Radio Communication

Second Edition

Radio Communication

Second Edition

D. C. Green

Longman

500477718

Pearson Education Limited
Edinburgh Gate
Harlow
Essex CM20 2JE, England
and Associated Companies throughout the world

First edition published as *Radio Systems Technology*

ISBN 0 582 36908 8

British Library Cataloguing-in-Publication Data
A catalogue record for this book is available from the British Library.

Set by 35 in 10/12pt Times
Produced by Pearson Education Asia Pte Ltd
Printed in Singapore

Contents

Preface   ix

1 Noise in radio systems   1
Noise generated within a radio receiver   2
Noise picked up by a receiving aerial   8
Signal-to-noise ratio   10
Noise factor   11
Noise temperature   17
Noise floor   21
Measurement of noise factor and noise temperature   22
Noise in digital radio systems   23
Exercises   24

2 Amplitude modulation   28
Double-sideband amplitude modulation; sinusoidal modulating signal   29
DSBAM: non-sinusoidal modulating signal   37
Phasor representation of an AM wave   42
Distortion of an AM wave   43
Double-sideband suppressed-carrier amplitude modulation   45
Single-sideband suppressed-carrier amplitude modulation   47
Single-sideband compared with double-sideband amplitude modulation   50
Exercises   51

3 Angle modulation   53
Frequency modulation   54
Phase modulation   65
Signal-to-noise ratio in an FM system   67
Pre-emphasis and de-emphasis   72
Advantages of frequency modulation over amplitude modulation   74
Exercises   75

4 Digital modulation   78
Signal waveforms   79
Binary phase shift keying   82
Quaternary PSK   86

8-phase PSK 93
16QPSK 97
Minimum shift keying 97
Gaussian minimum shift keying 100
Quadrature amplitude modulation 101
Spectral (bandwidth) efficiency and power efficiency 108
Bit error rate 109
Exercises 111

5 Transmission lines 113
Primary coefficients of a line 115
Secondary coefficients of a line 116
Mismatched transmission lines 118
Standing waves and voltage standing-wave ratio 126
Line mismatched at both ends 129
Transmission lines as components 131
Matching 134
The Smith chart 138
Exercises 151

6 Waveguides 154
Propagation in the rectangular waveguide 156
Impedance of a rectangular waveguide 165
Attenuation in a rectangular waveguide 166
Sizes of waveguides 167
Waveguide components 168
Exercises 174

7 Principles of aerials 176
Radiation from an aerial 177
Isotropic radiator 178
Current element 179
Effective length of an aerial 182
The monopole aerial 184
The $\lambda/2$ dipole 192
Gain of an aerial 194
Effective aperture of an aerial 195
Power received by an aerial 197
Long-wire radiator 199
Exercises 201

8 Aerials 203
Two-dipole array 204
Three-dipole array 210
Broadside array 211
End-fire array 215

Height factor 216
Pattern multiplication 219
Mutual impedances between dipoles 222
The rhombic aerial 225
The notch aerial 233
The slot aerial 235
The whip or rod aerial 237
The helical aerial 237
The loop aerial 239
The parabolic dish aerial 240
Exercises 245

9 Propagation of radio waves 247
The ionosphere 248
The troposphere 251
Ground-wave propagation 254
Sky-wave propagation 256
Fading 263
Space-wave propagation 266
Space-wave fading 279
Scatter propagation 279
Propagation via a communications satellite 281
Exercises 282

10 Radio circuits 285
Class C RF amplifiers 286
Amplitude modulators 288
AM detectors 292
Frequency modulators 298
FM detectors 306
Digital modulators and demodulators 313
Frequency synthesisers 313
Mixers 320
Miscellaneous circuits 322
Exercises 325

11 Radio transmitters 327
Radio regulations 327
Transmitter and receiver codes 332
AM transmitters 333
Sound broadcast transmitters 334
HF communication transmitters 337
VHF/UHF communication transmitters 337
Digital audio broadcasting transmitters 339
Exercises 340

12 Radio receivers 341
Superheterodyne radio receiver 342
Double-superheterodyne radio receiver 344
Level diagram 346
Parameters of superheterodyne radio receivers 346
Sensitivity 356
Selectivity 358
Noise factor 360
Stages in a radio receiver 361
Automatic gain control (AGC) 365
Communication radio receivers 367
Digital broadcast radio 378
Exercises 378

13 Radio-relay systems 381
Microwave radio-relay systems 382
Analogue radio-relay systems 385
Digital radio-relay systems 387
Link design 394
Tropospheric scatter systems 398
Exercises 398

14 Communications satellite systems 400
Communications satellite systems 401
Communications satellite orbits 403
Commercial operators 404
Link design 406
Multiple access 409
Path loss 414
Radiation techniques 417
Ground stations and satellites 417
Exercises 422

15 Mobile radio systems 424
Private land mobile radio 425
Cellular radio systems 431
GSM 435
DCS 1800 442
Digital cordless telephony 442
Digitally enhanced cordless telecommunications 443
Mobile telephones 444
Exercises 445

16 Electronic Workbench 448

Answers to exercises 457
Index 474

Preface

This book has been written to provide a comprehensive introduction to radio communications systems and covers the requirements of the BTEC Radio Communication Engineering Higher National Certificate/Diploma optional unit. A large part of the BTEC unit Transmission Lines For Telecommunications is also covered. The book should also prove useful to students on degree courses that include radio engineering.

In the first chapter the book discusses the sources of noise in a radio system and how the important parameter signal-to-noise ratio can be determined. The next three chapters cover the principles of amplitude modulation, angle modulation and digital modulation, and then transmission lines and waveguides are discussed. Transmission lines and waveguides are important components in any radio system since they are used both to provide feeders and to simulate components and tuned circuits. The basic concepts of aerials are introduced in Chapter 7 before some of the more commonly employed aerials are described in Chapter 8. Chapter 9 then deals with the propagation of radio signals from a transmitting aerial to one or more receiving aerials. The remaining chapters of the book deal with radio circuits and systems. Chapter 10 explains the operation of a number of circuits that are employed in radio systems; to keep the number of pages down to reasonable proportions circuits that are also covered in books on electronics, such as amplifiers and oscillators, have not been covered. Radio transmitters and radio receivers are the subjects of Chapters 11 and 12, respectively, and Chapters 13, 14 and 15 cover, in turn, microwave radio-relay systems, communications satellite systems and mobile radio. The final chapter presents a number of exercises that can be carried out using the electronic design software package Electronics Workbench. A reader with access to a PC and Electronics Workbench can download the relevant files from Pearson Education's website at ftp://ftp.pearsoned-ema.com/pub/awl-he/engineering/green. The circuit to be investigated will then appear in the circuit window.

A large number of worked examples are given throughout the book to illustrate various points and principles. Some chapters include one or more practical exercises which require only the use of components and equipment that should be available in any laboratory where such practical work is carried out. The circuits given in some of the practical exercises are best constructed using a breadboard of some kind that allows component leads and wires to be pushed into holes where they are held in place by spring contacts. This will allow circuits to be built (relatively) quickly and makes it easy to modify the circuit if an error is made and/or component values are changed.

Each chapter with the exception of the final one concludes with a number of exercises and at the end of the book a concisely worked answer is given to each numerical problem.

I would like to thank the Institution of British Telecommunication Engineers for their permission to use some diagrams from their publication *British Telecommunication Engineering*, and also Rohde Schwarz and the Radio Communication Agency for some useful information.

D.C.G.

1 Noise in radio systems

After reading this chapter you should be able to:

(a) List the sources of noise in a radio system, both internally and externally generated.
(b) Calculate the root mean-square thermal noise voltage generated in the resistive part of an impedance.
(c) Understand the meanings of the terms available noise power, noise bandwidth and available gain.
(d) Explain the importance of signal-to-noise ratio.
(e) Understand the importance of the noise factor of a circuit or radio receiver.
(f) Understand the relationship between signal-to-noise ratio and noise factor.
(g) Determine the noise output of a circuit.
(h) Calculate the overall noise factor of several circuits connected in cascade.
(i) Use effective noise factor when the source noise temperature is not 290 K.
(j) Explain what is meant by noise temperature and its relationship with noise factor.
(k) Calculate the overall noise temperature of several circuits connected in cascade.
(l) Measure both the noise factor and the noise temperature of a radio receiver.

The output of a radio receiver always has some unwanted superimposed interference and/or noise voltages that set a lower limit to the usable signal level at that output. The total noise is the summation of noise picked up by the aerial and noise generated within the receiver. For the output signal to be useful the signal power must be larger than the noise power by an amount specified by the required minimum signal-to-noise ratio. This minimum signal-to-noise ratio varies considerably depending upon the nature of the signal: for example, a mobile telephone needs a minimum signal-to-noise ratio of about 15 dB whereas a television receiver requires a figure that is more than 40 dB. The required minimum signal-to-noise ratio determines the power that a radio transmitter must supply to its aerial, the required sensitivity of a radio receiver, and the spacing of the relay stations in a microwave radio-relay system. Economic factors, therefore, require that the effects of any noise and interference are reduced to as low a figure as possible.

A noise source may consist of randomly occurring non-periodic voltages which have a mean value of zero but which may contain some relatively large voltage peaks.

Such noise sources have a uniform power density over a given bandwidth and are said to be *white*; it is possible to calculate the roof mean-square (r.m.s.) value of a white-noise source. Impulse noise usually originates from various artificial (i.e. human-made) sources such as electric motors, electric switches and neon signs. Interfering signals picked up by a receiving aerial may appear at the output of a receiver; the main culprits here are the adjacent-channel, co-channel, and image-channel signals (p. 347). Other interfering signals may be generated within the radio receiver itself as a direct result of *intermodulation* (p. 348).

The various sources of noise that may arise and degrade the performance of a radio system may be divided into two groups: (a) noise generated within the radio receiver itself, such as thermal noise, semiconductor noise and intermodulation noise; (b) noise that is picked up by the receiving aerial, which, in turn, may originate from either natural or artificial sources.

Noise generated within a radio receiver

Thermal noise

Thermal noise is generated within a conductor because thermal agitation of its atomic structure causes free electrons to move in a random manner within the conductor. The higher the temperature of the conductor the greater is the thermal energy and the more vigorous is the random movement of electrons. At any instant in time more electrons are moving in some directions than in others. The movement of each electron constitutes a very small current and hence the net current fluctuates continuously in both magnitude and direction. This net current flows in the resistance of the conductor and produces a noise voltage. Over a period of time the average noise voltage is zero but an r.m.s. noise voltage is developed.

The r.m.s. value of the thermal noise voltage is

$$V_n = \sqrt{(4kTBR)} \text{ V} \tag{1.1}$$

where k is Boltzmann's constant (1.38×10^{-23} J K^{-1}); T is the absolute temperature in K (K = °C + 273); B is the noise bandwidth in Hz; R is the resistance of the conductor or resistor, or the resistive part of the impedance, in which the noise is generated.

A resistance of R Ω can be represented by a noise voltage generator V_n in series with a noiseless resistor of R Ω, as shown by Fig. 1.1. Alternatively, the conductance $G = 1/R$ of that resistance can be represented by a noiseless conductance G connected in parallel with a current noise generator I_n.

The standard reference temperature is usually taken as 290 K and given the symbol T_0. This temperature, often called the *room temperature*, should always be assumed unless some other value is given. Thermal agitation noise is white.

The *noise bandwidth* of a circuit, or device, is the width along the frequency axis of a rectangular output frequency response curve whose area and height are the same as the actual frequency response characteristic of the circuit (see Fig. 1.2). The noise bandwidth of a circuit can be determined graphically or by the use of the expression

Fig. 1.1 *Representation of thermal noise generated in a resistance*

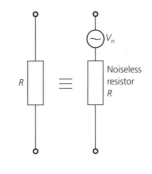

Fig. 1.2 *Noise bandwidth*

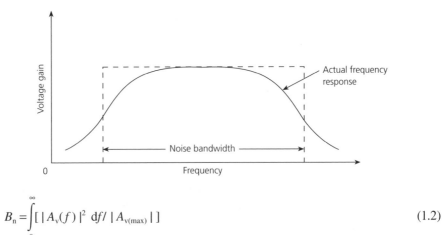

$$B_n = \int_0^\infty [\, |\, A_v(f)\, |^2 \; \mathrm{d}f /\, |\, A_{v(\mathrm{max})}\, |\,] \tag{1.2}$$

where $A_v(f)$ is the voltage gain of the circuit at any frequency f, and $A_{v(\mathrm{max})}$ is the maximum voltage gain.

EXAMPLE 1.1

Derive an expression for the noise bandwidth of the circuit shown in Fig. 1.3. Calculate the noise bandwidth if the output voltage falls by 3 dB at a frequency of 12 kHz.

Fig. 1.3

Solution

$$V_{out}/V_{in} = (1/j\omega C)/(R + 1j\omega CR) = 1/(1 + j\omega CR)$$

$$|V_{out}/V_{in}| = 1/\sqrt{(1 + \omega^2 C^2 R^2)}$$

and this ratio falls by 3 dB at a frequency $\omega_0/2\pi$, where $\omega_0 = 1/CR$. Hence

$$A_v(f) = 1/\sqrt{(1 + f^2/f_0^2)}$$

From equation (1.2)

$$B_n = \int_0^\infty df/(1 + f^2/f_0^2) = f_0^2 \int_0^\infty df/(f_0^2 + f^2)^\dagger$$

$$= f_0^2 [(1/f_0) \tan^{-1}(f/f_0)]_0^\infty = \pi f_0/2 \ (Ans.)$$

If $f_0 = 12$ kHz, $B_0 = 15\ 708$ Hz (*Ans.*)

It can be shown that:

- For a single-tuned circuit $B_n = 1.57\ B_{3\ dB}$.
- For two cascaded single-tuned circuits $B_n = 1.22\ B_{3\ dB}$.

If the noise bandwidth of a circuit is not known the 3 dB bandwidth will have to be used. This will introduce some error, of course, but this error will be small if the gain–frequency characteristic of the circuit has a rapid roll-off.

EXAMPLE 1.2

Calculate the thermal noise voltage produced at room temperature (a) in a 10 kΩ resistor in a 2 MHz bandwidth, and (b) in a parallel resonant circuit having an inductance of 40 µH and a Q factor of 48 that is resonant at a frequency of 2 MHz. Assume the noise bandwidth is equal to the 3 dB bandwidth.

Solution

(a) $V_n = \sqrt{(4 \times 1.38 \times 10^{-23} \times 290 \times 2 \times 10^6 \times 10 \times 10^3)} = 17.9$ µV (*Ans.*)
(b) $R_d = Q\omega_0 L = 48 \times 2\pi \times 2 \times 10^6 \times 40 \times 10^{-6} \approx 24.13$ kΩ
$B_{3\ dB} = f_0/Q = (2 \times 10^6)/48 \approx 41.67$ kHz
$V_n = \sqrt{(1.38 \times 10^{-23} \times 290 \times 24.13 \times 10^3 \times 41.67 \times 10^3)} = 2$ µV (*Ans.*)

† A standard integral is $\int dx/(x^2 + y^2) = (1/y) \tan^{-1}(x/y)$.

Fig. 1.4 *Available noise power*

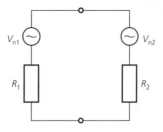

Available noise power

If a resistor R_1 at temperature T_1 is connected to another resistor R_2 at temperature T_2 as shown by Fig. 1.4, noise power will be transferred from each resistor to the other resistor.

The noise power P_1 delivered by resistor R_1 to resistor R_2 is

$$P_1 = [(V_{n1}R_2)/(R_1 + R_2)]^2/R_2$$

and the noise power P_2 delivered from R_2 to R_1 is

$$P_2 = [(V_{n2}R_1)/(R_1 + R_2)]^2/R_1$$

The net noise power transferred from source to load is

$$P_n = P_1 - P_2 = [4kB(R_1R_2T_1 - R_1R_2T_2)]/(R_1 + R_2)^2$$

or

$$P_n = [4kBR_1R_2(T_1 - T_2)]/(R_1 + R_2)^2 \qquad (1.3)$$

The maximum, or *available*, noise power P_A occurs when the two resistors are of equal value and $T_2 = 0$ (i.e. resistor R_2 is assumed to be noise free and its noise is referred back). Then

$$P_A = (V_n/2R)^2 = 4kTBR/4R$$
$$= kTB \text{ W} \qquad (1.4)$$

If P_A is divided by the bandwidth B the available noise power in a 1 Hz bandwidth is obtained; this is known as the *power density spectrum* (PDS) and it is constant up to about 300 GHz. The PDS is equal to $kT_0 = 4 \times 10^{-21}$ W Hz^{-1} = −204 dBW = −174 dBm

Very often it is convenient to quote the available noise power in decibels. Thus

$$P_A = -204 + 10 \log_{10} B_n \text{ dBW} \qquad (1.5)$$

$$P_A = -174 + 10 \log_{10} B_n \text{ dBm} \qquad (1.6)$$

Calculate the available noise power when the bandwidth is (a) 1 MHz, (b) 10 MHz and (c) 20 MHz.

Solution

(a) $P_A = -204$ dBm $+ 10 \log_{10}(1 \times 10^6) = -144$ dBm (*Ans.*)
(b) $P_A = -144$ dBm $+ 10$ dB $= -134$ dBm (*Ans.*)
(c) $P_A = -134$ dBm $+ 3$ dB $= -131$ dBm (*Ans.*)

Available power gain

There are a number of ways in which the power gain, or loss, of a network can be defined, but for noise calculations the *available power gain G* is often used. The available power gain is the ratio of output power to input power when *both* the input and the output impedances of the network are matched to the source and the load, respectively. Thus

available gain G = (available output power)/(available input power) $\qquad$ (1.7)

The expression for the noise bandwidth (1.2) can be written in terms of the available power gain:

$$B_n = \int_0^\infty [\,|\,G\,(f)\,|\,/G_{max}]\; df \qquad (1.8)$$

where $G(f)$ is the available power gain at any frequency f, and G_{max} is the mid-band available power gain.

Noise produced by resistors in series

If two, or more, resistances are connected in series the total mean-square noise voltage developed is equal to the sum of the mean-square noise voltages generated by each resistance. For two resistances R_1 and R_2, the total mean-square noise voltage V_n^2 is equal to $V_{n1}^2 + V_{n2}^2 = 4kB(R_1T_1 + R_2T_2)$. Usually, the two resistances are at the same temperature T, and then $V_n^2 = 4kBT(R_1 + R_2)$, which means that the total mean-square noise voltage is effectively generated in the total resistance $R_1 + R_2$ of the circuit.

Noise produced by resistors in parallel

If two resistors are connected in parallel and are at the same temperature the total mean-square noise voltage will be equal to $4kTBR_T$, where $R_T = R_1R_2/(R_1 + R_2)$.
    If the two resistors are not at the same temperature the superposition theorem will have to be used to calculate the total mean-square noise voltage generated.

An amplifier has an input resistance of 2000 Ω and is at a temperature of 290 K. It is connected to a source of 1000 Ω resistance at a temperature of 300 K. Calculate the total noise voltage across the input terminals of the amplifier if the noise bandwidth is 1 MHz.

Solution

The thermal noise voltages V_{ns} and V_{ni} generated in the source and input impedances respectively are

$$V_{ns} = \sqrt{(4 \times 1.38 \times 10^{-23} \times 300 \times 10^6 \times 10^3)} \approx 4 \ \mu V$$

$$V_{ni} = \sqrt{(4 \times 1.38 \times 10^{-23} \times 290 \times 2 \times 10^9)} \approx 5.7 \ \mu V$$

Referring to Fig. 1.5, the total noise voltage across the amplifier's input terminals is

$$V_{nt} = \sqrt{[(4 \times 2/3)^2 + (5.7 \times 1/3)^2]} \approx 3.3 \ \mu V \ (Ans.)$$

Fig. 1.5

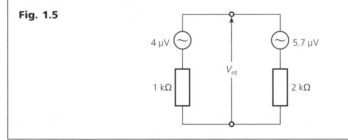

Semiconductor noise

All semiconductor devices are subject to the following sources of noise:

- *Thermal agitation noise* in the resistance of the semiconductor material. It occurs mainly in the base resistance of a bipolar transistor and in the channel resistance of a field-effect transistor (FET).
- *Shot noise* is caused by the random movement of electrons and holes across each p–n junction in the device. The r.m.s. value of the shot-noise current is:

$$I_n = \sqrt{(2eIB)} \qquad (1.9)$$

where e is the electronic charge (1.602×10^{-19} C), I is the d.c. current flowing across the junction and B is the bandwidth. Shot noise is white.
- *Flicker or 1/f noise* caused by fluctuations in the conductivity of the semiconductor material. Flicker noise is inversely proportional to frequency.

Intermodulation noise

A major cause of noise in radio systems carrying multi-channel analogue telephony signals is intermodulation. Intermodulation occurs whenever a complex signal is applied to a non-linear device. It results in the production of components at frequencies equal to the sums and the differences of the frequencies, and at the harmonics of the frequencies, contained in the input signal. When the input signal contains components at several different frequencies the number of intermodulation products may be very large; the effect at the output of the circuit is then very similar to that of thermal agitation noise. The main difference between them is that, whereas thermal agitation noise is constant, intermodulation noise is a function of the amplitude of the input signal.

Noise picked up by a receiving aerial

The noise picked up by a receiving aerial is generated by a number of sources of atmospheric, galactic and artificial origin. In urban areas there is more artificial noise than in rural areas. At frequencies in the low-, medium- and high-frequency bands the external noise is much larger than the noise generated within the radio receiver. At higher frequencies (in the VHF, UHF and SHF bands) externally generated noise falls to a relatively low level and the overall noise performance of a system is mainly determined by the receiver itself. Considerable attention is then given to reducing the noise factor of the receiver (p. 11) to as small a figure as possible.

Natural sources of noise

A receiving aerial will receive noise that originates from radiation from both the sky and the earth itself. Sky noise has a magnitude that varies both with frequency and with the part of the sky to which the aerial is pointed. Sky noise is normally expressed in terms of the *noise temperature* T_A of the aerial. This is the temperature at which the aerial must be assumed to be for thermal agitation in its radiation resistance (p. 182) to produce the same noise power as is actually supplied by the aerial. Thus $T_A = $ (noise power)/kB. If the aerial is used for terrestrial communications, so that its main beam has only a small upwards inclination, then its noise temperature is effectively the same as that of the earth, or of the lower atmosphere, and this is usually taken as 300 K. If, on the other hand, the aerial points upwards to the sky its noise temperature may be that of space, unless the aerial is pointing towards the sun when the noise temperature may be high.

At medium and high frequencies atmospheric noise or *static* is produced by electrical storms. Every time a flash of lightning occurs somewhere in the world impulse noise is generated. Since thunderstorms are always occurring somewhere above the earth's surface and the noise generated by a thunderstorm is able to propagate for very long distances, atmospheric noise is always present. The combined effect of a great many noise impulses produces a sound at the output of a receiver very like thermal agitation noise. Atmospheric noise has its greatest magnitude (approximately $10 \ \mu V \, m^{-1}$) at about 10 kHz and is negligible at frequencies above about 20 MHz. The level of

Fig. 1.6 *Variation of sky noise with frequency*

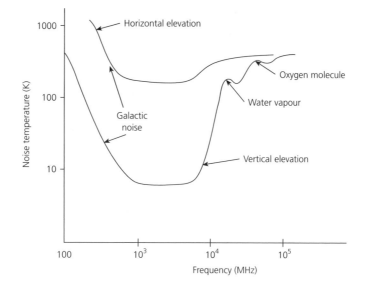

atmospheric noise varies considerably with the location of the aerial, with the time of day and year, and with frequency.

At frequencies above about 20 MHz solar and galactic noise start to be significant. Solar noise is produced by radiation from the sun and galactic noise is generated by radiation from distant stars. Galactic, or cosmic, noise originates from stars in both our galaxy and other galaxies and it is distributed more or less evenly throughout the sky. The manner in which sky noise varies with frequency above 100 MHz is shown, for both horizontal and vertical elevations, by Fig. 1.6. Galactic noise has its maximum value at about 20 MHz and then falls inversely proportional to (frequency)$^{2.4}$ to a minimum at about 1 GHz. At 50 MHz the noise temperature T_A of an aerial is in the region of 5000 K. Galactic noise is negligible at frequencies higher than about 500 MHz and then the main source of noise is radiation from the earth itself. Noise due to radiation from the earth also decreases with increase in frequency and, typically, the aerial noise temperature T_A is about 300 K at 200 MHz. Another source of sky noise is the sun. The sun has a noise temperature of about 6000 K or more and occasionally produces bursts of noise which are several times greater than this. The effect of solar noise can always be minimised by pointing the aerial away from the sun. At higher frequencies the noise temperature rises with peaks at 23 GHz, owing to water vapour molecules producing a peak in atmospheric absorption, and at about 60 GHz owing to oxygen molecules.

Artificial sources of noise

There are a large number of possible sources of artificial noise which may be received by an aerial. Whenever an electric current is switched on or off by a mechanical or an

Fig. 1.7 *Typical variation of total aerial noise in urban and rural areas*

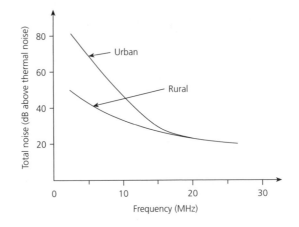

electronic switch, one, or more, voltage spikes will be generated because of the inevitable capacitance and inductance that exist in all circuits. The voltage spike may be a single transient, or several transients may occur in rapid succession. Three examples of the switching of electrical currents that generate noise are vehicle ignition systems, electric light switches and the brushes in electric motors. Each time an electrical switch is operated an audible click may occur that will adversely affect reception. Continuous interference spectra are generated by free-running circuits such as thyristor speed controls and switched-mode power supplies.

The interference produced by the switching of electrical currents may either be electromagnetic (EMI) or radio-frequency (RFI). EMI is of lower frequency (30 kHz to 30 MHz) than RFI but it is usually of higher voltage and may travel over the electrical mains wiring for a considerable distance. RFI is of high frequency (30 to 300 MHz) and is both conducted over, and radiated from, the mains wiring which acts as a rather inefficient aerial.

The total artificial noise received by an aerial cannot be separately identified from the atmospheric and galactic noise that is also present, but obviously this source of noise will be larger in an urban environment than in a rural area. Figure 1.7 shows how, typically, the total noise produced by atmospheric, galactic and artificial noise may vary in both urban and rural areas.

Artificial noise can often be suppressed at its source, although it may not always be an economic proposition to do so. Alternatively, it is often possible to position the receiving aerial at a site which is remote from most sources of interference.

Signal-to-noise ratio

As a signal is propagated over a radio link it will be subjected to various forms of noise and/or interference and it will also be attenuated. The radio receiver will have sufficient gain to compensate for the path attenuation and give the required output signal power, but each stage in the receiver will add further noise to the signal. The usefulness of the output signal for its intended purpose is expressed by means of its *signal-to-noise ratio*. This is defined as

signal-to-noise ratio = (wanted signal power)/(unwanted noise power)   (1.10)

Because signal-to-noise ratio is the ratio of two powers it is usual to quote it in decibels. The larger the output signal-to-noise ratio of a radio system the greater will be its ability to receive weak signals. The minimum permissible signal-to-noise ratio of a radio system is one of its most important parameters. Different minimum signal-to-noise ratio figures are specified for different kinds of signal and, for example, the minimum figure for a mobile radio-telephony system is about 15 dB.

The minimum required signal-to-noise ratio determines the minimum power that the distant transmitter must transmit. The transmitted signal is attenuated as it travels to the receiver – the loss is known as the *free-space attenuation* (p. 268) – and interference and noise are superimposed upon it. The minimum transmitted power P_T is given by

$$P_T = \text{required signal-to-noise ratio} + N + L - G_T - G_R \text{ dBW} \qquad (1.11)$$

where G_T and G_R are the gains in dB of the transmitting and receiving aerials respectively (p. 194), N is the noise power in dBW and L is the free-space loss in dB.

EXAMPLE 1.5

The minimum signal-to-noise ratio required at the input to a UHF mobile receiver is 22 dB. The total input noise is −118 dBm and the free-space loss is 80 dB. If the gains of the transmitting and receiving aerials are identical at 3 dB, calculate the minimum transmitted power necessary.

Solution

$$P_T = 22 - 118 + 80 - 6 = -22 \text{ dBm } (Ans.)$$

In radio receivers, particularly wideband microwave receivers, a distinction is usually made between signal-to-noise ratio and carrier-to-noise ratio. The carrier-to-noise ratio is the ratio of the signal power, including sidebands, to the noise power at the input to the demodulator, while the signal-to-noise ratio is at the output of the demodulator. The demodulation process can give an increase in the signal-to-noise ratio (p. 70).

Noise factor

Figure 1.8 shows a circuit that has an available power gain G and that introduces an internally generated noise power at the output terminals of N_c W. The input signal to the circuit is S_{in} with an associated noise power of $N_{in} = kT_0B$ W. This means that the input signal-to-noise ratio is S_{in}/N_{in}.

Fig. 1.8 *Noise factor*

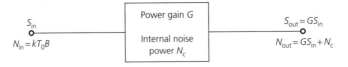

The noise factor, or noise figure, F of the circuit is defined as

$$F = \text{(total noise power at output)/(amplified input noise power)} \qquad (1.12)$$

Assuming that both the source and the circuit are at the standard temperature of 290 K and that the circuit is linear, then

$$F = (GN_{in} + N_c)/GN_{in} = 1 + N_c/GN_{in} \qquad (1.13)$$

The noise factor is unaffected by the value of the load impedance because any mismatch at the output terminals which might exist will reduce both the noise and the signal powers equally, and so it will not alter their ratio. If the circuit were noise free N_c would be zero and the noise factor would be $F = 1$ or 0 dB. This is the theoretical minimum figure for the noise factor. In practice, typical figures are 4 dB for a VHF amplifier, 0.5 to 3 dB for a low-noise amplifier (LNA), 7 dB for an HF radio receiver, and 5 dB for a VHF/UHF receiver.

It is often convenient to refer the internally generated noise to the input terminals of the circuit. Then $N_e = N_c/G$ and

$$F = (GN_{in} + GN_c) = 1 + N_e/N_{in} \qquad (1.14)$$

This expression can be rearranged to give $N_e = (F - 1)N_{in}$, which expresses the internally generated noise as a function of both the noise factor and the actual input noise. The internally generated noise may be regarded as being generated by thermal agitation in an equivalent input resistance.

When a coherent input signal is applied to the circuit the equation (1.14) can be written as

$$F = (1/GN_{in})/[1/(GN_{in} + N_c)] = (1/N_{in})/[G/(GN_{in} + N_c)]$$
$$= (S_{in}/N_{in})/[GS_{in}/(GN_{in} + N_c)]$$

or

$$F = \text{(input signal-to-noise ratio)/(output signal-to-noise ratio)} \qquad (1.15)$$

Using decibels,

$$F = \text{input signal-to-noise ratio} - \text{output signal-to-noise ratio} \qquad (1.16)$$

These two expressions show that the noise factor of a circuit indicates the extent to which the signal-to-noise ratio at the input terminals is degraded by the noise generated internally within the circuit to give a worse output signal-to-noise ratio.

The input signal to an RF amplifier is at a level of −102 dBm and the input noise level is −124 dBm. The gain of the RF amplifier is 24 dB and its noise factor is 2.8 dB. Calculate the output signal-to-noise ratio of the RF amplifier.

Solution

Method A:

input signal-to-noise ratio $= -102 - (-124) = 22$ dB

output signal-to-noise ratio $= 22 - 2.8 = 19.2$ dB (*Ans.*)

Method B:

$S_{out} = -102 + 24 = -78$ dBm

$N_{out} = -124 + 24 + 2.8 = -97.2$ dBm

output signal-to-noise ratio $= -78 - (-97.2) = 19.2$ dB (*Ans.*)

Output noise from a circuit

The available input noise power to a circuit is kT_0B W, and substituting this term into equation (1.15) gives

$$F = (S_{in}/kT_0B)/(GS_{in}/N_0) = N_0/(GkT_0B)$$

where N_0 is the output noise power. Therefore,

$$N_0 = FGkT_0B \tag{1.17}$$

Using decibels,

$$N_0 = -174 \text{ dBm} + 10 \log_{10} F + 10 \log_{10} G + 10 \log_{10} B \tag{1.18}$$

Equation (1.17) gives the total noise power at the output of the circuit and is the sum of (a) the amplified input noise and (b) the noise produced within the circuit. Since the amplified input noise is equal to GkT_0B, the internally generated noise is

$$N_e = (F - 1)GkT_0B \tag{1.19}$$

In the case of a radio receiver which has different bandwidths at different points in the circuit the narrowest bandwidth should be used.

Variation of noise factor with frequency

The gain of a circuit and the noise generated within it per unit bandwidth are often functions of frequency and this means that the noise factor of the circuit may also vary with frequency. Thus a distinction between the noise factor at a single frequency and the full-bandwidth noise factor may need to be made. If the bandwidth of the circuit is narrow enough for any variations in the gain and/or generated noise to be ignored, the *spot noise factor* is obtained. The spot noise factor can be measured at a number of points in the overall bandwidth of the circuit and then the *average noise factor* can be obtained.

Noise factor of a circuit with loss

Suppose the circuit has an attenuation (power ratio) of X. The available input noise power is kT_0B and hence the available output noise power is $(kT_0B)/X + N_c$. This power is the same as the available noise power kT_0B generated in the output resistance of the circuit. Therefore

$$(kT_0B)/X + N_c = kT_0B$$

or

$$N_c = kT_0B(1 - 1/X) = kT_0B(X - 1)/X$$

The same available output noise power would be obtained if a noiseless circuit having the same attenuation were to be supplied by a source that produces an available noise power of $kT_0B(X - 1)$. Hence

$$kT_0B(X - 1) = (F - 1)kT_0B$$

or

$$F = X \qquad\qquad (1.20)$$

This means that the noise factor of a lossy circuit, such as an attenuator or a length of coaxial or waveguide feeder, which is at temperature T_0 is equal to its attenuation.

EXAMPLE 1.7

A waveguide feeder has an attenuation of 2.5 dB. Calculate its noise factor.

Solution

Since 2.5 dB is a power ratio of 1.78, then

$$F = 1.78 \ (Ans.)$$

Overall noise factor of circuits in cascade

Figure 1.9 shows two circuits connected in cascade. The circuits have noise factors F_1 and F_2, and available gains G_1 and G_2, respectively, and equal bandwidths. If the overall noise factor of the combination is F_{ov} then the available output noise power N_0 is

$$N_0 = F_{ov}G_1G_2kT_0B$$

Fig. 1.9 *Noise factors in cascade*

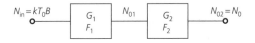

For the first circuit, the output noise power is

$$N_{01} = F_1 G_1 k T_0 B$$

and this is the input noise to the second circuit. Hence

$$N_{02} = G_2 F_1 G_1 k T_0 B + (F_2 - 1) G_2 k T_0 B$$

Since $N_0 = N_{02}$,

$$F_{ov} G_1 G_2 k T_0 B = G_1 G_2 F_1 k T_0 B + (F_2 - 1) G_2 k T_0 B$$

and

$$F_{ov} = F_1 + (F_2 - 1)/G_1 \tag{1.21}$$

This result can be extended to any number of circuits connected in cascade. For n circuits

$$F_{ov} = F_1 + (F_2 - 1)/G_1 + (F_3 - 1)/G_1 G_2 + \ldots + (F_n - 1)/(G_1 G_2 \ldots G_{n-1}) \tag{1.22}$$

If the first, and later, circuits shown in Fig. 1.9 are amplifiers the noise generated by the second, and following, amplifiers will be reduced because of its division by the product of the gains of the preceding amplifiers. If, however, the first circuit introduces a loss then the noise introduced by the second circuit will be increased. This means that to obtain a good, i.e. a low, overall noise factor, the first circuit *must* introduce the minimum possible loss and should, if possible, be an amplifier.

The derivation of equation (1.21) assumes that the bandwidth of the second stage is equal to or less than that of the first stage. If the bandwidth B_1 of the first stage is less than the bandwidth B_2 of the second stage the equation must be modified as

$$F_{ov} = F_1 + [(F_2 - 1)/G_1](B_2/B_1) \tag{1.23}$$

EXAMPLE 1.8

A radio receiver has a noise factor of 6 dB. An amplifier with a power gain of 10 dB is connected between the aerial and the receiver. The overall noise factor is then 6 dB. Calculate the noise factor of the amplifier. Calculate the overall noise factor if a 6 dB attenuator were to be connected (a) between the aerial and the amplifier, and (b) between the amplifier and the receiver. Assume the noise received by the aerial to have an effective noise temperature of 290 K.

Solution

Since 6 dB is a power ratio of 3.98 and 10 dB is a power ratio of 10, then, from equation (1.21),

$$3.98 = F_1 + (3.98 - 1)/10 \quad \text{or} \quad F_1 = 3.682 = 5.66 \text{ dB } (Ans.)$$

(a) $F_{ov} = 3.98 + (3.682 - 1)/(1/3.98) + (3.98 - 1)/(10 \times 1/3.98) = 15.84 = 12 \text{ dB } (Ans.)$
(b) $F_{ov} = 3.682 + (3.98 - 1)/10 + (3.98 - 1)/(10 \times 1/3.98) = 5.17 = 7.13 \text{ dB } (Ans.)$

Effective noise factor when $T_S \neq T_0$

The noise factor of a circuit is defined, measured and quoted with reference to a temperature of 290 K. If the source temperature is *not* at 290 K but is at some other temperature the degradation of the input signal-to-noise ratio will be different from that indicated by the noise factor. If the source temperature is less than 290 K the degradation will be greater than indicated, but if the source temperature is in excess of 290 K the reduction in the signal-to-noise ratio will be less than expected. To obtain the correct figure for the output signal-to-noise ratio the *effective noise factor* F_{eff} will have to be employed.

The noise factor of a circuit referred to the standard temperature of 290 K is $F = N_0/GkT_0B$, and hence the available output noise power due to the circuit alone is $(F - 1)GkT_0B$.

If, now, a source at temperature $T_S \neq T_0$ is applied to the input terminals of the network, the available noise output power will be $N_0 = GkT_SB + (F - 1)GkT_0B$. Now the effective noise factor $F_{eff} = N_0/GkT_SB$, or

$$F_{eff} = [GkT_SB + (F - 1)GkT_0B]/(GkT_SB) = 1 + (T_0/T_S)(F - 1) \tag{1.24}$$

EXAMPLE 1.9

A radio receiver has a noise factor of 10 and is connected by a feeder of 3 dB loss to an aerial. The noise delivered by the aerial is at an effective noise temperature of 145 K. Calculate the noise power at the output of the receiver if the receiver has a power gain of 50 dB and a bandwidth of 10 kHz.

Solution

The input noise power to the receiver system is

$$kT_AB = 1.38 \times 10^{-23} \times 145 \times 10^4 = 2 \times 10^{-17} \text{ W}$$

The noise factor of the feeder is 3 dB, or 2, and so the overall noise factor is

$$F_{ov} = 2 + (10 - 1)/(1/2) = 20$$

The effective noise factor at 145 K is

$$F_{eff} = 1 + [(20 - 1)290]/145 = 39$$

Therefore, the output noise power is

$$N_0 = F_{eff} GkT_A B = 39 \times 10^5 \times 2 \times 10^{-17} = 78 \text{ pW } (Ans.)$$

Noise temperature

The concept of noise temperature provides an alternative to noise factor for the specification of the noise performance of a radio system. The noise power N_c generated *within* a circuit and appearing at the output terminals may be considered to be the result of thermal agitation in the output resistance of the circuit. The output resistance must be regarded as being at a noise temperature $T_n = tT_0$, where t may be greater than, or less than, unity. Thus

$$N_c = kT_n B \quad \text{or} \quad T_n = N_c/kB \tag{1.25}$$

If the internally generated noise is referred to the input of the circuit it may be regarded as entering the input of the circuit as shown by Fig. 1.10. The internally generated noise is now equal to $kT_n B$ and so the total input noise is $kB(T_A + T_n)$, where T_A is the noise temperature of the aerial which also may, or may not, be equal to T_0.

The available noise power at the output of the circuit is

$$N_0 = Gk(T_S + T_c)B \tag{1.26}$$

The input signal-to-noise ratio of the system shown in Fig. 1.10 is $S_{in}/kT_A B$ and the output signal-to-noise ratio is

$$GS_{in}/[GkB(T_A + T_n)] = [\text{input signal-to-noise ratio}][T_A/(T_A + T_n)]$$

Relationship between noise factor and noise temperature

From equations (1.19) and (1.25) the noise generated within a circuit is

$$(F - 1)GkT_0 B = GktT_0 B$$

or

$$t = F - 1 \tag{1.27}$$

Fig. 1.10 *Noise temperature*

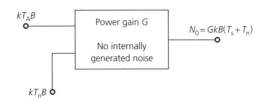

$kT_A B$

Power gain G

No internally generated noise

$N_0 = GkB(T_s + T_n)$

$kT_n B$

EXAMPLE 1.10

A circuit has a noise factor of 1.3 dB. Calculate its noise temperature.

Solution

Since 1.3 dB = 1.35, then $1.35 = 1 + T_c/290$, and

$$T_c = 0.35 \times 290 = 101.5 \text{ K } (Ans.)$$

EXAMPLE 1.11

A mobile telephone has an RF bandwidth of 30 kHz and a noise factor of 5.4 dB, and is connected to an aerial whose noise temperature is 290 K by a feeder of 2.7 dB loss. Calculate (a) the noise factor of the telephone and (b) the noise power.

Solution

(a) Now 5.4 dB ≈ 3.47 and 2.7 dB = 1.86 power ratio. Thus

$$F_{ov} = 1.86 + (3.47 - 1)1.86 = 6.45 \approx 8.1 \text{ dB } (Ans.)$$

(b) In this case

$$T_S = (6.45 - 1)290 = 1580.5 \text{ K}$$

$$T = T_A + T_S = 290 + 1580.5 = 1870.5 \text{ K}$$

and hence

$$N_0 = (1 + 1870.5/290)290 \times (1.38 \times 10^{-23} \times 30 \times 10^3)$$
$$= 8.95 \times 10^{-16} \text{ W} = -150.5 \text{ dBW} = -120.5 \text{ dBm } (Ans.)$$

The concept of noise temperature, instead of noise factor, is generally employed to express the noise picked up by an aerial and for low-noise circuits. The noise temperature of an aerial includes all types of noise that may be picked up by the aerial plus the noise generated in the ohmic resistance of the aerial, i.e.

$$T_A = T_{ext} + T_{int}$$

where T_{ext} represents the noise picked up by the aerial and T_{int} is the aerial ohmic noise temperature. For a low-noise circuit the use of noise factor to specify the noise performance will often lead to inconvenient numbers. Consider, for example, a noise factor of 1.068 97 is a noise temperature of 20 K. Table 1.1 shows equivalent noise factor and noise temperature values. The feeder is sometimes regarded as being a part of the aerial and their combined noise temperature is employed in calculations.

EXAMPLE 1.12

An aerial has a noise temperature of 22 K at a frequency of 11 GHz and waveguide feeder losses total 3 dB. Calculate the noise temperature of the aerial.

Solution

Since 3 dB = 2 power ratio, then

$$T_A = [(2 - 1)290 + 22]/2 = 156 \text{ K } (Ans.)$$

System noise temperature

The system noise temperature T_S of a radio receiving system is the sum of the aerial noise temperature T_A and the overall noise temperature of the system, i.e. $T_S = T_A + T_{ov}$. The overall noise temperature T_{ov} is easily obtained by combining equations (1.22) and (1.27). Subtracting one from both sides of equation (1.21) gives

$$t_{ov} = t_1 + t_2/G_1 + t_3/G_1G_2 \tag{1.28}$$

or

$$T_{ov} = T_1 + T_2/G_1 + T_3/G_1G_2 \tag{1.29}$$

The system output noise power N_0 is then given by equation (1.30), i.e.

$$N_0 = kT_SBG \tag{1.30}$$

This method of calculating the output noise power from a radio system is particularly useful when dealing with a system in which the aerial noise temperature is not equal to 290 K.

If an aerial of noise temperature T_A is connected to a receiving system the system noise temperature is

$$T_S = T_A + T_{ov} \tag{1.31}$$

EXAMPLE 1.13

The ground station in a communications satellite system has the following parameters: $T_A = 60$ K, $T_{LNA} = 50$ K, $T_{mix} = 500$ K, $G_{LNA} = 20$ dB and $G_{mix} = 0$ dB Calculate the system noise temperature.

Solution

Since 20 dB is a ratio of 100, then

$$T_S = 60 + 50 + 500/100 = 115 \text{ K } (Ans.)$$

When the aerial is connected to the receiving system by a coaxial or waveguide feeder of loss x dB the noise temperature of the feeder is $T_F = 290°(1 - L)$, where L is the loss quoted as a ratio less than unity. The effective aerial noise temperature is then

$$T_A^l = T_A L + 290°(1 - L) \tag{1.32}$$

EXAMPLE 1.14

In the system given in Example 1.13 a waveguide feeder of 2 dB attenuation is used to connect the aerial to the low-noise amplifier in the receiving system. Calculate the system noise temperature.

Solution

Since 2 dB is a ratio of 1.58, then

$$T_A^l = 60/1.58 + 290°(1 - 1/1.58) = 144.4 \text{ K}$$

$$T_S = 144.4 + 50 + 500/100 = 199.4 \text{ K } (Ans.)$$

EXAMPLE 1.15

Calculate (a) the system noise temperature, (b) the output noise power and (c) the output signal-to-noise ratio of the system shown in Fig. 1.11. The available signal power from the aerial is 3 pW and the bandwidth is 10 MHz.

Solution

(a) Converting from decibels to power ratios, 1 dB = 1.26, 20 dB = 100 and −10 dB = 0.1. The feeder has a noise factor of 1.26 and so $T_A^l = 40/1.26 + 290°(1 - 1/1.26) = 91.6$ K. The system noise temperature is

$$T_S = 91.6 + 50 + 630/100 + 500/10^4 \approx 148 \text{ K } (Ans.)$$

Fig. 1.11

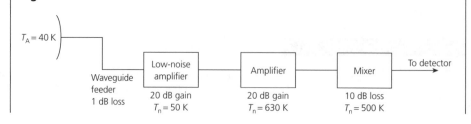

20   Radio Communication

(b) $N_0 = GkT_SB = (1/1.26) \times 100 \times 100 \times 0.1 \times 1.38 \times 10^{-23} \times 148 \times 10^7$
$= 16.2$ pW (*Ans.*)

(c)   The output signal power is

$1000 \times 1/1.26 \times 3 \times 10^{-12} = 2.38$ μW

Therefore, output signal-to-noise ratio is

$10 \log_{10}[(2.38 \times 10^{-6})/(20.4 \times 10^{-12})] = 51.7$ dB (*Ans.*)

EXAMPLE 1.16

A receiving system consists of an input LNA, a length of line and another amplifier. The LNA has a noise factor of 1.25 dB and 25 dB gain, the line has a loss of 2 dB, and the other amplifier has a noise factor of 7 dB and a gain of 30 dB. Calculate the overall noise temperature of the system.

Solution

Since 1.25 dB ≈ 1.33, 25 dB ≈ 316.23, 2 dB ≈ 1.59, 7 dB ≈ 38.45 and 30 dB = 1000 power ratio, then

$F_{ov} = 1.33 + (1.59 - 1)/316.23 + (38.45 - 1)/(316.23/1.59) = 1.52$

$T_S = (1.52 - 1)290 = 150.8$ K (*Ans.*)

Noise floor

The *noise floor* of a radio receiver is the smallest input signal level S_{in} that will give a specified output signal-to-noise ratio. It is also called the sensitivity. Since $F = (S_{in}/N_{in})/(S_{out}/N_{out})$,

noise floor $= S_{in} = FN_{in}S_{out}/N_{out}$ (1.33)

EXAMPLE 1.17

Calculate the noise floor for a radio receiver with a noise factor of 8 dB and a bandwidth of 20 kHz if the required minimum output signal-to-noise ratio is 12 dB.

Solution

The noise floor is

$8 - 204 + 10 \log_{10}(20 \times 10^3) + 12 = -141$ dBW (*Ans.*)

Measurement of noise factor and noise temperature

The measurement of the noise figure of a circuit is usually carried out using some kind of noise generator. For frequencies from zero hertz up to some hundreds of megahertz, the noise generator is usually a semiconductor diode. The shot noise produced by a diode is given by equation (1.9), i.e. $i_n = \sqrt{(2eIB)}$.

Fig. 1.12 *Measurement of noise factor*

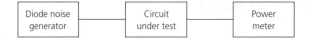

Figure 1.12 shows the arrangement used to measure the noise figure of a circuit. The r.m.s. noise current produced by the noise generator can be set to any desired value by varying the current passed by the diode. The noise generator has an output resistance R which is matched to the input resistance of the circuit under test. The total noise output power developed by the noise generator is

$$N_0 = kT_0B + (i_n/2)^2R$$

or

$$N_0 = kTB + 2eIBR/4 = kT_0B + eIBR/2$$

This is also the input noise to the circuit under test. With the noise generator switched off, the reading of the power meter, or true r.m.s. ammeter, at the output of the circuit is noted. This noise power is equal to $N_0 = FGkT_0B$ W. The noise generator is then switched on and its noise output is increased until the reading of the power meter is doubled. Then

$$2FGkT_0B = FGkT_0B + GeIBR/2 \quad \text{or} \quad FGkT_0B = GeIBR/2$$

Therefore,

$$F = eIR/2kT_0 = 20IR \tag{1.34}$$

Often $R = 50\ \Omega$ and then

$$F = I \tag{1.35}$$

where I is in mA.

The standard method of measuring the noise temperature of a circuit is to apply two noise sources of known temperatures T_1 and T_2 in turn to the circuit and then to obtain the ratio Y of the output powers thus obtained. Two separate standard noise sources are used only if precise measurements are being carried out; commonly a single noise generator is used and this is switched between two known temperatures.

The block diagram of the arrangement used to measure noise temperature is shown by Fig. 1.13. With the noise source at effective noise temperature T_1 connected to the circuit the reading of the output meter is noted. The circuit is then connected to the

Fig. 1.13 *Measurement of noise temperature*

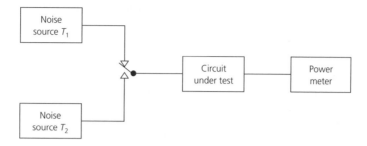

other noise generator at temperature T_2 (or the temperature of the sole generator is altered to T_2) and the new output meter reading is noted. It is customary to denote the ratio of the two meter readings as Y. Hence, if the noise temperature of the circuit is T_A,

$$Y = [Gk(T_1 + T_A)B]/[Gk(T_2 + T_A)B]$$
$$= (T_1 + T_A)/(T_2 + T_A)$$

and hence

$$T_A = (T_1 - YT_2)/(Y - 1) \tag{1.36}$$

Noise in digital radio systems

Probability of error and bit error rate

The *probability of error* $P(e)$ of a digital system is a mathematical expectation of the actual bit error rate (BER) that is obtained in the system. If, for example, a system has a $P(e)$ of 10^{-5} then it is expected that one bit will be in error for every 100 000 bits transmitted. If a system has a BER of 10^{-5} then there actually is, on average, one bit in error for every 100 000 bits transmitted. The probability of error is a function of the carrier-to-noise ratio and the number of possible encoding conditions employed (see Chapter 4).

In a digital radio system the carrier-to-noise ratio is

$$\text{carrier-to-noise ratio} = (\text{average energy per bit})/(\text{noise power density}) \tag{1.37}$$

The energy per bit E_B is equal to CT_b, where T_b is the time period occupied by a single bit, and C is the carrier power in W. E_B is often quoted in dBJ, i.e. $E_B = 10 \log_{10} E_B$ dBJ. Since $T_b = 1/R_B$, where R_B is the bit rate in bits per record, E_B can be written as $E_B = C/R_B$ J/bit. The energy per bit-to-noise power density ratio E_B/N_0 is used to compare two, or more, digital modulation systems that use different bit rates, modulation methods and/or encoding techniques (i.e. dibits, tribits, etc.). The energy per bit-to-noise ratio is the ratio

(energy of single bit)/(noise power in a 1 Hz bandwidth).

Therefore, E_B/N_0 normalises all modulation methods to a common noise bandwidth to make it easier to compare their performances in the presence of noise. Thus

$$E_B/N_0 = (C/R_B)/(N_0/B) = CB/N_0 R_B$$
$$= (C/N)(B/R_B) \qquad (1.38)$$

or in dB,

$$E_B/N_0 = 10 \log_{10}(C/N) + 10 \log_{10}(B/R_B) \qquad (1.39)$$

This means that the ratio E_B/N_0 is the product of the carrier-to-noise ratio and the ratio of the noise bandwidth to the bit rate.

The minimum carrier-to-noise ratio required from a quadrature amplitude modulation (QAM) system is generally less than is required from a phase shift modulation (PSK) system. The higher the encoding level employed, (the more bits per symbol), the higher will be the minimum carrier-to-noise power that is necessary to obtain a given BER.

EXAMPLE 1.18

A QPSK system has the following parameters: $C = 8 \times 10^{-13}$ W, $R_B = 100$ kb/s, $N = 1.1 \times 10^{-14}$ W, and $B = 125$ kHz. Calculate (a) the noise power, (b) the energy per bit, (c) the carrier-to-noise ratio and (d) the ratio E_B/N_0.

Solution

(a) $N_0 = 10 \log_{10}[(1.1 \times 10^{-14})/(1 \times 10^{-3})] - 10 \log_{10}(125 \times 10^3) = -160.6$ dBm (*Ans.*)
(b) $E_B = 10 \log_{10}[(8 \times 10^{-13})/(100 \times 10^3)] = -171$ dBJ (*Ans.*)
(c) $C/N = 10 \log_{10}[(8 \times 10^{-13})/(1.1 \times 10^{-14})] = 18.6$ dB (*Ans.*)
(d) $E_B/N_0 = 18.6 + 10 \log_{10}[(125 \times 10^3)/(100 \times 10^3)] = 19.6$ dB (*Ans.*)

EXERCISES

1.1 Define the terms 'noise factor' and 'noise temperature' and derive the relationship between them. Figure 1.14 shows a radio system. Calculate the required available signal power delivered by the aerial for the output signal-to-noise ratio to be better than 30 dB. The bandwidth is 10 MHz.

Fig. 1.14

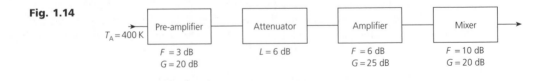

$T_A = 400$ K — Pre-amplifier $F = 3$ dB $G = 20$ dB — Attenuator $L = 6$ dB — Amplifier $F = 6$ dB $G = 25$ dB — Mixer $F = 10$ dB $G = 20$ dB

1.2 Explain how galactic noise and atmospheric noise vary with frequency. Hence explain why certain frequencies are used for communications satellite systems.

An aerial is connected to a radio receiver by a feeder of 1.46 dB loss, and a low-noise amplifier of 20 dB gain and a noise temperature of 89.9 K. If the noise factor of the radio receiver is 4.0 dB calculate (a) the overall noise factor of the feeder, amplifier and receiver, and (b) the system noise temperature.

1.3 A radio receiver has a noise factor of 5 dB and is connected to an aerial of noise temperature 133 K by a feeder of (a) 0 dB loss and (b) 1.76 dB loss. Calculate the output noise power if the bandwidth is 10 MHz, and the gain of the receiver is 60 dB.

1.4 An amplifier has a noise factor of 7 dB and its output terminals are connected to a radio receiver whose noise factor is 10 dB. Calculate the minimum gain the amplifier must have for the system noise temperature to be less than 1500 K.

1.5 Three amplifiers have the parameters shown in Table 1.2. Determine the order in which the amplifiers ought to be connected in order to give the lowest overall noise factor. What is the value of this minimum noise factor?

Table 1.2

Amplifier	Gain (dB)	Noise factor (dB)
1	20	7
2	10	5
3	6	2

1.6 An aerial is connected to an amplifier that has a gain of 26 dB and a noise factor of 3 dB. The noise temperature of the aerial is 300 K and it delivers a signal power of 1 nW to the amplifier. If the available noise power from the aerial is −110 dBm calculate (a) the input signal-to-noise ratio, (b) the output signal-to-noise ratio.

1.7 An aerial whose noise temperature is 20 K is connected by a waveguide feeder of 0.3 dB loss to a low-noise amplifier of noise temperature 10 K and gain 28 dB. The output of the low-noise amplifier is connected to a travelling-wave tube that has a noise factor of 10 dB and a gain of 25 dB. If the noise bandwidth of the system is 2.8 MHz, calculate what signal power must be delivered by the aerial to give an output signal-to-noise ratio of 30 dB.

1.8 The noise generated within an RF amplifier can be assumed to be generated in an equivalent resistance of 56 kΩ across the input terminals. The noise temperature of this resistance is 290 K and the bandwidth of the amplifier is 10 kHz. Calculate the output signal-to-noise ratio of the amplifier when the input signal is a 100 µV voltage sinusoidally modulated 30% at 1 kHz.

1.9 Explain why the first stage of a radio receiver should have a low noise factor and a high gain. Why, for the latter stages may gain be more important than noise factor? A radio receiver has a noise factor of 9 dB and a bandwidth of 100 kHz. Calculate the input signal power needed to give an output signal-to-noise ratio of 20 dB.

1.10 (a) Show that the r.m.s. noise voltage generated in the parallel combination of a resistor R and a capacitor C is given by $\sqrt{(kT/C)}$ V.
   (b) Calculate the variation in the noise temperature of a circuit as its noise factor is varied from 0 to 2 dB.

1.11 A network operates at 17°C with a bandwidth of 20 kHz. Calculate (a) the noise power density and (b) the output noise power.

1.12 Show that the output signal-to-noise ratio of an amplifier is less than the input signal-to-noise ratio by the ratio $T_S/(T_n + T_S)$, where T_S is the noise temperature of the source and T_n is the noise temperature of the amplifier.

1.13 The noise factor of a radio receiver is 5.8 dB. An amplifier of gain 8 dB is connected between the aerial and the receiver when the overall noise factor is found to be still 5.8 dB. Determine the noise factor of the amplifier.

1.14 A radio receiver has an RF amplifier of gain 20 dB and noise factor 2.2 dB which is followed first by a mixer of 4 dB loss and 10 dB noise factor, and then by an IF amplifier of 10 dB noise factor and 120 kHz bandwidth. The minimum allowable signal level (the sensitivity) is 1.2 µV. Calculate the minimum signal-to-noise ratio at the output of the IF amplifier (the input to the demodulator).

1.15 (a) A radio receiving system incorporates an LNA that has a noise factor of 1.45 dB and a bandwidth of 25 MHz. Determine in dBW the system noise referred to the input terminals.
   (b) Noise at a noise temperature of 18 K appears at the input of an LNA that has a noise temperature of 21 K and a bandwidth of 25 MHz. Calculate the output noise power in dBW.

1.16 An aerial of noise temperature $T_A = 12$ K is connected to an LNA of noise temperature 4.5 K by a feeder of 0.25 dB loss. Calculate the input noise power to the system in a bandwidth of 1 MHz.

1.17 (a) Determine an expression for the current noise generator in Fig. 1.1. (b) Calculate the noise current generated at room temperature in a bandwidth of 5 MHz if the conductance is 100 µS.

1.18 A radio receiver with a noise factor of 8 dB is connected to an aerial with a noise temperature of 60 K. Calculate the system noise temperature. An LNA is fitted at the front end of the receiver. If the noise factor of the receiver is 2.5 dB and its gain is 12 dB determine the new system noise temperature.

1.19 A radio receiver is required to produce a minimum output signal-to-noise ratio of 40 dB. The receiver has an RF stage with a noise factor of 3 dB and a large gain and is connected to the aerial by a feeder of loss 2 dB. Determine whether the system is satisfactory when the aerial noise temperature is 280 K and the input signal-to-noise ratio is 48 dB.

1.20 (a) Calculate in dBW the noise power in a 1 MHz bandwidth. (b) Calculate the noise power at the output of a radio receiver with a noise factor of 3 dB.

2 Amplitude modulation

After reading this chapter you should be able to:

(a) Understand the principle of double-sideband amplitude modulation (DSBAM).
(b) Determine the amplitudes and frequencies of the components of a DSBAM wave.
(c) Calculate the modulation factor of a DSBAM wave.
(d) Determine the r.m.s. value and the power content of a DSBAM wave.
(e) Measure the depth of modulation of a DSBAM wave.
(f) Understand why overmodulation must be avoided.
(g) Use phasor diagrams to represent amplitude-modulated waveforms.
(h) Understand the principles and uses of single-sideband amplitude modulation.
(i) Compare the relative merits of the different versions of amplitude modulation.

Modulation is the process by which an information-carrying signal – often known as the baseband signal – is shifted to another part of the frequency spectrum. There are two main reasons why modulation is necessary in a radio system.

1 For an aerial to radiate energy efficiently the wavelength of the signal must be of the same order as the physical dimensions of the aerial and this means that radio frequencies must be employed.
2 The various radio services have each been allocated particular frequency bands by the International Telecommunications Union (ITU). The different radio stations operating in an allocated frequency band must, of course, be positioned at different points within that frequency band so that a wanted signal can be selected from all those signals that are simultaneously present at the receiving aerial.

The modulation method employed may be either analogue or digital. Analogue modulation essentially consists of using the baseband, or modulating, signal to vary *one* of the three variables of a sinusoidal *carrier wave*. If the instantaneous voltage v_c of the carrier wave is

$$v_c = V_c \sin(\omega_c t + \theta) \tag{2.1}$$

then:

(a) The amplitude V_c of the carrier may be varied; this is *amplitude modulation*.
(b) The frequency $\omega_c/2\pi$ may be varied; this is *frequency modulation*.
(c) The phase θ can be varied to give *phase modulation*.

It will be seen in Chapter 3 that frequency and phase modulation are very similar processes and they are often jointly referred to as *angle modulation*. Amplitude modulation is commonly employed for a variety of radio applications and may use double-sideband, single-sideband or independent-sideband versions of the basic modulation scheme. Digital modulation is considered in Chapter 4.

Double-sideband amplitude modulation; sinusoidal modulating signal

For a sinusoidal carrier wave to be amplitude modulated the amplitude of the carrier must vary in the same way as the instantaneous voltage of the modulating signal. If the modulating voltage is $V_m(t)$ then the instantaneous voltage of the modulated carrier wave is

$$v_c = [V_c + V_m(t)] \sin \omega_c t \tag{2.2}$$

in which the phase angle θ of the unmodulated carrier is assumed, for convenience, to be zero.

When the modulating signal is a sine wave, i.e. $V_m(t) = V_m \sin \omega_m t$, equation (2.2) becomes

$$v_c = [V_c + V_m \sin \omega_m t] \sin \omega_c t \tag{2.3}$$

The amplitude or *envelope* of the modulated wave has the same waveform as the modulating signal which, in this case, is sinusoidal as shown by Fig. 2.1. The

Fig. 2.1 *Sinusoidally modulated AM wave*

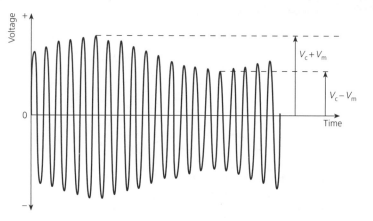

Fig. 2.2 *Spectrum diagram of a sinusoidally modulated AM wave*

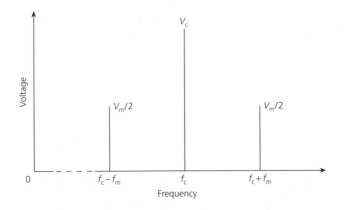

envelope varies sinusoidally between a maximum value of $V_c + V_m$ and a minimum value of $V_c - V_m$.

Equation (2.3) can be expanded, using the trigonometric identity $2 \sin A \sin B = \cos(A - B) - \cos(A + B)$, to give

$$v_c = V_c \sin \omega_c t + (V_m/2) \cos(\omega_c - \omega_m)t - (V_m/2) \cos(\omega_c + \omega_m)t \qquad (2.4)$$

The sinusoidally modulated carrier wave contains components at three different frequencies: (a) the lower side frequency $f_c - f_m$; (b) the carrier frequency f_c; and (c) the upper side frequency $f_c + f_m$. The modulating signal frequency f_m is *not* present in the modulated waveform. The component frequencies of a modulated waveform can be shown by a spectrum diagram and Fig. 2.2 gives the spectrum diagram for the amplitude-modulated wave described by equation (2.4).

EXAMPLE 2.1

A 5 V peak, 5 MHz carrier wave is amplitude modulated by a 2 kHz, 2 V sinusoidal signal. Determine the frequencies and amplitudes of each component contained in the amplitude-modulated waveform.

Solution

The components of the modulated wave are:

(a) the carrier frequency $f_c = 5$ MHz at 5 V;
(b) the lower side frequency $f_c - f_m = 4.998$ MHz at 1 V; and
(c) the upper side frequency $f_c + f_m = 5.002$ MHz at 1 V. (*Ans.*)

Modulation factor

The *modulation factor* of an amplitude-modulated waveform expresses the degree to which the amplitude of the carrier is varied from its unmodulated value. Modulation factor m is defined by equation (2.5):

$$m = (\text{r.m.s. value of } V_m(t))/(\text{r.m.s. value of unmodulated carrier}) \tag{2.5}$$

When m is expressed as a percentage it is generally known as the *depth of modulation*. For a sinusoidally modulated wave:

$$m = (V_m/\sqrt{2})/(V_c/\sqrt{2}) = V_m/V_c \tag{2.6}$$

or

$$m = [(V_c + V_m) - (V_c - V_m)]/[(V_c + V_m) + (V_c - V_m)]$$
$$= (\text{maximum voltage} - \text{minimum voltage})/(\text{maximum voltage} + \text{minimum voltage}) \tag{2.7}$$

EXAMPLE 2.2

A 12 V carrier wave is amplitude modulated to a depth of 40%. Calculate (a) the maximum and minimum voltages of the modulated waveform, (b) the modulating signal voltage, and (c) the voltage of each of the side-frequency components.

Solution

(a) $V_{max} = V_c + V_m = 12 + 0.4 \times 12 = 16.8$ V
 $V_{min} = V_c - V_m = 12(1 - 0.4) = 7.2$ V (*Ans.*)
(b) $V_m = mV_c = 0.4 \times 12 = 4.8$ V (*Ans.*)
(c) $V_{SF} = 4.8/2 = 2.4$ V (*Ans.*)

The maximum depth of modulation that a practical amplitude modulator is able to produce without generating distortion in excess of a specified limit is generally restricted to about 80%.

The expression, (2.3), for the instantaneous voltage of a sinusoidally modulated amplitude-modulated wave can be rewritten in terms of the modulation factor as

$$v_c = V_c(1 + m \sin \omega_m t) \sin \omega_c t \tag{2.8}$$

EXAMPLE 2.3

The instantaneous voltage of an amplitude-modulated wave is given by

$$v = 100(1 + 0.64 \sin 3000\pi t) \sin 2.5 \times 10^6 t \text{ V}$$

Determine (a) the carrier voltage, (b) the modulating signal voltage, and (c) the voltages of the upper and lower side frequencies.

Solution

(a) $V_c = 100$ V (*Ans.*)
(b) $V_m = 0.64 \times 100 = 64$ V (*Ans.*)
(c) $V_{SF} = 64/2 = 32$ V (*Ans.*)

The r.m.s. value

The r.m.s. value of an amplitude-modulated wave is the square root of the sum of the squares of the r.m.s. values of each of its component frequencies. Thus, for a sinusoidally modulated wave

$$V = \sqrt{[(V_c/\sqrt{2})^2 + (mV_c/2\sqrt{2})^2 + (mV_c/2\sqrt{2})^2]}$$
$$= \sqrt{[(V_c^2/2)(1 + m^2/2)]}$$

or

$$V = (\text{r.m.s. carrier voltage})[\sqrt{(1 + m^2/2)}] \tag{2.9}$$

EXAMPLE 2.4

A carrier has an r.m.s. current of 10 A. When the carrier is sinusoidally modulated the current rises to 11.2 A. Determine the depth of modulation.

Solution

$$11.2 = 10\sqrt{(1 + m^2/2)}$$

$$125.44/100 = 1.2544 = 1 + m^2/2$$

Therefore,

$$m = \sqrt{(2 \times 0.2544)} = 0.713 \ (\textit{Ans.})$$

PRACTICAL EXERCISE 2.1

Aim: To measure the depth of modulation of an amplitude-modulated wave.
Components and equipment: Signal generator. CRO. *True* r.m.s. responding ammeter.
Procedure:

(a) Connect the output of the signal generator to the Y1 input of the CRO. Then set the signal generator to a frequency of 1 MHz and a voltage of 10 V. Set the signal generator to deliver an amplitude-modulated wave and the modulating signal to 1 kHz at 2 V.

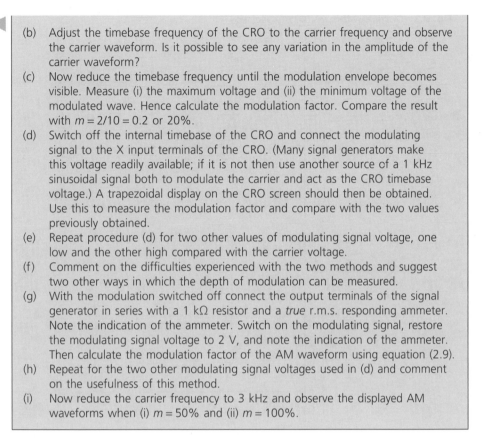

(b) Adjust the timebase frequency of the CRO to the carrier frequency and observe the carrier waveform. Is it possible to see any variation in the amplitude of the carrier waveform?

(c) Now reduce the timebase frequency until the modulation envelope becomes visible. Measure (i) the maximum voltage and (ii) the minimum voltage of the modulated wave. Hence calculate the modulation factor. Compare the result with $m = 2/10 = 0.2$ or 20%.

(d) Switch off the internal timebase of the CRO and connect the modulating signal to the X input terminals of the CRO. (Many signal generators make this voltage readily available; if it is not then use another source of a 1 kHz sinusoidal signal both to modulate the carrier and act as the CRO timebase voltage.) A trapezoidal display on the CRO screen should then be obtained. Use this to measure the modulation factor and compare with the two values previously obtained.

(e) Repeat procedure (d) for two other values of modulating signal voltage, one low and the other high compared with the carrier voltage.

(f) Comment on the difficulties experienced with the two methods and suggest two other ways in which the depth of modulation can be measured.

(g) With the modulation switched off connect the output terminals of the signal generator in series with a 1 kΩ resistor and a *true* r.m.s. responding ammeter. Note the indication of the ammeter. Switch on the modulating signal, restore the modulating signal voltage to 2 V, and note the indication of the ammeter. Then calculate the modulation factor of the AM waveform using equation (2.9).

(h) Repeat for the two other modulating signal voltages used in (d) and comment on the usefulness of this method.

(i) Now reduce the carrier frequency to 3 kHz and observe the displayed AM waveforms when (i) $m = 50\%$ and (ii) $m = 100\%$.

Overmodulation

The depth of modulation of a sinusoidally modulated AM wave must never be allowed to become greater than 100% because distortion of the modulation envelope would then occur. When the modulation factor is 1, or 100%, the envelope of the modulated voltage varies between a maximum value equal to twice the peak carrier voltage and a minimum value equal to zero volts. If the modulating voltage is increased to give a larger modulation factor, when $V_m > V_c$, the modulation envelope will no longer be sinusoidal. The modulation envelope will no longer have (more or less) the same waveform as the modulating signal and this means that the modulation envelope is distorted. The modulated waveform then contains extra, unwanted, frequency components. Overmodulation is sometimes known as *splatter*.

Two examples of the effects of overmodulation are shown by Fig. 2.3. Figure 2.3(a) shows a 100% modulated waveform whose envelope is sinusoidal. Figure 2.3(b) shows a 110% modulated waveform whose envelope is clearly not sinusoidal. The waveform given by Fig. 2.3(c) is 120% modulated and its envelope is even more distorted. This means that the greater the degree of overmodulation the more the modulation envelope is distorted.

Fig. 2.3 *Overmodulation: (a) 100% modulation*

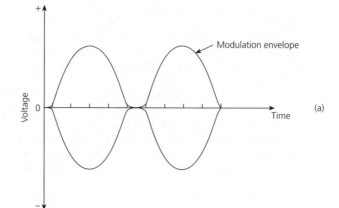

(a)

(b) 110% modulation

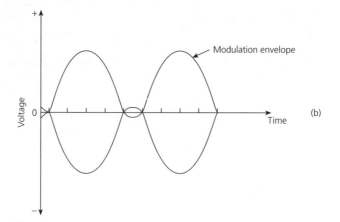

(b)

(c) 120% modulation

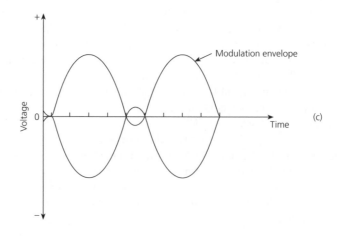

(c)

Aim: To observe the effects of overmodulating a carrier.
Components and equipment: Signal generator. CRO. Spectrum analyser.
Procedure:

(a) Connect the output terminals of the signal generator to the Y1 input of the CRO. Set the frequency of the signal generator to 1 MHz and turn on the amplitude modulation. Set the modulating frequency to 1 kHz with a modulation depth of 50%.
(b) Set the timebase of the CRO to about 0.1 ms and observe the modulation envelope.
(c) Increase the depth of modulation to 100% and note the modulation envelope.
(d) Increase the depth of modulation to (i) 105% and (ii) 110% and note the modulation envelope. With some signal generators it may be necessary to use an external modulating signal to increase the modulation depth above 100%.
(e) If a spectrum analyser is available use it to determine the frequencies contained in the overmodulated waves. Draw the spectrum diagram for each case. Hence give two reasons why overmodulation is not desirable.

Power

The power developed by an AM wave is the sum of the powers developed by the carrier component and by the lower and upper side-frequency components.

The total power P_T developed in a resistance R is

$$P_T = V^2/R = [(V_c/\sqrt{2})(1 + m^2/2)]^2/R = (V_c^2/2R)(1 + m^2/2) \text{ W} \tag{2.10}$$

or

$$P_T = \text{carrier power}(1 + m^2/2) \tag{2.11}$$

The carrier power is $V_c^2/2R$ W and the total power in the side frequencies is $m^2V_c^2/4R$ W.

The *transmission efficiency* η of an AM wave is the ratio

(total side-frequency power)/(total transmitted power)

Therefore,

$$\eta = [(m^2V_c^2)/4R]/[(V_c^2/2R)(1 + m^2/2)] \times 100\%$$
$$= m^2/(2 + m^2) \times 100\% \tag{2.12}$$

The maximum value for the modulation factor m is unity and then the transmission efficiency η is 33.3%. For any other value of m the side-frequency power will be an even smaller percentage of the total power. This means that DSBAM is not a very efficient method of transmitting information from one point to another. On the other hand, DSBAM can be demodulated by a relatively simple envelope (diode) detector that produces an output voltage which is proportional to the modulation envelope.

EXAMPLE 2.5

A 10 kW carrier wave is sinusoidally amplitude modulated to a depth of 70%.
(a) Calculate the total side-frequency power and (b) determine what percentage of
the total power it is.

Solution

(a)   From equation (2.11),

$$P_T = 10\,(1 + 0.7^2/2) = 12.45 \text{ kW}$$

Hence, the side-frequency power is

$$12.45 - 10 = 2.45 \text{ kW } (Ans.)$$

(b)   Expressed as a percentage of the total power,

$$\text{side-frequency power} = 19.68\% \ (Ans.)$$

Peak envelope power

The peak envelope power of an AM wave is of importance since it determines the
required power-handling capacity of the final RF amplifier in the radio transmitter.

If the carrier power is P_T and the depth of modulation is m then the average power
contained in the modulated wave is $P_T(1 + m^2/2)$. The peak carrier voltage is equal to
$\sqrt{(2P_c R)}$ V, where R is the resistance in which the power is developed, and the peak
voltage of each side-frequency component is $m\sqrt{(2P_c R)}/2$ V.

When the carrier, lower side-frequency and upper side-frequency components are
instantaneously in phase with one another the peak voltage of the modulated wave is

$$\sqrt{(2P_c R)} + 2m[\sqrt{(2P_c R)}]/2 = (1 + m)\sqrt{(2P_c R)} \text{ V}$$

Hence the instantaneous peak power is

$$P_{\text{peak}} = [(1 + m)\sqrt{(2P_c R)}]^2/R = 2P_c(1 + m)^2 \text{ W} \tag{2.13}$$

EXAMPLE 2.6

A 1 kW carrier is amplitude modulated to a depth of 60%. Calculate (a) the average
power and (b) the peak power dissipated.

Solution

(a) $P_T = 1000\,(1 + 0.6^2/2) = 1180 \text{ W } (Ans.)$
(b) $P_{\text{peak}} = 2 \times 1000 \times 1.6^2 = 5120 \text{ W } (Ans.)$

Fig. 2.4 *Amplitude modulation sidebands*

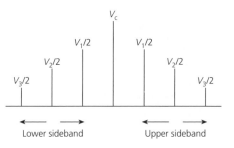

DSBAM: non-sinusoidal modulating signal

When a carrier is amplitude modulated by a non-sinusoidal modulating signal $V_m(t)$, extra frequency components appear in the modulated wave. Fourier analysis of a non-sinusoidal signal shows that it contains components at a fundamental frequency, plus one or more components at other frequencies. Each of these component frequencies will modulate the carrier to produce corresponding lower and upper side frequencies in the modulated waveform. If

$$V_m(t) = V_1 \sin \omega t + V_2 \sin 2\omega t + V_3 \sin 3\omega t \text{ V}$$

the instantaneous voltage of the modulated wave is

$$v_c = [V_c + V_1 \sin \omega t + V_2 \sin 2\omega t + V_3 \sin 3\omega t] \sin \omega_c t \text{ V} \tag{2.14}$$

Equation (2.14) can be expanded to give

$$
\begin{aligned}
v_c = {} & V_c \sin \omega_c t + (V_1/2)\cos(\omega_c - \omega)t + (V_2/2) \cos(\omega_c - 2\omega)t + (V_3/2) \cos(\omega_c - 3\omega)t \\
& - (V_1/2) \cos(\omega_c + \omega)t - (V_2/2) \cos(\omega_c + 2\omega)t - (V_3/2) \cos(\omega_c + 3\omega)t \tag{2.15}
\end{aligned}
$$

Equation (2.15) shows that the modulated wave now contains both lower and upper *sidebands* that are symmetrically situated either side of the carrier frequency. Figure 2.4 shows the spectrum diagram for the waveform represented by equation (2.15).

EXAMPLE 2.7

A 10 V, 1 MHz carrier is amplitude modulated by the signal

$$v = 5 \sin 2000\pi t + 2.5 \sin 4000\pi t + 1.25 \sin 8000\pi t \text{ V}$$

Determine the amplitude and frequency of each component in the modulated waveform.

Solution

The component frequencies of the modulated waveform are:

(a) carrier frequency: 1 MHz at 10 V;
(b) lower side frequencies: 0.999 MHz at 2.5 V; 0.998 MHz at 1.25 V and 0.996 MHz at 0.625 V;
(c) upper side frequencies: 1.001 MHz at 2.5 V; 1.002 MHz at 1.25 V and 1.004 MHz at 0.625 V *(Ans.)*

Modulation factor

The modulation factor of a non-sinusoidally modulated carrier wave is given by the ratio

$$\text{(r.m.s. value of modulating signal)/(r.m.s. value of carrier)} \qquad (2.16)$$

(i.e. equation (2.5) again).

EXAMPLE 2.8

A carrier wave $v_c = 10 \sin(8 \times 10^6 t)$ V is amplitude modulated by the signal $4 \sin(2 \times 10^3 t) + 1 \cos(6 \times 10^3 t)$ V. Calculate the depth of modulation of the modulated wave.

Solution

The r.m.s. value of the modulating signal voltage is

$$V = \sqrt{[(4^2 + 1^2)/2]} = 2.916 \text{ V}$$

and hence

$$m = 2.916/(10/\sqrt{2}) = 0.412 \quad \text{or} \quad 41.2\% \text{ (Ans.)}$$

Instantaneous voltage

The instantaneous value of an AM wave can be written in terms of the modulation factor:

- For two-tone modulation:

$$v_c = V_c(1 + m_1 \sin \omega_1 t + m_2 \sin \omega_2 t) \sin \omega_c t \qquad (2.17)$$

- For three-tone modulation:

$$v_c = V_c[1 + m_1 \sin \omega_1 t + m_2 \sin \omega_2 t + m_3 \sin \omega_3 t] \sin \omega_c t \qquad (2.18)$$

- For a general complex modulating signal $V_m(t)$:

$$v_c = V_c[1 + V_m(t)/V_c] \sin \omega_c t \qquad (2.19)$$

When a carrier is amplitude modulated by a voice signal whose peak amplitude is such that the peaks of the modulation envelope reach 100% modulation, the average modulation depth is then approximately 30%.

R.M.S. value

For a three-tone modulated wave,

$$V = \sqrt{[(V_c/\sqrt{2})^2 + m_1^2 V_c^2/4 + m_2^2 V_c^2/4 + m_3^2 V_c^2/4]}$$

or

$$V = (\text{r.m.s. carrier voltage})[\sqrt{(1 + m_1^2/2 + m_2^2/2 + m_3^2/2)}]$$

or

$$V = (\text{r.m.s. carrier voltage})[\sqrt{(1 + m_T^2/2)}] \tag{2.20}$$

where $m_T = \sqrt{(m_1^2 + m_2^2 + m_3^2)}$.

EXAMPLE 2.9

A carrier wave has an r.m.s. voltage of 10 V. It is amplitude modulated by a signal having components at frequencies f_1 and f_2 when its r.m.s. voltage rises to 11.5 V. If the depth of modulation due to one of the components is 60% calculate the depth of modulation caused by the other component.

Solution

From equation (2.20), $11.5 = 10\sqrt{(1 + m_T^2/2)}$. Hence,

$$1.3225 = 1 + m_T^2/2 \quad \text{or} \quad m_T = 0.803$$

Therefore,

$$m_2 = \sqrt{(0.803^2 - 0.6^2)} = 0.534 \quad \text{or} \quad 53.4\% \ (Ans.)$$

If the modulating signal is of rectangular shape the number of frequency components it contains is very large and an alternative approach to the determination of the modulation factor will give a simpler and more accurate result. Suppose that the rectangular waveform has a peak value of V_m V. The maximum value of the modulated carrier will be $V_c + V_m$ V and the minimum value will be $V_c - V_m$ V (see Fig. 2.5). The r.m.s. value of the modulated waveform is

$$V = \sqrt{(1/T) \int_0^T v^2 dt} = (V_c/\sqrt{2})^2 [\sqrt{(1 + m_T^2/2)}] \tag{2.21}$$

Fig. 2.5 *Carrier amplitude modulated by a rectangular signal*

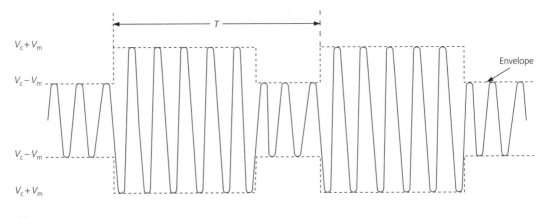

EXAMPLE 2.10

An 8 V peak carrier wave is amplitude modulated by a square waveform of peak value 5 V. Calculate (a) the r.m.s. value of the modulated waveform and (b) its depth of modulation.

Solution

(a) The maximum value of the modulated wave is 13 V and the minimum value is 3 V. Hence

$$V = \sqrt{\left[(1/T)\left(\int_0^{T/2} 13^2 \sin^2 \omega_c t \, dt + \int_{T/2}^{T} 3^2 \sin^2 \omega_c \, dt\right)\right]}$$

$$= \sqrt{\left[(1/T)\left(\int_0^{T/2} (169/2)(1 - \cos 2\omega_c t) \, dt + \int_{T/2}^{T} (9/2)(1 - \cos 2\omega_c t) \, dt\right)\right]}$$

$$= \sqrt{\left[(1/T)\left(\int_0^{T/2} 84.5 \, dt + \int_{T/2}^{T} 4.5 \, dt\right)\right]}$$

since the mean value of $\cos 2\omega_c t$ over half a cycle is zero,

$$V = \sqrt{\{(1/T)[84.5 \times T/2 + 4.5(T - T/2)]\}}$$
$$= \sqrt{44.5} = 6.67 \text{ V } (Ans.)$$

(b) $6.67 = (8/\sqrt{2})[\sqrt{(1 + m_T^2/2)}]$, or

$m_T = 0.884 = 88.4\% \ (Ans.)$

EXAMPLE 2.11

A 1 V carrier is amplitude modulated by the signal $v = V \cos \omega t + (V/2) \cos 2\omega t$. (a) Determine the maximum modulation factor that can be employed without overmodulation occurring. (b) Use the modulation factor calculated in (a) to tabulate and plot the modulation envelope.

Solution

The instantaneous voltage of the modulated wave is

$$v = [1 + m \cos \omega t + (m/2) \cos 2\omega t] \cos \omega_c t$$

To avoid overmodulation, the amplitude $A = [1 + m \cos \omega t + (m/2) \cos 2\omega t]$ of the modulated wave must be always equal to, or greater than, zero. The minimum value for A can be determined by differentiating A with respect to t and equating the result to zero. Thus

$$dA/dt = -m\omega \sin \omega t - (m/2)(2\omega) \sin 2\omega t$$
$$= -m\omega \sin \omega t - 2\omega m \sin \omega t \cos \omega t$$
$$= -m\omega \sin \omega t(1 + 2 \cos \omega t) = 0$$

This equation is true when $\sin \omega t = 0$ and also when $(1 + 2 \cos \omega t) = 0$. Thus $\cos \omega t = -1/2$, and $\omega t = 120°$. Hence $2\omega t = 240°$ and $\cos 2\omega t = -1/2$.
Then, at $\omega t = 120°$,

$$A = (1 - m/2 - m/4) = 1 - 3m/4 \quad \text{or} \quad m = 4/3 \; (Ans.)$$

(b) Tabulated values for the amplitude of each component in the modulated wave are given in Table 2.1, with extra points in the vicinity of 120° given in Table 2.2. The envelope of the modulated wave is shown plotted in Fig. 2.6. (Ans.)

Table 2.1

ωt (deg)	0	30	60	90	120	150	180
$\cos \omega t$	1	0.87	0.5	0	−0.5	−0.87	−1
4/3 $\cos \omega t$	1.33	1.16	0.67	0	−0.67	−1.16	−1.33
$\cos 2\omega t$	1	0.5	−0.5	−1	−0.5	0.5	1
4/6 $\cos 2\omega t$	0.67	0.33	−0.33	−0.67	−0.33	0.33	0.67
A	3	2.49	1.34	0.33	0	0.17	0.34

ωt (deg)	210	240	270	300	330	360
$\cos \omega t$	−0.87	−0.5	0	0.5	0.87	1
4/3 $\cos \omega t$	−1.16	−0.67	0	0.67	1.16	1.33
$\cos 2\omega t$	0.5	−0.5	−1	−0.5	0.5	1
4/6 $\cos 2\omega t$	0.33	−0.33	−0.67	−0.33	0.33	0.67
A	0.17	0	0.33	1.34	2.49	3

Table 2.2

ωt	100°	125°	130°	135°
cos ωt	−0.17	−0.57	−0.64	−0.71
4/3 cos ωt	−0.23	−0.77	−0.86	−0.94
cos 2ωt	−0.94	−0.34	−0.17	0
4/6 cos 2ωt	−0.63	−0.23	−0.12	0
A	0.14	0.007	0.03	0.06

Fig. 2.6

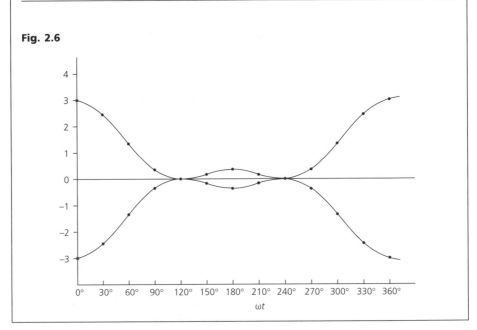

Phasor representation of an AM wave

The frequency spectrum of a sinusoidally modulated DSBAM wave contains components at the carrier frequency f_c and at the lower and upper side frequencies, $f_c \pm f_m$. Equation (2.4) can be rewritten as

$$v_c = V_c \sin \omega_c t + (V_m/2) \sin[(\omega_c - \omega_m)t + \pi/2] + (V_m/2) \sin[(\omega_c + \omega_m)t - \pi/2] \quad (2.22)$$

and this allows the spectrum to be represented by the phasor diagram given in Fig. 2.7(a). The figure contains three phasors, one for each component, whose length is proportional to voltage. Each phasor rotates in the anti-clockwise direction at its own angular velocity and the instantaneous envelope of the modulated wave is given by the phasor sum of the three phasors; in Fig. 2.7(a) the two side-frequency phasors are in anti-phase with one another and so mutually cancel out. Consequently, the instantaneous modulation envelope is equal to the unmodulated carrier voltage. To obtain the envelope over one cycle of the modulating signal it is more convenient to take the

Fig. 2.7 *Phasor representation of a DSB wave*

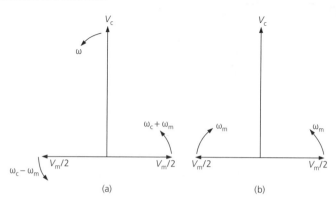

(a)   (b)

Fig. 2.8 *Phasor diagram of a DSB wave over one complete cycle of the modulating signal*

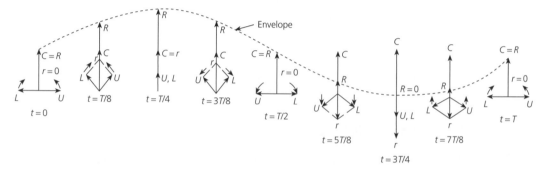

carrier phasor as the reference and assume it to be both stationary and in the vertical plane. This is shown by Fig. 2.7(b); the two side-frequency phasors will then rotate in opposite directions with angular velocity ω_m.

Figure 2.8 shows the positions of the side-frequency phasors, and of the phasor sum of all three phasors, for intervals of $T/8$, where T is the periodic time of the modulating signal. For each time interval the phasor sum gives the instantaneous value, represented by R, of the modulated wave; joining these together gives the positive envelope of the wave. The negative envelope can be obtained in similar fashion.

Distortion of an AM wave

A DSBAM waveform will suffer a reduction in its modulation depth and/or distortion if, in its transmission through a network or system, its side frequencies are either amplified or attenuated by a different amount from one another and/or from the carrier. If, for example, a sinusoidally modulated wave with a depth of modulation of 75% is applied to a tuned amplifier that has a gain of A_v at the carrier frequency and 3 dB less gain at each of the two side frequencies, then the output depth of modulation will be $75/\sqrt{2} = 53\%$.

EXAMPLE 2.12

A 1 MHz carrier is sinusoidally modulated to a depth of 80% by a 5 kHz signal. The modulated wave is passed through an amplifier which has a voltage gain of A_v at 1 MHz, $0.9A_v$ at 0.995 MHz, and $0.8A_v$ at 1.005 MHz. Calculate the depth of modulation of the output waveform.

Solution

At the output of the amplifier: carrier voltage $= V_c$; lower side-frequency voltage $= 0.9 \times 0.4V_c = 0.36V_c$; and upper side-frequency voltage $= 0.8 \times 0.4V_c = 0.32V_c$.
The r.m.s. voltage of the output waveform is

$$V = \sqrt{[(V_c/\sqrt{2})^2 + (0.36V_c/\sqrt{2})^2 + (0.32V_c/\sqrt{2})^2]}$$
$$= (V_c/\sqrt{2})^2[\sqrt{(1 + 0.1296 + 0.1024)}]$$
$$= (V_c/\sqrt{2})^2[1 + 0.232]$$

Hence,

$$m^2/2 = 0.232 \quad \text{or} \quad m = 68.1\% \ (Ans.)$$

Percentage distortion

The calculation of the percentage distortion caused by one side frequency being amplified more than the other is more difficult. To simplify the algebra, suppose that the upper side frequency is completely suppressed. Then the modulated wave is given by

$$v_c = V_c \sin \omega_c t + (mV_c/2) \cos(\omega_c - \omega_m)t$$
$$= V_c \sin \omega_c t[1 + (m/2) \sin \omega_m t] + (mV_c/2) \cos \omega_c t \cos \omega_m t$$

The envelope of the modulated waveform is given by

$$A = \sqrt{\{V_c^2[1 + (m/2) \sin \omega_m t]^2 + (mV_c/2) \cos \omega_m t)^2\}}$$
$$= V_c\sqrt{[1 + m \sin \omega_m t + (m^2/4) \sin^2 \omega_m t + (m^2/4) \cos^2 \omega_m t]}$$
$$= V_c\sqrt{[1 + m^2/4 + m \sin \omega_m t]}$$
$$= V_c\sqrt{(1 + m^2/4)}\left(1 + \frac{m \sin \omega_m t}{2(1 + m^2/4)} - \frac{m^2 \sin^2 \omega_m t}{8(1 + m^2/4)^2} + \ldots\right)$$
$$= V_c\sqrt{(1 + m^2/4)}\left(1 - \frac{m^2}{16(1 + m^2/4)^2} + \frac{m \sin \omega_m t}{2(1 + m^2/4)} + \frac{m^2 \cos 2\omega_m t}{16(1 + m^2/4)^2} + \ldots\right)$$

The percentage second-harmonic distortion is

$$\frac{m^2}{16(1 + m^2/4)^2} \times \frac{2(1 + m^2/4)}{m} \times 100 = \frac{m}{8(1 + m^2/4)} \times 100 \qquad (2.23)$$

A carrier wave is sinusoidally modulated to a depth of 30% and has one of its side frequencies suppressed. Calculate the percentage second-harmonic distortion of the modulation envelope.

Solution

From equation (2.23), the percentage second-harmonic distortion is

$$[0.3/8(1 + 0.3^2/4)] \times 100 = 3.67\% \ (Ans.)$$

Double-sideband suppressed-carrier amplitude modulation

Most of the power carried by a DSBAM wave is developed by the carrier frequency component and this means that the transmission efficiency is low. Since the carrier conveys zero information it is not necessary that it be transmitted and it can be suppressed at the modulation stage if a *balanced modulator* is used (p. 82).

Phasor diagram

The phasor diagram of a double sideband suppressed-carrier (DSBSC) AM wave is shown in Fig. 2.9. The envelope of the modulated wave is not sinusoidal, indicating that distortion has occurred. This means that the signal cannot be demodulated at the receiver unless the carrier component is reinserted with *both* the correct frequency *and* phase; this is known as *coherent detection*. A coherent detector recovers the baseband signal by multiplying the signal to be demodulated by a reinsert carrier that has the same frequency *and* phase as the original carrier at the transmitter.

If there is an error θ in the phase of the reinserted carrier the instantaneous voltage of the wave will be

$$v = V_c \sin(\omega_c t + \theta) + mV_c \sin \omega_c t \sin \omega_m t$$
$$= V_c[\cos \omega_c t \sin \theta + \sin \omega_c t(\cos \theta + m \sin \omega_m t)]$$

Fig. 2.9 *Phasor diagram of a DSBSC amplitude-modulated wave*

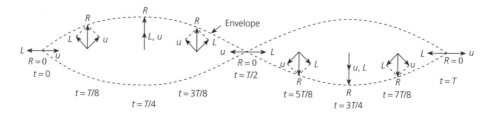

The envelope of this wave is $A = V_c\sqrt{[\sin^2\theta + (\cos\theta + m\sin\omega_m t)^2]}$, or

$$A = V_c\sqrt{[(1-\cos 2\theta)/2 + \cos^2\theta + 2\cos\theta\, m\sin\omega_m t + m^2\sin^2\omega_m t]}$$
$$= V_c\sqrt{[1/2 - \cos 2\theta/2 + 1/2 + \cos 2\theta/2 + 2m\cos\theta\sin\omega_m t + m^2/2 - (m^2/2)\cos 2\omega_m t]}$$
$$= V_c\sqrt{[1 + m^2/2 + 2m\cos\theta\sin\omega_m t - (m^2/2)\cos\omega_m t]}$$
$$= V_c\sqrt{(1 + m^2/2)[1 + (4m\cos\theta\sin\omega_m t)/(2 + m^2)}$$
$$- (m^2\cos 2\omega_m t)/(2 + m^2) + \dots\,]\qquad(2.24)$$

Equation (2.24) shows that the envelope of the reconstructed DSBSC AM waveform varies in a manner that is a function of both the modulating signal and the phase error. If the phase error θ is 90°, $\cos\theta = 0$ and then there will be no variation of the envelope at the signal frequency. What amplitude modulation there is occurs at twice the signal frequency and there is considerable phase modulation as well.

EXAMPLE 2.14

A 20 V carrier is amplitude modulated to a depth of 60%. The carrier is then removed and after a phase shift of 90° is reinserted. Calculate the resulting peak phase deviation of the envelope of the modulated wave.

Solution

The two side-frequency phasors both have a voltage of $(0.6 \times 20)/2 = 6$ V. The peak phase deviation is (see Fig. 2.10)

$$\phi_{max} = \tan^{-1}(12/20) = 31°\ (Ans.)$$

Fig. 2.10

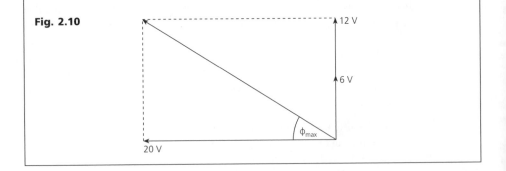

The requirement for the reinserted carrier to be correct in both frequency and phase is not simple to satisfy and requires the use of complex circuitry. This used to be a problem in the past but now, with the use of radio integrated circuits, is fairly easy to achieve. The DSBSC version of amplitude modulation is not used for ordinary radio communication purposes but it is employed for (a) the transmission of colour information in television broadcasting, and (b) the transmission of stereo information in VHF sound broadcasting.

Fig. 2.11 *Phasor diagram of a SSBSC amplitude-modulated wave*

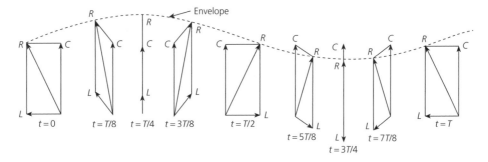

Single-sideband suppressed-carrier amplitude modulation

The information carried by an AM wave is contained in both sidebands and so it is not necessary for both sidebands to be transmitted. Either sideband can be suppressed at the transmitter without any loss of data. The instantaneous voltage of a *single-sideband suppressed-carrier amplitude modulated* (SSBSCAM – usually abbreviated to just SSB) wave is either

$$v = (mV_c/2) \cos(\omega_c + \omega_m)t \qquad\qquad (2.25)$$

or

$$v = (mV_c/2) \cos(\omega_c - \omega_m)t \qquad\qquad (2.26)$$

Figure 2.11 shows the phasor diagram of an SSBSCAM signal with its carrier component reinserted with the correct phase. The modulation envelope can be seen to be sinusoidal. The maximum phase error is 90° and if the phasor diagram is redrawn with this carrier reinsert error it will be found that the envelope is still sinusoidal. This means that the phase of the reinserted carrier is not important for a system transmitting voice signals.

Two methods of suppressing the unwanted sideband are employed: (a) the output of the balanced modulator can be passed through a filter of the appropriate bandwidth, or (b) the phasing technique shown in Fig. 2.12 can be used. The use of a filter to remove the unwanted sideband becomes more difficult at high frequencies because the frequency gap between the sidebands becomes a small percentage of the filter's centre frequency. A practical bandpass filter has an attenuation–frequency characteristic that does not roll off quickly enough with the result that either the low-frequency part of the SSB signal is attenuated, or a part of the unwanted sideband is transmitted. For this reason the modulation process is often carried out at a low frequency before the wanted sideband is shifted to the desired position in the frequency spectrum.

Fig. 2.12 *The phasing method of producing an SSBSCAM signal*

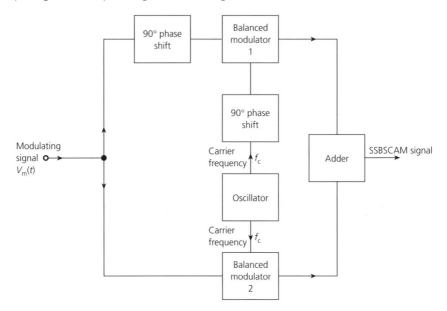

Referring to Fig. 2.12, the two balanced modulators have both the modulating and carrier voltages applied to them, but the upper modulator has both its inputs phase shifted by 90° before they are applied. The input signals to the upper modulator are $V_m \sin(\omega_m t + 90°)$ and $V_c \sin(\omega_c t + 90°)$ so that its output current contains the components

$$\cos[(\omega_c t + 90°) - (\omega_m t + 90°)] - \cos[(\omega_c t + 90°) + (\omega_m t + 90°)]$$

or

$$\cos(\omega_c t - \omega_m t) - \cos(\omega_c t + \omega_m t + 180°)$$

The inputs to the lower modulator are $V_m \sin \omega_m t$ and $V_c \sin \omega_c t$ and so its output current includes the components $\cos(\omega_c t - \omega_m t) - \cos(\omega_c t + \omega_m t)$.

The outputs of the two modulators are added together to give an output of $2 \cos(\omega_c - \omega_m)t$.

If it is required to transmit the upper sideband instead of the lower sideband *either* one of the 90° phase-shifting circuits must be moved to the lower part of the circuit.

The phasing method of suppressing one sideband has the advantage that it is easy to switch from transmitting one sideband to transmitting the other. One circuit which can be used as the audio phase-shifting circuit is shown by Fig. 2.12; here $\omega_1 = 1/C_1 R_1$ and $\omega_2 = 1/C_2 R_2$ specify the audio bandwidth that is shifted by 90°.

Aim: To investigate a 90° phase-shifting network

Components and equipment: Centre-tapped transformer, four variable 5 kΩ resistors, four 0.1 μF capacitors. Dual-beam CRO. Audio-frequency oscillator.

Procedure:

(a) Construct the circuit given in Fig. 2.13.

(b) Connect the Y1 input of the CRO to the modulating signal input, and the Y2 input to the output of the circuit. Adjust the oscillator to give a 2 kHz signal at 2 V.

(c) Vary the values of the resistors until the output waveform leads the input waveform by 90°. Vary the frequency of the oscillator and note the range of frequencies over which the phase change remains more or less equal to 90°.

(d) Determine the values of the resistors.

(e) Replace the variable resistors with (i) $R_1 = 56$ kΩ and (ii) $R_2 = 47$ kΩ. Calculate the theoretical frequency band for approximately 90° phase shift and then by measurement check the accuracy of the calculations.

Fig. 2.13   *90° phase-shifting circuit*

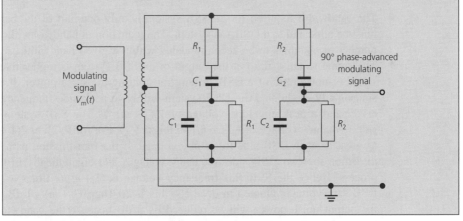

Demodulation of SSBSCAM signals

An SSBSCAM wave can be demodulated using either a product, or a switching, detector (p. 292). Suppose that the lower sideband is transmitted and arrives at the demodulator's input terminals. The output of a product detector is proportional to the product of the lower sideband signal and a locally generated carrier. Thus,

$$v_{out} = V \sin(\omega_c - \omega_m)t \; V_c \sin \omega_c t$$
$$= VV_c(\sin \omega_c t \cos \omega_m t - \sin \omega_m t \cos \omega_c t) \sin \omega_c t \qquad (2.27)$$

This expression includes the term $(VV_c/2) \cos \omega_m t$ which is the demodulated message signal and it can be extracted using a low-pass filter. If there is a frequency error $\delta \omega_c$ in the reinserted carrier the wanted output of the detector will be $(VV_c/2) \cos(\omega_m t + \delta\omega_c t)$. The frequency error that can be tolerated depends upon the type of signal involved. Since every frequency contained in the modulating signal is shifted by the same amount δf_c the harmonic relationship between the components is lost. The recommendation of the ITU-R is that the error should not be in excess of ± 2 Hz. However, it is found that for speech circuits an error of ± 20 Hz is hardly noticeable and as much as ± 50 Hz is tolerable.

If the reinserted carrier is of the correct frequency but there is a phase error θ the demodulated signal will contain a term $(VV_c/2) \cos(\omega_m t - \theta)$. For voice and music signals this error is of little consequence but it will matter for any system where the signal waveshape is of importance, e.g. the transmission of data signals.

Single-sideband compared with double-sideband amplitude modulation

Single-sideband operation of a radio system offers a number of advantages over double-sideband operation:

- The bandwidth required for an SSB system is only one-half of the bandwidth that must be allocated to a DSBAM system. The reduction in bandwidth allows a greater number of channels to be accommodated within a given bandwidth.
- The signal-to-noise ratio at the output of an SSB system is higher than the output signal-to-noise ratio of a DSB system transmitting the same power. If the carrier is sinusoidally modulated the DSB system will have peak side-frequency voltages of $mV_c/2$ and a peak envelope voltage of $V_c(1 + m)$ V. The SSB system will have a side-frequency voltage of $V_c(1 + m)$ V; this is $V_c(1 + m)/(mV_c/2)$, or $2(1 + m)/m$ times as great as each DSB side-frequency voltage. If the transmission path is free from distortion the two DSB side-frequency voltages add algebraically in the detection process. Hence the SSB side-frequency voltage is $(1 + m)/m$ times as great as the DSB sum voltage. Quoted in decibels, this is $20 \log_{10}[(1 + m)/m]$ dB. In addition, the output noise power will be reduced by 3 dB because the bandwidth has been halved. Therefore, the increase in the output signal-to-noise ratio given by SSB operation is

$$\text{signal-to-noise ratio increase} = 3 + 20 \log_{10}[(1 + m)/m] \text{ dB} \qquad (2.28)$$

The maximum possible value for the modulation factor m is unity and this gives the signal-to-noise ratio improvement as 9 dB. For any smaller value of m an even larger advantage is obtained.
- An SSB transmitter is more efficient than a DSB transmitter.
- Selective fading (p. 263) of DSB radio waves may cause considerable distortion when the carrier component fades relative to the side-frequencies. This effect does not occur in an SSB system because the received signal is demodulated against a reinserted carrier of constant amplitude.

A DSBAM system radiates a carrier power of 30 kW. The system is changed to operate using SSBSC and a radiated power of 10 kW. Calculate the change in the output signal-to-noise ratio of the system if the maximum depth of modulation is 75%.

Solution

From equation (2.28), the increase in the output signal-to-noise ratio is $3 + 20 \log_{10}(1.75/0.75) = 10.36$ dB. The decrease in the transmitted power is $10 \log_{10}(30/10) = 4.77$ dB. Therefore, the increase in output signal-to-noise ratio is

$10.36 - 4.77 = 5.59$ dB (*Ans.*)

Peak envelope power

The output power of an SSBSC radio transmitter is usually specified in terms of its *peak envelope power* (PEP). The PEP is the power developed by the peak value of the transmitted sideband and any pilot carrier. When there is no pilot carrier, or it is of very small amplitude, the term *peak sideband power* (PSP) is often employed instead.

2.1 A carrier wave has an r.m.s. value of 4 A when unmodulated which rises to 4.4 A when it is sinusoidally modulated. Calculate the depth of modulation. The carrier is then modulated by a bipolar square wave having the same peak value as the sine wave. Determine the r.m.s. value of the modulated wave.

2.2 A carrier wave has an r.m.s. value of 10 V when it is unmodulated and 10.8 V when it is sinusoidally modulated. Calculate its depth of modulation. The carrier is then modulated by a signal that contains components at two different frequencies and its r.m.s. value goes up to 10.8 V. If the depth of modulation due to one frequency is 40% calculate the depth of modulation produced by the other frequency. What is the overall depth of modulation?

2.3 A 1 MHz carrier wave is amplitude modulated to a depth of 80% by a 5 kHz sinusoidal signal and is then applied to a single tuned circuit that is resonant at 1 MHz and of Q factor 100. Calculate the depth of modulation of the output signal.

2.4 A carrier $12 \sin(8 \times 10^6 \pi t)$ V is amplitude modulated by the signal $v = 6 \sin(2000\pi t) + 3 \cos(4000\pi t)$ V. Calculate the depth of modulation. If the modulated wave is applied across a 100 Ω resistance calculate the power dissipated.

2.5 A tuned circuit has a Q factor of 60, a capacitance of 100 pF and is resonant at 455 kHz. It is effectively connected in parallel with the input resistance of a diode detector having a load resistance of 250 kΩ. If the detection efficiency is 86% calculate the effective Q-factor of the tuned circuit.

2.6 A carrier wave is amplitude modulated to a depth of 60%. One of its sidebands is then completely suppressed. Determine the percentage second-harmonic distortion of the modulation envelope.

2.7 Show that the improvement in system signal-to-noise ratio obtained by converting a DSB system to SSBSC working is given by $3 + 20 \log_{10}[(1 + m)/m]$ dB.

   The signal-to-noise ratio at the output of a radio system is 30 dB when an 80% modulated DSB 10 kW transmitter is used. Calculate the output signal-to-noise ratio when the system is converted to operate as SSBSC with a transmitted power of 4 kW.

2.8 A sinusoidal signal has an r.m.s. value of 10 V before it is amplitude modulated and 10.4 V after modulation. The modulated signal is passed through a network that attenuates the lower side frequency by 10 dB but leaves the carrier and upper side frequency unchanged. Calculate the r.m.s. value of the wave.

2.9 Show that a square-law device can be used for either amplitude modulation or demodulation.

2.10 A modulating signal has three frequency components of amplitudes 4.2 V, 2.1 V and 1.05 V respectively. If the carrier voltage is 10 V, calculate the modulation factor.

2.11 Expand equation (2.27) to show that it contains a term at the wanted modulating frequency.

2.12 A 20 kW radio transmitter is amplitude modulated by a sinusoidal signal to depth of 65%. Calculate (a) the total power transmitted, (b) the percentage of the total power in the carrier, and (c) the power in the lower side frequency.

2.13 A DSBAM transmitter has an unmodulated power output of 1 kW. The transmitter is simultaneously modulated by three sinusoidal voltages that respectively produce modulation factors of 0.25, 0.5 and 0.65. Calculate (a) the overall modulation factor, (b) the total power transmitted, and (c) the sideband power.

2.14 A carrier is amplitude modulated by the signal $v = V \cos \omega t + (V/3) \cos 2\omega t$. (a) Determine the maximum modulation factor that can be used without over-modulation occurring. (b) Using this value of modulation factor tabulate and sketch the envelope of the modulated waveform.

2.15 Explain the difference between *baseband* and *bandwidth*. Illustrate your answer with spectrum diagrams.

3 Angle modulation

After reading this chapter you should be able to:

(a) Analyse and describe frequency modulation.
(b) Understand the meanings of terms such as modulation index and deviation ratio.
(c) Explain that an FM wave contains a large number of frequency components and know how to determine the required bandwidth.
(d) Explain how phase modulation differs from frequency modulation and know why it is not often used in analogue systems.
(e) Calculate the signal-to-noise ratio in an FM system and understand why FM gives a better signal-to-noise ratio than AM.
(f) Understand why pre-emphasis and de-emphasis are employed.

When a sinusoidal carrier wave $V_c \sin(\omega_c t + \theta)$ is angle modulated the amplitude V_c of the carrier is maintained at a constant value and its instantaneous frequency and phase $\omega_c t + \theta$ are varied by the modulating signal. There are two possibilities: either the frequency $\omega_c t$ of the carrier wave or its phase θ can be made to vary in direct proportion to the instantaneous amplitude of the modulating signal voltage. The differences between *frequency modulation* and *phase modulation* are not obvious, since a change in frequency must inherently involve a change in phase and a change in phase alters the frequency. The differences between frequency and phase modulation are listed in Table 3.4 (p. 66).

Frequency modulation is much more commonly employed than phase modulation and it possesses a number of advantages over amplitude modulation, particularly if a wide bandwidth can be made available. In particular, it provides an improvement in the quality of the received signal as long as the signal level at the demodulator input is greater than a minimum value known as the FM threshold. Frequency modulation is employed for sound broadcasting in the VHF band, for the sound signal of UHF television broadcast transmissions, for some land, sea and air mobile systems, and for older UHF/SHF multi-channel telephony systems including those routed via communications satellites (all modern wideband systems use some form of digital modulation), and for analogue mobile telephones. Phase modulation is not often used in analogue radio communication and it finds its main application in the field of digital radio communication. It is, however, often employed as a stage in the generation of an FM wave.

Frequency modulation

Frequency modulation of a carrier wave occurs when the instantaneous deviation from the unmodulated carrier frequency is directly proportional to the instantaneous amplitude of the modulating signal voltage. A sinusoidally modulated carrier wave is shown by Fig. 3.1. When time $t = 0$ the instantaneous frequency of the wave is equal to the unmodulated carrier frequency. As the modulating signal voltage increases in the positive direction the frequency of the carrier wave increases also and it reaches its maximum value when the modulating signal voltage is at its peak positive value. When the modulating signal voltage starts to fall towards zero volts the instantaneous carrier frequency falls as well, and when the modulating signal voltage is zero the carrier frequency is back to its unmodulated value. When the modulating signal voltage goes negative the instantaneous carrier frequency falls below its unmodulated value and reaches its lowest value when the modulating signal voltage is at its negative peak value. After this point the modulating signal voltage decreases towards zero and the instantaneous carrier frequency increases towards its unmodulated value.

The amount by which the carrier frequency deviates from its unmodulated value is known as the *frequency deviation*. Frequency deviation has no inherent limit, like 100% modulation in an AM system, and for any particular FM system a maximum permissible frequency deviation must be specified. This maximum frequency deviation is known as the *rated system deviation* f_{d}. Once the rated system deviation has been determined it sets the maximum modulating voltage that can be applied to the frequency modulator. Most of the time the modulating voltage will be smaller than this maximum value and then the frequency deviation is kf_{d}, where

$k =$ (modulating signal voltage)/(maximum allowable modulating signal voltage)

(3.1)

Clearly, k can have any value between zero and unity.

Fig. 3.1 *Frequency modulated wave*

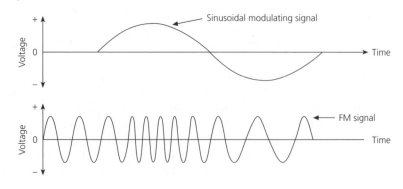

Instantaneous voltage

If the modulating signal is $V_m(t)$ the instantaneous carrier frequency f_i will be

$$f_i = f_c + kf_d V_m(t) \tag{3.2}$$

The instantaneous angular velocity ω_i of the modulated wave is

$$\omega_i = 2\pi f_i = d\theta/dt = 2\pi f_c + 2\pi kf_d V_m(t)$$

and

$$\theta = \int_0^t \omega_i \, dt = \int_0^t 2\pi f_c \, dt + \int_0^t 2\pi kf_d V_m(t) \, dt$$

or

$$\theta = \omega_c t + 2\pi kf_d \int_0^t V_m(t) \, dt \tag{3.3}$$

The instantaneous voltage v_c of the FM carrier wave is $v_c = V_c \sin \theta$ or

$$v_c = V_c \sin \left(\omega_c t + 2\pi kf_d \int_0^t V_m(t) \, dt \right) \tag{3.4}$$

The peak phase deviation of the carrier depends upon the integral with respect to time of the modulating signal voltage. If the modulating signal voltage is a sinusoidal waveform, i.e. $V_m(t) = V_m \cos \omega_m t$, then equations (3.2) and (3.3) become

$$f_i = f_c + kf_d \cos \omega_m t \tag{3.5}$$

and

$$\theta = \omega_c t + (kf_d/f_m) \sin \omega_m t \tag{3.6}$$

respectively. The instantaneous voltage of the wave is

$$v_c = V_c \sin[\omega_c t + (kf_d/f_m) \sin \omega_m t] \tag{3.7}$$

Modulation index

The peak phase deviation of an FM wave is known as the *modulation index* m_f. It is the ratio of the frequency deviation to the modulating frequency. Thus

$$m_f = kf_d/f_m \tag{3.8}$$

Very often the expression for the instantaneous voltage of a sinusoidally modulated FM wave is written in terms of the modulation index. Thus

$$v_c = V_c \sin(\omega_c t + m_f \sin \omega_m t) \tag{3.9}$$

Deviation ratio

When an FM system is designed the maximum permissible values for both the frequency deviation of the carrier and the modulating signal frequency must be used. Then the modulation index is known as the *deviation ratio D*:

$$D = f_d/f_{m(max)} \tag{3.10}$$

The deviation ratio of a particular FM system is fixed, whereas the modulation index varies continuously with change in the modulating signal voltage and/or frequency. In the BBC VHF sound broadcast system, $f_d = 75$ kHz and $f_{m(max)} = 15$ kHz so that $D = 5$.

EXAMPLE 3.1

When a 2 kHz sinusoidal signal is applied to a frequency modulator the 90 MHz carrier deviates by ±16 kHz. (a) Calculate the phase deviation of the carrier. (b) Calculate the new frequency and phase deviations if the modulating signal has both its voltage and its frequency doubled.

Solution

(a) The phase deviation is

$$(16 \times 10^3)/(2 \times 10^3) = 8 \text{ rad } (Ans.)$$

(b) The phase deviation is

$$(32 \times 10^3)/(4 \times 10^3) = 8 \text{ rad } (Ans.)$$

and

frequency deviation $= 32$ kHz $(Ans.)$

EXAMPLE 3.2

An FM system has a rated system deviation of 51 kHz and a maximum modulating signal frequency of 6.8 kHz. A 4 V, 2 kHz test tone produces a frequency deviation of 16 kHz. Calculate (a) the modulation index produced by the test tone, (b) the deviation ratio, (c) the frequency deviation produced by a 6 V, 2.5 kHz input signal, and (d) the voltage at 5 kHz needed to give the rated system deviation.

Solution

(a) $m_f = 16/2 = 8$ $(Ans.)$
(b) $D = 51/6.8 = 7.5$ $(Ans.)$
(c) $kf_d = 16 \times (6/4) = 24$ kHz $(Ans.)$
(d) The voltage for rated system deviation at 5 kHz is

$$4 \times (51/16) = 12.75 \text{ V } (Ans.)$$

Frequency spectrum of an FM wave

The frequency spectrum of an FM wave is much more complicated than that of an AM wave. For small values of modulation index, say $m_f \leq 0.25$, the FM wave consists of a carrier component f_c and two side frequencies $f_c \pm f_m$, just like a DSBAM waveform. If, however, the modulation index is increased, second-order side frequencies $f_c \pm 2f_m$ will also appear. Further increase in the value of m_f leads to the appearance of more and more higher orders of side frequencies, and the frequency spectrum rapidly becomes complex. Equation (3.9) can be rewritten (using the identity $\sin(A + B) = \sin A \cos B + \sin B \cos A$) in the form

$$v_c = V_c \sin \omega_c t \cos(m_f \sin \omega_m t) + V_c \cos \omega_c t \sin(m_f \sin \omega_m t) \tag{3.11}$$

If the value of m_f is less than unity equation (3.11) can be expanded using the series forms of $\sin \theta$ and $\cos \theta$, but if m_f is larger than unity expansion requires the use of Bessel functions.

Small values of m_f

The series forms of $\sin \theta$ and $\cos \theta$ are

$$\sin \theta = \theta - \theta^3/3! + \theta^5/5! - \ldots$$

$$\cos \theta = 1 - \theta^2/2! + \theta^4/4! - \ldots$$

If m_f is very small, say less than 0.25, m_f^2 and all higher powers of m_f will be negligibly small, and then $\cos(m_f \sin \omega_m t) \approx 1$ and $\sin(m_f \sin \omega_m t) \approx m_f \sin \omega_m t$.
Equation (3.11) can then be written as

$$\begin{aligned} v_c &= V_c \sin \omega_c t + V_c\, m_f \cos \omega_c t \sin \omega_m t \\ &= V_c \sin \omega_c t + (m_f V_c/2)[\sin(\omega_c + \omega_m)t - \sin(\omega_c - \omega_m)t] \end{aligned} \tag{3.12}$$

(using the identity $2 \cos A \sin B = \sin(A + B) - \sin(A - B)$. This equation shows that the spectrum of a narrow-band FM (NBFM) system consists of the carrier f_c and the lower and upper side frequencies $f_c \pm f_m$. Comparing equation (3.12) with equation (2.4) it can be seen that NBFM is equivalent to DSBAM with the lower side-frequency phase shifted by 180°.

0.25 < m_f < 1

If the modulation index m_f is greater than 0.25 and less than unity,

$$\cos(m_f \sin \omega_m t) \approx 1 - (m_f^2 \sin^2 \omega_m t)/2$$

$$\sin(m_f \sin \omega_m t) \approx m_f \sin \omega_m t$$

This means that the instantaneous voltage of the FM wave is

$$\begin{aligned} v_c &= V_c \sin \omega_c t[(1 - m_f^2 \sin^2 \omega_m t)/2] + m_f V_c \cos \omega_c t \sin \omega_m t \\ &= V_c \sin \omega_c t - (m_f^2 V_c \sin \omega_c t)/4 + (m_f^2 V_c \sin \omega_c t \cos 2\omega_m t)/4 + m_f\, V_c \cos \omega_c t \sin \omega_m t \end{aligned}$$

Hence, using the trigonometric identity $2 \cos A \sin B = \sin(A + B) - \sin(A - B)$,

$$\begin{aligned} v_c &= V_c \sin \omega_c t(1 - m_f^2/4) + (m_f V_c/2)[\sin(\omega_c + \omega_m)t - \sin(\omega_c - \omega_m)t] \\ &\quad + (m_f^2 V_c/8)[\sin(\omega_c + 2\omega_m)t + \sin(\omega_c - 2\omega_m)t] \end{aligned} \tag{3.13}$$

EXAMPLE 3.3

A 5 kHz sinusoidal modulating signal of amplitude 10 V produces a peak frequency deviation of 25 kHz in an FM transmitter. A 7.5 kHz, 24 V modulating signal is applied to the modulator. Calculate (a) the peak frequency deviation and (b) the number of side frequencies in a bandwidth ±50 kHz centred on the unmodulated carrier frequency.

Solution

(a) The frequency deviation is

$(24/10) \times 25 = 60$ kHz *(Ans.)*

(b) Side frequencies occur at 7.5 kHz intervals above and below the unmodulated carrier frequency, so 50 kHz can take six side frequencies ($6 \times 7.5 = 45$ kHz) and hence

total side frequencies $= 12$ *(Ans.)*

EXAMPLE 3.4

A 10 V, 100 MHz carrier wave is frequency modulated by a 2000 Hz tone when the frequency deviation is 1000 Hz. Calculate the amplitudes of the first-order and the second-order side frequencies in the FM wave.

Solution

Now $m_f = kf_d/f_m = 0.5$. From equation (3.13),

carrier amplitude $= 10(1 - 0.5^2/4) = 9.375$ V *(Ans.)*

first-order side-frequency amplitude $= (0.5 \times 10)/2 = 2.5$ V *(Ans.)*

second-order side-frequency amplitude $= (0.5^2 \times 10)/8 = 0.3125$ V *(Ans.)*

$m_f > 1$

When the modulation index m_f is equal to, or greater than, unity expansion of equation (3.11) requires the use of Bessel functions. The use of these functions shows the presence of a number of higher-order side frequencies in the FM wave. This is shown by.

$$v_c = V_c J_0(m_f) \sin \omega_c t$$
$$+ V_c J_1(m_f)[\sin(\omega_c + \omega_m)t - \sin(\omega_c - \omega_m)t]$$
$$+ V_c J_2(m_f)[\sin(\omega_c + 2\omega_m)t + \sin(\omega_c - 2\omega_m)t]$$
$$+ V_c J_3(m_f)[\sin(\omega_c + 3\omega_m)t - \sin(\omega_c - 3\omega_m)t]$$
$$+ V_c J_4(m_f)[\sin(\omega_c + 4\omega_m)t + \sin(\omega_c - 4\omega_m)t]$$
$$+ \ldots \tag{3.14}$$

Table 3.1 Bessel functions

Modulation index	1	2	3	4	5	6	7	8	9	10	11	12
Carrier	0.77	0.22	−0.26	−0.4	−0.18	0.15	0.30	0.17	−0.09	−0.25	−0.17	0.05
1st order	0.44	0.58	0.34	−0.07	−0.33	−0.28	−0.01	0.24	0.25	0.04	−0.18	−0.22
2nd order	0.12	0.36	0.49	0.36	0.05	−0.24	−0.30	−0.11	0.15	0.26	0.14	−0.09
3rd order	0.02	0.13	0.31	0.43	0.37	0.12	−0.17	−0.29	−0.18	0.06	0.23	0.20
4th order	–	−0.03	0.13	0.28	0.39	0.36	0.16	−0.11	−0.27	−0.22	−0.02	0.18
5th order	–	–	0.04	0.13	0.26	0.36	0.35	0.19	−0.06	−0.23	−0.24	−0.07
6th order	–	–	0.01	0.05	0.13	0.25	0.34	0.34	0.24	−0.02	−0.21	−0.24
7th order	–	–	–	0.02	0.05	0.13	0.23	0.32	0.33	0.22	0.02	−0.17
8th order	–	–	–	–	0.02	0.06	0.13	0.22	0.31	0.32	0.23	0.05
9th order	–	–	–	–	–	0.02	0.06	0.13	0.22	0.29	0.31	0.23

where $J_0(m_f)$, $J_1(m_f)$, $J_2(m_f)$, etc., are Bessel functions of order 0, 1, 2, etc., and give the amplitudes of the carrier and side-frequency components. Examination of equation (3.14) shows that the frequency spectrum contains the carrier component at frequency f_c, the odd-order side frequencies $f_c \pm f_m$, $f_c \pm 3f_m$, $f_c \pm 5f_m$, etc., and even-order side frequencies $f_c \pm 2f_m$, $f_c \pm 4f_m$, $f_c \pm 6f_m$, etc. All the odd-order lower side frequencies have a *minus* sign in front of the lower side-frequency component, whilst all the even-order lower side-frequency components are preceded by a *plus* sign. The side frequencies are spaced either side of the carrier frequency at intervals equal to the modulation frequency and its harmonics.

The amplitudes of the carrier, and of the various side frequencies, vary with the modulation index but not in a simple manner. The carrier and each order of side frequency reach a positive maximum value and then decrease and go cyclically through zero, reach a negative maximum value and then rise towards zero, and so on. Side frequencies of the same order have the same amplitude so that the frequency spectrum is symmetrical about the carrier frequency. Table 3.1 gives the values of $J_0(m_f)$, the carrier component, $J_1(m_f)$, the first-order side-frequency components, $J_2(m_f)$, the second-order side-frequency components, etc., for integer values of m_f from 1 to 8 and for side frequencies up to the 9th order. The greater the modulation index the larger is the number of side-frequency components in the FM wave. The data given in Table 3.1 is shown graphically by Fig. 3.2.

Table 3.2 shows the values of the modulation index, or the deviation ratio, at which the carrier, the first-, second- and third-order side frequencies are zero.

Figure 3.2 can be employed to determine the amplitudes, relative to the unmodulated carrier voltage, of each of the components of an FM wave. The amplitude of a component, for a particular value of m_f, or D, is obtained from the figure by projecting vertically upwards from the horizontal axis onto the required carrier, or nth-order side-frequency curve, and thence onto the vertical axis. Negative signs are (usually) ignored since only the magnitude of each component is (usually) required. The number of significant side frequencies, i.e. those of relative amplitude ±0.01 or greater, is equal to $(m_f + 1)$.

Fig. 3.2 *Showing how the amplitudes of the various components in an FM wave vary with the modulation index*

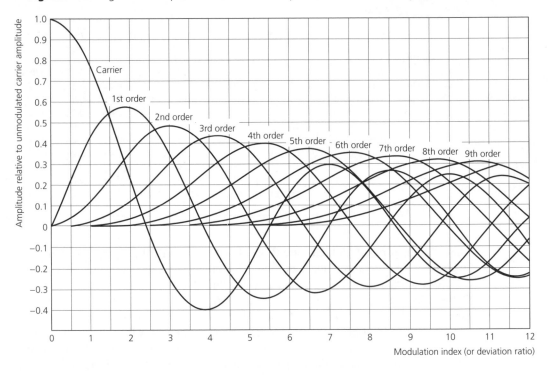

Table 3.2 **Modulation index m_f for zero carrier voltage**

Carrier	1st order	2nd order	3rd order
2.405	3.832	5.136	6.380
5.520	7.016	8.417	9.761
8.754	10.173	11.620	13.015
11.792	13.324	14.796	16.223
14.931	16.471	17.960	19.409

EXAMPLE 3.5

Plot the frequency spectrum diagrams of FM waves having a deviation ratio of (a) 0.5 and (b) 4.

Solution

The required spectrum diagrams are shown in Figs 3.3(a) and (b) respectively. The amplitudes of the components of Fig. 3.3(a) were calculated in Example 3.2 and should be compared.

Fig. 3.3 *Spectrum diagrams for FM waves with (a) $m_f = 0.5$ and (b) $m_f = 4$*

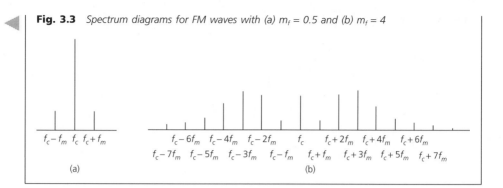

(a)

$f_c - f_m$ f_c $f_c + f_m$

(b)

$f_c - 6f_m$ $f_c - 4f_m$ $f_c - 2f_m$ f_c $f_c + 2f_m$ $f_c + 4f_m$ $f_c + 6f_m$

$f_c - 7f_m$ $f_c - 5f_m$ $f_c - 3f_m$ $f_c - f_m$ $f_c + f_m$ $f_c + 3f_m$ $f_c + 5f_m$ $f_c + 7f_m$

The phasor diagram of an FM wave

The phasor diagram of an NBFM wave that has first-order side frequencies only, has its lower and upper side-frequency phasors positioned symmetrically about a quadrature carrier phasor. This is shown by Fig. 3.4 for time intervals of $T/8$, where T is the periodic time of the modulating signal. As with the phasor diagram of the AM wave, it has been assumed that the carrier phasor is stationary in the vertical direction so that the lower and upper side-frequency phasors rotate in opposite directions with angular velocity $\pm\omega_m$. The phase of the resultant phasor, relative to the unmodulated carrier phasor, is varied in a linear manner either side of the carrier. The amplitude of the resultant phasor is *not* constant, which means that some amplitude modulation is present.

The phasor diagram of an FM wave having both first-order and second-order side frequencies is more complex. The second-order side frequencies have the same phase relationship to one another as do the AM side frequencies and they rotate with twice the angular velocity, i.e. at $\pm 2\omega_m$. Figure 3.5 shows the phasor diagram. The effect of the second-order side frequencies is to reduce the variations in the length of the resultant phasor and so reduce the amplitude modulation of the carrier. The second-order side frequencies do not affect the phase deviation of the resultant phasor from the carrier. In general, odd-order side frequencies contribute to the phase deviation of the carrier whilst even-order side frequencies tend to keep the amplitude of the modulated waveform constant. If *all* the side frequencies of an FM wave are included, the phasor diagram will have a constant-length resultant phasor R which deviates either side of the carrier phasor; this is shown by Fig. 3.6. The maximum phase deviation ϕ_{max} occurs when all the odd-order side-frequency phasors are instantaneously in phase with one another and in phase quadrature with the carrier phasor.

Fig. 3.4 *Phasor diagram of a NBFM wave*

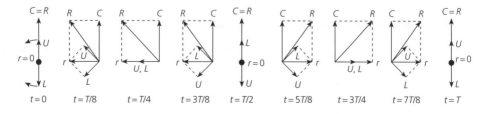

$t = 0$ $t = T/8$ $t = T/4$ $t = 3T/8$ $t = T/2$ $t = 5T/8$ $t = 3T/4$ $t = 7T/8$ $t = T$

Angle modulation **61**

Fig. 3.5 *Phasor diagram of an FM wave with both first-order and second-order side frequencies*

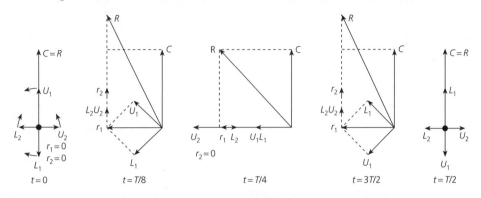

Fig. 3.6 *Resulting phasor diagram of an FM wave when all side frequencies are included*

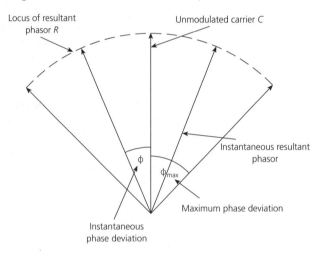

Any amplitude modulation that exists does not have any effect upon the output signal of the system. This is because FM receivers always incorporate an amplitude-limiting stage which provides a constant output voltage even when its input voltage varies. This means that any amplitude modulation is not pertinent to the recovery of the information signal.

Complex modulating signal

When a carrier is frequency modulated by a complex signal the resulting frequency spectrum is *not* the sum of the spectra produced by each component in the complex signal acting alone. The coefficient of each side frequency is no longer a single Bessel function but, instead, a series of products of Bessel functions.

Consider a carrier frequency modulated by the two-tone signal $V_m(t) = V_1 \sin \omega_1 t$ $+ V_2 \sin \omega_2 t$. Each component acting on its own will give a certain modulation index m_f and will produce a carrier and various side-frequency components. The magnitudes of these components can be obtained from Table 3.1. If the modulation index due to $V_1 \sin \omega_1 t$ acting alone is m_{f1} then the frequency components in the FM wave are J_{01} and J_{m1}; similarly $V_2 \sin \omega_2 t$ will give a modulation index of m_{f2} and components J_{02} and J_{m2}. For example, suppose that $m_{f1} = 2$; then from Table 3.1, $J_{01} = 0.2239$ and $J_{m1} = 0.5767$, 0.3528, 0.1289 and 0.0340.

When the carrier is modulated by the two-tone signal, the FM wave will contain components at the following frequencies:

(a) carrier frequency f_c of relative amplitude $J_{01} \times J_{02}$;
(b) side frequencies $f_c \pm m_{f1} f_1$ of relative amplitude $J_{m1} \times J_{02}$;
(c) side frequencies $f_c \pm m_{f2} f_2$ of relative amplitude $J_{m2} \times J_{01}$; and
(d) side frequencies $f_c \pm m_{f1} f_1 \pm m_{f2} f_2$ of relative amplitude $J_{m1} \times J_{m2}$.

Clearly, even two-tone modulation will give rise to a large number of frequencies in the FM wave.

Bandwidth required for an FM wave

It is difficult to determine the exact bandwidth that is occupied by an FM wave because of the large number of side frequencies that it may contain. Usually, it is necessary to band-limit the wave and not transmit all of the higher-order side frequencies. Between 98% and 99% of the signal power will be retained if $(m_f + 1)$ pairs of side frequencies are transmitted. The minimum bandwidth required is hence

$$\text{bandwidth} = 2f_m(m_f + 1) \tag{3.15}$$

or

$$\text{bandwidth} = 2(kf_d + f_m) \tag{3.16}$$

An FM system will, of course, be designed to transmit the most demanding modulating signal without excessive distortion. This signal is the one that produces the rated system deviation and which contains components at up to the maximum frequency $f_{m(max)}$ to be transmitted. The minimum bandwidth that must be provided for the transmission of this signal is given by equation (3.16), i.e.

$$\text{system bandwidth} = 2(f_d + f_{m(max)}) \tag{3.17}$$

The energy associated with the side frequencies outside of this bandwidth is small. Restricting the system bandwidth to the value specified by equation (3.17) will cause more distortion to a sinusoidally modulated wave than to a speech signal that contains random voltages at random frequencies and a distributed spectrum. If an FM signal is passed through a network whose bandwidth is smaller than specified by equation (3.17) it is said to be *overdeviated*.

EXAMPLE 3.6

The bandwidth occupied by an FM signal is 80 kHz when the modulating signal is 5 V at 10 kHz. What will be the occupied bandwidth if (a) the signal voltage increases to 10 V, (b) the frequency decreases to 5 kHz, or (c) both (a) and (b) occur together?

Solution

From equation (3.16), 80 kHz = $2(kf_d + 10)$ kHz or $kf_d = 30$ kHz.

(a) New $kf_d = 10/5 \times 30 = 60$ kHz; $B = 2(60 + 10) = 140$ kHz (*Ans.*)
(b) $B = 2(30 + 5) = 70$ kHz (*Ans.*)
(c) $B = 2(60 + 5) = 130$ kHz (*Ans.*)

EXAMPLE 3.7

An NBFM system has a frequency deviation of $0.1f_m$. Determine (a) the amplitudes of the side frequencies if $V_c = 10$ V when unmodulated, and (b) the percentage power in the carrier and first-order side frequencies.

Solution

Carrier voltage = $10(1 - 0.1^2/4) \approx 9.975$ V.

(a) First-order side-frequency voltage = $(0.1 \times 10)/2 \approx 0.5$ V (*Ans.*)
     Second-order side-frequency voltage = $(0.1^2 \times 10)/8 \approx 0.0125$ V (*Ans.*)
(b) Assuming that $R = 1\ \Omega$, then
     power at the carrier frequency = 99.5 W
     power at first-order side frequencies = $0.25 \times 2 = 0.5$ W
     power at second-order side frequencies = $1.5625 \times 10^{-4} \times 2 = 3.12 \times 10^{-4}$ W
     The percentage of power in carrier and first-order side frequencies is

$$(99.5 + 0.5 + 3.125 \times 10^{-4})/10^2 \approx 100\% \ (Ans.)$$

EXAMPLE 3.8

(a) Use Table 3.1 to determine the amplitudes of the side frequencies of an FM VHF sound broadcast system having $f_d = 75$ kHz and $f_{m(max)} = 15$ kHz. (b) Determine the required bandwidth for the system if 99% of the power is to be transmitted. (c) Compare the result with the bandwidth determined using equation (3.17). Assume $V_c = 1$ V and $R = 1\ \Omega$.

Solution

(a) $m_f = 75/15 = 5$. From Table 3.3 the following relative amplitudes are obtained:
     carrier 0.18, first order 0.33, second order 0.05, third order 0.37, fourth order

Table 3.3

	Carrier	1st	2nd	3rd	4th
Voltage (V)	0.1776	0.3276	0.0466	0.3648	0.3912
Power (mW)	31.54	107.32	2.17	133.08	153.04
Both SF (×2)	31.54	214.64	4.34	266.16	306.08
Cumulative					
Power (mW)	31.54	246.18	250.52	516.68	822.76
	5th	6th	7th	8th	
Voltage (V)	0.2611	0.1316	0.0534	0.0184	
Power (mW)	68.17	17.16	2.85	0.39	
Both SF (×2)	136.34	34.32	5.70	0.78	
Cumulative					
Power (mW)	959.1	999.42			

0.39, fifth order 0.26, sixth order 0.13, seventh order 0.05 and eighth order 0.02 (*Ans.*)

(b) Over 99% of the power is contained in the first six side frequencies. Hence

required bandwidth $= \pm 6 \times 15 = \pm 90$ kHz $= 180$ kHz (*Ans.*)

(c) From equation (3.17),

$B = 2(75 + 15) = 180$ kHz (*Ans.*)

Phase modulation

When a carrier is phase modulated the phase deviation of the carrier is directly proportional to the instantaneous amplitude of the modulating signal. Thus

$$\theta(t) = \omega_c t + k\Phi_d V_m(t) \tag{3.18}$$

where Φ_d is the peak phase deviation permitted in the system, known as the rated system deviation, and k (as for frequency modulation) is the ratio (modulating signal voltage)/(maximum permissible modulating signal voltage). The instantaneous voltage of a phase-modulated (PM) wave is

$$v_c = V_c \sin[\omega_c t + k\Phi_d V_m(t)] \tag{3.19}$$

or

$$v_c = V_c \sin[\omega_c t + m_p V_m(t)] \tag{3.20}$$

where m_p is the modulation index and is equal to the peak phase deviation of the carrier.

Table 3.4 *Frequency and phase modulation differences*		
Modulation	*Frequency deviation*	*Phase deviation*
Frequency	Proportional to the voltage of the modulating signal	Proportional to the voltage and inversely proportional to the frequency of the modulating signal
Phase	Proportional to both the voltage and the frequency of the modulating signal	Proportional to the voltage of the modulating signal

The instantaneous angular velocity ω_i of the PM wave is the rate of change of its phase, so

$$\omega_i = d[\omega_c t + k\Phi_d V_m(t)]/dt = \omega_c + k\Phi_d dV_m(t)/dt$$

and the instantaneous frequency is

$$f_i = f_c + (k\Phi_d/2\pi)dV_m(t)/dt \tag{3.21}$$

If the modulating signal is of sinusoidal waveform so that $V_m(t) = V_m \sin \omega_m t$, then

$$\theta = \omega_c t + k\Phi_d \sin \omega_m t \tag{3.22}$$

$$v_c = V_c \sin(\omega_c t + k\Phi_d \sin \omega_m t) \tag{3.23}$$

$$f_i = f_c + k\Phi_d f_m \cos \omega_m t \tag{3.24}$$

The differences between frequency modulation and phase modulation can now be seen by comparing equations (3.5) and (3.6) with (3.22) and (3.24). The results are shown in Table 3.4.

Equation (3.23) is of the same form as equation (3.8), where $m_p = k\Phi_d$, and it can be similarly expanded to show the presence of various orders of side frequencies. Although the two forms of angle modulation are similar their applications differ. Frequency modulation is used for VHF sound broadcasting and for some mobile systems, while some forms of phase modulation (see Chapter 4) are employed in wideband terrestrial and satellite systems (see Chapters 13 and 14). Phase modulation is more difficult to demodulate since demodulation requires the presence of an accurate reference phase; also it makes less efficient use of an available bandwidth than does frequency modulation, and so its signal-to-noise ratio is inferior. The phase modulation techniques used in wideband systems are forms of digital modulation. Table 3.4 shows that an FM signal is the same as a PM signal in which the modulating signal was integrated before it modulated the carrier. Conversely, an PM signal is a FM signal in which the modulating signal was differentiated before it modulated the carrier.

Consider two analogue systems, one frequency modulated and the other phase modulated, having a maximum modulating frequency of 15 kHz and a modulation index of 5. The number of significant side frequencies is then six so that a minimum bandwidth of

Table 3.5 FM and PM bandwidths

Modulating signal frequency (kHz)	Frequency modulation		Phase modulation	
	Modulation index	Bandwidth (kHz)	Modulation index	Bandwidth (kHz)
15	5	$6 \times 15 \times 2 = 180$	5	$6 \times 15 \times 2 = 180$
5	15	$16 \times 5 \times 2 = 160$	5	$6 \times 5 \times 2 = 60$
3	25	$26 \times 3 \times 2 = 156$	5	$6 \times 3 \times 2 = 36$
1	75	$76 \times 1 \times 2 = 152$	5	$6 \times 1 \times 2 = 12$

$6 \times 15 \times 2 = 180$ kHz must be provided. If the modulating frequency is reduced, in turn, to 5, 3 and 1 kHz, the modulation index will increase in the FM system but will remain constant in the PM system. Consequently, the number of significant side frequencies, and hence the occupied bandwidth, will vary as shown by Table 3.5.

Signal-to-noise ratio in an FM system

During the transmission of an FM signal both noise and interference voltages are superimposed upon the FM signal and these voltages will both amplitude and phase modulate the signal. The amplitude modulation is easily removed by passing the FM signal through a *limiter* in the FM receiver. Phase modulation of an FM signal, on the other hand, cannot be removed and it is only possible to minimise its effects upon the output signal-to-noise ratio of the system.

If an unmodulated carrier frequency of voltage V_s has a sinusoidal interfering voltage V_n superimposed upon it, the phasor diagram of the voltages is as shown by Fig. 3.7. In general, the noise voltage will not be at the same frequency as the unmodulated carrier and so its phasor will rotate about the top of the carrier phasor with an angular velocity ω_{diff}, where ω_{diff} is 2π times the difference in their frequencies. If the noise

Fig. 3.7 *Interference in an FM system*

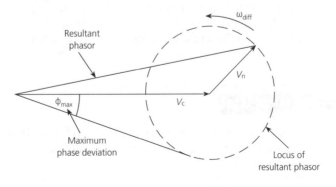

voltage is at a higher frequency than the carrier voltage the noise phasor will rotate in the anti-clockwise direction as shown in the figure, otherwise it will rotate in the clockwise direction.

The total voltage is given by the resultant phasor. Thus

$$v = V_c \sin \omega_c t + V_n \sin(\omega_c + \omega_{diff})t$$
$$= V_c \sin \omega_c t + V_n \sin \omega_c t \cos \omega_{diff}t + V_n \cos \omega_c t \sin \omega_{diff}t$$
$$= (V_c + V_n \cos \omega_{diff}t) \sin \omega_c t + V_n \cos \omega_c t \sin \omega_{diff}t$$
$$= V \sin(\omega_c t + \phi)$$

where

$$V = \sqrt{[(V_c + V_n \cos \omega_{diff}t)^2 + V_n^2 \sin^2 \omega_{diff}t]}$$
$$= \sqrt{[V_c^2 + V_n^2 + 2V_c V_n \cos \omega_{diff}t]}$$

$$\phi = \tan^{-1}[(V_n \sin \omega_{diff}t)/(V_c + V_n \cos \omega_{diff}t)]$$

Usually, $V_c \gg V_n$ and then

$$V \approx V_c[1 + (V_n/V_c) \cos \omega_{diff}t]$$

$$\phi = \tan^{-1}[(V_n/V_c) \sin \omega_{diff}t] \approx (V_n/V_c) \sin \omega_{diff}t$$

The magnitude V of the resultant voltage varies between the limits $V_c \pm V_n$ so that the FM signal is amplitude modulated. The resultant voltage has a sinusoidally varying phase, relative to the unmodulated carrier, with a peak phase deviation of V_n/V_c. The resulting frequency deviation f_{dev} is

$$f_{dev} = \omega_{dev}/2\pi = (1/2\pi)[d(V_n/V_c) \sin \omega_{diff}t]/dt$$
$$= (1/2\pi)[(V_n/V_c)\omega_{diff} \cos \omega_{diff}t]$$

or

$$f_{dev} = f_{diff}(V_n/V_c) \cos \omega_{diff}t \tag{3.25}$$

The peak frequency deviation is $f_{diff}(V_n/V_c)$ and the r.m.s. frequency deviation is $f_{diff}V_n/\sqrt{2}V_c$.

When the carrier and noise voltages are at the same frequency their difference frequency is zero and there is no output noise. The FM receiver will produce an output that consists solely of the stronger signal, the weaker signal being suppressed. This is sometimes known as the *capture effect*. This improvement in the signal-to-noise ratio at the output of the detector stage, which may be as large as 20 dB, is only obtained provided the input carrier-to-noise ratio is greater than a threshold value which is typically about 10 dB. The capture effect ensures that FM has a better performance than AM in the presence of fading.

EXAMPLE 3.9

A 10 mV, 100 MHz carrier has a 25 μV, 100.1 MHz interfering signal super-imposed upon it. Calculate the peak phase and frequency deviations of the carrier that are produced.

Solution

The peak phase deviation is

$$(25 \times 10^{-6})/(10 \times 10^{-3}) = 2.5 \times 10^{-3} \text{ rad } (Ans.)$$

The peak frequency deviation is

$$2.5 \times 10^{-3} \times 0.1 \times 10^{6} = 250 \text{Hz } (Ans.)$$

EXAMPLE 3.10

A 6 V, 100 MHz carrier wave is frequency modulated to have a rated system deviation of 51 kHz. During its transmission it has an interfering signal of 0.25 V at 99.985 MHz superimposed upon it. Calculate (a) the carrier-to-noise ratio at the detector input, and (b) the signal-to-noise ratio at the detector output.

Solution

Frequency deviation due to interfering signal $= (0.25/6) \times 15 \times 10^{3} = 625$ Hz.
Frequency deviation due to modulation $= 51$ kHz.
(a) Carrier-to-noise ratio is

$$20 \log_{10}(6/0.25) = 27.6 \text{ dB } (Ans.)$$

(b) Signal-to-noise ratio is

$$20 \log_{10}[(51 \times 10^{3})/625] = 38.24 \text{ dB } (Ans.)$$

Noise output power

The noise power δN_0 at the output of the detector in an FM receiver in an audio bandwidth of 0 to $f_{\text{m(max)}}$ is proportional to $(V_n^2 f^2)/(2V_c^2)$. Now $V_n^2/2 = N_0 = P\delta f$, where P is the noise power density spectrum in W Hz^{-1}. Hence

$$\delta N_0 = (KPf^2\delta f)/V_c^2$$

(K is the transfer function of the FM detector, i.e. an input Δf produces $K\Delta f$ volts at the output.)

The total noise output power in the audio bandwidth of 0 to $f_{\text{m(max)}}$ is

$$N_0 = \int_{-B}^{+B}(KPf^2/V_c^2) \ df = (2KP/V_c^2)\int_{0}^{B} f^2 \ df$$

$$= [(2KP/V_c^2) \ (f^3/3)]_0^B = (2KP/V_c^2)(B^3/3)$$

The bandwidth is from 0 to $f_{\text{m(max)}}$, so $B = f_{\text{m(max)}}$. Hence,

$$N_0 = 2KPf_{\text{m(max)}}^3/3V_c^2 \tag{3.26}$$

Thus the noise output power is proportional to $Pf_{\text{m(max)}}^3/V_c^2$.

Output signal-to-noise ratio

In an FM receiver the signal-to-noise ratio at the input to the detector, which is often known as the carrier-to-noise ratio, is determined by the receiver bandwidth up to the detector input, the received carrier power and the received noise and interference. The signal-to-noise ratio at the output of the detector is a function of the maximum modulating signal frequency, the modulation index and the carrier-to-noise ratio. Provided the carrier-to-noise ratio is greater than about 10 dB the FM detection process will give an improvement in the system signal-to-noise ratio.

The input signal-to-noise ratio, or carrier-to-noise ratio C/N, is

$$C/N = V_c^2/2PB_{IF} \tag{3.27}$$

where B_{IF} is the bandwidth of the receiver preceding the detector.

The r.m.s. output signal power is $Kf_{d(rms)}^2$ and hence, from equation (3.26), the output signal-to-noise ratio (S/N) is

$$
\begin{aligned}
S/N &= f_{d(rms)}^2/[2Pf_{m(max)}^3/3V_c^2] \\
&= (3V_c^2/2PB_{IF})[f_{d(rms)}^2 B_{IF})/f_{m(max)}^3) \\
&= (3C/N)(f_{d(rms)}^2 B_{IF}/f_{m(max)}^3)
\end{aligned}
\tag{3.28}
$$

For sinusoidal modulation $f_{d(rms)} = f_d/\sqrt{2}$ and hence equation (3.28) can be modified to give

$$
\begin{aligned}
S/N &= (C/N)\tfrac{3}{2}(B_{IF}f_d^2/f_{m(max)}^3) \tag{3.29} \\
&= (C/N)\tfrac{3}{2}B_{IF}D^2/f_{m(max)} \tag{3.30}
\end{aligned}
$$

where D is the deviation ratio.

EXAMPLE 3.11

The carrier-to-noise ratio at the input to the detector in an FM radio receiver is 12 dB. Calculate the output signal-to-noise ratio if $B_{IF} = 180$ kHz, $f_{m(max)} = 15$ kHz, and $f_d = 75$ kHz.

Solution

Since 12 dB is a voltage ratio of 3.98 and $D = 5$, then

$$S/N = (3.98 \times 1.5 \times 180 \times 10^3 \times 25)/(15 \times 10^3) = 1791 = 32.5 \text{ dB } (Ans.)$$

The triangular noise spectrum

Random noise can be considered to consist of a large number N of equal-amplitude, equally spaced, sinusoidal voltages in a bandwidth of N Hz. The previous analysis can then be applied to demonstrate that an FM system has a triangular noise voltage spectrum and a parabolic noise power spectrum.

Fig. 3.8 *The triangular noise spectrum*

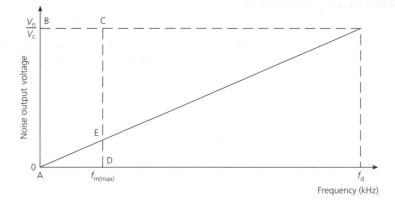

The output voltage of an FM detector is proportional to the frequency deviation of the input voltage. This means that the noise output voltage is proportional to frequency and hence has a triangular spectrum. The output noise voltage rises linearly from zero volts at zero frequency to a maximum, equal to V_n/V_c, at the frequency equal to the rated system deviation f_d (see Fig. 3.8). Usually, the passband of the audio amplifier which follows the detector will be less than the rated system deviation and it will remove all noise voltages at frequencies higher than $f_{m(max)}$. The output noise voltage of an AM receiver with the *same* signal and noise voltages would be proportional to V_n/V_c; thus the areas enclosed by the points ADE and ABCD represent, respectively, the output noise voltages of FM and AM systems having the same audio passband. Area ADE is smaller than area ABCD, which is an indication that the FM system has a smaller output noise than the AM system. This means that the use of frequency modulation instead of amplitude modulation can provide an increase in the output signal-to-noise ratio of a system.

Signal-to-noise ratio improvement of frequency modulation over amplitude modulation

The signal output power of an FM system is $K(kf_d)^2/2$ and the noise output power is equal to $2KPB^3/3V_c^2$, and so the output signal-to-noise ratio is

$$[(\sqrt{3}kf_d)/B]^2(V_c^2/4PB) = (\sqrt{3}m_f)^2(V_c^2/4PB)$$

An AM system, modulated to a depth of $m\%$, has an output signal-to-noise ratio of

$$(m^2P_c/2PB) = (m^2V_c^2/4PB)$$

For a proper comparison of the signal-to-noise ratios assume that both systems are 100% modulated, i.e. $m_f = D$ and $m = 1$. Then,

$$[\text{signal-to-noise ratio (FM)}]/[\text{signal-to-noise ratio (AM)}] = 3(D)^2 \tag{3.31}$$

or, in decibels,

$$\text{signal-to-noise ratio improvement} = 20\log_{10}(\sqrt{D}) \tag{3.32}$$

EXAMPLE 3.12

An AM system has an output signal-to-noise ratio of 30 dB. What output signal-to-noise ratio could be obtained if frequency modulation with a deviation ratio of 5 were employed instead and the transmitted power were reduced by 50%?

Solution

From equation (3.32) the improvement in signal-to-noise ratio is $20 \log_{10}(\sqrt{3} \times 5)$ = 18.75 dB. The 50% reduction in the transmitted power is equivalent to a reduction of $10 \log_{10} 2 = 6$ dB. Therefore, the new signal-to-noise ratio is

$$30 + 18.75 - 6 = 42.75 \text{ dB } (Ans.)$$

Pre-emphasis and de-emphasis

An improvement in the output signal-to-noise ratio of an FM system can be achieved if the modulating signal is *pre-emphasised* before it modulates the carrier. The signal is passed through a pre-emphasis network, Fig. 3.9(a), which amplifies the high-frequency components of the signal more than the low-frequency components. The voltage gain A_v of a transistor amplifier is

$$A_v = h_{fe}Z_L/R_{in} \approx h_{fe}Z_L/h_{ie} = g_m Z_L$$

where Z_L is the effective collector load impedance, h_{fe} and h_{ie} are the current gain and input resistance respectively of the transistor, and $g_m = h_{fe}/h_{ie}$ is the mutual conductance of the transistor. In the pre-emphasis circuit of Fig. 3.9(a) the collector load impedance is $Z_L = R_L + j\omega L$ and hence the voltage gain of the circuit is

$$A_v = g_m(R_L + j\omega L) = g_m R_L(1 + \omega\tau)$$

where τ is the time constant, L/R seconds, of the circuit.

The voltage gain of the circuit therefore varies with frequency and so the amplified output signal is distorted. Pre-emphasis ensures that the deviation ratio of an FM wave does not vary with the modulation frequency. Since a pre-emphasised FM signal has had its amplitude–frequency relationship distorted it will be necessary at the receiver to restore the various components of the signal to their original relative amplitudes. This process is carried out by passing the signal through a *de-emphasis circuit* such as the one shown in Fig. 3.9(b). For this circuit,

$$V_{out} = (V_{in}/j\omega C)/(R + 1/j\omega C) = V_{in}/(1 + j\omega CR)$$

and so

$$|V_{out}/V_{in}| = 1/\sqrt{(1 + \omega^2 R^2 C^2)}$$

Fig. 3.9 *(a) A pre-emphasis circuit, (b) a de-emphasis circuit and (c) pre-emphasis and de-emphasis characteristics for 50 μs time constant*

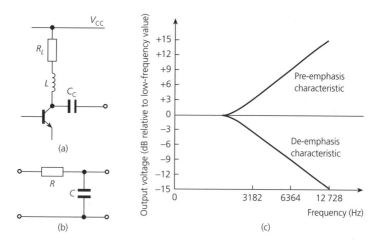

The circuit will have 3 dB loss at frequency $f_1 = \omega_1/2\pi$ when

$$|V_{out}/V_{in}| = 1/\sqrt{2} = 1/\sqrt{(1 + \omega_1^2 R^2 C^2)}$$

i.e. when $f_1 = 1/(2\pi RC)$ Hz. Thus

$$|V_{out}/V_{in}|^2 = 1/(1 + f^2/f_1^2)$$

At frequency, $f = 2f_1$, $|V_{out}/V_{in}|^2 = 1/(1 + 4)$ or -7 dB; at frequency $f = 4f_1$, $|V_{out}/V_{in}|^2 = 1/(1 + 16)$ or -12 dB, and so on.

Therefore at higher frequencies than f_1 the attenuation of the network falls at the rate of 6 dB/octave. To ensure that the component frequencies are restored to their original amplitude relationships in the receiver the time constants of the pre-emphasis and de-emphasis networks must be equal to one another. In the UK sound broadcast system a time constant $\tau = L/R = CR = 50$ μs is used. Then

$$f_1 = 1/(2\pi \times 50 \times 10^{-6}) = 3183 \text{ Hz}$$

giving the pre-emphasis and de-emphasis characteristics shown in Fig. 3.9(c).

To determine the effectiveness of pre-/de-emphasis in increasing the output signal-to-noise ratio of an FM system, the FM system must be compared with an AM system having the same maximum audio frequency $f_{(max)}$. Assume a 1 Ω resistance; then for the AM system the output noise voltage V_{no} is constant with frequency and hence

$$\text{AM noise power} = \int_0^{f_{m(max)}} [V_{no}^2/(1 + (f/f_1)^2)] \, df$$

Using the standard integral

$$\int [1/(1 + a^2 x^2)] \, dx = (1/a)\tan^{-1}(ax)$$

gives $V_{no}^2 f_1[\tan^{-1}(f/f_1)]$. Therefore,

$$N_{o(AM)} = V_{no}^2 f_1 \tan^{-1}(f/f_1) \Big|_0^{f_{m(max)}} = V_{no}^2 f_1 \tan^{-1}(f_{m(max)}/f_1) \tag{3.33}$$

The noise output voltage of an FM system is proportional to frequency, i.e. $V_{no} f/f_d$. Hence

$$\text{FM noise power} = V_{no}^2 \int_0^{f_{m(max)}} [(f/f_d)^2/(1 + (f/f_1)^2)] \, df$$

$$= (V_{no}^2/f_d^2) \int_0^{f_{m(max)}} [f^2/(1 + f^2/f_1^2)] \, df$$

Using another standard integral

$$\int [x^2/(1 + a^2 x^2)] \, dx = x^3[ax - \tan^{-1}(ax)]$$

gives

$$\text{FM noise power} = (V_{no}^2 f_1^3/f_d^2)[f_{m(max)}/f_1 - \tan^{-1}(f_{m(max)}/f_1)] \tag{3.34}$$

If $f_1 = 3183$ Hz, $f_{m(max)} = 15$ kHz and $f_d = 75$ kHz, the ratio

(AM noise power)/(FM noise power) $= 4334/19.2 = 225.68$ or   23.54 dB

Without pre-emphasis the signal-to-noise ratio improvement of frequency modulation over amplitude modulation was 18.75 dB so that the increase provided by the use of pre-emphasis is $23.54 - 18.75$ or 4.8 dB.

Advantages of frequency modulation over amplitude modulation

Frequency modulation has a number of advantages over amplitude modulation if a wide bandwidth is employed. If the bandwidth is narrow the last of these advantages is not obtained. These advantages are as follows:

- The dynamic range is larger.
- Since the modulation envelope is constant high-efficiency Class C RF amplifiers can be used in the radio transmitter. This means that an FM radio transmitter is more efficient than an AM transmitter.
- Because of the capture effect fading is less of a problem.
- An improvement in the output signal-to-noise ratio is obtained if the deviation ratio is larger than unity. This advantage is not obtained with NBFM systems.

Aim: To observe an FM waveform and measure the deviation ratio.
Components and equipment:
FM signal generator. CRO. Spectrum analyser.
Procedure:

(a) Set the FM signal generator to an available carrier frequency f_c and the modulation frequency to $f_c/10$ with a modulation factor of (i) 0.2, (ii) 1, (iii) 5 and (iv) 10. Connect the generator output terminals to the CRO Y1 terminal. Is it possible to see the FM wave in each case? Explain why it is much harder to see the modulation in some cases than others.

(b) With the modulation factor left at 10 vary the modulation frequency to (i) $f_c/8$, (ii) $f_c/5$ and (iii) $f_c/4$. Draw the displayed waveforms and account for their shapes.

(c) Remove the CRO and connect the spectrum analyser to the FM signal generator. Set the modulation factor to 0.2 and vary the modulation frequency to the same frequencies as in (b). Use the spectrum analyser to determine the frequencies contained in the FM waveform. Sketch the spectrum diagram observed.

(d) Now keep the modulation frequency constant at one of the values in (b) and vary the modulation index between the values used in (a). Each time note the spectrum of the FM waveform. State what difficulties were experienced.

(e) A spectrum analyser can be employed to determine the frequency deviation of an FM wave. It is necessary to count the number of spectral lines displayed and then, knowing (i) the display range and (ii) the modulation frequency, calculate the deviation ratio. Try this method and comment on its effectiveness.

The alternative method of measuring frequency deviation is to make use of the carrier nulls that occur at different values of deviation ratio (or modulation index). If the modulation frequency is held constant at a convenient figure and the modulation voltage is increased from 0 V until the first carrier null appears, then $D = 2.405$ and since the modulating frequency is known the frequency deviation can easily be calculated. Try this method by setting the modulation frequency to $f_c/10$ and then increasing the modulating signal voltage until the carrier spectral line disappears. Then increase the modulating signal voltage further until the second carrier null appears at $D = 5.52$ and again calculate the frequency deviation.

EXERCISES

3.1 The RF power output of a radio transmitter is 1 kW when it is not modulated. Calculate the power output when the transmitter is modulated (a) in amplitude with a depth of modulation of 50%, and (b) in frequency with a modulation index of 0.5. For each case draw frequency spectrum diagrams showing the relative amplitudes of the components.

3.2 A single-channel AM radio-telephony system has an output signal-to-noise ratio of 30 dB. If the system is changed to frequency modulation with a rated system deviation of 10 kHz and the transmitted power is doubled, what will then be the output signal-to-noise ratio? The maximum modulating frequency is 3 kHz.

3.3 Explain the effect that pre-emphasis and de-emphasis have on the output signal-to-noise ratio of an FM system. If the de-emphasis network has a time constant of 75 μs, calculate the improvement in signal-to-noise ratio for a baseband signal having a maximum frequency of 15 kHz and a rated system deviation of 75 kHz.

3.4 Derive an expression for the instantaneous voltage of a 100 MHz carrier that is frequency modulated by a 5 kHz, 6 V tone if a signal voltage of 10 V produces the rated system deviation of 75 kHz. Use Table 2.1 to determine the amplitudes of the various components in the FM wave and then find the percentage power in the first $(m_f + 1)$ side frequencies.

3.5 Explain what is meant by the triangular noise spectrum of an FM system. A carrier of 1.5 mV at 100 MHz is received together with an interfering signal of 50 μV at 100.1 MHz. Calculate the peak frequency deviation of the carrier.

3.6 (a) Discuss the relative merits of frequency and phase modulation and explain how they differ from one another. (b) Draw spectrum diagrams for a carrier wave (i) frequency modulated by a 2 MHz signal with a rated system deviation of 4.8 MHz, and (ii) phase modulated by a 2 MHz signal with a peak phase deviation of 2.4 rad.

3.7 (a) The output of a phase modulator is an FM carrier of 1 MHz and a frequency deviation of 1 kHz. The FM signal is passed through three frequency multipliers in turn that have, respectively, multiplication factors of 6, 8 and 6. The signal is then applied to a mixer together with a 200 MHz tone. Calculate the centre frequency and the frequency deviation of the output of the mixer.
(b) Deduce a combination of multipliers and mixers that will turn the modulator output into a 96 MHz carrier with 75 kHz frequency deviation.

3.8 An FM system that carries modulating signals at frequencies up to 12 kHz has a deviation ratio of 5.8. The rated system deviation is obtained when the modulator delivers a peak output of 18 V at 5 kHz. Calculate the modulation index when the modulator output is (a) 15 V at 5 kHz and (b) 8 V at 8 kHz.

3.9 An FM system provides a channel whose bandwidth is 300 to 3400 Hz. The unmodulated carrier frequency is 100 MHz with a deviation ratio of 15. A 12 V, 600 Hz test tone input signal is used to produce the rated system deviation. Calculate (a) the rated system deviation, (b) the frequency deviation produced by a 10 V, 3 kHz signal, (c) the modulation index for an 8 V, 1.7 kHz input signal, and (d) the bandwidth required for (c).

3.10 Draw the phasor diagram for an FM wave with a modulation index of 1.0.

3.11 A sinusoidal modulating signal $v = 5\cos(6000\pi t)$ V is applied to an FM modulator that has a sensitivity of 11 kHz V^{-1}. Calculate (a) the peak frequency deviation and (b) the modulation index.

3.12 (a) Explain the difference between frequency deviation and rated system deviation.

(b) Explain the difference between modulation index and deviation ratio.

(c) The deviation ratio of an FM system is increased from 2.5 to 4. Determine the resulting increase in signal-to-noise ratio.

3.13 The signal $v = 1.5 \cos(6000\pi t)$ V is applied to an FM modulator having a sensitivity of 8 kHz V^{-1}. Calculate (a) the peak frequency deviation and (b) the modulation index.

3.14 (a) What is meant by the 'FM threshold'?

(b) The output signal-to-noise ratio of an FM detector is increased over the input signal-to-noise ratio by the ratio $\frac{3}{2}(\Delta f/b)^2(B/b)$. Explain the meaning of each term in the equation. Insert typical figures to illustrate the effect.

4 Digital modulation

After reading this chapter you should be able to:

(a) List the different kinds of digital modulation that are commonly employed and state that a digitally modulated carrier is an analogue waveform.
(b) Explain the basic principles of operation of BPSK, state the theoretical minimum bandwidth necessary and know why the practical bandwidth must be larger.
(c) Understand the operation of QPSK and 8PSK and draw their constellation diagrams.
(d) Draw, and explain the operation of, BPSK, QPSK and 8PSK modulators and demodulators.
(e) Know why offset QPSK is sometimes used.
(f) Describe MSK and GMSK and explain their advantages for mobile telephones.
(g) Explain that QAM is a combination of amplitude and phase modulation and explain its advantages.
(h) List the different versions of QAM and draw their constellation diagrams.
(i) Explain the operation of a QAM modulator and a QAM demodulator.
(j) Calculate the bandwidth and power efficiencies of a modulation system.
(k) Understand how error probabilities are determined.

With digital modulation both the modulating signal and the demodulated signal at the receiver are digital pulses but both the carrier and the modulated wave are analogue as with AM and FM signals. Digital modulation methods fall into either one of two main classes: *phase shift keying* (PSK) and *quadrature amplitude modulation* (QAM). With PSK a digital signal is applied to a PSK modulator to shift the phase of a carrier wave to any one of a number of specified values; with QAM both the amplitude and the phase of the carrier are shifted by the modulating digital signal to represent the data. Digital modulation has become feasible since the advent of VLSI devices and it offers several advantages over analogue modulation. These advantages are:

- The noise immunity is higher.
- It is easier to multiplex a digitally modulated signal.

- Digital ICs are able to support signal conditioning, coding, encryption and equalisation.
- Digital signal processors (DSPs) can implement digital modulation and demodulation in software; this allows changes to the operation of the circuit to be implemented without change to the hardware.

Signal waveforms

A rectangular pulse waveform contains a large number of frequency components and hence occupies a wide bandwidth. This bandwidth must be limited before the pulse is transmitted through a system in order to make full use of the available frequency spectrum. If a rectangular waveform is passed through a band-limiting filter *pulse spreading* will occur which, if severe enough, may cause *intersymbol interference* (ISI). The greater the band limitation of a rectangular pulse the more pronounced the pulse-spreading effect becomes. In digital work the term *bandwidth* is sometimes taken as the null-to-null bandwidth (see Fig. 4.3), or as the range of frequencies which contain 90% of the signal power. The 3 dB bandwidth of the main lobe in the spectrum diagram is also sometimes quoted.

Figure 4.1(a) shows two *non-return-to-zero* (NRZ) pulse waveforms, one unipolar and the other bipolar, while Fig 4.1(b) shows two *return-to-zero* (RZ) unipolar and bipolar pulse waveforms. The voltage of the RZ bipolar pulse waveform falls to 0 V during each symbol period, whereas an NRZ bipolar waveform never returns to 0 V but switches from +V to −V, or from −V to +V, during each symbol period.

Fig. 4.1 *(a) unipolar and bipolar NRZ waveforms, (b) unipolar and bipolar RZ waveforms*

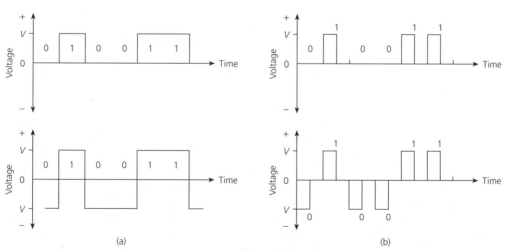

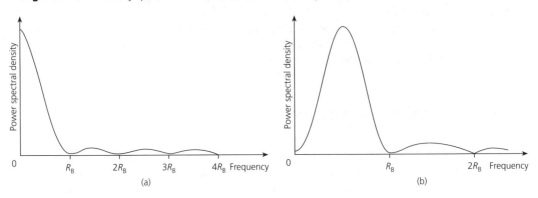

Fig. 4.2 *Power density spectrum curves for (a) NRZ and (b) RZ pulse waveforms*

Power spectral density

The *power spectral density* (PSD) $G(f)$ of a periodic or random waveform is the average power dissipated in a 1 Ω resistance at a frequency f. The PSD of a pulse waveform can be found by taking the Fourier transform of its autocorrelation function. In a narrow frequency range df the average power dissipated is equal to $G(f)df$. The average power dissipated by a periodic or random signal is given by

$$P = \int G(f)\, df \qquad (4.1)$$

Figures 4.2(a) and (b) respectively show the PSD curves for NRZ and RZ pulse waveforms. An RZ waveform has a d.c. component while an NRZ waveform does not. The d.c. component of an RZ signal becomes zero when equal numbers of ones and zeros are transmitted during a message and this condition is often instigated by the use of scrambling and bit stuffing. The use of an RZ waveform offers an advantage over NRZ in that the extra signal transitions make synchronisation at the receiver easier. With NRZ pulse waveforms synchronisation may be difficult if a long sequence of ones (or zeros) should occur. An NRZ waveform may be differentially encoded; this means that binary 1 is indicated by a change from the previous bit and binary 0 is indicated by zero change from the previous bit.

If only the frequencies contained in the main lobe of the NRZ waveform are transmitted by a filter the output waveform will be sinusoidal. When later this sinusoidal wave is applied to a circuit like a Schmitt trigger, the original rectangular waveform can be recreated. The minimum bandwidth required to transmit an NRZ waveform is equal to the bit rate R_B and this has a maximum fundamental frequency equal to one-half of the bit rate when alternate ones and zeros are transmitted.

Digital pulses are often 'shaped' prior to entering a modulator so that they are no longer rectangular in order to reduce the bandwidth that the modulated signal will occupy. Different kinds of filter can be used to shape a pulse waveform in an attempt to obtain a suitable compromise between bandwidth and ISI. The most commonly employed of these filters are the raised-cosine filter and the Gaussian filter.

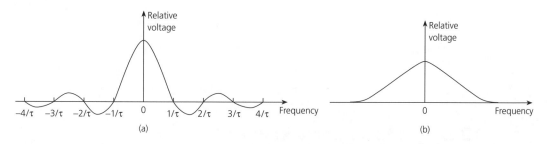

Fig. 4.3 *Frequency spectrum of (a) rectangular pulse, (b) Gaussian pulse*

(a)

(b)

Rectangular pulse

A rectangular pulse of width τ has a frequency spectrum with the envelope, known as sinc x, shown by Fig. 4.3(a), the negative values indicating a 180° phase reversal. The sidelobes have one-half the width of the main lobe. The spectrum extends to infinity and the peak values of the sidelobes decrease in inverse proportion to the reciprocal of the frequency. To retain the rectangular waveshape it would be necessary to transmit many harmonics, probably up to about the 12th, of the fundamental frequency. This wide frequency spectrum cannot be transmitted because of interference with other channels. The frequency spectrum must be band limited to the narrowest bandwidth that will still allow the receiver to detect the presence of the pulse with the required bit error rate.

Nyquist filter

A *Nyquist filter* is an idealised filter that has a response such that at every sampling instant at the receiver the response to all symbols except the wanted one will be zero. This means that a Nyquist filter could reduce the bandwidth occupied by a pulse waveform without producing ISI. Unfortunately, the sinc x shape of the response cannot be achieved and hence the Nyquist filter is not practical.

Raised-cosine filter

A pulse shape that has a greater percentage of the total signal power in the main lobe of the spectrum diagram and hence less pulse distortion than the rectangular shape is the raised-cosine shape. This consists of a cosine wave that is squared to give

$$f(t) = \cos^2(\pi t/\tau) = 0.5 + 0.5\cos(2\pi t/\tau) \tag{4.2}$$

The frequency spectrum of the output signal of a raised-cosine filter with a rectangular pulse applied to the input terminals is also of sinc x shape but it has a faster roll-off of the main lobe and smaller amplitude sidelobes than shown by Fig. 4.3(a). A raised-cosine pulse has 50% of the signal energy in a bandwidth of one-half the bit rate and so it provides a good compromise between pulse shape and bandwidth.

Gaussian filter

A Gaussian pulse has a shape that is defined by the expression $e^{-0.5(f/f_c)^2}$. The frequency spectrum of a Gaussian pulse has a smooth shape that does not cross the zero-voltage axis as shown by Fig. 4.3(b).

Fig. 4.4 *BPSK Modulator*

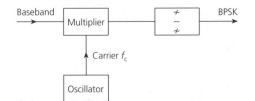

Binary phase shift keying

Binary phase shift keying varies the phase of a carrier to represent the information contained in an input data stream. The number M of phase states that are used is $M = 2^n$; where n varies from two up to 16. Although higher multiples of two than 16 are theoretically possible, practical difficulties mean that such systems are rarely used. In an M-phase PSK modulator the modulating signal voltage puts the phase of the carrier into one out of M different states. When $M = 2$ a binary PSK system is obtained, and if $M = 4$ a quaternary PSK system results.

Binary phase shift keying switches the carrier appearing at the output of the mdulator to either one of two phases that are 180° apart. One of these phases is used to represent binary 1, while the other phase represents binary 0. As the input data signal changes state from 1 to 0, or from 0 to 1, the phase of the output carrier is changed by 180°. If the two phases are ±90° the carrier voltage is

$$v = V_c \cos(\omega_c t \pm \pi/2) \tag{4.3}$$

(Throughout the remainder of this chapter the carrier voltage will be taken as being 1 V.)

The block diagram of a BPSK modulator is shown by Fig. 4.4. The input data bit stream is applied to a multiplier along with the carrier voltage generated by an oscillator or a frequency synthesiser. The multiplier is often a balanced modulator of the type shown by Fig. 4.5(a). The action of the balanced modulator is to reverse repeatedly the polarity of the carrier at the output terminals under the control of the data waveform and its operation is shown by Fig. 4.5. When the input data waveform is at the binary 1 voltage level diodes D_1 and D_2 are turned ON and diodes D_3 and D_4 are turned OFF, and then the carrier appears at the output terminals with the same phase as at the input. When the input data waveform is at the binary 0 voltage level diodes D_1 and D_2 are turned OFF and diodes D_3 and D_4 are turned ON. Now the carrier voltage appears at the output terminals with a 180° phase shift relative to the previous case. Effectively the modulator acts as a multiplier that multiplies the carrier voltage $\cos \omega_c t$ by either +1 (logic 1) or by −1 (logic 0). This means that the output voltage of the balanced modulator is $\pm\cos \omega_c t$.

The amplitude and phase relationships in a digitally modulated carrier are usually shown by a *constellation diagram*. The constellation diagram of a BPSK signal is shown by Fig. 4.6. The two phases that represent binary 1 and binary 0 are spaced 180° apart. The wide separation makes it easier for the receiver to distinguish between the two states even in the presence of noise and interference. The theoretical minimum bandwidth needed to transmit the BPSK signal can be determined by considering the maximum fundamental frequency component of the input data waveform. This occurs

Fig. 4.5 *(a) Balanced modulator, (b) and (c) operation of balanced modulator*

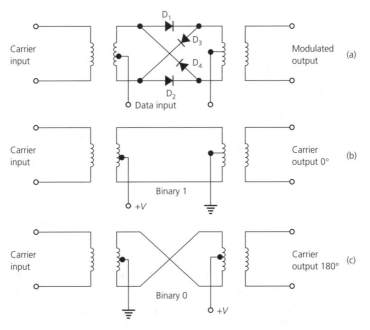

Fig. 4.6 *BPSK constellation diagram*

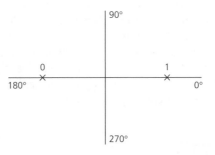

when the data bit stream consists of alternate ones and zeros. If the maximum fundamental frequency is $f_{m(max)}$ then $f_{m(max)} = $ (bit rate)/2 and the output of the multiplier is

$$V_{out} = \sin \omega_{m(max)}t \, \sin \omega_c t = 0.5 \cos(\omega_c - \omega_{m(max)})t - 0.5 \cos(\omega_c + \omega_{m(max)})t$$

The minimum bandwidth B that is required to pass the modulated signal is

$$B = (\omega_c + \omega_{m(max)}) - (\omega_c + \omega_{m(max)}) = 2\omega_{m(max)} = 2(\text{bit rate})/2 = \text{bit rate} = R_B$$

The theoretical minimum bandwidth can only be approached because of the wide frequency spectrum of a rectangular pulse. If the pulses are shaped before they are applied to the modulator the occupied frequency spectrum will be reduced. If a raised-cosine pulse is employed the minimum bandwidth required is increased to twice the bit rate. The PSD–frequency plot of a BPSK waveform is of the form shown in Fig. 4.7. The 3 dB bandwidth of the main lobe is 0.88 times the bit rate, and the null-to-null width

Fig. 4.7 *Power spectral density of a BPSK waveform*

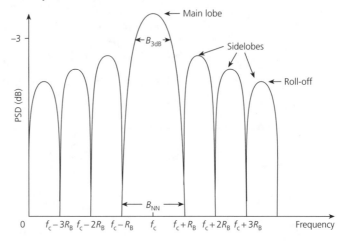

of the main lobe is twice the bit rate. Other digital modulation schemes have similar shaped spectra with differences occurring in the main lobe 3 dB bandwidth, the null-to-null main lobe bandwidth, the rate of roll-off of the sidelobes, and the gap between the peak value of the main lobe and the peak of the highest sidelobe. In all cases the use of a raised-cosine filter to shape the pulses makes the width of the main lobe narrower than if rectangular pulses are transmitted.

Since the carrier is switched by a rectangular waveform the frequency spectrum of the output waveform will be much wider than the minimum bandwidth (see Fig. 4.7 which shows that the null-to-null bandwidth is equal to $2R_B$) and it will be necessary to employ a bandpass filter at the output to band-limit the signal. The question is, of course, by how much? 90% of the signal energy is contained in a bandwidth of 1.6 times the bit rate if rectangular pulses are employed, and in a bandwidth of 1.5 times the bit rate if raised-cosine pulses are used.

EXAMPLE 4.1

A BPSK modulator has a carrier frequency of 70 MHz and an input bit rate of 5 Mb/s. Calculate (a) the theoretical minimum bandwidth necessary, (b) the null-to-null bandwidth, and (c) the 90% signal energy bandwidth. Assume rectangular input pulses.

Solution

$$V_{out} = \cos(2\pi \times 70 \times 10^6) \sin(2\pi \times 2.5 \times 10^6)$$
$$= 0.5[\sin(2\pi \times 72.5 \times 10^6) - \sin(2\pi \times 67.5 \times 10^6)]$$

(a) Minimum bandwidth $= 72.5 - 67.5 = 5$ MHz $=$ bit rate (*Ans.*)
(b) Null-to-null bandwidth $= 2f_B = 10$ Mb/s $= 10$ MHz (*Ans.*)
(c) 90% energy bandwidth $= 1.6 \times 5$ Mb/s $= 8$ Mb/s $= 8$ MHz (*Ans.*)

Fig. 4.8 *Carrier recovery circuit*

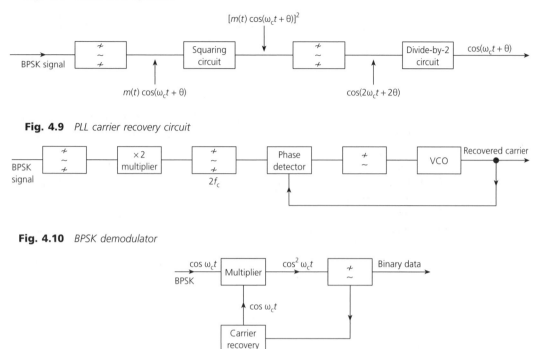

Fig. 4.9 *PLL carrier recovery circuit*

Fig. 4.10 *BPSK demodulator*

The receiver for a BPSK system uses coherent detection in which the demodulator compares the phase of the received signal with the phase of a locally generated carrier which has the same phase as the original carrier at the transmitter. Thus coherent detection requires that the original carrier, correct in both frequency and phase, is available and hence a *carrier recovery* circuit is necessary. The block diagram of a carrier recovery circuit is given by Fig. 4.8. The received signal $m(t) \cos(\omega_c t + \theta)$ is applied to a squaring circuit that generates an output of

$$m(t)^2 + 2m(t) \cos(\omega_c t + \theta) + \cos^2(\omega_c t + \theta)$$

The last term can be rewritten to give $0.5 - 0.5 \cos(2\omega_c t + 2\theta)$ and only the second term is passed by the bandpass filter which has a narrow passband centred on $2f_c$. The filter output is then applied to a divide-by-2 circuit to produce an output of $\cos(\omega_c t + \theta)$ and this is the required carrier component. Other carrier recovery circuits are also possible; Fig. 4.9 shows one which employs a phase-locked loop (PLL).

The basic block diagram of a BPSK demodulator is shown by Fig. 4.10. The input signal is either $\cos \omega_c t$ or it is $-\cos \omega_c t$. The coherent carrier recovery circuit is able to detect the input signal and regenerate the original carrier accurate in both amplitude and phase. The output of the multiplier is the product of the BPSK signal and the recovered carrier, i.e.

$$\text{output} = \pm\cos^2 \omega_c t = \pm[0.5 + 0.5 \cos 2\omega_c t] \quad \text{or}$$
$$\pm[-\cos^2 \omega_c t] = \pm[-0.5 - 0.5 \cos 2\omega_c t]$$

Fig. 4.11 *Alternative BPSK demodulator*

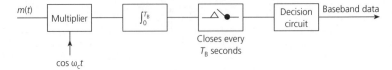

The second-harmonic terms are suppressed by the low-pass filter and hence the output of the demodulator is either 0.5, which represents binary 1, or −0.5, which represents binary 0.

An alternative form of demodulator consists of a multiplier, whose inputs are the BPSK signal and the recovered carrier $\cos \omega_c t$, an integrator, a switch that operates every T_B seconds, and a decision circuit. Figure 4.11 shows the basic circuit of this type of BPSK modulator. The input signal $\pm\cos \omega_c t$ is applied to the multiplier along with the recovered carrier $\cos \omega_c t$. The output of the multiplier is applied to the integrator. The signal is integrated for a time equal to the period of a bit to give $\int_0^{T_B} \pm\cos^2 \omega_c t\; dt$. At the end of each bit period a switch is closed and the integrated voltage is passed on to a decision circuit that decides whether the voltage represents binary 1 or binary 0. The threshold, or decision, point of the decision circuit is set at a value that will minimise errors due to noise.

Quaternary PSK

Quaternary PSK (QPSK), which is also known as *quadrature PSK* (QPSK), uses four equally spaced different phases of the output carrier to represent the *dibits* 00, 01, 11 and 10. Each input dibit shifts the carrier phase to any one of four different phases. Two bits are transmitted in each modulation symbol period which gives QPSK twice the bandwidth efficiency (p. 108) of BPSK.

The instantaneous voltage of a QPSK signal is

$$v = \cos(\omega_c t - \phi) \tag{4.4}$$

where ϕ has any one of the specified four values. There are different ways in which the four states may be assigned to the phases of the output carrier and three alternative schemes are listed in Table 4.1.

Expanding equation (4.4),

$$v = \cos \omega_c t \cos \phi + \sin \omega_c t \sin \phi \tag{4.5}$$

This equation shows that a QPSK waveform can be generated by combining two quadrature BPSK waveforms. The first term is a BPSK signal in phase with the carrier

Table 4.1 QPSK schemes

	00	01	11	10
V22	90°	0°	270°	180°
V26	0°	90°	180°	270°
V26bis	45°	135°	225°	315°

Fig. 4.12 *QPSK modulator*

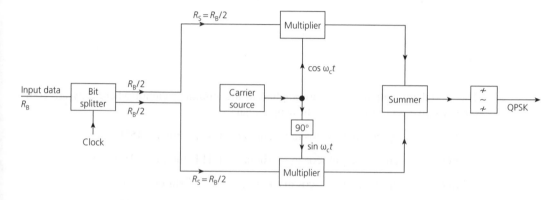

and the second term is a BPSK signal in quadrature with the carrier. Hence equation (4.5) can be written as

$$v = I \cos \omega_c t + Q \sin \omega_c t \qquad (4.6)$$

where I represents the data stream in the in-phase channel and Q represents the data in the quadrature channel. In both channels binary 1 is indicated by I or $Q = +1$ and binary 0 is indicated by I or $Q = -1$. If the input data does not change from one symbol $(T_S = 2T_B)$ period to the next the phase of the carrier is unchanged. If there is a one-bit change the carrier phase is shifted by 90°, and if both bits in a dibit are altered the carrier phase changes by 180°. Whenever a 180° phase shift occurs the waveform at the output of the following bandpass filter is no longer of constant amplitude.

Figure 4.12 shows the block diagram of a QPSK modulator. The incoming bit stream, at bit rate R_B, is applied to a bit-splitting circuit (or dividing unit) which directs alternate bits into the I (for in-phase) and Q (for quadrature) channels. The two channels are identical except that the carrier for the Q multiplier is phase shifted by 90°. Since the data in the I and Q channels is grouped in dibits the symbol rate in each channel is $R_S = R_B/2$.

The outputs of the two multipliers are

I channel: $+\cos \omega_c t$ and $-\cos \omega_c t$

Q channel: $+\sin \omega_c t$ and $-\sin \omega_c t$

Fig. 4.13 *QPSK constellation diagram*

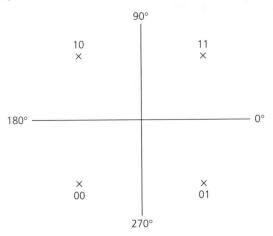

The modulator output signals are applied to the summing circuit where they are combined to give one of the four following signals:

$I,Q = 11$ represented by $\cos \omega_c t + \sin \omega_c t = 1.414 \sin(\omega_c t + 45°)$

$I,Q = 10$ represented by $\cos \omega_c t - \sin \omega_c t = 1.414 \sin(\omega_c t + 135°)$

$I,Q = 01$ represented by $-\cos \omega_c t + \sin \omega_c t = 1.414 \sin(\omega_c t - 45°)$

$I,Q = 00$ represented by $-\cos \omega_c t - \sin \omega_c t = 1.414 \sin(\omega_c t - 135°)$

The constellation diagram for a QPSK signal is given in Fig. 4.13. Each of the four output states has the same amplitude and an angular separation of 90°. This means that noise and distortion could shift a point in the constellation diagram by almost 45° before information would be lost. Successive points in the constellation diagram follow a Gray code sequence.

The bit rate in both the *I* channel and the *Q* channel is $R_B/2$ and hence the maximum fundamental frequency of either bit waveform is $R_B/4$. The output of the modulator is

$$V_{out} = \sin(2\pi R_B/4)t \cos(2\pi f_c t) = 0.5 \sin[2\pi(f_c + R_B/4)t] - 0.5 \cos[2\pi(f_c - R_B/4)t]$$

The theoretical minimum bandwidth necessary is

$$B = (f_c + R_B/4) - (f_c - R_B/4) = R_B/2 \tag{4.7}$$

To allow for filtering the practical bandwidth is increased to about $0.7R_B$.

QPSK has the same BER as BPSK but it is able to transmit data in the same bandwidth at twice the rate. The PSD–frequency plot for a QPSK waveform has the same form as the BPSK plot given in Fig. 4.7, but the widths of the lobes are narrower. The main lobe extends from $f_c - R_B/2$ to $f_c + R_B/2$ and the sidelobes are $R_B/2$ wide as opposed to a width of R_B for BPSK. As with BPSK the use of a raised-cosine filter prior to the modulator reduces the widths of the lobes. The 3 dB bandwidth of the main lobe is equal to 0.44 times the bit rate. The heights of the sidelobes relative to the main lobe are the same for both modulation schemes.

EXAMPLE 4.2

A QPSK modulator has an input bit rate of 5 Mb/s and a carrier frequency of 70 MHz. Calculate (a) the minimum bandwidth needed and (b) the null-to-null bandwidth. Assume rectangular input pulses.

Solution

(a) The bandwidth is $5/2 = 2.5$ Mb/s $= 2.5$ MHz *(Ans.)*
(b) Null-to-null bandwidth $= R_B = 5$ Mb/s $= 5$ MHz *(Ans.)*

The block diagram of a QPSK demodulator is shown by Fig. 4.14. The incoming bit stream is band limited before it is split into two parts to produce the I and Q channel bit streams which are each applied to a multiplier. The input signal is also applied to a carrier recovery circuit to generate the wanted carrier signal; the carrier recovery circuit is similar to that given in Fig. 4.8 but now it uses a ×4 multiplier and a divide-by-4 divider. The recovered carrier is applied directly to the I channel multiplier and is phase shifted by 90° before it is applied to the Q channel multiplier. In the multipliers the input signals are multiplied together and, since the inputs are at the same frequency, the output is a d.c. voltage whose magnitude varies with the phase modulation. Since the output is a d.c. signal the multipliers are sometimes known as *phase detectors*.

The incoming signal is $1.414 \sin(\omega_c t + \theta)$, where θ is one of the angles given in Table 4.2.

If $\theta = -135°$ then the voltage $v = -\cos \omega_c t - \sin \omega_c t$ is applied to both the I and Q multipliers.

The output of the I multiplier is

$$I = (-\cos \omega_c t - \sin \omega_c t) \cos \omega_c t = -\cos^2 \omega_c t - \sin \omega_c t \cos \omega_c t$$
$$= -0.5(1 + \cos 2\omega_c t) + 0.5(\sin 2\omega_c t + 0)$$
$$= -0.5 + 0.5 \cos 2\omega_c t + 0.5 \sin 2\omega_c t \qquad (4.8a)$$

Fig. 4.14 *QPSK demodulator*

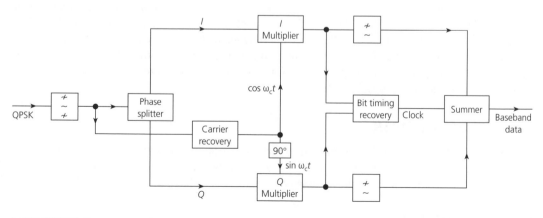

Table 4.2 QPSK angles		
I	Q	θ
0	0	$-135°$
1	0	$+135°$
0	1	$-45°$
1	1	$+45°$

Fig. 4.15 *Bit recovery circuit*

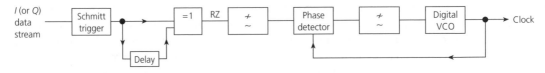

The low-pass filter following the multiplier passes only the d.c. component -0.5 V which represents binary 0. Hence $I = 0$.

The output of the Q multiplier is

$$Q = (-\cos \omega_c t - \sin \omega_c t) \sin \omega_c t$$
$$= -\cos \omega_c t \sin \omega_c t - \sin^2 \omega_c t = 0.5 \sin 2\omega_c t - 0.5(1 - \cos 2\omega_c t)$$
$$= -0.5 + 0.5 \sin 2\omega_c t + 0.5 \cos 2\omega_c t \qquad (4.8b)$$

Only the d.c. component is able to pass through the low-pass filter. Hence $Q = 0$. The output of the demodulator is the dibit 00.

The bit recovery circuit is required to convert the outputs of the two multipliers into a serial bit stream. The circuit of a one-bit recovery circuit is shown in Fig. 4.15. The I, or Q, data is applied to a Schmitt trigger for shaping and the output voltage of the trigger circuit is applied to the two inputs of an exclusive-OR gate: one input is supplied directly and the other via a delay circuit. The output of the exclusive-OR gate is an RZ waveform and this contains spectral lines at both the symbol rate and the harmonics of the symbol rate. The RZ waveform is applied via a low-pass filter to the PLL. The signal is band limited so that only the fundamental frequency component remains, and the action of the PLL is to synchronise the digital voltage-controlled oscillator (VCO) to this frequency. The output of the digital VCO is the recovered clock which is used to time the output serial bit stream.

Offset QPSK

A QPSK waveform is supposed to have a constant amplitude but, since transitions of the I and Q symbol streams occur simultaneously, phase changes of 180° result in amplitude variations after the modulated signal has been band limited. In some applications the lack of a constant-amplitude envelope may be a disadvantage and then a variation of QPSK, known as *offset QPSK* (OQPSK), can be employed. OQPSK introduces a delay of one bit period into the *I* channel so that *I* and *Q* channel transitions occur one bit (half a symbol) apart. One channel switches phase state at the beginning of each symbol period while the other channel changes state at the mid-point of each symbol period. This causes phase states to be switched every $T_B = 1/R_B$ seconds instead of every $2T_B$ seconds. The maximum phase change that can now occur is $\pm 90°$. Limiting the phase changes of the carrier to $\pm 90°$ prevents amplitude variations when the modulated wave-form is band limited to reduce the bandwidth to the first lobe in the spectrum diagram. Although more sidelobes are created when the OQPSK signal is amplitude limited so it can be amplified by a Class C RF amplifier, their frequencies are such that they can be filtered off.

PRACTICAL EXERCISE 4.1

To investigate the operation of a 90° phase shifter.
Components and equipment:
Two resistors, two capacitors. Breadboard. Sinusoidal voltage source. CRO.
Procedure:

(a) Build the circuit given in Fig. 4.16 with $R = 10$ kΩ and $C = 1$ nF.
(b) Apply the signal generator to the input terminals of the circuit. Connect output terminal 1 to the Y1 input of the CRO and output terminal 2 to the Y2 CRO input.
(c) The phase shift through the circuit ought to be 90° at all frequencies. Confirm if this is so.
(d) Although the phase shift is always 90° the amplitudes of the two output voltages are only equal to one another at a frequency given by $f = 1/(2\pi RC)$ Hz. Vary the frequency of the signal generator until the two output signals are of equal amplitude. Check that their phase difference is 90°. Note this frequency and compare with the theoretical value. Account for any difference between the two frequencies.
(e) Use an alternative method to determine the phase difference between the two equal-amplitude output voltages.

Fig. 4.16

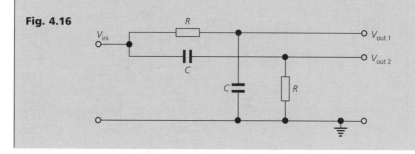

To investigate a digital method of obtaining 90° phase difference between two carriers.

Components and equipment: One 74HC112 dual J–K flip-flop, one 74HC86 quad 2-input exclusive-OR gate, one 20 kΩ resistor, one 1 nF capacitor, sundry other resistors and capacitors. Breadboard. Sinusoidal 50 kHz signal source. CRO.

(a)   Build the circuit shown in Fig. 4.17(a).

(b)   Connect the signal source to the input terminals of the circuit and set it to 5 V at 50 kHz. Connect the CRO Y1 input to the Q output of the J–K flip-flop and the Y2 terminal to the output of the exclusive-OR gate. Observe the displayed waveforms and note their frequencies. The output square-wave signal should be at a frequency that is twice the frequency of the input. The time constant of the CR circuit is equal to the periodic time of the input sine wave. Investigate the effect on the output waveform and frequency of altering this time constant. With the time constant at its original figure observe the effect of changing the frequency of the input signal.

(c)   To obtain a 90° phase difference between two signals it is necessary to use another J–K flip-flop connected as a divide-by-2 circuit, but this flip-flop must be driven by the inverted exclusive-OR gate output. Modify the circuit to give the circuit shown by Fig. 4.17(b).

(d)   Use the CRO to observe the waveforms at the outputs of the two J–K flip-flops and their relative phase. The output waveforms are rectangular but passing them through suitable low-pass filters will produce a sinusoidal signal.

(e)   Discuss the need for a 90° phase-shifting circuit in digital modulators/demodulators and compare this circuit with the one in Practical Exercise 4.1.

Fig. 4.17

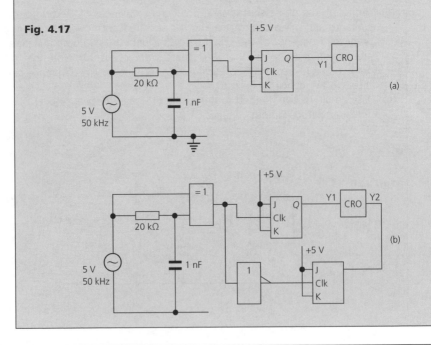

Fig. 4.18 *8PSK modulator*

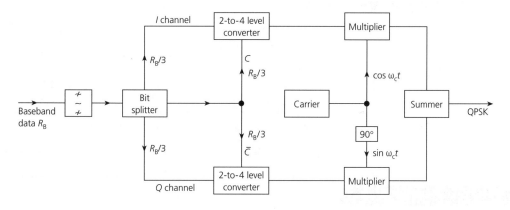

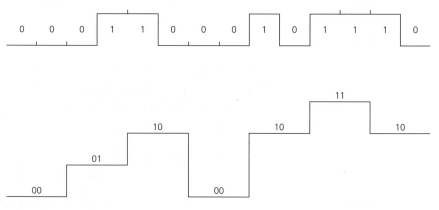

Fig. 4.19 *Multi-level signal*

8-phase PSK

The principle of QPSK can be extended to group the incoming bit stream into groups of three, or *tribits*, i.e. $M = 3$. The eight tribits, 000, 001, 010, etc. are represented by eight different phases of the output carrier wave. The block diagram of an 8PSK modulator is shown by Fig. 4.18. The incoming bit stream is applied to the three-way bit splitter circuit which has I, Q and C (control) outputs. Both true and inverted control output signals are provided. The bit rate in each channel and also in the two control lines is $R_B/3$. The I and Q channel bit streams are each applied to a 2-to-4 level converter to determine the polarity of the output signal (binary 1 = positive and binary 0 = negative polarity). The C signal is applied to the I converter where it controls the amplitude of the output signal (binary 1 = 1.307 V and binary 0 = 0.541 V). The other control signal is inverted before it is applied to the Q channel level converter to vary the amplitude of the output signal. Since two phases and two amplitudes are possible there are four different output states. Figure 4.19 shows a typical multi-level signal.

Table 4.3 shows the available output states for each combination of I, Q and C bits.

Table 4.3 8PSK voltages

I	C	Output (V)	Q	C	Output (V)
0	0	−0.541	0	1	−1.307
0	1	−1.307	0	0	−0.541
1	0	+0.541	1	1	+1.307
1	1	+1.307	1	0	+0.541

000 gives −0.541 cos $\omega_c t$ − 1.307 sin $\omega_c t$, 100 gives 0.541 cos $\omega_c t$ − 1.307 sin $\omega_c t$, 010 gives −0.541 cos $\omega_c t$ + 1.307 sin $\omega_c t$, etc.

EXAMPLE 4.3

The tribit 101 is applied to an 8PSK modulator. Determine the output of the modulator.

Solution

$I = 1$, $Q = 0$ and $C = 1$. From Table 4.3, $I = 1$, $C = 1$ gives +1.307 V and $Q = 0$ $\bar{C} = 0$ gives −0.541 V. Hence the output of the I multiplier is 1.307 cos $\omega_c t$ V and the output of the Q multiplier is −0.541 sin $\omega_c t$ V. Therefore,

$$\text{output of modulator} = 1.307 \cos \omega_c t - 0.541 \sin \omega_c t$$
$$= 1.414 \cos(\omega_c t + 22.5°) \text{ V } (Ans.)$$
$$= 1.414 \sin(\omega_c t + 112.5°) \ (Ans.)$$

In a similar manner the modulator output for other tribits can be calculated. Thus

000 gives −0.541 cos $\omega_c t$ − 1.307 sin $\omega_c t$ = 1.414 cos($\omega_c t$ + 112.5°)
$\qquad\qquad\qquad\qquad\qquad\qquad\quad$ = 1.414 sin($\omega_c t$ − 157.5°)

001 gives −1.307 cos $\omega_c t$ − 0.541 sin $\omega_c t$ = 1.414 cos($\omega_c t$ + 157.5°)
$\qquad\qquad\qquad\qquad\qquad\qquad\quad$ = 1.414 sin($\omega_c t$ − 112.5°)

010 gives −0.541 cos $\omega_c t$ + 1.307 sin $\omega_c t$ = 1.414 cos($\omega_c t$ − 112.5°)
$\qquad\qquad\qquad\qquad\qquad\qquad\quad$ = 1.414 sin($\omega_c t$ − 22.5°)

011 gives −1.307 cos $\omega_c t$ + 0.541 sin $\omega_c t$ = 1.414 cos($\omega_c t$ − 157.5°)
$\qquad\qquad\qquad\qquad\qquad\qquad\quad$ = 1.414 sin($\omega_c t$ − 67.5°)

100 gives 0.541 cos $\omega_c t$ − 1.307 sin $\omega_c t$ = 1.414 cos($\omega_c t$ + 67.5°)
$\qquad\qquad\qquad\qquad\qquad\qquad\quad$ = 1.414 sin($\omega_c t$ + 157.5°)

110 gives 0.541 cos $\omega_c t$ + 1.307 sin $\omega_c t$ = 1.414 cos($\omega_c t$ − 67.5°)
$\qquad\qquad\qquad\qquad\qquad\qquad\quad$ = 1.414 sin($\omega_c t$ + 22.5°)

111 gives 1.307 cos $\omega_c t$ + 0.541 sin $\omega_c t$ = 1.414 cos($\omega_c t$ − 22.5°)
$\qquad\qquad\qquad\qquad\qquad\qquad\quad$ = 1.414 sin($\omega_c t$ + 67.5°)

Fig. 4.20 *8PSK constellation diagram*

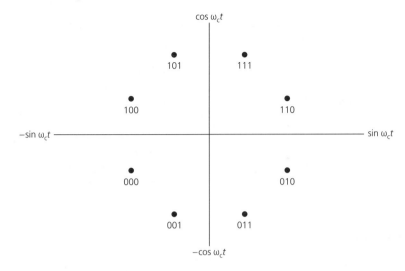

The constellation diagram for an 8 QPSK signal may be drawn using these values and is given by Fig. 4.20. The angular separation between points in the constellation is 22.5°. As the distance between adjacent states is reduced it becomes harder for the receiver to make the correct decision because the received signals are degraded by noise and distortion. Since each point in the constellation diagram is the same distance from the origin all the information is contained in the phase of the signal.

The output bit rate of each 2-to-4 level converter is at $R_B/3$ and hence the highest fundamental frequency of the modulated signal is $R_B/6$. The output of the modulator is $V \sin(2\pi R_B/6)t \cos \omega_c t$, where V is either ± 0.541 V or ± 1.307 V. Therefore,

$$\text{output} = (V/2)[\sin 2\pi(f_c + R_B/6) - \sin 2\pi(f_c - R_B/6)]$$

Thus the theoretical minimum required bandwidth is

$$B = (f_c + R_B/6) - (f_c - R_B/6) = R_B/3 \tag{4.9}$$

EXAMPLE 4.4

An 8PSK modulator has an input data rate of 6 Mb/s and a carrier frequency of 70 MHz. Calculate the minimum bandwidth necessary. Assume rectangular input pulses.

Solution

Now $R_B = 6/3 = 2$ Mb/s and $f_{m(max)} = R_B/2 = 1$ Mb/s $= 1$ MHz. Thus

$$\text{bandwidth} = 71 - 69 = 2 \text{ MHz } (Ans.)$$

Fig. 4.21 *8PSK demodulator*

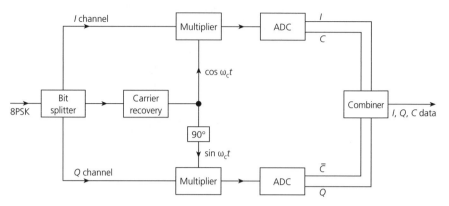

Fig. 4.22 *Alternative 8PSK demodulator*

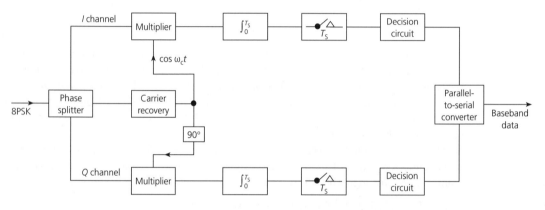

Figure 4.21 gives the basic circuit of an 8PSK demodulator. The input bit splitter directs the incoming bit stream to the I and Q channels and to the carrier recovery circuit. The carrier recovery circuit is able to reproduce the original carrier that was used to generate the 8PSK signal. The I and Q channel signals are mixed with the in-phase $\cos \omega_c t$ and quadrature $\sin \omega_c t$ carriers respectively to generate 4-level signals. The 4-level signals are then passed on to the analogue-to-digital converters (ADCs) which convert the I and Q channel amplitude-modulated bit streams into the required serial bit streams. These bit streams are then applied to a combining circuit which outputs the baseband data.

An alternative form of 8PSK demodulator is shown in Fig. 4.22. The incoming 8PSK signal is applied to a bit-splitting circuit which provides the I and Q channel bit streams as well as an input to the carrier recovery circuit. The carrier recovery circuit reproduces the original carrier $\cos \omega_c t$ which is then applied to the I multipler directly and to the Q multiplier via a 90° phase-shifting circuit. The I channel signal is multiplied by the recovered carrier $\cos \omega_c t$ and the Q channel signal is multiplied by $\sin \omega_c t$.

Fig. 4.23 *16PSK constellation diagram*

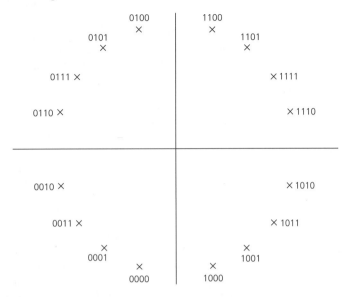

The outputs of the multipliers are integrated for a time T_S equal to the period of each symbol and the integrated output signals are dumped onto the decision circuit at the end of each symbol period by the switch closing. The function of the decision circuit is to determine whether the data signal that is present at the end of the integration time T_S is at the binary 1 or binary 0 voltage level. Finally, the outputs of the two decision circuits are applied to the parallel-to-serial converter which multiplexes alternate dibits to convert them into a single serial bit stream.

8PSK is used for microwave radio-relay systems and communications satellite systems.

16QPSK

In a 16QPSK system the data bit stream is divided into groups of four known as quadbits, e.g. 0001, 0101 and 1110. The output only changes phase once for every four bits, which means that the theoretical minimum bandwidth necessary is equal to (bit rate)/4. The constellation diagram of a 16QPSK signal is shown by Fig. 4.23. The angular separation between points is now only 22.5°, which means that the likelihood of errors has increased.

Minimum shift keying

Minimum shift keying (MSK) is a modification of OQPSK in which rectangular pulses are shaped to become half-sinusoidal pulses. Several versions of MSK exist in which

Fig. 4.24 *Power spectrum density of MSK signal*

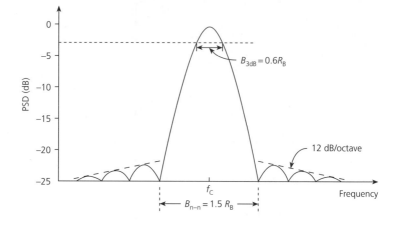

the half-sinusoids are positive only, negative only, or alternating positive/negative. In all versions of MSK the phase changes make smooth transitions between their values instead of discrete steps. The modulation envelope is of constant amplitude and the frequency spectrum falls off more rapidly than with OQPSK. The carrier frequency is chosen to be equal to ($n \times$ bit rate/4), where n is an integer and the minimum required bandwidth B is

$$B = 1.2/T \qquad (4.10)$$

where T is the symbol period.

This should be compared with $8/T$ for QPSK but, on the other hand, the main lobe of the spectrum diagram is wider as shown by Fig. 4.24. The 3 dB bandwidth of the main lobe is equal to 0.6 times the bit rate R_B and the null-to-null bandwidth is $1.5R_B$. The amplitudes of the sidelobes fall off at the rate of 12 dB per octave. The amplitudes of the sidelobes can be reduced by filtering the modulated signal. Band limitation of an MSK signal does not make the modulation envelope vary and the envelope remains more or less constant. This means that MSK signals can be amplified by a Class C RF amplifier. Another advantage claimed for MSK is that it is easy both to demodulate and to synchronise and this is why it is used for some mobile radio systems.

MSK can be regarded as a form of frequency shift modulation (known as *frequency shift keying* or FSK, which is itself a form a digital frequency modulation where the carrier frequency is deviated to either one of two frequencies to indicate binary 1 or binary 0). MSK differs from FSK in that the two frequencies used are synchronised with the bit rate and are separated from the unmodulated carrier frequency by an odd multiple of (bit rate)/2. The lower frequency is equal to $nR_B/2$ and the higher frequency is $[(n + 2)R_B]/2$, where n is an odd integer.

The deviation ratio of a MSK signal is given by

$$D = (\text{peak-to-peak frequency shift})/(\text{bit rate}) \qquad (4.11)$$

(note: peak-to-peak and not peak as with analogue frequency modulation).

The peak frequency deviation f_D is equal to (bit rate)/4 and so $D = (R_B/2)/R_B = 0.5$. This is the smallest frequency separation that allows two FSK signals to be orthogonal and detectable:

$$\omega_D = 2\pi f_D = \pi R_B/2 = \pi/2T_B$$

Hence the instantaneous voltage of an MSK signal is given by

$$v(t) = \cos(\pm\pi t/2T)\cos\omega_c t - \sin(\pm\pi t/2T)\sin\omega_c t \qquad (4.12)$$

EXAMPLE 4.5

(a) Calculate the frequency deviation of an MSK system that operates at 58 Mb/s.
(b) Calculate the minimum bandwidth necessary.

Solution

(a) Frequency deviation is

$$\omega_D = \pi/[2 \times 1/(58 \times 10^6)] = 91.106 \text{ Mrad s}^{-1} \quad \text{and}$$
$$f_D = 91.106/2\pi = 14.5 \text{ MHz } (Ans.)$$

(b) Minimum bandwidth is

$$1.2 \times 58 = 69.6 \text{ MHz } (Ans.)$$

The block diagram of an MSK modulator is shown by Fig. 4.25. The carrier signal $\cos \omega_c t$ is multiplied by the signal $\cos(\pi t/2T)$ to generate two output signals at frequencies of $f_c + 1/4T$ and $f_c - 1/4T$. The two FSK signals are band limited to produce sinusoidal signals and then the filter outputs are combined to give in-phase and quadrature carriers. One carrier is then applied to the I product modulator and the other carrier is applied to the Q product modulator and here they are modulated by the odd and even bit streams I and Q. The outputs of the product modulators are then combined in an adder to form the MSK signal.

Fig. 4.25 *MSK modulator*

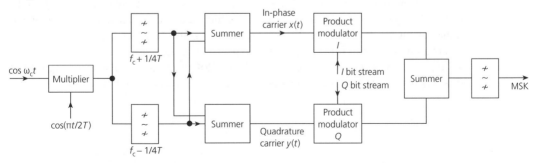

Fig. 4.26 *MSK demodulator*

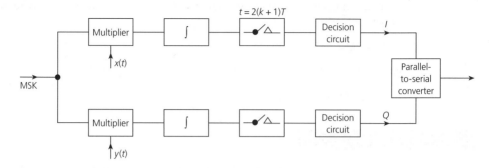

The MSK signal arriving at the MSK demodulator, shown by Fig. 4.26, is applied to two multipliers where they are multiplied respectively by in-phase and quadrature carriers. The outputs of the multipliers are integrated over a symbol period and the integrated voltages are passed to a threshold circuit. Here a decision is made at the end of each symbol period whether the integrated voltage input represents binary 1 or binary 0. The outputs of the two decision circuits are the I and Q bit streams which must be combined to obtain the baseband signal.

Gaussian minimum shift keying

Gaussian minimum shift keying (GMSK) is the modulation scheme that is employed in the digital GSM cellular mobile radio-telephony system (see Chapter 15). Essentially, GMSK is a form of MSK in which the sidelobe levels of the transmitted spectrum diagram are reduced. This reduction is achieved by passing the modulating signal's NRZ waveform through a Gaussian pulse-shaping filter before the signal is applied to an MSK modulator. This is shown by Fig. 4.27. More simply, a GMSK signal can be generated by applying the output of the Gaussian low-pass filter to a VCO in an FM transmitter. GMSK is employed as the modulation system for GSM mobile radio because it gives a good compromise between a good spectrum efficiency of about 1.4 bits/Hz, and resistance to both adjacent-channel and co-channel interference (Chapter 12).

The Gaussian filter has a Gaussian response with a bandwidth–modulation bit period (BT) product of between 0.25 and 0.3 which makes the bandwidth of the baseband signal about 81.25 kHz. As the BT product falls the level of the sidelobes in the spectrum diagram fall off rapidly at the expense of an increase in ISI.

Figure 4.28 gives the block diagram of a GMSK demodulator. The incoming GMSK signal is applied to two multipliers and to a clock recovery circuit. The clock recovery

Fig. 4.27 *GMSK modulator*

Fig. 4.28 *GMSK demodulator*

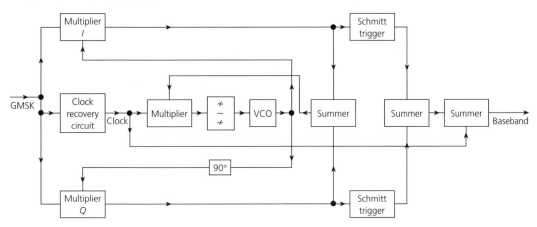

circuit is used to synchronise a VCO that provides in-phase and quadrature carriers to the two multipliers. In the *I* multiplier one of the inputs is multipled by the in-phase recovered carrier and the input to the *Q* multiplier is multiplied by the quadrature recovered carrier. The multiplier outputs are shaped into digital form by Schmitt trigger circuits before they are combined and the combined signal is applied to another summer where the recovered clock is added to the demodulated signal.

Quadrature amplitude modulation

Quadrature amplitude modulation (QAM) is a combination of phase modulation and amplitude modulation in which both the amplitude and the phase of the carrier are varied by the modulating bit stream. The spectral efficiency of MQAM is the same as the MPSK but MQAM has a better power efficiency.

8QAM

In 8QAM the amplitude of the carrier can take up either one of two different values and the phase of the carrier can be varied between four discrete values to give a total of eight different states. The block diagram of an 8QAM modulator is shown by Fig. 4.29 and is similar to the 8PSK modulator shown in Fig. 4.21, differing only in that the control (*C*) input to the *Q* channel 2-to-4 level converter is not inverted. The control input determines the magnitude of the voltage at the output of the 2-to-4 level converter, while the *I*, or *Q*, bit determines the polarity of the output voltage. Since the two *C* inputs are identical to one another the amplitude and phase of the converter output voltages are always equal to one another. This means that, unlike 8PSK, 8QAM does not have the same energy per symbol. The polarities and magnitudes of the modulator outputs for various combinations of *I*, *Q* and *C* are given in Table 4.4.

Fig. 4.29 *8QAM modulator*

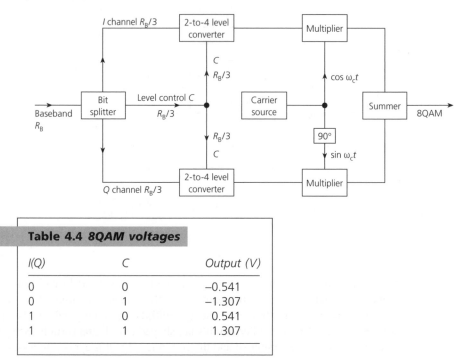

Table 4.4 **8QAM voltages**

I(Q)	C	Output (V)
0	0	−0.541
0	1	−1.307
1	0	0.541
1	1	1.307

EXAMPLE 4.6

An 8QAM modulator has the tribit *I*, *Q*, *C* = 110 inputted. Determine the amplitude and phase of the output signal.

Solution

The inputs to the *I* converter are *I* = 1 and *C* = 0; hence from Table 4.4 the output is +0.541 V. The inputs to the *Q* converter are also 10 and so its output is also 0.541 V. Therefore,

$$\begin{aligned}
\text{modulator output} &= 0.541 \cos \omega_c t + 0.541 \sin \omega_c t \\
&= 0.765 \cos(\omega_c t - 45°) \text{ V } (Ans.) \\
&= 0.765 \sin(\omega_c t + 45°) \text{ V } (Ans.)
\end{aligned}$$

In the same way the outputs for all the other possible tribits can be determined:

$$\begin{aligned}
000 \text{ gives } -0.541 \cos \omega_c t - 0.541 \sin \omega_c t &= 0.765 \cos(\omega_c t + 135°) \\
&= 0.765 \sin(\omega_c t - 135°)
\end{aligned}$$

$$\begin{aligned}
001 \text{ gives } -1.307 \cos \omega_c t - 1.307 \sin \omega_c t &= 1.848 \cos(\omega_c t + 135°) \\
&= 1.848 \sin(\omega_c t - 135°)
\end{aligned}$$

Fig. 4.30 *8QAM constellation diagram*

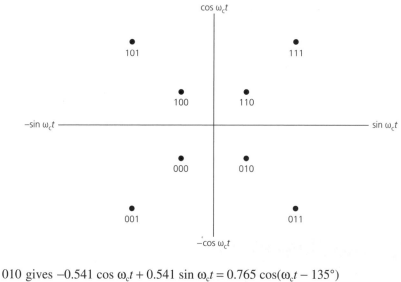

010 gives $-0.541 \cos \omega_c t + 0.541 \sin \omega_c t = 0.765 \cos(\omega_c t - 135°)$
$$= 0.765 \sin(\omega_c t - 45°)$$

011 gives $-1.307 \cos \omega_c t + 1.307 \sin \omega_c t = 1.848 \cos(\omega_c t - 135°)$
$$= 1.848 \sin(\omega_c t - 45°)$$

100 gives $0.541 \cos \omega_c t - 0.541 \sin \omega_c t = 0.765 \cos(\omega_c t + 45°)$
$$= 0.765 \sin(\omega_c t + 135°)$$

101 gives $1.307 \cos \omega_c t - 1.307 \sin \omega_c t = 1.848 \cos(\omega_c t + 45°)$
$$= 1.848 \sin(\omega_c t + 135°)$$

111 gives $1.307 \cos \omega_c t + 1.307 \sin \omega_c t = 1.848 \cos(\omega_c t - 45°)$
$$= 1.848 \sin(\omega_c t + 45°)$$

Using these figures the constellation diagram can be plotted and is shown by Fig. 4.30. The equation for the instantaneous voltage of an 8QAM waveform is

$$v = a \cos \omega_c t + b \sin \omega_c t$$

where a and b are ±0.541 or ±1.307.

The minimum bandwidth required for an 8QAM signal is the same as for an 8PSK signal.

16QAM

With 16QAM information is still represented by both the amplitude and phase of the modulated carrier but now the incoming data is divided into groups of four, known as *quabits*. Figure 4.31 shows a 16QAM modulator. The input bit stream which has a bit rate of R_B is split into four streams each of which has a bit rate of $R_B/4$. Every quabit

Fig. 4.31 *16QAM modulator*

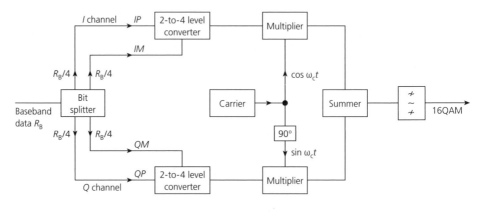

Table 4.5 *16QAM voltages*

IP	IM	Output (V)	QP	QM	Output (V)
0	0	−0.22	0	0	−0.22
0	1	−0.821	0	1	−0.821
1	0	0.22	1	0	0.22
1	1	0.821	1	1	0.821

clocked into the bit splitter produces a change in the state of the output. The *IP* bits set the polarity of the output of the *I* channel 2-to-4 level converter, and the *QP* bits determine the polarity of the signal at the quadrature 2-to-4 level converter output (1 = positive and 0 = negative). The *IM* and *QM* bits determine the magnitude of the respective 2-to-4 level converter outputs, (1 = 0.821 V and 0 = 0.22 V). The outputs of the two 2-to-4 level converters are therefore two-level, two-phase signals.

The 2-to-4 level converter output signals are applied to their respective multipliers to modulate the in-phase $\cos \omega_c t$ and quadrature $\sin \omega_c t$ carriers. The output of each balanced modulator may have any one of four different values:

$0.821 \cos \omega_c t$, $-0.821 \cos \omega_c t$, $0.22 \cos \omega_c t$ and $-0.22 \cos \omega_c t$ for the *I* balanced modulator

$0.821 \sin \omega_c t$, $-0.821 \sin \omega_c t$, $0.22 \sin \omega_c t$ and $-0.22 \sin \omega_c t$ for the *Q* balanced modulator

The balanced modulators' outputs are applied to the summer to produce a 16QAM waveform. Table 4.5 shows the amplitudes and phases obtained at the output of each balanced modulator for different *IP*, *IM*, *QP* and *QM* inputs.

A 16QAM modulator has the quabit *IP, IM, QP, QM* = 1001 applied to its input terminals. Determine its output signal.

Solution

The input to the *I* modulator = 10; hence, from Table 4.5, the output is 0.22 V. The input to the *Q* modulator = 01; hence the output = −0.821 V. Therefore,

$$\text{output of modulator} = 0.22 \cos \omega_c t - 0.821 \sin \omega_c t$$
$$= 0.85 \cos(\omega_c t + 75°) \text{ V } (Ans.)$$
$$= 0.85 \sin(\omega_c t + 165°) \text{ } (Ans.)$$

The output waveform generated by each of the possible input quabits can similarly be calculated with the results given in Table 4.6 (see Exercise 4.7).

The constellation diagram for a 16QAM signal is shown by Fig. 4.32. Each quadrant is divided into three with either one or two amplitudes. The quabit represented by each position in the constellation diagram will be different if the inputs to the *I* and *Q* modulators are changed. One alternative to the diagram of Fig. 4.32 has, reading from top to bottom and from left to right, 0010, 0110, 1110, 1010, 0011, 0111, 1111, 1011, 0001, 0101, 1101, 1001, 0000, 0100, 0100, 1100 and 1000. The maximum fundamental frequency is equal to $R_B/8$ and since there is one change in output state for every four input bits the baud speed is $R_B/8$ also.

Table 4.6 16QAM

IP	IM	QP	QM	Output (V)
0	0	0	0	0.311∠−135°
0	1	0	0	0.85∠−165°
1	0	0	0	0.311∠−45°
1	1	0	0	0.85∠−15°
0	0	0	1	0.85∠−105°
0	1	0	1	1.161∠−135°
1	0	0	1	0.85∠−75°
1	1	0	1	1.161∠−45°
0	0	1	0	0.311∠135°
0	1	1	0	0.85∠165°
1	0	1	0	0.311∠45°
1	1	1	0	0.85∠15°
0	0	1	1	0.85∠105°
0	1	1	1	1.161∠135°
1	0	1	1	0.85∠75°
1	1	1	1	1.161∠45°

Fig. 4.32 *16QAM constellation diagram*

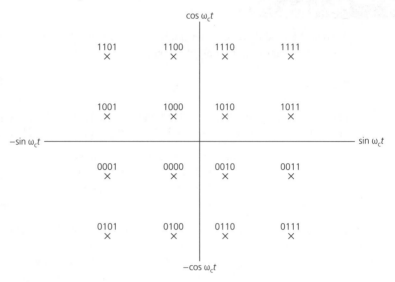

The output of the modulator is

$$\text{output} = V \sin(2\pi R_B t/8) \sin(2\pi f_c t) = 0.5V \cos[2\pi(f_c - R_B/8)]$$
$$- 0.5V \cos[2\pi(f_c + R_B/8)]$$

where V is either ± 0.22 V or ± 0.821 V. The bandwidth is $R_B/4$.

EXAMPLE 4.8

A 16QAM modulator has an input bit stream at 5 Mb/s and a carrier frequency of 70 MHz. Calculate the theoretical minimum bandwidth required.

Solution

$B = R_B/4 = 5/4 \approx 1.24$ Mb/s *(Ans.)*

Figure 4.33 shows the block diagram for a 16QAM demodulator.

Higher QAM

Higher orders of QAM are employed in digital radio-relay systems: 32QAM uses five bits per symbol and has the constellation diagram given in Fig. 4.34; 64QAM uses six bits per symbol and its constellation diagram is given by Fig. 4.35; 128QAM and 256QAM systems also exist and employ seven and eight bits per symbol respectively.

Fig. 4.33 *16QAM demodulator*

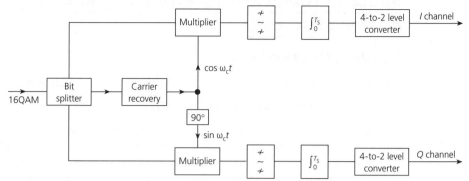

Fig. 4.34 *32QAM constellation diagram*

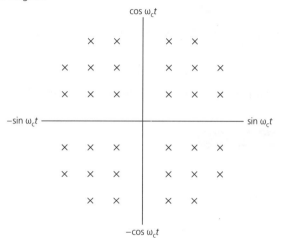

Fig. 4.35 *64QAM constellation diagram*

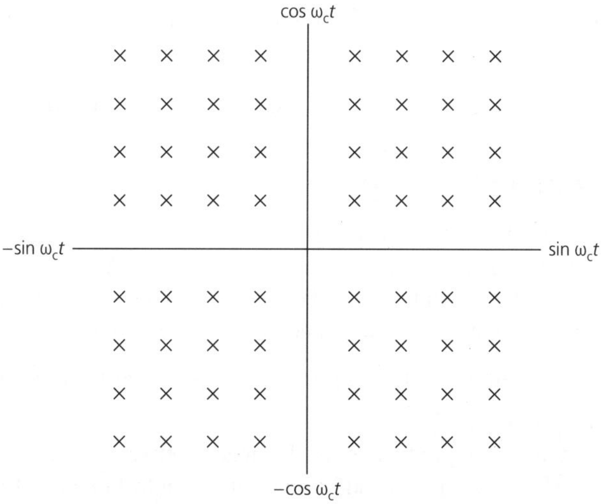

Spectral (bandwidth) efficiency and power efficiency

Bandwidth efficiency

The bandwidth efficiency η of a digital modulation method is the ratio

$$\eta = \text{(bit rate)/(required bandwidth) bits/s/Hz} \tag{4.13}$$

The bandwidth efficiency (also known as the *information density*) provides a means by which the various digital modulation schemes can be compared. The bandwidth efficiency determines the ability of a modulation method to transmit a certain quantity of data in a specified bandwidth. Assuming that the bandwidth is required to transmit the main lobe of the frequency spectrum, i.e. the null-to-null bandwidth, then

$$\text{bandwidth} = 2/T_S \tag{4.14}$$

where T_S is the symbol period equal to $T_B \log_2 M = \log_2 M/R_B$. Therefore, bandwidth $= 2R_B/\log_2 M$ and

$$\text{bandwidth efficiency} = R_B/B = (\log_2 M)/2 \text{ bits/s/Hz} \tag{4.15}$$

Note that the bandwidth efficiency increases with M.

EXAMPLE 4.9

Determine the bandwidth efficiency of (a) BPSK, (b) QPSK and (c) 8PSK.

Solution

(a) $\eta = (\log_2 2)/2 = 0.5$ bits/s/Hz (*Ans.*)
(b) $\eta = (\log_2 4)/2 = 1$ bit/s/Hz (*Ans.*)
(c) $\eta = (\log_2 8)/2 = 1.5$ bits/s/Hz (*Ans.*)
(In practice these figures are reduced to allow for filtering.)

The bandwidth efficiency of MSK is 2 bits/s/Hz and of 16QAM is 4 bits/s/Hz.

Power efficiency

The *power efficiency* of a digital modulation method is the value of E_B/N_0 needed to give a specified BER. It is the ability of a digital modulation method to preserve the integrity of a digital word when the signal level is low. It is another way in which different digital modulation schemes may be compared:

$$\text{power efficiency } \eta = \text{(signal energy per bit)/(noise power density)} = E_B/N_0$$

for a specified BER.

Often a compromise must be made between spectral efficiency and power efficiency. For example, the addition of error control bits to a transmitted signal will reduce

---

the signal level required for satisfactory reception, increasing the power efficiency but, at the same time, increasing the required bandwidth, which reduces the bandwidth efficiency.

Bit error rate

The BER of a digital radio system is its figure of merit and is the probability that a bit will be incorrectly received. It is quoted as a number, typically 1×10^{-3}. BER is the digital equivalent of signal-to-noise ratio in an analogue system. An error may occur in a received symbol because it has been corrupted by noise to such an extent that the receiver is unable to identify it correctly as a one or a zero.

If only thermal noise is present in the system the BER can be calculated from the ratio E_B/N_0, where E_B is the energy per bit in J and N_0 is the noise power density in W Hz^{-1}. The energy per bit E_B is equal to PT_B, where P is the carrier power and T_B is the time duration of a single bit. Most of the digital modulation methods use dibits, tribits or quabits and then the time T_S occupied by a symbol must be used instead of T_B. If the power transmitted during the time period T_S of one symbol is P W, then the received energy in that time period is $PT_S = C/R_S$, where R_S is the symbol rate.

The noise power density

N_0 = (received noise power)/(noise bandwidth)
$\quad = N/B = kTB/B = kT$ W Hz^{-1}

Therefore,

$$E_S/N_0 = (C/N)(B/R_S) \tag{4.16}$$

Some practical filters have a bandwidth $B \approx R_S$ and then $E_S/N_0 \approx C/N$. The calculation of the BER in a digital radio system is complex and graphs are available from which the BER for a given value of C/N can be determined for each digital modulation method.

EXAMPLE 4.10

A QPSK system operates at a bit rate of 100 kb/s in a bandwidth of 220 kHz. If the received carrier power is 4 pW and the noise temperature is 290 K calculate (a) the noise power density, (b) the noise power, (c) the energy per symbol, and (d) the ratio E_B/N_0.

Solution

(a) $N_0 = kT = 1.38 \times 10^{-23} \times 290 = 4 \times 10^{-21}$ W Hz^{-1} *(Ans.)*
(b) $N = kTB = 4 \times 10^{-21} \times 220 \times 10^3 = 8.8 \times 10^{-16}$ W *(Ans.)*
(c) $E_B = (4 \times 10^{-12})/(100 \times 10^3) = 4 \times 10^{-17}$ J/bit *(Ans.)*
(d) $E_B/N_0 = (4 \times 10^{-17})/(4 \times 10^{-21}) = 10 \times 10^3$ *(Ans.)*

Table 4.7 erfc(x)

x	erfc(x)	x	erfc(x)	x	erfc(x)	x	erfc(x)
0.1	0.887 54	0.9	0.203 09	1.7	0.0621	2.5	4.1×10^{-4}
0.2	0.777 3	1.0	0.157 3	1.8	7.24×10^{-3}	2.6	2.4×10^{-4}
0.3	0.671 37	1.1	0.119 79	1.9	7.21×10^{-3}	2.7	1.3×10^{-4}
0.4	0.571 61	1.2	0.089 69	2.0	4.68×10^{-3}	2.8	7×10^{-5}
0.5	0.479 51	1.3	0.065 99	2.1	2.98×10^{-3}	2.9	4×10^{-5}
0.6	0.396 15	1.4	0.047 72	2.2	1.86×10^{-3}	3.0	2×10^{-5}
0.7	0.322 20	1.5	0.033 89	2.3	1.15×10^{-4}		
0.8	0.257 90	1.6	0.023 65	2.4	6.9×10^{-4}		

For values of x greater than 3, erfc(x) ≈ 0. Its value can be calculated using erfc(x) ≈ $e^{-x}/(x\sqrt{\pi})$.

Probability of error

The probability of error P_e of the reception of an incoming digitally modulated signal can be calculated for each form of modulation if tabulated values of the *complementary error function* erfc(x) are available. The erfc(x) function is related to the *error function* erf(x) by erfc(x) = 1 − erf(x). Sometimes P_e is quoted in terms of the *Q function*; this is related to the complementary error function by the relationship erfc(x) = $2Q(\sqrt{2}x)$. Table 4.7 gives values of erfc(x) for x = 0.1 to 3.0 in steps of 0.1.

The expressions for the error probability for BPSK and QPSK are identical and given by

$$P_e = 0.5 \ \text{erfc}[\sqrt{(E_B/N_0)}] \tag{4.17}$$

and for 16QAM

$$P_e = 0.5 \ \text{erfc}[\sqrt{(2E_B/N_0)}] \tag{4.18}$$

EXAMPLE 4.11

Calculate the carrier-to-noise ratio required to give a BER of 1×10^{-5} at a bit rate of 140 Mb/s using (a) BPSK and (b) QPSK. Assume that the bandwidth is 1.2 times the theoretical minimum bandwidth.

Solution

$1 \times 10^{-5} = 0.5 \ \text{erfc}[\sqrt{(E_B/N_0)}]$, and erfc(x) = 2×10^{-5}. From Table 4.7, $E_B/N_0 = 3.0$. Thus
(a) Carrier-to-noise ratio is

$$R_B/B \times E_B/N_0 = [(140 \times 10^6)/(1.2 \times 140 \times 10^6)] \times 3 = 2.5 = 4 \ \text{dB} \ (Ans.)$$

(b) Again, $E_B/N_0 = 3.0$ and the carrier-to-noise ratio is

$$[(140 \times 10^6)/(1.2 \times 70 \times 10^6) \times 3 = 5 = 7 \ \text{dB} \ (Ans.)$$

EXAMPLE 4.12

Calculate the error probability for a 3200 b/s BPSK system. The peak carrier voltage is 2 V and $N_0 = 2.5 \times 10^{-4}$ V^2 Hz^{-1}.

Solution

Now $T_B = 1/3200 = 3.125 \times 10^{-4}$ s and $E_B = (2/\sqrt{2})^2 \times 3.125 \times 10^{-4} = 6.25 \times 10^{-4}$ J/b. Therefore,

$$P_e = 0.5 \text{ erfc}\{\sqrt{[(6.25 \times 10^{-4})/(2.5 \times 10^{-4})]}\}$$
$$= 0.5 \text{ erfc}(2.5) = 0.5 \times 2.4 \times 10^{-4} = 1.2 \times 10^{-4} \text{ (Ans.)}$$

EXERCISES

4.1 Explain the operation of the carrier recovery circuit given in Fig. 4.9.

4.2 (a) Explain what is meant by (i) bandwidth efficiency and (ii) power efficiency in a digital modulation scheme.
(b) Explain the effect of using a modulation method with $M = 4$ instead of $M = 2$ on (a)(i) and (a)(ii).

4.3 (a) State the reason why MSK can be regarded as a form of fast FSK.
(b) If the nominal carrier frequency of 1500 Hz is shifted between 1200 and 1800 Hz by a digital signal with a symbol rate of 1200 baud calculate the modulation index of the system.
(c) State the disadvantage of MSK for use in a digital cellular mobile radio system.
(d) Explain how that disadvantage is overcome by GMSK.

4.4 The necessary bandwidth for a PSK system is given by $B = (2 \times \text{bit rate})/(\log_2 M)$. Calculate the necessary bandwidth for (a) BPSK, (b) QPSK and (c) 8PSK if the bit rate is 1 Mb/s.

4.5 Describe the operation of the carrier recovery circuit for a QPSK receiver.

4.6 Show how the carrier component can be recovered from the BPSK waveform $m(t) \cos(\omega_c t + \theta)$, by first squaring and then dividing by 2.

4.7 Calculate values for the output of a 16QAM modulator for the input quabits 0000, 0001, 0010, 0011, 0100, 0101 and 0110.

4.8 Explain the meanings of the terms bandwidth efficiency and power efficiency when used in conjunction with digital modulation. Calculate the bandwidth efficiency for (a) 16PSK and (b) 16QAM if the bit rate is (i) 1 kb/s and (ii) 1 Mb/s. (c) Determine the bandwidth efficiency of 64QAM.

4.9 The signal produced by the dibit 01 is applied to a QPSK demodulator. Determine the I and Q bits at the demodulator output.

4.10 Calculate and plot the constellation diagram for 8PSK when the I channel is supplied with $\sin \omega_c t$ and the Q channel with $\cos \omega_c t$.

4.11 An 8QAM system has a carrier power of 5×10^{-14} W, noise level of 5×10^{-17} W, and provides a bit rate of 33 kb/s in a bandwidth of 70 kHz. Calculate (a) the energy per bit, (b) the energy per symbol, and (c) the E_B/N_0 ratio.

4.12 The E_B/N_0 ratio needed for an 8PSK system to have a BER of 10^{-7} is 14.7 dB. If the bit rate is 12 Mb/s and the bandwidth is 20% larger than the minimum possible calculate the required carrier-to-noise ratio.

5 Transmission lines

After reading this chapter you should be able to:

(a) Know the different kinds of transmission line that exist.
(b) Understand the concepts of characteristic impedance, propagation coefficient and velocity of propagation.
(c) Be able to quote typical values for the characteristic impedance for different lines.
(d) Explain why reflections occur on mismatched lines and be able to solve problems.
(e) Explain what is meant by the reflection coefficient of a line and distinguish between the voltage and current reflection coefficients.
(f) Explain how standing waves are developed on mismatched lines.
(g) Explain the term voltage standing-wave ratio and calculate its value for given values of load and characteristic impedance.
(h) Know how to solve a line that is mismatched at both its sending and load terminals.
(i) List reasons why a high VSWR is usually undesirable.
(j) Describe how resonant lines can be used to simulate components and tuned circuits.
(k) Use the Smith chart to solve problems on mismatched transmission lines.

A transmission line consists of two conductors separated from one another by a dielectric which may be either air or some kind of plastic. A transmission line provides a means for guiding an electromagnetic wave from one point to another. Lines are employed in radio systems as feeders to connect a radio transmitter or radio receiver to its aerial and, at the higher frequencies, to simulate a component and/or a tuned circuit. There are several kinds of transmission line and each one may be classified as being either *balanced* or *unbalanced*. The two conductors of a balanced line are symmetrically positioned with respect to earth, with the signal travelling out in one conductor and returning in the other conductor. The signal voltage is the potential difference between the two conductors. Any noise or interference voltages that may exist are induced equally into both conductors and produce *longitudinal* currents that cancel out at the end of the line. An unbalanced line has one of its conductors connected to earth while the other conductor carries the signal. Any noise or interference voltages that are induced into the conductors are of unequal amplitudes and so they will not cancel out.

Fig. 5.1 *Types of transmission line (a) open-air pair, (b) twin-wire, (c) twisted-pair, (d) shielded-pair, (e) air-spaced coaxial pair, (f) solid dielectric coaxial pair, and (g) microstrip*

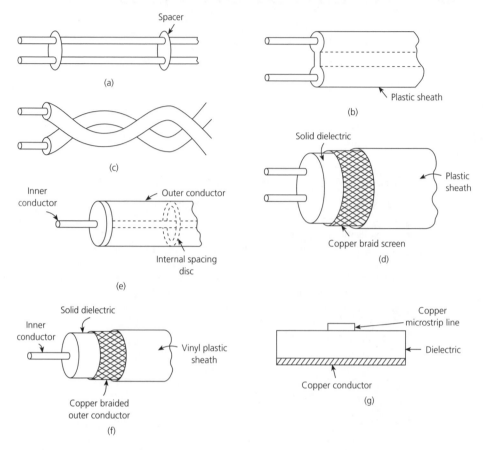

Types of balanced line include the open-air pair, the twin wire, the twisted wire and the shielded pair and these are shown in Figs 5.1(a) to (d). Unbalanced lines such as the coaxial pair and microstrip are shown in Figs 5.1(e), (f) and (g). When a dielectric material is employed it is usually one of polythene, polyethylene, polyproplene, Teflon, or tetrafluorethylene. An open-wire line has two parallel lines that are held a constant distance apart by plastic spacers and has an air dielectric. An open-wire line is prone to interference and noise and, because it readily radiates energy, it has relatively high losses. The twin-pair line has the two conductors held apart by a continuous solid dielectric. The twisted-pair line has its two conductors individually insulated and then twisted together. Shielded-pair cable is designed to reduce both radiation losses and interference. The braid is connected to earth so that it acts as a screen to prevent external noise and interference reaching the conductors which are kept apart by a sold dielectric. The coaxial pair has the advantage that electromagnetic fields are confined within its outer conductor and propagating signals are screened from external noise and interference. An air-cored coaxial pair has its inner conductor held in position by polythene discs spaced apart at regular intervals; this type of cable is relatively expensive but it is more or less unaffected by external noise and interference. Flexible coaxial cables have a solid polythene dielectric and a copper braid outer conductor and are not quite as good at eliminating noise. Stripline and microstrip are used at microwave frequencies for interconnections and also to produce components such as couplers and circulators.

The behaviour of an RF transmission line is determined by the values of its *secondary coefficients*. The secondary coefficients are: the *characteristic impedance* Z_0, the *propagation coefficient* γ, and the *velocity of propagation* v. These, in turn, are functions of the *primary coefficients* of the line, i.e. the resistance R, the conductance G, the inductance L and the capacitance C. The *electrical length* λ of a transmission line is measured in wavelengths:

$$\lambda = c/(f\sqrt{\varepsilon_r}) \tag{5.1}$$

where c is the velocity of light ($\approx 3 \times 10^8$ m s^{-1}) and ε_r is the relative permitivity of the dielectric.

EXAMPLE 5.1

A transmission line is 10 m in length. Calculate its electrical length at (a) 1 MHz, (b) 10 MHz and (c) 100 MHz.

Solution

(a) $\lambda = (3 \times 10^8)/(1 \times 10^6) = 300$ m. Therefore the electrical length is $\lambda/30$ (*Ans.*)
(b) $\lambda = 30$ m. Electrical length $= \lambda/3$ (*Ans.*)
(c) $\lambda = 3$ m. Electrical length $= 10\lambda/3$ (*Ans.*)

Primary coefficients of a line

The inductance per metre L and the capacitance per metre C of an RF transmission line are quantities whose values are determined by the physical dimensions of the line and the relative permitivity of the dielectric. Neither L nor C is a function of frequency but both the resistance R per metre and the conductance G per metre are frequency-dependent quantities. The resistance increases in proportion to the square root of frequency, and the conductance increases in direct proportion to the frequency.

PRACTICAL EXERCISE 5.1

To measure the primary coefficients of a line
Components and equipment: Q meter. Inductor. Known length of line. Signal source
Procedure:

(a)   Connect a suitable value of inductance across the appropriate terminals of the Q meter. (Terminals used may differ with the actual instrument employed.) Set the tuning capacitor dial to a convenient capacitance value and call the chosen value C_1.

(b) Resonate the test circuit by adjusting the frequency of the signal source. Call the indicated Q reading Q_1. Open-circuit the output terminals of the line.
(c) Connect the input terminals of the line across the test terminals of the Q meter. Resonate the circuit by means of the tuning capacitor. Call the new tuning capacitance at resonance C_2 and the new Q factor Q_2.
(d) Then the capacitance of the line is $C_1 - C_2$ and the conductance is $\omega C_1 (Q_1 - Q_2)/Q_1 Q_2$.
(e) Short-circuit the output terminals of the line and repeat procedure (c).
(f) Then the inductance of the line is $(C_1 - C_2)/(\omega^2 C_1 C_2)$ and the resistance of the line is $[1/C_2 Q_2 - 1/C_1 Q_1]/\omega$.

Secondary coefficients of a line

The performance of an RF transmission line is determined by its secondary coefficients. The full expressions for the secondary coefficients involve all four of the primary coefficients and also the frequency, but at radio frequencies these expressions can be reduced to simpler, and more convenient, forms.

Characteristic impedance

The characteristic impedance of a line is the input impedance of a long length of that line; alternatively, it is the input impedance of a line that is terminated in the characteristic impedance. At radio frequencies the characteristic impedance Z_0 of a line is purely resistive and is given by

$$Z_0 = \sqrt{(L/C)} \ \Omega \tag{5.2}$$

If a line has a solid dielectric its characteristic impedance is reduced to

$$Z_0 = \sqrt{[L/(\varepsilon_r C)]} \ \Omega \tag{5.3}$$

When the inner conductor of a coaxial line is held in position by spacing discs of thickness t and relative permitivity ε_r, spaced a distance d apart, the characteristic impedance is

$$Z_0 = \sqrt{(L/C)}/\sqrt{[1 + (\varepsilon_r - 1)t/d]} \tag{5.4}$$

EXAMPLE 5.2

The inner part of a coaxial cable is supported by discs 0.64 cm thick spaced 5 cm apart. The disc material has a relative permitivity of 2.3 and the air-spaced value of the characteristic impedance is 70 Ω. Calculate the characteristic impedance of the cable.

Solution

$$Z_0 = 70/\sqrt{[1 + (2.3 - 1)(0.64/5)]} = 64.8 \ \Omega \ (Ans.)$$

Propagation coefficient

As a radio wave travels along a line it is attenuated and phase shifted because of the effects of the primary coefficients. The attenuation and phase shift introduced per metre length of line are determined by the propagation coefficient of the line. The propagation coefficient γ of an RF transmission line is

$$\gamma = R/2Z_0 + GZ_0/2 + j\omega\sqrt{(LC)} \tag{5.5}$$

The real part of γ is known as the *attenuation coefficient* α in nepers per metre (or dB m^{-1}), and the imaginary part is known as the *phase-change coefficient* β in rad m^{-1}. The attenuation coefficient is not a constant quantity but instead increases with increase in frequency; this is because the resistance R of the line is proportional to the square root of the frequency and the conductance G is directly proportional to frequency. Usually, the conductor losses, $R/2Z_0$, are much greater than the dielectric losses, $GZ_0/2$, and then the dielectric loss can be neglected. The attenuation coefficient α is then equal to the conductor loss $R/2Z_0$ in nepers per metre. In addition to the losses predicted by the attenuation of the line there may also be losses due to radiation from a line (but not from a coaxial line).

The attenuation of an RF line is proportional to the square root of the frequency while wavelength is inversely proportional to frequency. This means that the attenuation per wavelength *decreases* with increase in frequency. At the higher radio frequencies, in particular, the electrical length of a line is often small, perhaps only a fraction of a wavelength, and then the line loss will be small. Such lines are often described as being *low-loss* or even, if the losses are small enough to be neglected, as *loss-free*.

Velocity of propagation

The velocity with which a sinusoidal signal travels along a line is known as the *phase velocity of propagation* v_P and the velocity with which a complex signal travels is known as the *group velocity* v_G. At radio frequencies the phase and group velocities are of equal value and their common value is given by

$$v_P = v_G = \omega/\beta = 1/\sqrt{(LC)} \tag{5.6}$$

PRACTICAL EXERCISE 5.2

Aim: To measure (a) the characteristic impedance of a transmission line, and (b) the attenuation coefficient of the line.

Components and equipment: 10 m length of 50 Ω (or 75 Ω) line, 50 Ω (or 75 Ω resistor, RF signal source (5 MHz), CRO, multi-meter (able to work at 5 MHz).

Procedure:

(a) Set the signal source to 10 V at 5 MHz and connect it to the input terminals of the line. Connect the multi-meter across the input terminals, and the Y1 terminal of the CRO across the output terminals of the line.

(b) Measure the voltage V_{oc} across the input terminals of the line. Short-circuit the line's output terminals and measure the input voltage V_{sc}.

(c) Now connect the multi-meter in series with the signal source and the line and set it to measure current. Measure the input current I_{sc}. Then open-circuit the output terminals and measure the input current I_{oc}.

(d) Calculate (i) $Z_{oc} = V_{oc}/I_{oc}$ and $Z_{sc} = V_{sc}/I_{sc}$.

(e) Calculate $Z_0 = \sqrt{(Z_{oc} Z_{sc})}$. Compare the result with the quoted value of characteristic impedance.

(f) Connect the 50 Ω (or 75 Ω) resistor across the output terminals of the line so it is correctly terminated. Connect the Y2 terminal of the CRO to the input terminals of the line. Use the CRO to measure as accurately as possible the input and output voltage waveforms and hence estimate the loss of the cable. Then state the value of the attenuation coefficient α. Increase the frequency of the signal source and note the effect on the output waveform.

Mismatched transmission lines

When a transmission line is used to transmit energy from one point to another the load impedance is chosen, as far as possible, to be equal to (match) the characteristic impedance of the line. This will ensure that no reflection of energy occurs at the load. The behaviour of a matched transmission line is fairly straightforward and an understanding of it is assumed in this chapter.

Whenever the load terminals of an RF line are closed in an impedance that is not equal to the characteristic impedance of the line, the load will be unable to absorb all of the incident power. A fraction of the incident power will be *reflected* by the load and transmitted back towards the sending end of the line. If the sending-end terminals are matched to the source impedance all of the reflected power will be dissipated in the source impedance. If, however, the sending-end terminals are also mismatched some of the returning energy will be further reflected and *multiple* reflections will take place on the line.

Figure 5.2 shows a line of length l metres, having secondary coefficients Z_0 and γ, which is terminated in a load impedance Z_L that is *not* equal to Z_0. The sending-end terminals of the line are matched, i.e. the source impedance is equal to the characteristic impedance. When the source is first connected to the line the impedance presented to it is equal to the characteristic impedance of the line Z_0. The *incident* current I_i and voltage

Fig. 5.2 *Currents and voltages on a mismatched line*

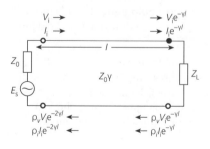

V_i into the line are therefore equal to $E_s/2Z_0$ and $E_s/2$, respectively. The incident current and voltage waves propagate along the line and experience both attenuation and phase change as they travel. At the distant end of the line the magnitudes of the incident current and voltage waves are $I_i e^{-\gamma l}$ and $V_i e^{-\gamma l}$, respectively.

Since the load impedance Z_L is *not* equal to the characteristic impedance Z_0, both the incident current and the incident voltage are reflected by the load. The values of the reflected waves are determined by the current, and voltage, reflection coefficients ρ_i and ρ_v, respectively. The reflected current is equal to $\rho_i I_i e^{-\gamma l}$ and the reflected voltage is $\rho_v V_i e^{-\gamma l}$. The reflected power is equal to the product of the reflected current and the reflected voltage. The reflected current and voltage waves propagate along the line towards its sending end and are further attenuated and phase shifted as they travel. At the sending end of the line the reflected current is $\rho_i I_i e^{-2\gamma l}$ and the reflected voltage is $\rho_v V_i e^{-\gamma l}$. Since the source impedance is equal to the characteristic impedance of the line no further reflections occur.

At any point along the line the total current and voltage are equal to the phasor sum of the incident and the reflected waves. At a distance x from the sending end of the line

$$V_x = V_i e^{-\gamma x} + \rho_v V_i e^{-\gamma(2l-x)} \tag{5.7}$$

This equation can be written as

$$V_x = V_i e^{-\gamma x} + V_r e^{\gamma x} \tag{5.8}$$

where V_r is the reflected voltage at the receiving end of the line, i.e. $V_r = \rho_v V_i e^{-\gamma l}$. Similarly, the current at any point distance x from the sending-end terminals is

$$I_x = I_i e^{-\gamma x} + I_r e^{\gamma x} \tag{5.9}$$

or

$$I_x = (V_i e^{-\gamma x})/Z_0 - (V_r e^{\gamma x})/Z_0 \tag{5.10}$$

The minus sign is necessary in equation (5.10) because the reflected current is *always* in anti-phase with the reflected voltage.

General line equations

It is sometimes convenient to be able to express the current and voltage on a mismatched line in terms of the hyperbolic functions $\cosh x = (e^x + e^{-x})/2$ and $\sinh x = (e^x - e^{-x})/2$. At the sending end of the line, $x = 0$, and from equations (5.8) and (5.9)

$$V_S = V_i + V_r \quad \text{and} \quad I_S = V_i/Z_0 - V_r/Z_0$$

Adding these two equations together gives $V_i = (V_S + I_S Z_0)/2$, and subtracting gives $V_r = (V_S - I_S Z_0)/2$. Equation (5.8) can now be written as

$$V_x = [(V_S + I_S Z_0)/2]e^{-\gamma x} + [(V_S - I_S Z_0)/2]e^{\gamma x}$$
$$= V_S[(e^{\gamma x} + e^{-\gamma x})/2] - I_S Z_0[(e^{\gamma x} - e^{-\gamma x})/2]$$

or

$$V_x = V_S \cosh \gamma x - I_S Z_0 \sinh \gamma x \tag{5.11}$$

Similarly,

$$I_x = I_S \cosh \gamma x - (V_S/Z_0) \sinh \gamma x \tag{5.12}$$

Equations (5.11) and (5.12) are known as the *general line equations*.

The current and voltage at any point on a mismatched line may also be expressed in terms of the current and the voltage at the load terminals. At a distance x from the load terminals

$$V_x = V_I e^{\gamma x} + V_R e^{-\gamma x} \tag{5.13}$$

$$I_x = (V_I e^{\gamma x})/Z_0 - (V_R e^{-\gamma x})/Z_0 \tag{5.14}$$

where V_I is the incident voltage at the load, i.e. $V_I = V_i e^{-\gamma l}$, and V_R is the reflected voltage at the load, i.e. $V_R = \rho_v V_I$.

At the load terminals $x = 0$ and the load voltage V_L is $V_L = V_I + V_R$. Also, $I_L Z_0 = V_I - V_R$, where I_L is the load current. Following the same steps as before leads to

$$V_x = V_L \cosh \gamma x + I_L Z_0 \sinh \gamma x \tag{5.15}$$

$$I_x = I_L \cosh \gamma x + (V_L/Z_0) \sinh \gamma x \tag{5.16}$$

Equations (5.15) and (5.16) are the alternative form of the general line equations.

Voltage and current reflection coefficients

The voltage reflection coefficient ρ_v of a mismatched line is the ratio (reflected voltage)/(incident voltage) at the load. Similarly, the current reflection coefficient ρ_i is the ratio (reflected current)/(incident current) at the load. Putting $x = 0$ into equations (5.13) and (5.14) makes it possible to obtain the load impedance in terms of the load current and voltage. Thus

$$Z_L = V_L/I_L = (V_I + V_R)/(V_I/Z_0 - V_R/Z_0)$$

Rearranging gives

$$Z_L/Z_0 = (1 + V_R/V_I)/(1 - V_R/V_I) = (1 + \rho_v)/(1 - \rho_v).$$

Therefore,

$$\rho_v = (Z_L - Z_0)/(Z_L + Z_0) \tag{5.17}$$

Since the reflected current is *always* in anti-phase with the reflected voltage,

$$\rho_i = -\rho_v = (Z_0 - Z_L)/(Z_0 + Z_L) \tag{5.18}$$

EXAMPLE 5.3

An RF line has a characteristic impedance of 50 Ω, 3 dB loss, and it is $\lambda/2$ in length. The line is terminated by a load of $100 + j20\ \Omega$. (a) Calculate the voltage reflection coefficient at the load. (b) The line is fed by a source of 50 Ω impedance and 2 V e.m.f. Calculate the voltages across the sending-end terminals of the line and across the load impedance.

Solution

From equation (5.17),

(a)   The voltage reflection coefficient is

$$\rho_v = (100 + j20 - 50)(100 + j20 + 50) = 0.345 + j0.087 = 0.36\angle 14°\ (Ans.)$$

(b)   The incident voltage is 1 V and 3 dB is a voltage ratio of $\sqrt{2}: 1$. Hence the incident voltage at the load is $0.707\angle{-}180°$ V.
The reflected voltage at the load is $0.707\angle{-}180° \times 0.36\angle 14° = 0.255\angle{-}166°$ V.
The reflected voltage at the sending end of the line is $0.255\angle{-}166° \times 0.707\angle 180°$ or $0.18\angle 14°$ V.
The sending-end voltage is

$$1 + 0.18\angle 14° = 1.175 + j0.044 = 1.176\angle 2.2°\ V\ (Ans.)$$

The load voltage is

$$0.707\angle{-}180° + 0.255\angle{-}166° = 0.956\angle{-}176°\ (Ans.)$$

Voltage reflection coefficient at any point on a line

At the mismatched load $\rho_v = V_I/V_R$. At any distance x from the load

$$\rho_{v(x)} = (V_R e^{-\gamma x})\,/(V_I e^{\gamma x})$$

or

$$\rho_{v(x)} = \rho_v e^{-2\gamma x} \tag{5.19}$$

EXAMPLE 5.4

A loss-free line has a characteristic impedance of 60 Ω and a load impedance of 120 Ω. Calculate the voltage reflection coefficient at (a) the load, (b) a distance of $\lambda/8$ from the load, and (c) a distance $\lambda/8$ from the load if the line loss is 8 dB per wavelength.

Solution

(a) $\rho_v = (120 - 60)/(120 + 60) = 1/3\ (Ans.)$
(b) $\rho_{v(x)} = (1/3)e^{-2(0+j\pi/4)} = (1/3)e^{-j\pi/2} = (1/3)\angle{-}90°\ (Ans.)$
(c) $\rho_{v(x)} = (1/3)e^{-2(0.115+j\pi/4)} = (1/3)e^{-0.23}\angle{-}90° = 0.265\angle{-}90°\ (Ans.)$

Input impedance of a mismatched line

The impedance at any point along a mismatched line is the ratio of the total voltage to the total current at that point. Hence the input impedance of a line is the ratio (sending-end voltage)/(sending-end current). Using equations (5.7) and (5.10) with $x = 0$ gives

$$Z_S = V_S/I_S = (V_i + V_r)/(V_i/Z_0 - V_r/Z_0) = Z_0[(V_i + V_r)/(V_i - V_r)]$$

Now, $V_r = \rho_{v(l)}V_i = \rho_v V_i e^{-\gamma l} = \rho_v V_i e^{-2\gamma l}$, so that

$$Z_S = Z_0[(1 + \rho_v e^{-2\gamma l})/(1 - \rho_v e^{-2\gamma l})] \tag{5.20}$$

Alternatively, from equations (5.15) and (5.16),

$$Z_S = [V_L \cosh \gamma l + I_L Z_0 \sinh \gamma l]/[I_L \cosh \gamma l + (V_L/Z_0) \sinh \gamma l]$$

or

$$Z_S = Z_0[(Z_L \cosh \gamma l + Z_0 \sinh \gamma l)/(Z_0 \cosh \gamma l + Z_L \sinh \gamma l)] \tag{5.21}$$

If the load terminals are short-circuited so that $Z_L = 0$, then

$$Z_S = Z_0 \tanh \gamma l \tag{5.22}$$

Similarly, for an open-circuited line $Z_L = \infty$ and

$$Z_S = Z_0 \cosh \gamma l \tag{5.23}$$

EXAMPLE 5.5

A line is $3\lambda/2$ long and has a characteristic impedance of 50 Ω and 3 dB loss. Calculate its input impedance when the load impedance is 100 Ω.

Solution

(a) $\rho_v = (100 - 50)/(100 + 50) = 1/3$, and 3 dB $= 0.345$ nepers.
  Substituting into equation (5.20)

$$Z_S = 50\{[1 + (1/3)e^{-2(0.345+j3\pi)}]/[1 - (1/3)e^{-2(0.345+j3\pi)}]\}$$
$$= 50\{[1 + (1/3)e^{-0.69}]/[1 - (1/3)e^{-0.69}] = 70 \ \Omega \ (Ans.)$$

(b) Working from first principles (see Fig. 5.3), the total sending-end voltage is

$$V_S = V_i + V_i/6 = 7V_i/6$$

and the total sending-end current is

$$I_S = I_i - I_i/6 = 5I_i/6$$

Therefore,

$$Z_S = V_S/I_S = (7V_i/6) \times (6/5I_i) = 7Z_0/5 = 70 \ \Omega \ (Ans.)$$

Fig. 5.3

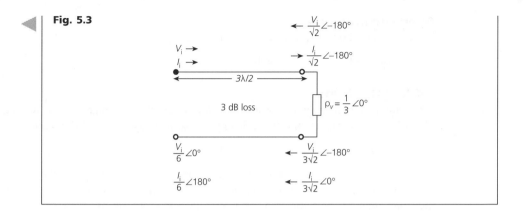

Low-loss lines

A low-loss line is one whose attenuation αl is small enough for the approximations $\cosh \alpha l \approx 1$ and $\sinh \alpha l \approx \alpha l$ to be valid. The input impedance of a short-circuited line (see equation (5.21)) can then be written as

$$Z_S = Z_0\{[\sinh(\alpha + j\beta)/[\cosh(\alpha + j\beta)]\}$$
$$= Z_0[(\sinh \alpha l \cosh j\beta l + \sinh j\beta l \cosh \alpha l)/(\cosh \alpha l \cosh j\beta l + \sinh \alpha l \sinh j\beta l)]$$
$$= Z_0[(\sinh \alpha l \cos \beta l + j \cosh \alpha l \sin \beta l)/(\cosh \alpha l \cos \beta l + j \sinh \alpha l \sin \beta l)]$$

Because $\sinh jx = j \sin x$ and $\cosh jx = \cos x$, then

$$Z_S \approx Z_0[(\alpha l \cos \beta l + j \sin \beta l)/(\cos \beta l + j\alpha l \sin \beta l)] \tag{5.24}$$

(a)   When $l = \lambda/4$, $\cos \beta l = 0$ and $\sin \beta l = 1$. Then

$$Z_S = Z_0[j/(j\alpha l)] = Z_0/\alpha l \tag{5.25}$$

(b)   When $l = \lambda/2$, $\cos \beta l = -1$ and $\sin \beta l = 0$. Then

$$Z_S = Z_0[(-\alpha l)/(-1)] = Z_0\alpha l \tag{5.26}$$

Loss-free lines

Very often the attenuation of an RF line is small enough to be neglected so that $\alpha l \approx 0$ and $\gamma l \approx j\beta l$. Then equation (5.21) becomes

$$Z_S = Z_0[(Z_L \cos \beta l + jZ_0 \sin \beta l)/(Z_0 \cos \beta l + jZ_L \sin \beta l)] \tag{5.27}$$

Short-circuited line

If the load terminals of the line are short-circuited

$$Z_L = 0 \quad \text{and} \quad Z_S = jZ_0 \tan \beta l \tag{5.28}$$

This means that the input impedance of a loss-free short-circuited line is a pure reactance whose magnitude and sign are determined by both the characteristic impedance and the length of the line.

Open-circuited line

If the load terminals of a line are left open circuit,

$$Z_L = \infty \quad \text{and} \quad Z_S = -jZ_0 \cos \beta l \qquad (5.29)$$

λ/4 length of line

When the electrical length of a loss-free line is exactly one-quarter of a wavelength, $\gamma l = j\beta l = j\pi/2$. Then $\cos \beta l = 0$ and $j \sin \beta l = j$ so that equation (5.27) becomes

$$Z_S = Z_0^2/Z_L \qquad (5.30)$$

Note that if the load impedance Z_L is zero, i.e. the line is short-circuited, the input impedance is very high and acts like an open circuit. It might seem that the reverse was also true – that an open-circuited line would have an input impedance of zero. However, it is very difficult to obtain a true open circuit at very high frequencies because the open-circuited end of the line tends to radiate energy.

λ/2 length of line

For a λ/2 length of loss-free line, $\gamma l = j\beta l = j\pi$ and so $\cos \beta l = -1$ and $\sin \beta l = 0$, giving an input impedance of

$$Z_S = Z_0[-Z_L/-Z_0] = Z_L \qquad (5.31)$$

This means that the input impedance of a λ/2 length of loss-free line is equal to the load impedance.

There are several applications of this 'impedance transformation' action of λ/4 and λ/2 loss-free lines. One of the most important is in connection with the matching of a load impedance to a line and this is dealt with on pp. 134 and 146. Two other applications are given by Figs 5.4(a) and (b). Figure 5.4(a) shows a choke joint which is used in

Fig. 5.4 (a) Choke joint, (b) inner conductor support

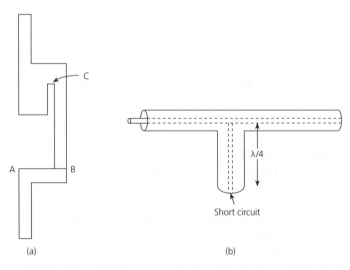

(a)

(b)

radio/radar systems that employ a rotating aerial. It is required to transmit RF currents through a rotating joint without the use of any kind of sliding contact (which would generate noise). The connection between the stationary and moving parts of the aerial is shaped as shown so that the L-shaped channel is $\lambda/2$ long from point A to point C, and $\lambda/4$ in length from point A to point B. The physical sliding junction is at point B. Since the short circuit at point C is $\lambda/2$ from point A a very low impedance is 'seen' at point A even though there may be a small gap at B.

Figure 5.4(b) shows how a $\lambda/4$ short-circuited line may be used to support the inner conductor of a coaxial line. The short circuit appears as an open circuit at the point where the inner conductor is supported and therefore has little electrical effect. This arrangement results in fewer reflections than an insulating disc would cause, but it is more expensive to use.

$\lambda/8$ length of line

Now $\beta l = \pi/4$ and $\cos \beta l = \sin \beta l = 1/\sqrt{2}$. Hence

$$\begin{aligned} Z_S &= Z_0 \left[(Z_L/\sqrt{2} + jZ_0/\sqrt{2})/(Z_0/\sqrt{2} + jZ_L/\sqrt{2}) \right] \\ &= Z_0 \angle \tan^{-1}(Z_0/Z_L - Z_L/Z_0) \end{aligned} \qquad (5.32)$$

This means that the magnitude of the input impedance of a $\lambda/8$ length of loss-free line is equal to the characteristic impedance of the line.

Calculate the impedance Z_0' of the $\lambda/4$ section of line shown in Fig. 5.5, if the input impedance Z_S is equal to 50 Ω.

Fig. 5.5

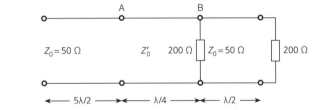

Solution

Since the length of line from the load to the point B is $\lambda/2$ the input impedance at B is 200 Ω and the total load impedance for the $\lambda/4$ section is 100 Ω. The impedance required at the point A, for the input impedance of the system to be 50 Ω, is also 50 Ω. Hence,

$$Z_0' = \sqrt{(50 \times 100)} = 70.7 \ \Omega \ (Ans.)$$

Fig. 5.6 *Standing wave on a line with zero loss*

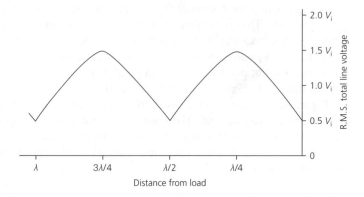

Standing waves and voltage standing-wave ratio

At any point along a mismatched line the total voltage, or current, is the phasor sum of the incident and the reflected waves at that point. If the r.m.s. values of the total current and voltage are plotted against distance from the load, *standing waves* will be obtained. The maximum voltage V_{max} on a loss-free line will occur whenever the incident and reflected waves are in phase with one another. Therefore,

$$V_{max} = V_i + V_r = V_i(1 + |\rho_v|)$$

The minimum voltage V_{min} occurs at those points on the line where the incident and the reflected waves are in anti-phase with one another. Therefore,

$$V_{min} = V_i - V_r = V_i(1 - |\rho_v|)$$

The points at which the maximum voltage occurs are known as anti-nodes, whilst the points of minimum voltage are known as nodes. Figure 5.6 shows the standing wave of voltage on a line of characteristic impedance 600 Ω and load impedance 200 Ω. The voltage reflection coefficient is equal to $(200 - 600)/(200 + 600) = -0.5$ and so the maximum and minimum voltages on the line are 1.5 V and 0.5 V, respectively. The minimum voltage occurs at the load and at multiples of $\lambda/2$ from the load. The maximum voltage occurs at $\lambda/4$ from the load and then at multiples of $\lambda/2$ from that point.

The *voltage standing-wave ratio* (VSWR), S, is either the ratio (maximum voltage)/(minimum voltage) or the ratio (minimum voltage)/(maximum voltage). Either definition can be used as required; no confusion should result since the VSWR will always be either greater than, or less than, unity. Using the first definition of VSWR,

$$S = V_{max}/V_{min} = V_i(1 + |\rho_v|)/V_i(1 - |\rho_v|)$$
$$= (1 + |\rho_v|)(1 - |\rho_v|) \qquad (5.33)$$

For the line whose standing wave is shown by Fig. 5.6, $|\rho_v| = 0.5$ and $S = 3$.

There are a number of reasons why the presence of standing waves on a line used to transmit energy from one point to another is undesirable. These reasons are as follows:

- If the load is not matched to the line the maximum transfer of power to the load will not take place. The incident power is $V_i^2/4$ and the reflected power is $V_r^2/4$. The power dissipated in the load is the difference between the two, i.e.

$$P_L = (V_i^2 - V_r^2)/Z_0 = V_i^2(1 - |\rho_v^2|)/Z_0 = P_{inc}(1 - |\rho_v|^2) \qquad (5.34)$$

The load power can also be expressed in terms of the maximum voltage on the line:

$$P_L = (V_i + V_r)(V_i - V_r)/Z_0 = (V_{max}V_{min})/Z_0$$

or

$$P_L = V_{max}^2/SZ_0 \qquad (5.35)$$

- The reflected current and voltage waves are attenuated as they travel back towards the sending end of the line. This means that the total attenuation of the line is increased.
- At an anti-node the maximum voltage is equal to $V_{max} = V_i(1 + |\rho_v|)$ and it may be anything up to twice as great as the incident voltage. Since the breakdown voltage of the dielectric between the conductors of a line must not be exceeded to avoid damage to the line, this factor limits the maximum possible peak value of the incident voltage, and hence the incident power which the line can transmit. The power-handling capacity of a coaxial line is determined by the voltage breakdown of the dielectric and is independent of frequency. A peak power rating is quoted by the manufacturer of the cable. Then, for a sinusoidal signal, or for an FM wave,

$$P_{max} = P_{peak}/S \qquad (5.36)$$

and for an AM wave

$$P_{max} = P_{peak}/[(1 + m)^2 S] \qquad (5.37)$$

VSWR on a line with attenuation

When the loss of a line is not negligibly small the incident and reflected waves are attenuated as they propagate along the line. As the distance from the load increases the incident voltage will get bigger and the reflected voltage will get smaller, and so the VSWR will become smaller (see Fig. 5.7).

The voltage reflection coefficient at distance x from the load is $\rho_{v(x)} = \rho_v e^{-2\gamma x}$, and therefore the VSWR at this point is

$$S_{(x)} = (1 + |\rho_v e^{-2\gamma x}|)/(1 - |\rho_v e^{-2\gamma x}|) = (1 + |\rho_v|e^{-2\alpha x})/(1 - |\rho_v|e^{-2\alpha x}) \qquad (5.38)$$

Fig. 5.7 *Standing wave on a lossy line*

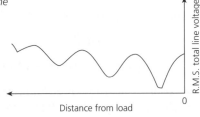

Distance from load

R.M.S. total line voltage

0

This result means that the VSWR on a line that is not loss-free has its maximum value near the load.

EXAMPLE 5.7

A line has an attenuation of 6 dB and the VSWR near to the load is 2. Calculate the VSWR near the sending end of the line.

Solution

From equation (5.38),

$$S_{(x)} = \{1 + [(S-1)/(S+1)]e^{-2\alpha x}\}/\{1 - [(S-1)/(S+1)]e^{-2\alpha x}\}$$
$$= [(S+1)e^{\alpha x} + (S-1)e^{-\alpha x}]/[(S+1)e^{\alpha x} - (S-1)e^{-\alpha x}]$$

$\alpha x = 6/8.686 = 0.69$ nepers, so $e^{\alpha x} = 2$ and $e^{-\alpha x} = 0.5$. Hence,

$$S_{(x)} = (3 \times 2 + 1 \times 0.5)/(3 \times 2 - 1 \times 0.5) = 6.5/5.5 = 1.18 \ (Ans.)$$

Voltage transmission coefficient

Reflections will occur wherever there is a change of impedance on a transmission line and not just at the two ends of the line. If a discontinuity of any kind exists along the length of the line, perhaps due to a change in characteristic impedance at the junction of two different cables, or the parallel connection of another line or device, it will cause some of the incident current and voltage waves to be reflected. The reflected voltage is $\rho_{vd}V_i$, where ρ_{vd} is the voltage reflection coefficient at the discontinuity and V_i is the incident voltage. The *transmitted voltage* V_t is equal to the voltage across the discontinuity and is equal to the sum of the incident voltage and the reflected voltage. Thus

$$V_t = V_i + V_r = V_i(1 + \rho_{vd})$$

The *voltage transmission coefficient* T_v is thus

$$T_v = 2Z_D/(Z_0 + Z_D) \tag{5.39}$$

where Z_D is the total impedance at the discontinuity.

Return loss

The fraction of the incident power that is reflected by the load is

$$| (V_R I_R)/(V_I I_I) | = | \rho_v(-\rho_v) | = | \rho_v |^2$$

This fraction is generally quoted in decibels when it is known as the *return loss*:

$$\text{return loss} = 10 \log_{10}[(\text{incident power})/(\text{reflected power})] \text{ dB}$$
$$= 20 \log_{10}(1/| \rho_v |) \text{ dB} = 20 \log_{10}[(S+1)/(S-1)] \text{ dB} \tag{5.40}$$

Reflection loss

Reflection loss = 10 $\log_{10}$[(incident power)/(load power)] dB

$\qquad\qquad$ = 10 $\log_{10}$[1/(1 $-$ | ρ_v |^2) dB $\qquad\qquad\qquad\qquad\qquad\qquad$ (5.41)

Transmission loss

Transmission loss = 10 $\log_{10}$[(incident power)/(transmitted power)]

$\qquad\qquad$ = 10 $\log_{10}$[1/(1 $-$ | ρ_v |^2)] dB = 10 $\log_{10}$[(S + 1)^2/4S] dB $\qquad$ (5.42)

Note that the expressions for reflection loss and transmission loss are exactly the same; the former term is used for a mismatched load while the latter term refers to a discontinuity.

EXAMPLE 5.8

A line with $Z_0 = 70$ Ω is connected to another line having $Z_0 = 50$ Ω. Calculate (a) the return loss and (b) the transmission loss at the junction.

Solution

At the junction $\rho_v = (50 - 70)/120 = -0.167$.

(a) $\quad$ Return loss = 20 $\log_{10}$(1/0.167) = 15.6 dB *(Ans.)*
(b) $\quad$ Transmission loss = 10 $\log_{10}$[1/(1 $-$ 0.167^2)] = 0.13 dB *(Ans.)*

Line mismatched at both ends

If both ends of an RF transmission line are connected to a mismatched impedance reflections will occur at both ends of the line. The voltage and current waves reflected at the load will travel back to the sending end of the line and here some of the reflected energy will be reflected again to travel along the line towards the load. When this reflected energy reaches the load terminals another reflection occurs and the reflected energy is transmitted back towards the source, and so on. Multiple reflections will occur until the effect of line attenuation reduces the reflected waves to a negligibly small value. The situation on a line mismatched at both ends is illustrated by Fig. 5.8, where ρ_L and ρ_S are the voltage reflection coefficients at the load and at the sending-end terminals, respectively, and $V'_S = E_S Z_0/(Z_S + Z_0)$. The total voltage at any point along the line is the sum to infinity of the incident and reflected voltages at that point. The incident and reflected voltages at any point on the line have values that form a geometric series, and thus their sum to infinity is

$\qquad$ S = (initial term)/(1 $-$ common ratio)

Fig. 5.8 *Line mismatched at both ends*

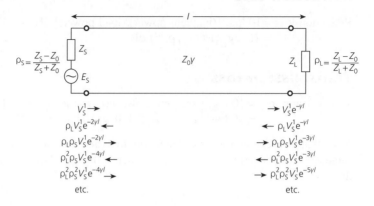

Sending-end voltage

Source-to-load direction

The initial term is V'_S and the common ratio is $\rho_L\rho_S e^{-2\gamma l}$. Hence,

$$V_1 = V'_S/(1 - \rho_L\rho_S e^{-2\gamma l})$$

Load-to-source direction

The initial term is $\rho_L V'_S e^{-2\gamma l}$ and the common ratio is $\rho_L\rho_S e^{-2\gamma l}$. Hence,

$$V_2 = (\rho_L V'_S\, e^{-2\gamma l})/(1 - \rho_L\rho_S e^{-2\gamma l})$$

The sending-end voltage is the sum of these voltages, i.e.

$$V_S = V'_S(1 + \rho_L e^{-2\gamma l})/(1 - \rho_L\rho_S e^{-2\gamma l}) \tag{5.43}$$

Load voltage

Source-to-load direction

The initial value is $V'_S e^{-\gamma l}$ and the common ratio is $\rho_L\rho_S e^{-2\gamma l}$. Hence,

$$V_1 = (V'_S e^{-\gamma l})/(1 - \rho_L\rho_S e^{-2\gamma l})$$

Load-to-source direction

The initial value is $\rho_L V'_S\, e^{-\gamma l}$ and the common ratio is $\rho_L\rho_S e^{-2\gamma l}$. Hence,

$$V_2 = (\rho_L V'_S e^{-\gamma l})/(1 - \rho_L\rho_S e^{-2\gamma l})$$

The total load voltage V_L is the sum of V_1 and V_2, or

$$V_L = (V'_S e^{-\gamma l})(1 + \rho_L)/(1 - \rho_L\rho_S e^{-2\gamma l}) \tag{5.44}$$

EXAMPLE 5.9

A line of characteristic impedance 600 Ω and 3 dB loss is λ/2 in length. It is fed by a source of e.m.f. 5 V and impedance 1000 Ω and it is terminated by a load of 400 Ω impedance. Calculate the load voltage.

Solution

$\rho_S = (1000 - 600)/(1000 + 600) = 0.25$ and
$\rho_L = (400 - 600)/(400 + 600) = -0.25$

$V'_S = (5 \times 600)/(600 + 1000) = 1.875$ V

$e^{-\gamma l} = e^{-(\alpha + j\beta)} = 0.707\angle{-180°} = -0.707$

$e^{-2\gamma l} = e^{-2(\alpha + j\beta)} = 0.5\angle{-360°} = 0.5$

Therefore,

$V_L = (1.875 \times -0.707 \times 0.75)/[1 - (-0.25 \times 0.25 \times 0.5)] = -0.964$ V *(Ans.)*

Transmission lines as components

At the higher end of the VHF band, and above, the use of discrete components such as capacitors and, particularly, inductors becomes increasingly difficult because the values of L and C required are very small. Inductors have interturn and interwinding capacitances, and both capacitors and resistors have inductance in their connecting wires. Wire-wound resistors will also have capacitance. A capacitor intended for use at microwave frequencies may have its capacitance swamped by the lead inductance. Because of these parasitic effects any component may behave like a tuned circuit at a particular self-resonant frequency and at frequencies above this resonant frequency may act like a different kind of component, e.g. an inductor may act like a capacitor and a capacitor may act like an inductor. Also, it is difficult to obtain a high Q factor at these frequencies using discrete devices because of the inherent losses of these components. It is therefore common to use a length of transmission line to simulate a wanted component or resonant circuit.

The input impedance Z_S of a loss-free line short-circuited at its load terminals is given by $Z_S = jZ_0 \tan \beta l$ and this input impedance is very nearly a pure reactance. If the electrical length βl of the line is less than λ/4 the line will simulate an inductor; if λ/4 < βl < λ/2 then a capacitor will be simulated. Longer lengths of line are not often employed, except at UHF, because the line losses will no longer be negligibly small. Suppose, for example, that an inductance of 100 nH is wanted at a frequency of 600 MHz and that it is to be simulated by a short-circuited line of characteristic impedance 50 Ω. The reactance required is $j2\pi \times 600 \times 10^6 \times 100 \times 10^{-9} = j377$ Ω. Hence, $377 = 50 \tan \beta l$, or $\beta l = \tan^{-1} 7.54 = 1.439$ rad. Therefore, $2\pi/\lambda = 1.439$, or $l = 1.439\lambda/2\pi = 0.229\lambda$.

The wavelength λ is 0.5 m so that the physical length of the short-circuited line should be $0.229 \times 0.5 = 0.1145$ m $= 11.45$ cm.

A similar calculation can be made to determine the length of line needed to simulate a capacitive reactance. If the length thus calculated is inconveniently long an open-circuited line will give a shorter length but there may well be radiation problems from the open-circuited end of the line. When the electrical length of the line is very short, certainly less than $\lambda/8$, $\tan \beta l \approx \beta l$ and so the simulated inductive reactance X_L is

$$X_L \approx Z_0 \beta l = \sqrt{(L/C)} \times \omega\sqrt{(LC)} \times l = \omega L l$$

Then,

$$\text{simulated inductance} = Ll \qquad (5.45)$$

where L is the inductance per metre and l is the length of the line.

Q factor

The Q factor of the simulated inductance is

$$Q = \omega L/r, \text{ and } \alpha = r/2Z_0 \text{ or } r = 2\alpha Z_0.$$

Hence,

$$Q = \omega L/[2\alpha\sqrt{(L/C)}] = [\sqrt{(LC)}\omega]/2\alpha = \beta/2\alpha = 2\pi/(2\alpha\lambda)$$

or

$$Q = \pi/\alpha\lambda \qquad (5.46)$$

Clearly, the Q factor will increase with both frequency and with a reduction in the attenuation of the line.

EXAMPLE 5.10

A line is used to simulate an inductor at 600 MHz. If the attenuation factor α is 8×10^{-3} N m^{-1} determine the Q factor of the line.

Solution

Since $\lambda = (3 \times 10^8)/(600 \times 10^6) = 0.5$ m, then

$$Q = \pi/(8 \times 10^{-3} \times 0.5) = 785 \text{ (Ans.)}$$

Transmission lines as tuned circuits

If the length of a line is approximately equal to $\lambda/4$, or to $\lambda/2$, its impedance will vary with frequency in a similar manner to that of a series- or parallel-tuned circuit. The possible simulations are given in Table 5.1.

Consider a low-loss short-circuited line whose input impedance is

$$Z_S = Z_0[(\alpha l \cos \beta l + j \sin \beta l)/(\cos \beta l + j\alpha l \sin \beta l)]$$

(a) For $l \approx \lambda/4$, $\beta l = \pi/4$, so that $\cos \beta l$ is small and $\sin \beta l \approx 1$. Therefore,

$$Z_S \approx Z_0[j/(\cos \beta l + j\alpha l)] = (Z_0/\alpha l)/\{[1 - (j \cos \beta l)/\alpha l]\}$$

Now $\cos \beta l = \sin(90° - \beta l) \approx 90° - \beta l = \beta_0 l - \beta l = \beta_0 (1 - \beta_0/\beta)l$. $\beta = \omega/v_P$, so that $\cos \beta l = \beta_0(1 - \omega/\omega_0)l = \beta_0[(\omega_0 - \omega)/\omega_0]l$. Therefore,

$$Z_s = (Z_0/\alpha l)\left\{ \frac{1}{1 - \left[j2\beta_0\left(\frac{\omega_0 - \omega}{\omega}\right)l \right]/2\alpha l} \right\} \tag{5.47}$$

The impedance of a parallel-tuned circuit can be written in the form

$$Z = R_d/[1 + jQ2(\omega_0 - \omega)/\omega_0] \tag{5.48}$$

and it is evident that the impedances in equations (5.47) and (5.48) vary with frequency in a similar manner. Comparing the two equations gives

$$Q = \beta_0/2\alpha = 2\pi/2\lambda\alpha = \pi/\lambda\alpha$$

(b) For $l \approx \lambda/2$, $\beta l = \pi$, $\cos \beta l = -1$ and $\sin l$ is small. Hence

$$Z_S = Z_0[(-\alpha l + j \sin \beta l)/(-1)] = Z_0\alpha l[1 - (j \sin \beta l)/\alpha l]$$

Now, $\sin \beta l = -\sin(-\beta l) = -\sin(-\pi + \beta l) = -\sin(-\beta_0 l + \beta l) \approx \beta_0 l - \beta l = \beta_0(1 - \omega/\omega_0)l$. Hence,

$$Z_S = Z_0\alpha l\{[1 - \beta_0(\omega_0 - \omega)/\omega_0]/\alpha\} \tag{5.49}$$

which is of the same form as the impedance of a series-tuned circuit, i.e.

$$Z = R[1 + jQ(\omega_0 - \omega)/\omega_0] \tag{5.50}$$

Applications of resonant line effects

Resonant cavities

If a length of low-loss coaxial line is short-circuited at both ends it is able to act as a *resonant cavity*. The minimum frequency at which the cavity is resonant is the frequency at which the line is λ/2 long. (The other resonant frequencies will be at integral multiples of that frequency.) Resonant cavities are often employed as the tuned circuit of a VHF/UHF oscillator when the oscillator is connected to one end of a short-circuited line. The oscillator circuit imposes a shunt capacitance across the line and this reduces

Fig. 5.9 *Use of a λ/4 matching section*

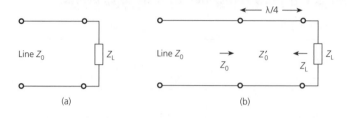

(a)   (b)

the length of line required to be resonant, i.e. $\lambda/2$ long. Then, essentially, the self-capacitance of the source resonates with the inductive reactance of the line and

$$1/\omega C_s = Z_0 \tan(\omega l/v_p) \tag{5.51}$$

Matching

For the maximum transfer of energy from a line to its load the impedance of the load must be equal to the characteristic impedance of the line. Wherever possible the load impedance is selected to satisfy this requirement. Very often, however, the load impedance cannot be chosen to be equal to the characteristic impedance and then some form of matching device must be used if the line is to be matched. The majority of line matching systems are of one or another of the following forms: (a) $\lambda/4$ low-loss matching sections, (b) single or double stubs, or (c) baluns.

λ/4 matching sections

A quarter-wavelength ($\lambda/4$) length of loss-free line has an input impedance Z_S given by $Z_S = Z_0^2/Z_L$. This means that a load impedance Z_L can be transformed into a desired value of input impedance Z_S by the suitable choice of the characteristic impedance Z_0. The required value of Z_0 is easily obtained by transposing equation (5.30) to give

$$Z_0 = \sqrt{(Z_S Z_L)} \tag{5.52}$$

If the impedance of the load is purely resistive the $\lambda/4$ matching section can be connected between the line and the load as shown by Fig. 5.9. If, however, the load has a reactive component the $\lambda/4$ section must be inserted into the line at the distance from the load at which the impedance of the line is purely resistive. This is a calculation that is best performed with the aid of a Smith chart (p. 146).

EXAMPLE 5.11

A 100 Ω load is to be matched to a 50 Ω line by a $\lambda/4$ matching section. Determine the required charateristic impedance of the section.

Solution

$$Z_0' = \sqrt{(100 \times 50)} \approx 71 \ \Omega \ (Ans.)$$

Fig. 5.10 *Wideband λ/4 matching system*

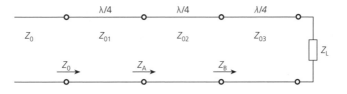

Fig. 5.11 *Single-stub matching*

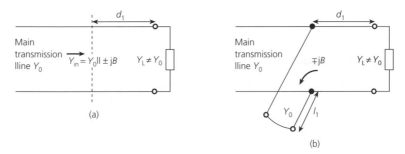

(a)

(b)

Wideband matching

The main disadvantage of the λ/4 matching section is that it is a narrow-band device. The bandwidth can be increased if several sections are employed connected in tandem as shown by Fig. 5.10. The optimum results are obtained when the characteristic impedances of the individual sections are related in the manner shown by equation (5.52):

$$Z_L/Z_{03} = Z_{03}/Z_B = Z_B/Z_{02} = Z_{02}/Z_A = Z_A/Z_0 \qquad (5.53)$$

Stub matching

The admittance of a mismatched line varies with the distance from the load. At some particular distance d_1 the admittance will be equal to the *characteristic admittance* $Y_0 = 1/Z_0$ of the line, in parallel with a susceptance B. At this point $Y_{in} = Y_0 \pm jB$, as in Fig. 5.11(a). If this susceptance can be cancelled out by another susceptance of equal magnitude but of opposite sign, the input admittance of the line will become $Y_{in} = Y_0$. The line will then be matched at this point. The necessary susceptance could be provided by either an open-circuited stub or a short-circuited stub. A short-circuited stub is normally preferred to an open-circuit stub because a true open circuit is difficult to obtain because of the radiation of energy from the open circuit. The short-circuited stub is connected in parallel with the line at distance d_1 from the load. This is shown by Fig. 5.11(b). Not all values of load impedance can be matched in this way and it will sometimes be necessary to employ two stubs, as shown by Fig. 5.12. An alternative to this method is to connect an adjustable short-circuit stub across the load and then adjust its length until it has the input susceptance required to cancel out the load susceptance. The resistive part of the load impedance can then be matched to the characteristic impedance of the line by a λ/4 section.

Fig. 5.12 *Double-stub matching*

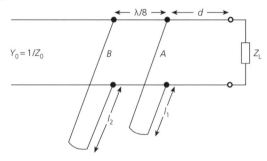

EXAMPLE 5.12

A 600 Ω radio feeder is to supply power at 50 MHz to an aerial of input impedance $60 + j60$ Ω. Calculate (a) the loss when the feeder is directly connected to the aerial, (b) the required short-circuit load stub, and (c) the required $\lambda/4$ matching section.

Solution

(a) $\rho_v = (60 + j60 - 600)/(660 + j60) = 0.82\angle168.5°$. Then $S = 1.82/0.18 = 10.1$ and load power $= P_{max}/S = P_{max}/10.1$. Therefore,

  loss ≈ 10 dB (*Ans.*)

(b) $Y_L = 1/(60 + j60) \approx 11.8 \times 10^{-3}\angle-45°$ S. Load susceptance $= -8.34$ mS. Therefore,

  required stub susceptance $= +8.34$ mS (*Ans.*)

(c) $Y_L = 8.33$ mS and $R_L = 1/(8.33 \times 10^{-3}) \approx 120$ Ω. Therefore,

  $Z'_0 = \sqrt{(600 \times 120)} \approx 268$ Ω (*Ans.*)

Stub matching problems are best tackled with the aid of a Smith chart.

Stub matching of an aerial

The input impedance of an aerial varies with frequency since the aerial's impedance acts in a similar fashion to an open-circuited $\lambda/4$ line. At the resonant frequency of the aerial the input impedance is purely resistive, but (a) just below the resonant frequency it is capacitive, and (b) just above the resonant frequency it is inductive. The matching of an aerial to its feeder can be improved by the use of a short-circuited stub line that is connected across the input terminals of the aerial as shown by Fig. 5.13. The stub must be $\lambda/4$ long at the resonant frequency so that the load then presented to the feeder is purely resistive.

At frequencies just below the resonant frequency the inductive reactance of the stub will tend to cancel the capacitive reactance of the aerial's input impedance. Conversely, at frequencies above the resonant frequency the capacitive reactance of the stub will tend to cancel the inductive reactance of the aerial input impedance.

Fig. 5.13 *Stub matching an aerial*

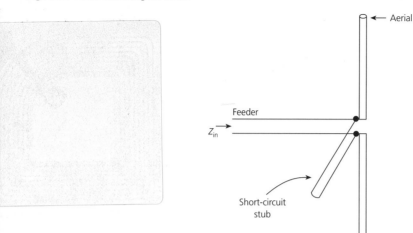

← Aerial

Feeder

Z_{in} →

Short-circuit
stub

Fig. 5.14 *Double-stub matching*

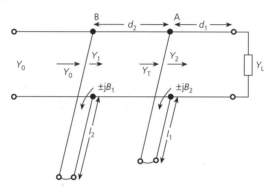

The double-stub tuner

A double-stub tuner consists of two short-circuited stubs of adjustable lengths that are connected across the line at fixed positions. The spacing between the two stubs is not critical but it is usually chosen to be $n\lambda/8$, where n is an odd integer. Figure 5.14 shows a double-stub tuner in which the stub spacing is $\lambda/8$. The action of the matching system is to make the total admittance at the point B equal to the characteristic admittance of the line $Y_0 = 1/Z_0$. Stub B is used to add susceptance to the line to cancel out the susceptance to the right of point B; hence the admittance to the right of B is $Y_0(1 + jB)$. The length l_2 of stub B is chosen so that the input susceptance of stub B is equal to $-jB$ so that the total admittance is $Y_0 + jB - jB = Y_0$. The total admittance at point A must be equal to $Y_0(1 + jA)$ and stub A is required to cancel out the susceptance A and so its length l_1 is chosen to give the required susceptance. Calculations on double-stub matching systems are best carried out using a Smith chart.

Fig. 5.15 *Baluns (a) to feed a dipole aerial and (b) to connect a 75 Ω unbalanced line to a balanced 300 Ω line*

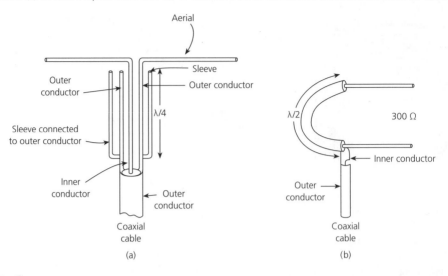

(a)   (b)

Baluns

A balun is a transmission line device that is used to connect an unbalanced RF line to a balanced RF line. Several different versions of balun exist but they are all based upon the properties of λ/4 and λ/2 loss-free lines. Two relatively simple examples are shown in Figs 5.15(a) and (b). The balun in Fig. 5.15(a) uses a λ/4 length of coaxial cable to enable an unbalanced feeder to supply a dipole aerial. The balun in Fig. 5.15(b) is used to connect a 75 Ω unbalanced line to a 300 Ω balanced line.

The Smith chart

The Smith chart is a plot of normalised impedance, i.e. impedance/(characteristic impedance), against the magnitude and angle of voltage reflection coefficient. It can be used in the solution of many problems involving transmission lines (and waveguides) since it can often greatly simplify a problem. The Smith chart consists of: (a) a real axis with values which vary from zero to infinity, with unity in the centre; (b) a series of circles centred on the real axis; and (c) a series of arcs of circles that start from the infinity point on the real axis. This is shown by Figs 5.16(a) and 5.16(b). The circles represent the real parts of the normalised impedances, i.e. R/Z_0 and the arcs represent the imaginary parts of the normalised impedances, i.e. $\pm jX/Z_0$.

Figure 5.17 shows a full Smith chart. In addition to the circles and the arcs of circles representing normalised resistance and reactance the edge of the chart is marked with scales of (a) angle of reflection coefficient (in degrees), and (b) distance (in wavelengths). Movement around the edge of the chart in the clockwise direction corresponds to movement along the line towards the source; this is usually marked as backward. Conversely, anti-clockwise movement around the chart represents movement along the line towards the load and is usually marked as forward. A complete journey around the edge of the chart represents a movement of one-half wavelength (λ/2) along the line.

Fig. 5.16 *(a) Real parts, and (b) imaginary parts of normalized impedance Z/Z₀*

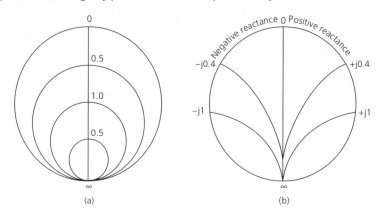

(a)

(b)

Fig. 5.17 *The Smith chart. A represents z = 4 + j4, B represents z = 1.2 − j0.8 and C represents y = 2 − j2*

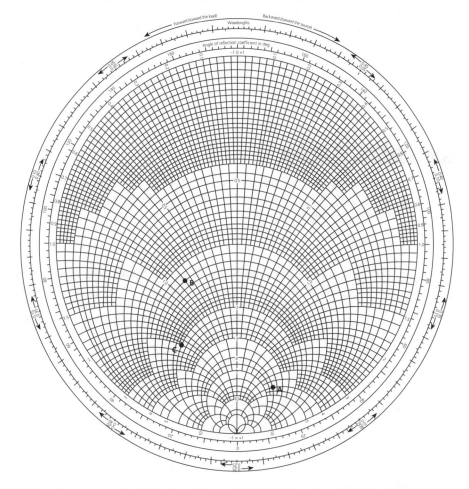

Any value of normalised impedance can be located on the chart. Suppose that $Z = 200 + j200 \ \Omega$ and $Z_0 = 50 \ \Omega$. The normalised impedance is then $z = (200 + j200)/50 = 4 + j4$; z is shown plotted in Fig. 5.17 by the point marked as A. Similarly, an impedance $60 - j40 \ \Omega$ is normalised to $(60 - j40)/50 = 1.2 - j0.8$ and is represented on the chart by the point B. Admittances can also be plotted on the Smith chart; the admittance must first be normalised by dividing it by the characteristic admittance Y_0 of the line. Thus, if $Y = 0.04 - j0.04 \ \text{S}$ and $Z_0 = 50 \ \Omega$ then $y = (0.04 - j0.04)/0.02 = 2 - j2$ and is plotted on the chart as the point C.

Use of the Smith chart

Essentially, the Smith chart deals with lines of negligible loss; the effect of any line attenuation can be taken into account by the use of a separate scale and this will be dealt with later.

Voltage reflection coefficient

To determine the voltage reflection coefficient produced by a mismatched load impedance the load impedance must first be normalised (divide by Z_0 to get $z_L = Z_L/Z_0$) and then marked on the chart. A straight line should then be drawn from the centre of the chart (the point $1 + j0$), through the plotted point z to the edge of the chart. The distance of the point from the centre of the chart, divided by the distance of the centre to the edge, is equal to the magnitude of the voltage reflection coefficient. The phase angle of the voltage reflection coefficient is then read from the scale at the edge of the chart at the point where the extended z_L line intersected it.

EXAMPLE 5.13

Calculate the voltage reflection coefficient of a 50 Ω line having a load impedance of (a) $100 - j150 \ \Omega$ and (b) $100 + j50 \ \Omega$. Compare with the value obtained in (a) using equation (5.17).

Solution

(a) $z_{L1} = 2 - j3$. This point is plotted on the Smith chart as shown by Fig. 5.18. The line drawn from the point $1 + j0$ through z_{L1} passes through the voltage reflection coefficient angle scale at $-26.6°$. The distance from the point $(1 + j0)$ to z_{L1} is 37.5 mm and the distance from $(1 + j0)$ to the edge of the chart is 50 mm and so $|\rho_v| = 37.5/50 = 0.75$. Hence

$\rho_v = 0.75\angle{-26.6°}$ (*Ans.*)

Using equation (5.17),

$\rho_v = [(100 - j150) - 50]/[(100 - j150) + 50] = 0.75\angle{-26.6°}$ (*Ans.*)

(b) $Z_{L2} = 2 + j1$. Drawing a line from the point $1 + j0$ through z_{L2} to the chart edge gives

$|\rho_v| = 22.5/50 = 0.45$ and $\angle\rho_v = 26.5°$ (*Ans.*)

Fig. 5.18

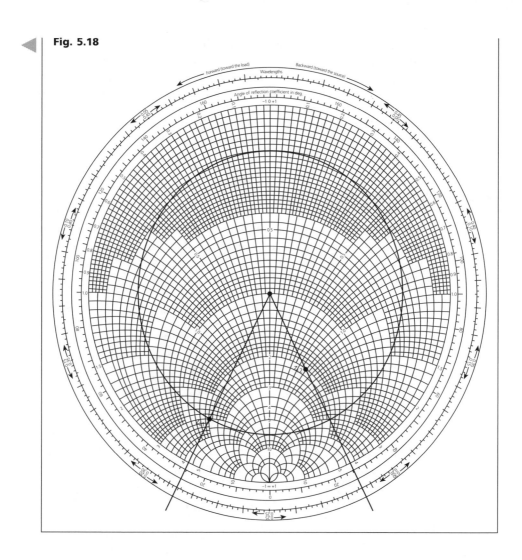

The procedure is slightly different when a load admittance is involved. First, locate the normalised admittance y_L on the chart and then draw a straight line from y_L through the centre of the chart, to the edge of the chart. Then the magnitude of the voltage reflection coefficient $|\rho_v|$ is equal to the ratio (distance y_L to centre)/(distance edge to centre), and the angle of y_L is read from the scale at the edge of the chart.

Voltage standing-wave ratio

To calculate the VSWR on a line locate the normalised impedance z_L (or the normalised admittance y_L) on the chart and draw a circle, centred on the point $(1 + j0)$, which passes through the point z_L. The VSWR is then equal to the value of the real axis at the point where it is cut by the circle. Two values will be obtained: one greater than, and the other less than, unity and each will be the reciprocal of the other. Referring to Fig. 5.18, the VSWR is $S = 7$ or 0.14.

Input impedance of a length of line

To determine the input impedance of a length of loss-free line locate the normalised load impedance on the chart and draw an arc of a circle, centred on the centre of the chart, i.e. the point $(1 + j0)$, moving clockwise. The length of the arc, measured on the wavelength scale, should be equal to the electrical length of the line. The normalised input impedance of the line is then given by the location of the end of the arc. The procedure can be reversed if the input impedance is known and the load impedance is to be determined.

EXAMPLE 5.14

A 50 Ω line has a load impedance of $80 - j100$ Ω. Use a Smith chart to find (a) the voltage reflection coefficient, (b) the VSWR, (c) the input impedance of a 0.3λ length of this line, and (d) the lengths of line that have a purely resistive input impedance and the values of these resistances.

Fig. 5.19

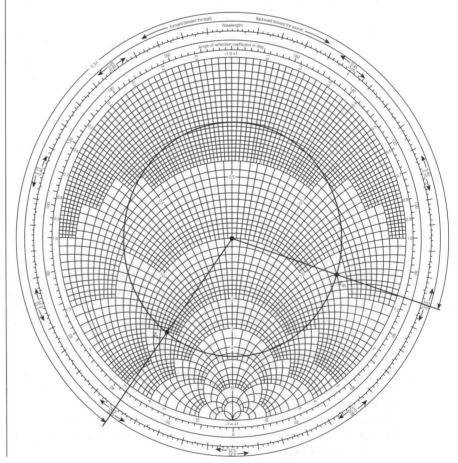

Solution

The normalised load impedance is $z_L = (80 - j100)/50 = 1.6 - j2$ and this point is plotted on the Smith chart as shown by Fig. 5.19. From the chart:

(a) $|\rho_v| = 32.5/50 = 0.65$, and $\angle\rho_v = -37°$. Therefore,

$$\rho_v = 0.65\angle{-37}° \ (Ans.)$$

(b) $S = 4.6$ or 0.22 (*Ans.*)

(c) Travelling around the $S = 4.6$ circle a distance of 0.3λ from z_L towards the source gives $z_{in} = 0.34 + j0.7$. Therefore,

$$Z_{in} = (0.34 + j0.7)50 = 17 + j35 \ \Omega. \ (Ans.)$$

(d) Travelling from z_L towards the source a distance of 0.202λ gives $z_{in} = 0.22 + j0$, and hence

$$Z_{in} = 0.22 \times 50 = 11 \ \Omega \ (Ans.)$$

Travelling from z_L towards the source $(0.202 + 0.25)\lambda = 0.452\lambda$ makes $z_{in} = 4.6 + j0$ and $Z_{in} = 4.6 \times 50 = 230 \ \Omega$ (*Ans.*)

Determination of an unknown load impedance

If both the length of the line and its input impedance are known the method previously described to find the input impedance of a line can be used. If not, the procedure to be adopted is as follows:

(a) Measure the VSWR with the unknown load connected to the line and note the position of any voltage minimum.
(b) Remove the load from the line and short-circuit the load terminals. This will cause the noted position of the voltage minimum to shift to a new point (which is less than $\lambda/4$ away). Note this new position.
(c) Measure the distance in centimetres between two adjacent voltage minima – this corresponds to one-half a wavelength on the line.
(d) Draw the VSWR circle.
(e) Starting from the point where the VSWR circle cuts the real axis at a value less than unity, move around the VSWR circle a distance equal to the distance moved by the voltage minimum and in the *same* direction. The point reached is the normalised load impedance.

If an unknown load admittance is to be determined follow the same procedure but start on the Smith chart at the point where the VSWR circle cuts the real axis at a value greater than unity.

EXAMPLE 5.15

A 50 Ω line has a VSWR of 2 when an unknown load impedance is connected to its output terminals. Adjacent voltage minima are found to be 20 cm apart. When the unknown load is removed from the line and is replaced by a short circuit the voltage minima move by 6 cm towards the source. Calculate the value of the unknown load impedance.

Solution

See Fig. 5.20. The VSWR = 2 circle has been drawn centred on $1 + j0$; 20 cm = $\lambda/2$ so that 6 cm = 0.15λ. Starting from the point $0.5 + j0$ and moving around the VSWR circle for a distance of 0.15 in the clockwise direction gives $z_L = 0.98 + j0.7$. Therefore,

$$Z_L = 50(0.98 + j0.7) = 49 + j35 \text{ } \Omega \text{ } (Ans.)$$

Fig. 5.20

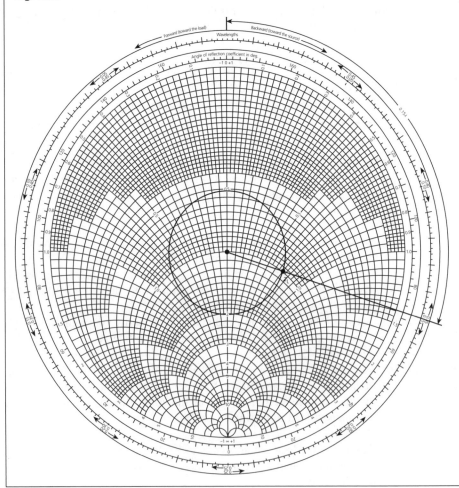

Fig. 5.21 *Scales used to take into account line attenuation*

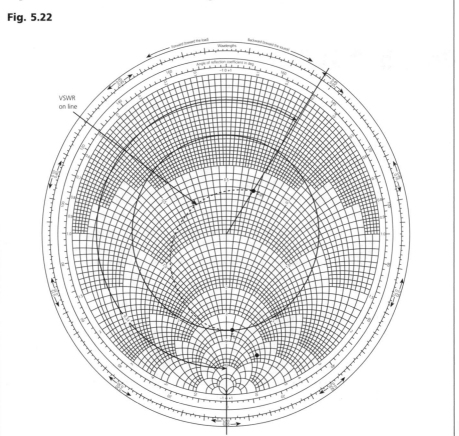

Voltage standing-wave ratio

Towards load → Effect of line attenuation (1 dB steps) ← Towards generator

Centre of chart

Edge of chart

Effect of line attenuation

The effect of line attenuation upon the VSWR and the input impedance can be taken into account by the use of the scales shown in Fig. 5.21. The line attenuation scale is marked in 1 dB steps and may be entered at any point since only distances along the scale are of any significance. The use of the scales will be illustrated by an example.

EXAMPLE 5.16

A 50 Ω line has a 3 dB loss and is terminated in a $200 + j25$ Ω load. Calculate its input resistance if the line is 0.3λ long.

Fig. 5.22

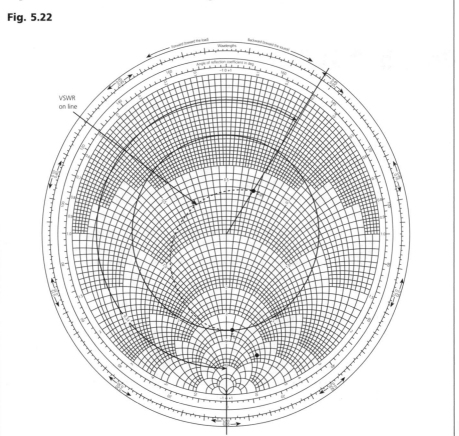

Solution

Refer to Fig. 5.22: $z_L = (200 + j25)/50 = 4 + j0.5$. This point is located on the chart and the loss-free VSWR circle drawn to give $S = 4$. Locate $S = 4$ on the VSWR scale of Fig. 5.22 and move across onto the line attenuation scale; this point is slightly less than 2.25 dB. Move along this scale towards the source a distance equal to 3 dB and then move back onto the VSWR scale. This gives $S = 1.89$ (approximately). The VSWR circle therefore becomes a spiral, as shown. The point reached is $z_{in} = 0.54 + j0.22$ so that

$$Z_{in} = 27 + j11 \ \Omega \ (Ans.)$$

Matching

λ/4 section

If the load impedance is not purely resistive the λ/4 matching section must be inserted at the distance from the load at which the line impedance is wholly real.

EXAMPLE 5.17

The load impedance $z_L = 20 + j10 \ \Omega$ is to be matched to a 50 Ω line by a λ/4 length of loss-free line. Calculate the position and impedance of the matching section.

Solution

The normalised impedance $z_L = (20 + j10)/50 = 0.4 + j0.2 \ \Omega$. This point has been plotted on the Smith chart shown in Fig. 5.23 and the VSWR circle drawn. Moving around the VSWR circle towards the source until the real axis is reached covers a distance of 0.214λ. At this point $z = 2.6$; hence $Z = 50 \times 2.6 = 130 \ \Omega$ and $Z_0' = \sqrt{(50 \times 130)} = 80.6 \ \Omega$. Therefore the λ/4 section should be of 80.6 Ω impedance and be connected 0.214λ from the load (*Ans.*)

Single-stub matching

When a single-stub matching system is employed a short-circuited stub line is connected in parallel with the line at the distance from the load where the normalised conductance of the line is unity. The length of the stub must be such that its input susceptance is of equal magnitude but opposite sign to the susceptance of the line at that point.

Fig. 5.23

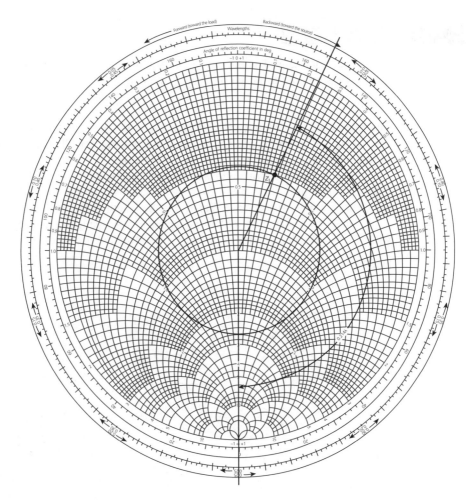

The design procedure is as follows:

(a) Plot the normalised load admittance on the Smith chart.
(b) Draw the VSWR circle.
(c) Move around this circle towards the source until the unity conductance circle is reached and note the distance travelled.
(d) Determine from the chart the susceptance of the line at this point, say $+jB$; the required susceptance of the stub is then equal but opposite, i.e. $-jB$.
(e) Determine the necessary length of the stub by moving in the clockwise direction from the point of infinite susceptance to the wanted susceptance and note the distance travelled.

EXAMPLE 5.18

A load has a normalised admittance of 0.4 + j0.6. Calculate the length and position of a single stub used to match the load to the line.

Solution

The normalised load admittance y_L is plotted on the Smith chart shown in Fig. 5.24 and the VSWR circle drawn. The distance that must be travelled around the circle to reach the unity conductance circle is 0.078λ (*Ans.*)

At this point the normalised susceptance of the line is +j1.35. To find the required length of the stub move from the point −j1.35 on the edge of the chart to the point of infinite susceptance. This gives the length of the stub as 0.102λ (*Ans.*)

A single-stub matching system is satisfactory for single-frequency operation with a constant value of load impedance, but of limited usefulness otherwise.

Fig. 5.24

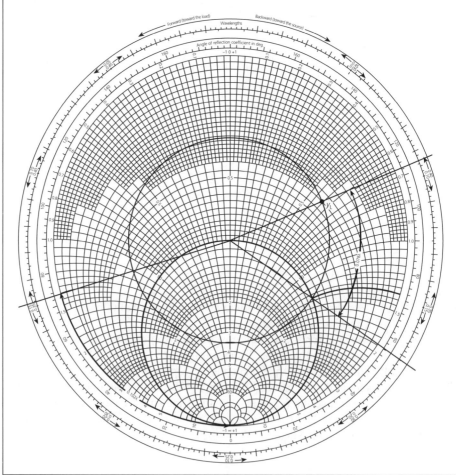

Double-stub matching

If two short-circuited stubs are connected across a mismatched line at two different locations a much greater range of load impedances can be successfully matched together, but again only at a specified frequency. The basic concept was illustrated by Fig. 5.14; the distance d_1 of the stub nearest the load may sometimes be zero. The stub nearest the source is only used to cancel out the susceptance of the line at the point at which the normalised admittance is $1 + jb$. This means that the admittance to the right of the stub/line junction must lie on the unity conductance circle so that the normalised admittance of the line at this point is $y_1 = 1 + j0$. At this point therefore the total admittance is $Y_1 = Y_0$. The stub nearest the load must have an input susceptance B_2 such that the total normalised admittance y_T ($y_T = (Y_0 + jB_2)/Y_0$) at the point of connection, when transformed by the length of line d_2, to become y_{in}, falls somewhere on the unity conductance circle.

Fig. 5.25 *Design of a double-stub matching system*

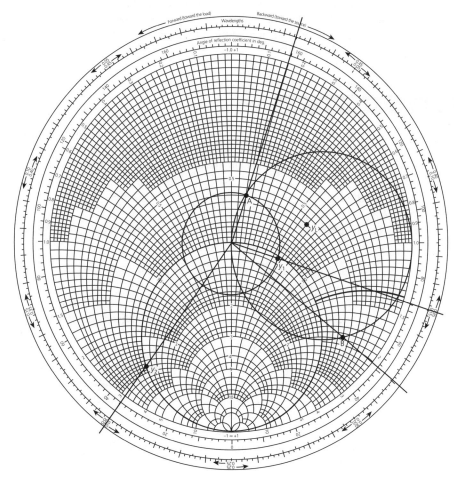

In most cases the distance d_2 between the two stubs is either $\lambda/8$ or $3\lambda/8$. Any closer spacing will distort the field distribution so that the two stubs would act more or less as though they were in parallel with one another. Spacings between $\lambda/8$ and $3\lambda/8$ reduce the number of loads that can be matched. Suppose that d_2 is chosen to be $\lambda/8$; then the normalised admittance y_T must lie on the unity conductance circle rotated $\lambda/8$ towards the load (see Fig. 5.25). Then the $\lambda/8$ length of line will transform all admittances that lie on the unity conductance circle to corresponding points on the rotated circle.

Suppose, for example, that the normalised load admittance is $y_L = 0.6 + j0.6$ and that the second stub is connected at the load so that $d_1 = 0$. There are two points, marked as A and B, at which the addition of load susceptance will make the resultant load admittance lie on the $\lambda/8$ rotated unity conductance circle. At point A, $y_T = 0.6 + j0.1$, and at point B, $y_T = 0.6 + j1.96$. When transformed by the $\lambda/8$ section of line the normalised admittances at A and B become either $y_1 = 1 + j0.58$ or $y_2 = 1 - j2.76$. Thus, the source-end stub must provide a normalised susceptance of either $j0.525$ or $+j2.6$. The necessary lengths of the two stubs can then be found in the same manner as for a single stub, i.e. 0.4λ or 0.05λ, respectively.

The disadvantage of double-stub matching is that not all loads can be matched. This disadvantage can be eliminated either by making the distance between load and load stub adjustable, or by using a third stub. As with single-stub matching the system has a narrow bandwidth.

EXAMPLE 5.19

A 50 Ω line has a load impedance of $49\angle 78.7°$ Ω. The load is to be matched to the line by a double-stub system with the load stub 0.1λ from the load and a stub spacing of $\lambda/8$. Determine the necessary lengths of the two stubs.

Solution

The admittance of the load is $Y_L = 1/(49\angle 78.7°) = 20.4\angle -78.7°$ mS. The normalised load admittance is $[(20.4) \times 10^{-3}]/0.02 = 0.2 - j1$.

(a) Plot $0.2 - j1$ on the Smith chart, as in Fig. 5.26.
(b) Draw the VSWR circle through the point.
(c) Move around the circle towards the source a distance of 0.1λ. The point reached is $0.1 - j0.164$ and this is the normalised admittance to the right of the load stub.
(d) The load stub must have a normalised input admittance of $+j0.164$ (i) to cancel out the $-j0.16$ term and (ii) to place the real part of the normalised admittance on the circle B. Hence, move along the constant-conductance circle from the point $(0.1 - j0.164)$ until circle B is reached. There are two choices: point A where y is $0.1 + j0.48$ and point B where y is $0.5 + j1.75$.
(e) Choosing point A, this stub must have a susceptance of $(0.1 + j0.48) - (0.1 - j0.16) = +j0.64$. Moving along the infinite admittance circle towards the source from ∞ to $+j0.64$, the length l_1 of the load stub is $l_1 = 0.322\lambda$ (*Ans.*)

Fig. 5.26

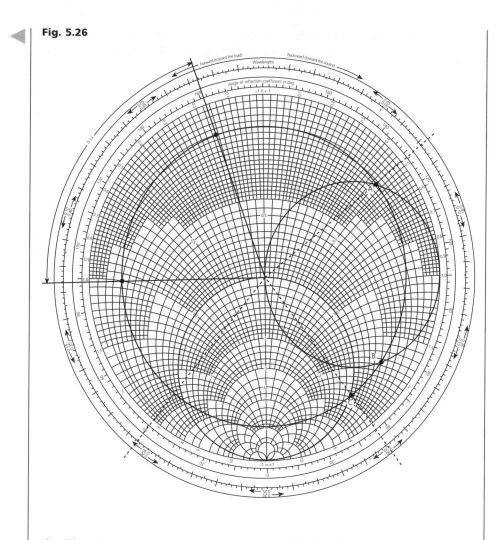

(f) The change in admittance produced by the λ/8 section of line separating the two stubs is found by moving along the VSWR circle that passes through the point a distance of λ/8 towards the source. Once the circle A is reached at point C it gives the normalised admittance of the source stub as $1 + \text{j}2.72$.

(g) The source stub is required to have an input susceptance of $-\text{j}2.72$. Following step (e) again gives $l_2 = 0.053\lambda$ (*Ans.*)

EXERCISES

5.1   An RF line is λ/2 long, has a characteristic impedance of 600 Ω, 6 dB loss and it is terminated by a load impedance of $1200 + \text{j}300$ Ω. Calculate the input impedance of the line.

5.2 List the factors that limit the use of inductors and capacitors at very high frequencies. Calculate the length of 50 Ω loss-free line that would simulate an inductance of 20 nH at 600 MHz.

5.3 A $\lambda/8$ length of loss-free line has a characteristic impedance of 600 Ω and a load of 800 Ω. Calculate the input impedance of the line. Also calculate the ratio, in dB, of the powers in the load with and without the insertion of a $\lambda/4$ section of loss-free matching line of the appropriate impedance.

5.4 A 75 Ω transmitting aerial, operating at 500 MHz, is connected to the transmitter by a 6 m length of coaxial cable of 75 Ω characteristic impedance. A cable fault causes an effective capacitance of 4.244 pF to be in series with the line at a distance of 2 m from the aerial. Calculate the value of the voltage reflection coefficient on the cable (a) at the fault and (b) at the input to the line. Also calculate the power delivered to the aerial before and after the fault occurs if the transmitter power output is 30 W.

5.5 A load of $210 - j180\ \Omega$ is connected to the output terminals of a 150 Ω loss-free line at 100 MHz. Use a Smith chart to find the position and the length of a single matching stub made of the same cable. Calculate the voltage across the resistive part of the load if the sending-end voltage is 100 μV.

5.6 An unknown load presents an impedance of $80 + j110\ \Omega$ when supplied via a line of characteristic impedance 100 Ω and length 0.154λ. Use a Smith chart to find (a) the load impedance, (b) the VSWR, (c) the shortest distance from the load at which a single matching stub could be connected, and (d) the length of this stub.

5.7 A load of $100 - j100\ \Omega$ is to be matched to a 50 Ω feeder by connecting a short-circuit stub across the line 0.1λ from the load, and then using a $\lambda/4$ section to connect this point to the rest of the feeder. Use a Smith chart to calculate the length of the stub and the impedance of the $\lambda/4$ section.

5.8 A coaxial cable has an attenuation of 0.2 dB m^{-1}. Calculate the Q factor of a length of this cable that is resonant at a frequency of 900 MHz.

5.9 A loss-free line divides into two sections A and B. The length of section A is 16.28 cm and that of section B is 14.5 cm. The impedances of the loads connected to the two sections of line are $166 + j0\ \Omega$ onto A and $37.5 + j0\ \Omega$ onto B. The frequency of operation is 258 MHz and the characteristic impedance is 100 Ω. Calculate the voltage reflection coefficient on each line and also the VSWR on the source side of the junction.

5.10 A 50 Ω slotted line is used to measure the impedance of an unknown load. With this load connected the VSWR on the line was $S = 2.0$. Adjacent voltage minima were found to be at 41.2 cm and 71.2 cm from the load. With the load disconnected and replaced with a short circuit the voltage minima were found to be at 33.7 cm and 63.7 cm from the load. Use a Smith chart to calculate the impedance of the load.

5.11 A low-loss coaxial cable is $3\lambda/4$ long and has a characteristic impedance of 75 Ω. The load impedance of 150 Ω has a peak voltage of 40 V across it. Calculate (a) the peak voltage at the sending end of the line, (b) the peak input current, (c) the distance from the load of the nearest current maximum, and (d) the fraction of the incident power reflected by the load.

5.12 Use a Smith chart to design a single-stub matching system to match a 50 Ω load to its $100 + j50$ Ω load.

5.13 A loss-free 100 Ω line is $\lambda/3$ in length. Calculate its input impedance when the load impedance is $150 - j60$ Ω.

5.14 A 50 Ω loss-free line has a VSWR of 5. The nearest voltage minimum to the load is $\lambda/3$ from it. Determine the load impedance.

5.15 Prove equation (5.12).

5.16 A 50 Ω line has a load of (i) 100 Ω and (ii) $100 + j100$ Ω connected across its output terminals. (a) Calculate the VSWR on the line and (b) determine the return loss in each case.

5.17 An RF line has an inductance of 12 μH m^{-1} and a capacitance of 4.8 nF m^{-1}. Determine the input impedance of a 1 m length of the line at a frequency of 15 MHz if the far end is short-circuited.

6 Waveguides

After reading this chapter you should be able to:

(a) State the boundary conditions for E and H fields at a conducting surface.
(b) Explain how a TE wave is propagated in a rectangular waveguide.
(c) Understand the difference between group velocity and phase velocity and derive an expression for each.
(d) Explain why a rectangular waveguide acts like a high-pass filter.
(e) Explain how a waveguide mode is energised.
(f) State the higher-order modes of propagation in a rectangular waveguide and say why they are not normally employed.
(g) Describe what is meant by the wave impedance of a waveguide.
(h) State that waveguides are manufactured in a number of standard sizes and know at least one labelling scheme.
(i) Describe some commonly employed waveguide components.

When a signal is propagated along a transmission line some of its energy is always lost because of the inevitable I^2R power dissipation in the resistance of the conductors. Even with a coaxial cable these losses become excessively high at frequencies above about 3 GHz. To minimise losses the use of coaxial cable is only feasible for very short connections and a rectangular waveguide must be used for longer lengths. At microwave frequencies it becomes necessary to employ a rectangular waveguide as the transmission medium in which electromagnetic energy is guided in the space enclosed by its walls. The rectangular waveguide shown in Fig. 6.1 consists of a hollow rectangular metal tube that has two horizontal walls of internal dimensions a and two vertical walls of internal dimensions b; always $a > b$. Usually, the waveguide is made of copper, although sometimes other materials, such as aluminium or brass, are used. The dimensions a and b of the waveguide must be comparable with the wavelength of the signal and it is only at frequencies in excess of about 1 GHz that these dimensions become small enough for the use of a waveguide to be both practical and economic.

The use of waveguides is made possible by the skin effect which limits the flow of current to an area very close to the surface of a metal when the frequency is high enough. Energy can therefore be completely confined to the interior of the waveguide. Electromagnetic energy directed into the waveguide cannot radiate in the sideways direction and so it is propagated along the waveguide in the z direction with very little

Fig. 6.1 *Rectangular waveguide*

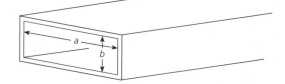

Fig. 6.2 *Electromagnetic wave*

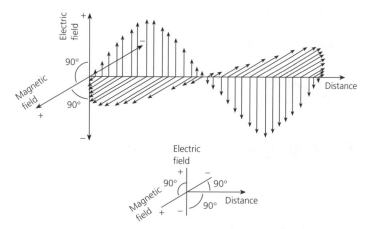

attenuation. An electromagnetic wave has both an electric component and a magnetic component that are always in phase quadrature, and are also mutually at right angles to the direction of propagation. This is shown by Fig. 6.2.

When an electromagnetic wave is incident upon a perfect conductor no energy can be absorbed by the conductor and so the wave must be completely reflected. At the surface of the conductor the following boundary conditions must be satisfied:

- The electric field at the surface of the conductor must be perpendicular to the surface; there can be no tangential component. This must be so, or else the field would be short-circuited by the (assumed) perfect conductor.
- Any magnetic field at the surface of the conductor must be parallel to the surface; there cannot be any perpendicular components.

The *polarisation* of an electromagnetic wave is the plane in which the electric field lies; this plane is usually either horizontal or vertical but less often the polarisation may be circular. A horizontally polarised transverse electromagnetic (TEM) wave that is incident on a horizontal conducting surface will produce a reflected wave having a horizontal electric field that is always of equal amplitude and opposite phase to the incident wave at the point of reflection. This satisfies the second condition. The tangential magnetic component produces a current in the surface of the conducting walls at right angles to the field that, in turn, produces a magnetic component in the reflected wave equal and opposite to the corresponding component in the incident wave. This results in a reflected wave of equal magnitude but opposite phase to the incident wave.

The incident and reflected waves combine to give a transverse electric (TE) wave that propagates in a direction parallel to the surface and which consists of a series of closed magnetic field loops. (TE means that the electric field lines are transverse, or *perpendicular*, to the walls of the waveguide.)

A TEM wave, which has its electric E and magnetic H fields in quadrature to each other and to the direction of propagation, cannot be propagated along a waveguide. This is because the magnetic field would be at right angles to the sides of the waveguide containing the y axis and this would not satisfy one of the boundary conditions.

There are a large number of distinct electromagnetic field configurations that can exist in a rectangular waveguide and they are known as *waveguide modes*. Waveguide modes are classified by their electric and magnetic field components. Two main types of waveguide mode are possible:

1   TE modes in which the electric field is perpendicular, or *transverse*, to the waveguide axis; and
2   TM modes in which the magnetic field is always transverse to the axis.

Propagation in the rectangular waveguide

Figure 6.3 shows one point in the positive peak wavefront of an electromagnetic wave entering a rectangular waveguide. The wave is incident upon one of the two vertical walls of the waveguide. The polarisation of the wave is assumed to be such that the electric field is perpendicular to the plane of the paper and the magnetic field lies in the plane of the paper. When the electric field arrives at a wall it will be completely reflected with 180° phase reversal. This is indicated in the figure by the + and − signs. The total field at the surface of the wall is equal to the phasor sum of the incident and reflected fields and hence is zero. The angle of reflection θ_r is always equal to the angle of incidence θ_i. The reflected wave travels across the waveguide to the other vertical wall and here it is again totally reflected with another reversal in its polarity. This reflected wave travels across the waveguide to the other vertical wall, is again reflected, and so on. The electromagnetic wave will therefore propagate down the waveguide by means of a series of reflections from each of the vertical guide walls.

Group velocity

The wave travels from one vertical wall to the other with a velocity equal to the velocity of light c, i.e. 3×10^8 m s^{-1}. This velocity can be resolved into two components, V_G and

Fig. 6.3 *Single point on a wavefront propagating down a waveguide*

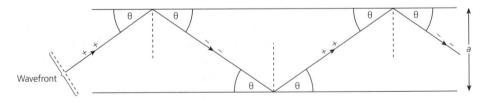

Fig. 6.4 *Velocities in a waveguide*

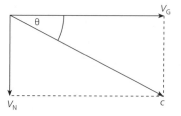

Fig. 6.5 *Wavefronts propagating down a waveguide (• = positive, o = negative)*

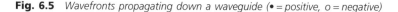

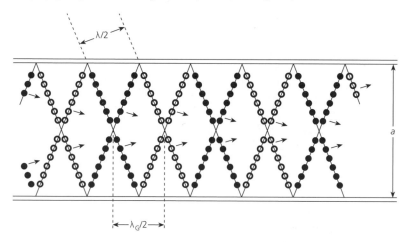

V_N, as shown by Fig. 6.4. The *group velocity* V_G is the component of velocity parallel to the walls of the waveguide and is the velocity with which the electromagnetic energy propagates down the waveguide. From Fig. 6.4, $V_G = c \cos \theta$ and this means that the group velocity is always less than the velocity of light. The component V_N of the velocity normal to the guide walls is equal to $c \sin \theta$. Figure 6.4 shows one particular point on the wavefront of a propagating electromagnetic wave. If the complete wavefront is considered the situation is somewhat more complex and is shown by Fig. 6.5. As each successive peak of the wavefront travels across the waveguide, one end of the wavefront will arrive at a wall some time before its other end. As each part of the wavefront reaches the wall it is reflected, with a change in polarity, whilst the remainder of the wavefront continues to move in its original direction. Eventually, the entire wavefront will have reached the wall and have been reflected to travel in the new direction. Figure 6.5 shows only the complete wavefronts; clearly, alternate positive and negative wavefronts propagate in both directions across the waveguide. The zigzag path followed by the wave causes the wavelength of the mode to be longer than the free-space wavelength.

The distance between two successive wavefronts propagating in the same direction is equal to one-half of the free-space wavelength λ_0. The distance between the intersection of two positive wavefronts and the intersection of two negative wavefronts is equal to one-half of the waveguide wavelength λ_G. These two different wavelengths are indicated in Fig. 6.5.

Fig. 6.6 *Field configurations in a rectangular waveguide, (a) end view, (b) side view, and (c) top view.*

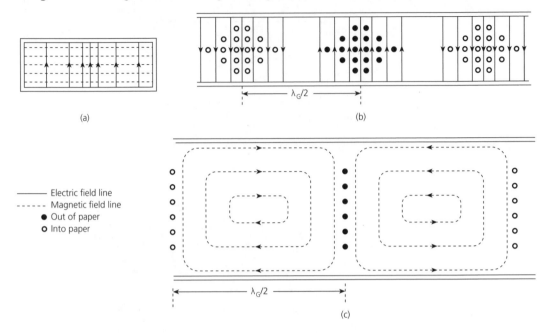

(a)

(b)

Electric field line
Magnetic field line
● Out of paper
○ Into paper

(c)

At every point in the waveguide the electric and the magnetic field strengths are the algebraic sum of the two components at that point. Whenever the peak of one of the waves intersects with a peak of another wave of the same polarity the resultant field will have its maximum value. Wherever two peaks of opposite polarity coincide they cancel out and the resultant field is zero; for the electric field this only occurs at the vertical walls of the waveguide. In this way the resultant electric and magnetic field configurations can be deduced and are shown in Fig. 6.6. Figure 6.6(a) shows the field configurations looking into the end of the waveguide; the electric field consists of straight lines between the two horizontal walls, and the magnetic field consists of lines of force parallel to the horizontal walls. The electric field strength has its maximum amplitude at the centre of the guide and falls to zero at each of the vertical walls. The electric field is normal to the horizontal walls and so it conforms to boundary condition (a). If the viewpoint is changed to the side of the waveguide, as shown by Fig. 6.6(b), the electric field between the horizontal walls changes its direction at regular intervals along the length of the guide. Lastly, the top view of the waveguide, Fig. 6.6(c), shows only the magnetic field and this can be seen to consist of a series of closed loops of lines of force that are at right angles to the electric field.

Phase velocity

The field patterns propagate along the waveguide, without any change in their shape, with a velocity known as the *phase velocity* V_P which is always greater than the velocity of light. This is possible because the patterns do not convey energy – which travels at the group velocity. The product of the group and phase velocities is equal to the square of the velocity of light, i.e.

$$V_G V_P = c^2 \qquad (6.1)$$

Figure 6.6 shows that while the magnetic field has a component which lies in the direction of propagation, the electric field does not. For this reason this mode of propagation is known as a transverse electric (TE) mode and it is labelled as TE_{10}. The first subscript 1 denotes that there is only one half-cycle in the field configurations in the a dimension of the waveguide. The second subscript 0 denotes that there are no half-cycle variations in the field strengths in the b dimension of the waveguide.

Other modes of propagation are also possible but the TE_{10} mode is both the easiest to set up and of the lowest frequency. The TE_{10} mode is by far the most commonly employed mode and it is known as the *dominant mode*. Higher-order modes may be generated whenever energy is delivered to, or taken from, the waveguide, at a discontinuity, and also at any point where some field distortion occurs. Usually, the narrow guide dimension b is chosen to ensure that all modes other than the dominant mode are suppressed. Usually, b is about one-half of a.

Cut-off frequency

If the frequency of the signal is varied, the angle of incidence, and hence of reflection, will also vary to ensure that the dimension a is always equal to an integer number of half-wavelengths. If the frequency is increased the angle of incidence θ becomes larger and eventually the point is reached where only one half-wavelength is no longer possible and then two half-wavelengths become established. If this occurs the higher mode TE_{20} has been set up in the waveguide. On the other hand, if the frequency is decreased the angle of incidence θ becomes smaller and smaller and eventually the point is reached, when $\theta = 0°$, where the wave merely moves perpendicularly between the two walls of the waveguide. There is then *no* propagation of energy down the waveguide; this means that a rectangular waveguide acts like a high-pass filter whose cut-off frequency is determined by the dimension a.

The free-space wavelength λ_C at which this happens is known as the *cut-off wavelength*. The *cut-off frequency* $f_C = c/\lambda_C$ is the lowest frequency at which the waveguide is able to transmit energy:

$$f_C = c/[2a\sqrt{(\mu_r \varepsilon_r)}] = c/2a \quad \text{for an air-filled waveguide} \qquad (6.2)$$

Referring to Fig. 6.7, which is an expanded version of the pattern between a positive peak and a negative peak, from the triangle ABC

$$\cos \theta = (\lambda_G/2)/\sqrt{[a^2 + (\lambda_G/2)^2]}$$

From the triangle ADC, $\cos \theta = \lambda_0/2a$, and from the triangle BCD, $\sin \theta = \lambda_0/\lambda_G$. Therefore,

$$(\lambda_G/2)/\sqrt{[a^2 + (\lambda_G/2)^2]} = \lambda_0/2a$$

$$\lambda_G^2 a^2/4 = (\lambda_0^2/4)(a^2 + \lambda_G^2/4)$$

Fig. 6.7 *Calculation of group wavelength*

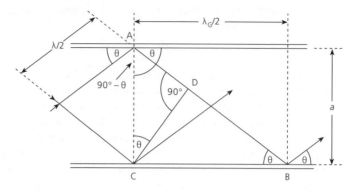

$$\lambda_G^2 a^2 = \lambda_0^2 a^2 + \lambda_0^2 \lambda_G^2/4, \quad \lambda_G^2(a^2 - \lambda_0^2/4) = \lambda_0^2 a^2$$

$$\lambda_G^2(4a^2 - \lambda_0^2)/4 = \lambda_0^2 a^2, \quad \lambda_G^2 = (4\lambda_0^2 a^2)/(4a^2 - \lambda_0^2) = \lambda_0^2/(1 - \lambda_0^2/4a^2)$$

or

$$\lambda_G = \lambda_0/\sqrt{[1 - (\lambda_0/2a)^2]} \tag{6.3}$$

If $\lambda_0/2a < 1$, λ_C is real and the wave is able to propagate along the waveguide. If, however, $\lambda_0/2a > 1$, λ_C will be an imaginary quantity and this means that no propagation of energy takes place. The cut-off wavelength λ_C is the wavelength at which λ_C changes from a real to an imaginary quantity, i.e. $\lambda_C = 2a$.

The cut-off wavelength of the next higher mode is equal to the wide dimension a of the waveguide. If the operation of the waveguide is to be restricted to the dominant mode only, the waveguide must be operated at some frequency between the cut-off frequencies of the dominant and the next higher mode. It is normally recommended that a rectangular waveguide should be used with signals having a free-space wavelength within ±20% of $4a/3$. The nominal operating frequency should be $1.5f_C$ with a recommended bandwidth from $1.25f_C$ to $1.87f_C$ to ensure that only the dominant mode is transmitted. The next higher modes have cut-off wavelengths of a (TE_{20}) and $2b$ (TE_{01}). Hence, if $\lambda_0/2 < a < \lambda_0$ and $2b < \lambda_0$ these nearest modes to the dominant mode will both be suppressed. Usually, b is approximately one-half of a so that the TE_{01} mode is suppressed and the attenuation of the waveguide is as low as possible.

The lowest frequency for which the dominant mode is able to propagate down a waveguide is the frequency at which the wider dimension a is equal to one-half a wavelength. Therefore

$$\lambda_G = \lambda_0/\sqrt{[1 - (\lambda_0/\lambda_C)^2]} = \lambda_0/\sqrt{[1 - (f_C/f)^2]} \tag{6.4}$$

Equation (6.4) is very often written in the form

$$1/\lambda_G^2 = 1/\lambda_0^2 - 1/\lambda_C^2 \tag{6.5}$$

EXAMPLE 6.1

The internal dimensions of a rectangular waveguide are 0.7112 cm by 0.3556 cm. Calculate (a) the cut-off frequency and (b) the group wavelength at a frequency of 25 GHz.

Solution

$\lambda_C = 2a = 2 \times 0.7112 = 1.4224$ cm

(a) $f_C = c/\lambda_C = (3 \times 10^8)/(14.224 \times 10^{-3}) = 21.09$ GHz (*Ans.*)
(b) From equation (6.5), $1/\lambda_G^2 = [(25 \times 10^9)/(3 \times 10^8)]^2 - [1/(14.224 \times 10^{-3})^2 \approx 2000$. Hence, $1/\lambda_G = 1/44.72$, and $\lambda_G = 2.236$ cm (*Ans.*)

Waveguide equations

The electromagnetic field components at any point in a rectangular waveguide are given by the following equations:

$$\frac{\partial^2 E_z}{\partial x^2} + \frac{\partial^2 E_z}{\partial y^2} + \frac{\partial^2 E_z}{\partial z^2} = -\omega^2 \mu \varepsilon E_z \tag{6.6}$$

$$\frac{\partial^2 H_z}{\partial x^2} + \frac{\partial^2 H_z}{\partial y^2} + \frac{\partial^2 H_z}{\partial z^2} = -\omega^2 \mu \varepsilon H_z \tag{6.7}$$

The solutions to these equations are

$$E_z = E_0 \sin(m\pi x/a) \sin(n\pi y/b) e^{j(\omega t - \beta z)} \tag{6.8}$$

$$H_z = H_0 \cos(m\pi x/a) \cos(n\pi y/b) e^{j(\omega t - \beta z)} \tag{6.9}$$

In a TE mode of propagation $E_z = 0$. If $E_y = 0$ at $x = 0$ and at $x = a$, and if $E_x = 0$ at $y = 0$ and at $y = b$, then $\partial H_z/\partial t = 0$.

For the TE$_{10}$ mode of propagation $m = 1$ and $n = 0$ and the cut-off wavelength $\lambda_C = 2a$. Then the propagation coefficient β of the waveguide is

$$\beta = \sqrt{(\omega^2/c^2 - \pi^2/a^2)} = 2\pi/\lambda_G \tag{6.10}$$

Hence, for the TE$_{10}$ mode,

$$E_x = E_z = H_y = 0 \tag{6.11}$$

$$E_y = A \sin(\pi x/a) \sin(\omega t - \beta x) \tag{6.12}$$

$$H_x = -A(\beta/a\omega\mu_0) \sin(\pi x/a) \cos(\omega t - \beta z) \tag{6.13}$$

$$H_y = A(\beta/a\omega\mu_0) \cos(\pi x/a) \cos(\omega t - \beta z) \tag{6.14}$$

Fig. 6.8 *Calculation of group and phase velocity*

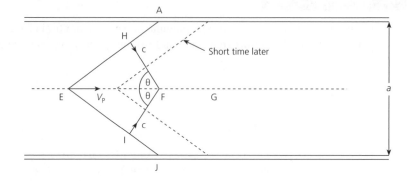

Velocity of propagation

The phase velocity V_P is the rate at which any particular point in a field pattern propagates along the waveguide. The group velocity V_G is the rate at which energy is propagated along the waveguide. From Fig. 6.8 the point on a wavefront marked as E will propagate along the waveguide to reach first the point F, and then the point G. To keep the phase of the wave constant the point E must arrive at F at the same time as any other point on the wavefront. The two wavefronts AE and EJ move in the directions perpendicular to the wavefronts at the velocity of light c. Their point of intersection E, a particular phase in the field pattern, moves parallel to the walls with phase velocity V_P. For the two wavefronts and the point E to arrive at the point F simultaneously, $c/V_P = \text{HF/EF} = \cos \theta$, and therefore

$$V_P = c/\cos \theta \tag{6.15}$$

Since $\cos \theta < 1$ the phase velocity is always greater than, or equal to, the velocity of light. Further,

$$V_P = f\lambda_G = c\lambda_G/\lambda_0 \tag{6.16}$$

The group velocity is the velocity with which energy is propagated along the waveguide and it is equal to

$$V_G = c \cos \theta = c\lambda_0/\lambda_G \tag{6.17}$$

Also,

$$V_P V_G = c^2 \tag{6.18}$$

EXAMPLE 6.2

A rectangular waveguide has internal dimensions 3.485 cm and 1.580 cm. Calculate the phase and group velocities at a frequency of 7 GHz.

Solution

Now $\lambda_C = 2a = 2 \times 3.485 = 6.97$ cm. Hence

$$1/\lambda_G^2 = [(7 \times 10^9)/(3 \times 10^8)]^2 - [1/(6.97 \times 10^{-2})]^2 = 338.6$$

$$1/\lambda_G = 18.4 \quad \text{and} \quad \lambda_G = 5.435 \text{ cm}$$

From equation (6.16),

$$V_P = 7 \times 10^9 \times 5.435 \times 10^{-2} = 3.805 \times 10^8 \text{ m s}^{-1} \text{ (Ans.)}$$

From equation (6.18),

$$V_G = (3 \times 10^8)^2/(3.805 \times 10^8) = 2.3653 \times 10^8 \text{ m s}^{-1} \text{ (Ans.)}$$

Coaxial inputs

A coaxial input is often employed to energise a waveguide in the dominant TE_{01} mode as shown by Fig. 6.9. The outer conductor of the coaxial cable is connected to the centre of the broad side of the waveguide. The inner conductor passes through a hole in the wall to a rod, or probe, that is approximately $\lambda/4$ long. The rod is supported by a cross-bar which does not affect the electric field inside the waveguide since it is parallel to the vertical rod. The current in, and the voltage across, the rod excite the TE_{01} mode in the waveguide. Other modes are also excited but these are rapidly attenuated as they travel along the waveguide. Energy that travels in the reverse direction is reflected back in the required direction by the short-circuit plunger; this is adjusted to be exactly $\lambda_G/4$ behind the rod. The reflected waves are then in phase with the wave forward transmitted from the rod.

Higher-order modes of propagation

At higher frequencies other modes of propagation become possible since the waveguide dimensions then exceed the free-space wavelength λ_0. One example of a higher mode is the TE_{20} mode shown in Fig. 6.10 which consists of two sets of TE_{10} wave patterns. When the waveguide is even larger it also becomes possible to transmit the TM series of modes, the simplest of which is the TM_{11} mode shown in Fig. 6.11.

Fig. 6.9 *Two views of a coaxial input to a waveguide*

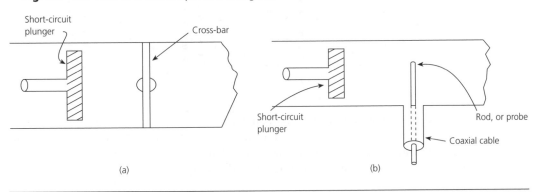

(a)　　　　　(b)

Fig. 6.10 *The TE$_{20}$ mode of propagation*

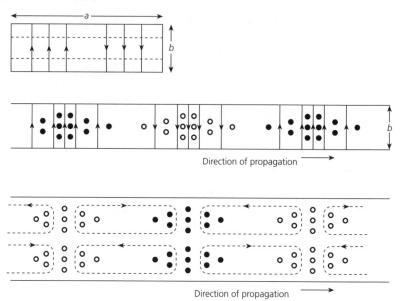

Fig. 6.11 *The TM$_{11}$ mode of propagation*

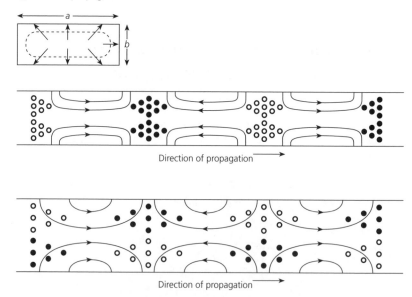

The presence in a waveguide of more than one mode makes it difficult to design an efficient system because the different modes travel with different velocities. The resultant differential delays vary with frequency and this effect (a) causes distortion in an FM system and (b) increases the error rate in a digital system.

Fig. 6.12 *(a) Capacitive iris, (b) inductive iris, and (c) parallel-resonant circuit iris*

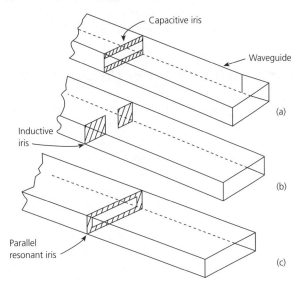

Impedance of a rectangular waveguide

The ratio of the electric and the magnetic field strengths in a rectangular waveguide is known as the *wave impedance* Z_W and it is constant at all points in the guide. Thus,

$$Z_W = |E_y/H_x| = \omega\mu_0/\beta = (2\pi c\mu_0/\lambda)/(2\pi/\lambda_G) = c\mu_0\lambda_G/\lambda$$
$$= [\mu_0/\surd(\mu_0\varepsilon_0)](\lambda_G/\lambda) = (\lambda_G/\lambda)\surd(\mu_0/\varepsilon_0) = 120\pi\lambda_G/\lambda \qquad (6.19)$$

Alternatively,

$$Z_W = 377/\surd[1 - (f_C/f)^2] \qquad (6.20)$$

Since $\lambda_C > \lambda_0$ the wave impedance is always greater than 120π or 377 Ω and at frequencies near to the cut-off frequency it becomes very large. If the wave impedance is matched to the waveguide's load then maximum power transfer from the waveguide to the load will be obtained. If, however, the load is mismatched, reflections and hence standing waves will be set up in the guide. The effect is exactly the same as occurs in a transmission line, and problems can be solved in a similar way.

Matching

When two lengths of waveguide are joined together or a waveguide is terminated in a load impedance reflections will occur unless the main waveguide is matched to its load. Capacitive and inductive irises are placed into the waveguide to act like shunt susceptances. An iris consists of two thin metal plates that are positioned perpendicular to the waveguide walls and joined to the walls at the edges with a gap left between the plates. An iris will give either a positive or a negative susceptance depending on its orientation. A horizontal iris provides a capacitive susceptance and a vertical iris provides an inductive iris. Figures 6.12(a) and (b) show capacitive and inductive irises respectively. The magnitude of the susceptance is determined by the size of the gap separating the two plates. If a parallel resonant circuit is required in the waveguide then a combined iris can be used, and this is shown by Fig. 6.12(c).

Attenuation in a rectangular waveguide

At frequencies below the cut-off frequency the propagation coefficient β is an imaginary quantity and it describes a wave that is not travelling along the waveguide but merely bouncing back and forwards between the b walls. Such a wave is known as an *evanescent* wave and its attenuation is independent of frequency. At frequencies above the cut-off frequency, as a signal is propagated down a waveguide the magnetic field induces e.m.f.s into the walls of the guide and these induced voltages cause currents to flow in the walls. The direction of the current flow is always at right angles to the direction of the magnetic field adjacent to the wall. In the b dimension walls the current flows vertically, but in the a dimension walls the current distribution is as shown by Fig. 6.13. Because the walls must possess some resistance this flow of current results in power dissipation and, since this power can only be supplied by the propagating wave, attenuation of the propagating wave occurs. Further losses are introduced because the surfaces of the inner walls are not perfectly smooth. For all sizes of rectangular waveguide the variation of attenuation with frequency is of the form shown by Fig. 6.14. At the

Fig. 6.13 *Currents in waveguide walls*

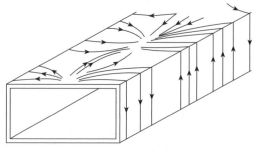

Fig. 6.14 *Attenuation–frequency characteristics of a rectangular waveguide*

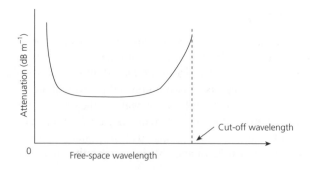

Table 6.1 *Waveguide dimensions and parameters*

Waveguide dimensions (cm) Internal		External		Frequency limit (GHz) Lower	Upper	Cut-off frequency (GHz)	Power rating at 1.5f_C (MW)	Attenuation (dB m^{-1})
a	b	a	b					
16.51	8.255	16.92	8.661	1.14	1.73	0.908	13.47	5×10^{-3}
10.92	5.461	11.33	5.867	1.72	2.61	1.373	5.90	9.4×10^{-3}
7.214	3.404	7.62	3.81	2.60	3.95	2.080	2.43	0.018
4.755	2.215	5.08	2.54	3.94	5.99	3.155	1.04	0.034
3.485	1.580	3.81	1.905	5.38	8.18	4.285	0.544	0.056
2.850	1.262	3.175	1.588	6.58	10.0	5.260	0.355	0.077
2.286	1.016	2.54	1.270	8.2	12.5	6.560	0.229	0.106
1.580	0.7899	1.783	0.9931	11.9	18.0	9.49	0.123	0.171
1.067	0.4318	1.27	0.635	17.6	26.7	14.08	0.048	0.357
0.7112	0.3556	0.9144	0.5588	26.4	40.1	21.1	0.025	0.5767
0.569	0.2845	0.7722	0.4877	33.0	50.1	26.35	0.016	0.787
0.4775	0.2388	0.6807	0.4420	39.3	59.7	31.4	0.010	1.026
0.3759	0.1880	0.5791	0.3921	49.9	75.8	39.9	0.007	1.466
0.3099	0.1549	0.5131	0.3581	60.5	92.0	48.4	0.005	1.957

low-frequency end of the range the attenuation is high because of the cut-off effect mentioned earlier. There is then a relatively wide bandwidth over which the attenuation has a fairly flat minimum value rising only slowly with frequency, and then at higher frequencies the attenuation rises rapidly.

Attenuation figures for each size of waveguide are given in Table 6.1.

Power-handling capability

The maximum power that can be transmitted by a rectangular waveguide is limited by the need to avoid voltage breakdown of the air within the guide. This means that it is necessary to ensure that the maximum electric field strength is always less than the breakdown value; for dry air at atmospheric pressure, for example, this is 3×10^6 V m^{-1}. The maximum power that a waveguide can transmit using the dominant mode is given by equation (6.21), i.e.

$$P_{max} = [(E_{max}^2 ab)/(480\pi)]\{\sqrt{[1 - (\lambda_0/2a)^2]}\}$$ (6.21)

Sizes of waveguides

A range of standard sizes of rectangular waveguides has been developed and these are given by Table 6.1. For each size there are recommended upper and lower frequency limits, a power rating and the attenuation at 1.5 times the cut-off frequency. The microwave spectrum is often said to be divided into a number of bands each of which is given a label. Unfortunately the labeling methods are not universally agreed but Fig. 6.15 shows one version that is employed in the USA.

Fig. 6.15 *Microwave bands: L, 0.39–1.55; S, 1.55–5.2; X, 5.2–10.9; K, 10.9–36; Q, 36–46; V, 46–56; and W, 56–100 GHz*

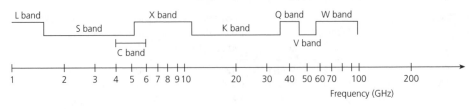

Two other microwave labelling schemes are also in use:

1   UK IEE:

C, 0.5–1; D, 1–2; E, 2–3; F, 3–4; G, 4–6; H, 6–8; I, 8–10; J, 10–20; K, 20–40; L, 40–60; and M, 60–100 GHz

2   NATO:

L, 1–2; S, 2–4; C, 4–8; X, 8–12; J, 12–18; K, 18–26; Q, 26–40; V, 40–60; and O, 60–90 GHz

Often the bands between 12.5 and 40 GHz are labelled as Ku 12.5–18 GHz, K 18–26.5 GHz and Ka 16.5–40 GHz.

Waveguide components

A variety of waveguide components are used in microwave systems, such as choke flanges, bends, junctions, E–plane and H–plane tees, hybrid rings and magic Ts.

Choke flange

A choke flange is used to join two lengths of rectangular waveguide together. Figure 6.16 shows two views of a choke flange. The flange incorporates a series-connected branching line ABC that is formed by the gap section AB and the slot BC. The lengths AB and BC are equal to one another. The distance ACB is λ/2 long so that the short

Fig. 6.16 *Choke flange*

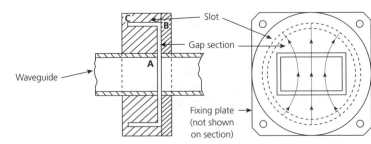

Fig. 6.17 *Waveguide bends (a) H-plane and (b) E-plane*

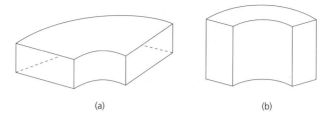

(a)   (b)

Fig. 6.18 *E-plane tee, and (b) H-plane tee*

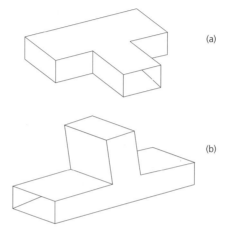

(a)

(b)

circuit at C presents zero impedance at A. The mechanical contact of the joint is at point B which is the high-impedance point half-way along the λ/2 line. The currents flowing in the waveguide wall cross the joint on the wide sides only. On the narrow sides the wall currents are parallel to the gap so that the segments of the slot adjacent to the narrow sides are not necessary.

Bends

Figures 6.17(a) and (b) show the two types of bends that are used to allow a waveguide to go around a corner. The H–plane bend is used to change the direction of wave propagation while the E–plane bend is used to minimise reflections by making a bend several wavelengths long.

The E–plane and H–plane tees shown by Figs 6.18(a) and (b) are used to combine signals from two sources into a single guide.

Hybrid ring

The hybrid ring is a power-splitting device and an example of one is shown in Fig. 6.19. Power entering port 2 is divided equally between ports 3 and 1 and no power enters port

Fig. 6.19 *Hybrid ring*

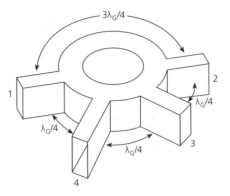

Fig. 6.20 *Magic T (a) appearance, (b) use of*

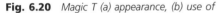

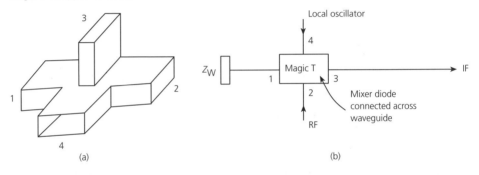

4; similarly, power entering port 4 splits equally between ports 1 and 3 and zero power reaches port 2.

Magic T

A magic T device is employed in a waveguide system to provide a high degree of isolation between two ports. Figure 6.20(a) shows the appearance of a magic T device, and Fig. 6.20(b) shows how the device might be employed. RF energy entering at port 2 splits equally between ports 1 and 3; provided port 3 is terminated in an impedance equal to the characteristic impedance of the system the energy entering this port is completely absorbed and there are no reflections. The energy reaching port 3 is passed on to the next mixer stage in the system. None of the RF energy reached port 4. Similarly, the output of the local oscillator enters port 4 and splits equally between ports 1 and 3. The oscillator energy that reached port 3 is applied to the mixer along with the RF energy and the mixer produces the wanted difference frequency (along with many other unwanted frequencies that must be filtered out).

Fig. 6.21 *(a) Probe coupling, (b) loop coupling*

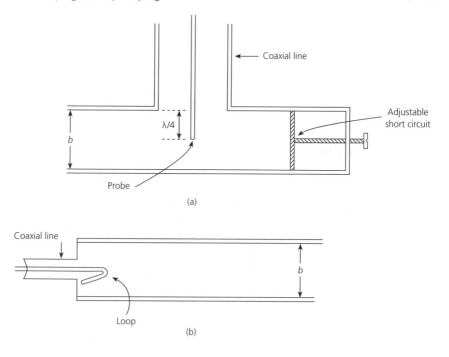

Couplers

The energy that is to be transmitted along a waveguide has first to be coupled into that waveguide. The two coupling methods that are most often used are the *probe* and the *loop*.

The probe couples the input energy with the E field within the waveguide and is usually approximately $\lambda_0/4$ (at the desired frequency of operation) in length. Figure 6.21(a) shows one way in which a probe can be used to couple to the dominant TE_{10} mode. The inner conductor of the coaxial line protrudes into the waveguide for a distance of about $\lambda_0/4$ parallel to the electric field and it is centrally placed to couple to the point of maximum field strength within the waveguide. A short-circuited section of waveguide is situated behind the probe to reflect backward-radiated energy forward and in phase with the energy propagated directly by the probe. The short-circuited section of waveguide must be exactly $\lambda_G/4$ long to maintain the correct phase relationship. A short-circuiting plunger is employed whose position in the waveguide is adjusted to ensure that the short-circuited section of waveguide is exactly $\lambda_G/4$ long.

Probe coupling is also used to couple the output of a microwave device known as a *klystron* to a waveguide.

Loop coupling is shown by Fig. 6.21(b). The coaxial line input is now connected to one end of the waveguide and the extended inner conductor is bent into the shape of a loop. The input energy now couples with the H field in the waveguide. Loop coupling is employed to couple the output of a *magnetron* to a waveguide.

Fig. 6.22 *Circulator*

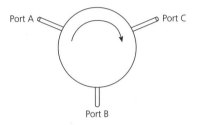

Circulators

A circulator is a three-port device that is used to couple two, or three, pieces of micro-wave radio equipment to a single aerial. A circulator consists of three waveguide sections that transmit RF energy from port to port in one direction only. The centre section of a circulator contains a ferrite phase-shifting device and an external permanent magnet is employed. The magnet causes the ferrite device to have phase-shifting characteristics because of the interaction between the RF magnetic fields and the magnetic field set up by the magnet. The attenuation of a circulator in the clockwise direction is low, approximately 0.5 dB, but in the anti-clockwise direction it is much higher, in the region of 20 dB.

The basic use of a circulator is shown by Fig. 6.22: the attenuation from port A to port B, from B to C, or from C to A is 20 dB, but the attenuation from A to C, from C to B, and from B to A is only 0.5 dB. Each of the ports must be terminated in a matched load for the circulator to work correctly. Any mismatch reduces the isolation between two ports that ought not to be connected.

The most common application of a circulators is as a diplexer that allows a micro-wave aerial to be connected to both a receiver and a transmitter without the transmitted energy entering the receiver.

Isolators

An isolator is a two-port device which allows RF energy to pass in one direction only. In one direction the isolator has a small insertion loss, probably less than 1 dB, while in the other direction the insertion loss is large, being 20 dB or more. An isolator is employed to prevent RF energy travelling in the wrong direction in a radio system, probably as a result of unwanted reflections from a mismatched load.

Resonant cavities

A resonant cavity is a closed section of waveguide that contains a whole number of complete E field and H field patterns, as shown by Fig. 6.23(a) which assumes dimensions of 10 cm $\times$ 6 cm. The cavity can be energised by a probe inserted into one of the wide walls at the exact mid-point A, or by a loop inserted at the mid-point of a narrow wall, point B. The H field pattern consists of a series of circles around the probe and is the resultant of two waves moving in opposite directions over a $\lambda_G/2$ length of waveguide. The pattern shown in (b) and (c) is that for the lowest resonant frequency and is the TE_{011} pattern, i.e. the field produced by the TE_{01} mode in a short-circuited waveguide

Fig. 6.23 *(a) Resonant cavity, (b) E field, and (c) H field*

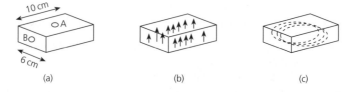

(a)   (b)   (c)

Fig. 6.24 *Fields in a resonant cavity using the TE$_{102}$ Mode*

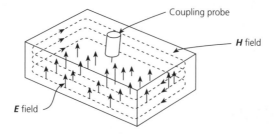

Coupling probe

H field

E field

one λ_G in length. The maximum E field occurs at the point where the probe is inserted into the waveguide. The resonant frequency of the cavity can be determined using equation (6.3) with $\lambda_c = 2a$ and $\lambda_G = 2l$, where l is the length of the cavity.

The cavity may be made to resonate at a higher frequency by exciting the cavity with a probe or a loop in the optimum position for the required higher mode. Different integers for m, n, and l can be chosen for the TE$_{mnl}$ and TM$_{mnl}$ modes, where m, n and l represent the number of E field or H field half-period patterns repeated parallel to the narrow and broad dimensions, and longitudinally in the length of the cavity, respectively. These patterns can occur in three different orientations in a cavity. It would not be possible to excite the TE$_{102}$ mode using the probe position shown in Fig. 6.24 because the TE$_{102}$ mode requires two sets of electric field along the length of the resonator and this would leave a point of zero field intensity in the centre of the resonator, where no power could be coupled in.

EXAMPLE 6.3

A resonant cavity is made from a waveguide of dimensions $a = 60$ mm, $b = 30$ mm, and is 80 mm in length. Calculate its resonant frequency.

Solution

From equation (6.3),

$$\lambda_0 = 1/\sqrt{[1/(160 \times 10^{-3})^2 + 1/(120 \times 10^{-3})^2]} = 96 \text{ mm}$$

Therefore,

$$f = (3 \times 10^8)/(96 \times 10^{-3}) = 3.125 \text{ GHz } (Ans.)$$

Q factor

The Q factor of a resonant cavity is

$$Q = \omega(\text{energy stored in cavity})/(\text{energy dissipated per cycle}) \qquad (6.22)$$

The Q factor is a measure of the sharpness of tuning of a cavity which behaves in similar manner to a tuned LC circuit.

The stored energy is proportional to $\mu H_{\text{average}}^2 V$, where μ is the permeability of free space, H is the magnetic field strength, and V is the volume of the cavity.

The energy dissipated at the internal surface area S of the cavity is proportional to $H_{\text{average}}^2 S$, for any given configuration and mode of oscillation. Therefore,

$$Q = (\omega k \mu H_{\text{average}}^2 V)/(H_{\text{average}}^2 S)$$

where k is a constant.

This means that the Q factor is directly proportional to the ratio V/S.

EXERCISES

6.1 Explain why a transverse electromagnetic wave cannot be propagated down a rectangular waveguide. Show how a TE wave can be regarded as being the resultant of two TEM waves. A waveguide of dimensions 2.8 cm by 1.3 cm has a group wavelength equal to the cut-off wavelength. Calculate the frequency of the propagating signal.

6.2 Explain why the cut-off frequency is an important parameter of a waveguide. Also explain why the power-handling capability of a waveguide is limited by dielectric breakdown. A waveguide operating at 3.2 GHz has a breakdown electric field strength of 3×10^6 V m^{-1}. If a safety factor of 2 is used calculate the maximum power that can be transmitted.

6.3 A rectangular waveguide has internal dimensions of 0.569 cm and 0.285 cm. Calculate (a) the cut-off frequency, (b) the guide wavelength, and (c) the phase and group velocities if the frequency is 40 GHz.

6.4 A rectangular waveguide has internal dimensions of 1.067 cm and 0.4318 cm. It is connected to another similar waveguide that is filled with a dielectric of relative permittivity 2. This second waveguide is matched to its load. If the frequency of operation is 20 GHz calculate the VSWR in the air-filled waveguide.

6.5 What is meant by the term dominant mode in a rectangular waveguide? What are higher modes and why are they generally undesirable? How can the higher-order modes be suppressed? A rectangular waveguide has dimensions of 1.580 cm and 0.7899 cm and transmits a signal whose frequency is twice the cut-off frequency. Calculate the angle at which reflection from the walls occurs.

6.6 In a test on a 31 cm length of mismatched waveguide the measured VSWR pattern has adjacent minima of 2.9 cm and the normalised input impedance is $33 - j2$ Ω. A matching iris having an admittance of $-j1.43$ S is then connected in parallel with the mismatched load. Use a Smith chart to find the VSWR on the waveguide.

6.7 A rectangular waveguide has internal dimensions of 1 cm and 2.3 cm and is operated at 10 GHz. Calculate (a) the free-space wavelength, (b) the cut-off frequency, (c) the phase velocity, (d) the group velocity, and (e) the guide wavelength.

6.8 A rectangular waveguide has internal dimensions of 2.8 cm and 1.3 cm and is operated at a frequency equal to twice the cut-off frequency of the dominant mode. Calculate (a) the guide wavelength and (b) the angle at which reflection from the waveguide wall takes place.

6.9 A rectangular waveguide has wide dimension a of 2.3 cm. A wave travelling down this guide makes an angle of reflection of 60° at each wall. Calculate (a) the phase velocity, (b) the group velocity, (c) the frequency of operation, (d) the guide wavelength, and (e) the cut-off wavelength.

6.10 A wave using the TE_{10} mode propagates in a waveguide having dimensions 28 mm × 13 mm. The guide wavelength is equal to the cut-off wavelength. Calculate the frequency of the signal source.

6.11 A resonant cavity is made from a 10 cm length of 6 cm × 3 cm waveguide that is short-circuited at both ends. It is excited to operate in the TE_{101} mode. Calculate its resonant frequency.

6.12 A 2.86 cm × 1.27 cm waveguide operates in the dominant mode when $\lambda_G = 2\lambda_C$. Calculate the signal frequency.

6.13 The attenuation of a 24 mm × 50 mm waveguide is at its minimum value when $\lambda_G = 60$ mm. Calculate the frequency of minimum attenuation.

6.14 The wavelength measured in a waveguide energised in the dominant mode at a frequency of 6.25 GHz is 8 cm. Calculate (a) λ_C and (b) the frequency at which $\lambda_G = 10$ cm.

6.15 Show that $\lambda_G = c/\sqrt{(f^2 - f_C^2)}$. Calculate λ_G if $f = 2f_C$ if the waveguide dimensions are 2.85 cm and 1.262 cm.

6.16 A resonant cavity consists of 8 cm of waveguide closed at both ends. The lowest resonant frequency is 3.125 GHz. Calculate the critical frequency for this resonance mode.

6.17 A resonant cavity is made by closing the ends of a 10 cm length of 6 cm × 3 cm waveguide. The cavity is excited by a coaxial cable which may be connected in either of the ways shown in Figs 6.25(a) and (b). (a) For each position state whether a loop of a probe would be employed and briefly explain why. (b) For the loop coupling show how it would be positioned. (c) Calculate the lowest frequency at which the cavity will resonate.

6.18 (a) Explain the disadvantage of operating a rectangular waveguide at $1.1 f_C$.
   (b) A rectangular waveguide has dimensions of 4 cm × 2 cm. Calculate (i) the lowest recommended frequency of operation and (ii) the guide wavelength if it is operated at 5 GHz.

7 Principles of aerials

After reading this chapter you should be able to:

(a) Describe how an aerial radiates RF energy and say why an aerial will not work at audio frequencies.
(b) Understand the meanings of the terms impedance of free space, isotropic radiator, power density and current element.
(c) Distinguish between the induction field and the radiation field of an aerial.
(d) Calculate the effective length of an aerial.
(e) State the meaning of radiation resistance.
(f) Describe the use of a monopole aerial, calculate its effective height and understand why top loading is sometimes employed.
(g) Explain the importance of the $\lambda/2$ dipole, calculate its effective length, its effective aperture and its gain, and quote its radiation resistance.
(h) Calculate the power received by an aerial and calculate the free-space attenuation.
(i) Understand the principle of a long-wire radiator and say how it may be used as the basis of other types of aerial.

Transmitting and receiving aerials provide the link between the radio transmitter and receiver, and the propagation path via the atmosphere and/or space. All types of aerial are able both to transmit and receive RF electromagnetic waves equally well, and for each purpose will have the same gain and radiation pattern. It is customary to consider the operation of most aerials in their transmitting mode and to use the principle of reciprocity to obtain the receiving characteristics if, and when, required. Some aerials, such as those employed in broadcast systems, are required to transmit energy equally well in all directions in the horizontal plane. Other aerials are required to concentrate their radiation in one direction and these aerials must have a directive radiation pattern to achieve the maximum gain in the wanted direction. Thus the directivity of an aerial, expressed graphically by means of its radiation pattern, is one of its most important parameters. A radiation pattern is a plot of relative field strength at various angular positions from an aerial.

For the maximum efficiency in the radiation of energy an aerial should be of resonant length; this means that its electrical length should be one-half a wavelength ($\lambda/2$) at the frequency of operation. This requirement can easily be satisfied at frequencies in the HF, VHF, UHF and SHF bands, and it is possible, although more difficult, at the higher frequencies in the MF band. However, it is not possible to obtain a $\lambda/2$ aerial at frequencies in the VLF and LF bands because of the enormous physical structures that would be necessary. Transmitting aerials for use in the VLF, LF and MF bands always employ vertical structures that are mounted upon the earth and are supplied between the base of the aerial and the earth. Ground reflections then make the aerial appear to be up to twice its physical height. An aerial whose electrical length is less than one-quarter wavelength, including the ground-plane image, is said to be an electrically short (or small) aerial.

Radiation from an aerial

When an RF current flows in a conductor a magnetic H field is set up around that conductor, the magnitude of which is directly proportional to the instantaneous value of the current. As the magnitude of the current varies with time the magnetic strength of the H field will also vary. The changing H field produces a changing electric E field, not only in the vicinity of the H field but also in the region surrounding it. Whenever the H field is constant the E field no longer exists. The direction of the E field depends upon whether the H field is growing or collapsing into the aerial. Similarly, the changing electric field produces a further changing magnetic field in the next surrounding region of space, and so on. This means that a conductor that is carrying an RF current is always surrounded by continually changing interdependent E and H fields.

When a sinusoidal current flows in a conductor the E and H fields surrounding the conductor will attempt to vary sinusoidally as well. When the current changes its direction of flow in the conductor the H field must first collapse into the conductor before it can then build up in the reverse direction. The associated E field will fall to zero and then build up with the reverse polarity. The H fields are unable to collapse into the conductor instantaneously and at frequencies higher than about 15 kHz, not all of the energy contained in the H field has returned into the conductor before the current starts to increase in the opposite direction as before to produce new E and H fields. When this happens the energy that remains outside of the conductor as the new H field grows in the opposite direction as before is unable to return to the conductor. This RF energy is propagated away from the conductor in the form of an electromagnetic wave. Figure 7.1

Fig. 7.1 *Radiation from an aerial*

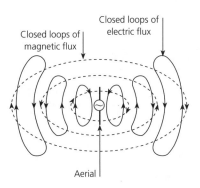

Closed loops of electric flux

Closed loops of magnetic flux

Aerial

shows electromagnetic waves moving away from an aerial. The electromagnetic wave has the form given in Fig. 6.2. The plane that contains the electric field and the direction of propagation is known as the *polarisation* of the wave. If, for example, the electric field is in the vertical plane the wave is said to be vertically polarised. For optimum reception the receiving aerial should be mounted in the same plane as the polarisation of the signal, i.e. a vertical aerial should be employed to receive a vertically polarised wave. If a vertical aerial receives a horizontally polarised wave, or a horizontal aerial receives a vertically polarised wave, an extra loss of anything up to 20 dB may be experienced.

The electromagnetic wave propagates through the atmosphere with a velocity equal to the velocity of light c which is generally (for radio work) taken as being equal to 3×10^8 m s^{-1}. At all times during its travel the two fields making up the electromagnetic wave vary in time phase with one another.

The majority of radio systems employ either horizontal or vertical polarisation but circular polarisation is sometimes used for television aerials. Circular polarisation is also used for mobile telephones because the telephone may be held by the user in any position while a call is in progress. When circular polarisation is employed there is some extra loss introduced because the aerial is never in the same plane as the signal, but on the other hand the aerial is never positioned at 90° to the signal when reception would be very poor.

Impedance of free space

The ratio of the amplitude of the electric field strength to the amplitude of the magnetic field strength in an electromagnetic wave has a constant value that is known as the *impedance of free space*.

$$\text{impedance of free space} = [E \text{ (V m}^{-1})]/[H \text{ (A m}^{-1})] = 120\pi \ \Omega = 377 \ \Omega \qquad (7.1)$$

Power density

The power density P_d of the electromagnetic wave is equal to the product of the r.m.s. values of the electric field strength and the magnetic field strength, i.e.

$$P_d = EH \text{ W m}^{-1} = E^2/120\pi \text{ W m}^{-1} \qquad (7.2)$$

Since both the electric field and the magnetic field lie in a plane that is at right angles to the direction of propagation a radio wave is a transverse electromagnetic or TEM wave.

Isotropic radiator

An *isotropic radiator* is a theoretical aerial, which cannot be realised in practice, which is able to radiate energy equally well in all possible planes. The radiated energy will therefore have a spherical wavefront with its power spread uniformly over the surface of a sphere. The surface area of a sphere of radius r is $4\pi r^2$ and so the power density P_d of the radiated energy is

$$P_d = P_T/4\pi D^2 \text{ W m}^{-1} \qquad (7.3)$$

where P_T is the transmitted power and D is the distance from the radiator. Clearly, the power density is inversely proportional to the square of the distance from the isotropic radiator. The power density is also, from equation (7.2), equal to $E^2/120\pi$, and equating the two relationships gives the electric field strength at distance D from the isotropic radiator as

$$E = [\sqrt{(30P_T)}]/D \text{ V m}^{-1} \qquad (7.4)$$

The electric field strength is inversely proportional to the distance from the transmitter. If the transmitted power is given in kW and the distance D is quoted in km, then

$$E = (173\sqrt{P_T})/D \text{ mV m}^{-1} \qquad (7.5)$$

Although the isotropic radiator is not a practical aerial it is commonly employed as a reference against which practical aerials can be compared.

Current element

A current element consists of a current of uniform amplitude I A which flows in a very short length dl of conductor. It is sometimes known as a short, or Hertzian, dipole and, like the isotropic radiator, it cannot be practically realised. The current element is an extremely useful concept because the results obtained from a study of its characteristics can be applied to practical cases if another concept, that of the *effective length* of an aerial, is employed. Many practical aerials may be conveniently regarded as consisting of a large number of current elements in cascade.

When an RF current flows in a very short electrical length dl of conductor (see Fig. 7.2) to form a current element, the magnetic field set up will have a field strength given by

$$H = [(I \text{ d}l \sin \theta)/4\pi][(\omega/cD) \cos\omega(t - D/c) + (1/D^2) \sin\omega(t - D/c)] \qquad (7.6)$$

where c is the velocity of light, D is the distance in m from the current element, and θ is the angle shown in Fig. 7.2.

Fig. 7.2 *Current element*

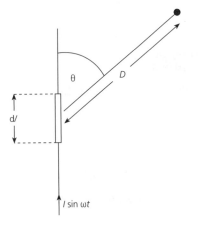

Unlike the isotropic radiator, the current element does not radiate energy equally well in all directions but, instead, it produces a field that is proportional to sin θ. Equation (7.6) indicates that the magnetic field has two components which are known, respectively, as the *radiation field* and the *induction field*.

Radiation field

The first term in equation (7.6) has a magnitude that is directly proportional to the frequency of the current flowing in the element and inversely proportional to distance. This term therefore represents the energy that is radiated away from the current element and is known as the radiation field or the *far field*.

Induction field

Near to the aerial, an induction field or *near field* also exists and is given by the second term in equation (7.6). The induction field contains the energy that returns to the aerial when the current is reversed and is therefore not radiated. Near the aerial the induction field is larger than the radiated field, but since the magnitude of the induction field decreases inversely with the square of the distance from the aerial the radiation field soon becomes the larger. The induction field is inversely proportional to the square of the distance from the current element and, therefore, its amplitude rapidly falls to a negligible value.

The induction and radiation fields are of equal magnitude at the distance from the current element at which $\omega/cD = 1/D^2$, or

$$D = c/\omega = \lambda/2\pi \tag{7.7}$$

The distance $D = \lambda/2\pi$ marks the boundary between the near field and the far field. At distances greater than $\lambda/2\pi$ the induction field makes an insignificant contribution to the total field strength and hence may be neglected. The boundary is often quoted in terms of the largest physical linear dimension L of the transmitting aerial:

$$D \approx 2L^2/\lambda \tag{7.8}$$

EXAMPLE 7.1

Determine the far-field distance for an aerial of 1.2 m length at a frequency of 1 GHz.

Solution

$\lambda = (3 \times 10^8)/(1 \times 10^9) = 0.3$ m

$D = (2 \times 1.2^2)/0.3 = 9.6$ m *(Ans.)*

Fig. 7.3 *Radiation patterns of a current element: (a) meridian plane and (b) equatorial plane*

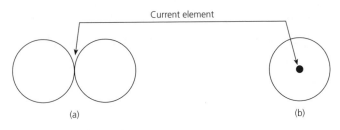

(a)   (b)

Fig. 7.4 *Power radiated by a current element*

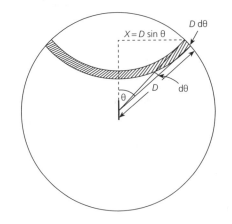

The magnetic radiation field has an r.m.s. value of

$$H = (I \, dl \, \omega \sin \theta)/(4\pi cD) = (I \, dl \sin \theta)/(2\lambda D) \tag{7.9}$$

An expression for the r.m.s. electric field strength is obtained by multiplying H by 120π to give

$$E = (60\pi \, I \, dl \sin \theta)/\lambda D \tag{7.10}$$

If $I \, dl = 1$ mA and $D = 1$ km then the field strength is equal to 188 mV m^{-1}.

In the meridian plane (the plane that contains the current element) the field strength varies with $\sin \theta$ and the radiation pattern is shown by Fig. 7.3(a). In the equatorial plane, where $\theta = 90°$ and hence $\sin \theta = 1$, the current element radiates equally well in all directions and so the radiation pattern is a circle (see Fig. 7.3(b)).

Radiated power

The total power radiated by a current element is determined by finding the power that passes through a small area and then integrating that power over the surface of a sphere. Referring to Fig. 7.4, the area of the shaded zone is

$$2\pi x D \, d\theta = 2\pi D^2 \sin \theta \, d\theta$$

The power that passes through this zone is

$$(E^2/120\pi)(2\pi D^2 \sin \theta \, d\theta) = (60\pi^2 I^2 (dl)^2 \sin^3 \theta \, d\theta)/\lambda^2 \text{ W}$$

The total power P_T radiated over the surface of the sphere is

$$P_T = 2\int_0^{\pi/2} [(60\pi^2 I^2 (dl)^2 \sin^3 \theta)/\lambda^2] \, d\theta$$

$$= [(120\pi^2 I^2 (dl)^2)/\lambda^2] \int_0^{\pi/2} [(3 \sin \theta - \sin 3\theta)/4] \, d\theta$$

$$= [(120\pi^2 I^2 (dl)^2)/4\lambda^2][-3 \cos \theta + (\cos 3\theta)/3]_0^{\pi/2}$$

$$= [(30\pi^2 I^2 (dl)^2)/\lambda^2][3 - 1/3]$$

or

$$P_T = (80\pi^2 I^2 (dl)^2)/\lambda^2 \text{ W} \tag{7.11}$$

Expressing both equations (7.10) and (7.11) in terms of I^2 and then equating them gives

$$I^2 = P_T\lambda^2/[80\pi^2(dl)^2] = E^2\lambda^2 D^2/[60\pi^2(dl)^2]$$

or

$$E = \sqrt{(45P_T)}/D \tag{7.12}$$

Radiation resistance

The total power P_T radiated from an aerial may be considered to be equal to the product of the square of the input current to the aerial and a non-physical resistance R_r, i.e. $P_T = I^2 R_r$. This concept gives the *radiation resistance* of a current element as

$$R_r = [80\pi^2(dl)^2]/\lambda^2 \ \Omega \tag{7.13}$$

Effective length of an aerial

The equations previously obtained for the electric field produced by, and the power radiated from, a current element cannot be directly applied to a practical aerial. They can, however, be usefully employed if another concept, that of the *effective length* of an aerial, is introduced.

The effective length l_{eff} of an aerial is that length which, if it carried a uniform current at the same amplitude as the input current I to the aerial, would produce the same field strength at a given point in the equatorial plane of the aerial. This means that the product of the physical length of the aerial and the mean current flowing in the aerial must be equal to the product of the effective length and the assumed uniform current. Thus

$$l_{phy} I_{mean} = l_{eff} I$$

Fig. 7.5 *Current distribution on an electrically short aerial*

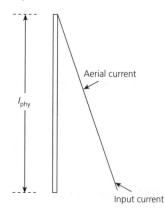

I_{phy}

Aerial current

Input current

or

$$l_{\text{eff}} = l_{\text{phy}}I_{\text{mean}}/I \qquad (7.14)$$

$$= (l_{\text{phy}}/I)\left((1/l_{\text{phy}})\int_0^{l_{\text{phy}}} I(y)\ dy \right) \qquad (7.15)$$

$$= (1/I)\int_0^{l_{\text{phy}}} I(y)\ dy \qquad (7.16)$$

Alternatively, the effective length of a receive aerial may be defined as

$$l_{\text{eff}} = V_{\text{oc}}/E \qquad (7.17)$$

where V_{oc} is the voltage that appears at the open-circuited terminals of the aerial when it is situated in an electric field of strength of E V m^{-1}.

For an electrically short aerial, such as that shown in Fig. 7.5, the current distribution can be assumed to vary linearly from its maximum value I at the input terminals to zero at the top of the aerial. Clearly, the mean value of the aerial current is $I/2$ and, from equation (7.14), $l_{\text{eff}} = l_{\text{phy}}/2$.

Using equation (7.15),

$$l_{\text{eff}} = (l_{\text{phy}}/I)\left((1/l_{\text{phy}})\int_0^{l_{\text{phy}}} (I/l_{\text{phy}})(l_{\text{phy}} - y)\ dy \right)$$

$$= (1/l_{\text{phy}})\int_0^{l_{\text{phy}}} (l_{\text{phy}} - y)dy$$

$$= (1/l_{\text{phy}})[l_{\text{phy}}y - y^2/2]_0^{l_{\text{phy}}}$$

$$= (1/l_{\text{phy}})[l_{\text{phy}}^2 - l_{\text{phy}}^2/2]$$

$$= l_{\text{phy}}/2$$

Using equation (7.16),

$$l_{\text{eff}} = (1/I) \int_0^{l_{\text{phy}}} (I/l_{\text{phy}})(l_{\text{phy}} - y) \; \mathrm{d}y = l_{\text{phy}}/2$$

The radiation resistance of such an aerial is given by

$$R_{\text{r}} = 80\pi^2 (l_{\text{phy}}/2\lambda)^2 = 20\pi^2 (l_{\text{phy}}/\lambda)^2 \; \Omega \qquad (7.18)$$

For longer aerials the assumption of a linear current distribution is no longer valid and it is customary to assume the distribution to be sinusoidal.

The monopole aerial

A monopole aerial is one which is mounted vertically upon a conducting surface, such as the surface of the earth, and which is fed between the base of the aerial and earth. This type of aerial is employed in the VLF, LF and MF bands where the aerial is mounted vertically upon the earth's surface. In the VLF and LF bands the aerial must, of necessity, be electrically short, but in the MF band it is possible to employ aerials whose electrical length is $\lambda/4$ or even longer. In the VHF and UHF bands monopole aerials are used where the aerial is a short metal rod mounted, for example, on the roof or wing of a car.

Figure 7.6 shows an aerial of physical height l_{phy} which is mounted vertically upon the earth. The aerial will radiate energy equally well in all directions in the horizontal plane but it will exhibit some *directivity* in the vertical plane. Some energy is directed upwards towards the sky whilst some other energy is radiated downwards towards the earth. The aerial site is chosen to ensure that the earth in the neighborhood of the aerial

Fig. 7.6 *Monopole aerial*

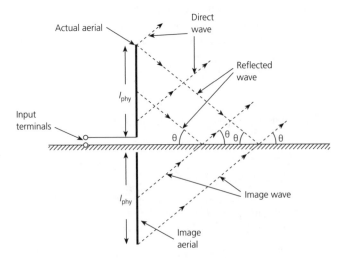

is both flat and of high conductivity. Therefore the waves radiated towards the earth are totally reflected with an angle of reflection equal to the angle of incidence. This makes the ground-reflected waves travel in the same direction as the direct waves. At a distant point P from the aerial energy is received by means of both the direct and the ground-reflected waves. The total field strength at this point is the phasor sum of the individual field strengths produced by the direct and reflected waves. From the viewpoint of an observer at the point P it appears as though the ground-reflected wave has originated from an *image aerial* beneath the earth. This effect makes the aerial appear to be of *twice* its actual physical height and so doubles the effective length of the aerial. This means that an electrically short monopole aerial has an effective length equal to its physical length.

The electric field strength produced at the distant point P is hence

$$E = (120\pi I l_{\text{eff}} \sin \theta)/\lambda D \text{ V m}^{-1} \tag{7.19}$$

The monopole aerial produces a similar radiation pattern, in both the horizontal and the vertical planes, as a balanced dipole of twice the physical length that is situated in free space.

The power radiated by a monopole aerial is obtained by the use of equation (7.11) but since there is no electric field beneath the ground the actual power is only one-half of that predicted, i.e.

$$P_T = [40\pi^2 I^2 (2l_{\text{eff}})^2]/\lambda^2 = 160\pi^2 (l_{\text{eff}})^2 I^2 \text{ W} \tag{7.20}$$

If both equations (7.19) and (7.20) are expressed in terms of I^2 and then equated to one another:

$$I^2 = P_T^2 \lambda^2/(160\pi^2 l_{\text{eff}}^2) = (E^2\lambda^2 D^2)/(120^2\pi^2 l_{\text{eff}}^2)$$

or

$$E = \sqrt{(90P_T)}/D \tag{7.21}$$

If P_T is in kW and D is in km, then

$$E = [\sqrt{(90 \times 10^3)}\sqrt{P_T}]/D = (300\sqrt{P_T})/D \text{ mV m}^{-1} \tag{7.22}$$

EXAMPLE 7.2

A monopole aerial is 25 m high and is supplied with a current of 100 A at 200 kHz. Assuming the current distribution on the aerial is linear, calculate (a) the power radiated by the aerial and (b) the field strength produced at ground level at a point 100 km distant.

Solution

$$\lambda = (3 \times 10^8)/(200 \times 10^3) = 1500 \text{ m}$$

The electrical length of the aerial is $25/1500 = 0.017\lambda$

(a) $P_T = 160\pi^2(12.5/1500)^2 \times 10^4 = 1097$ W (*Ans.*)

(b) From equation (7.19),

$$E = (120\pi \times 100 \times 12.5)/(1500 \times 100 \times 10^3) = 3.14 \text{ mV m}^{-1} \text{ (Ans.)}$$

Alternatively, using equation (7.21),

$$E = [\sqrt{(90 \times 1097)}]/100 = 3.14 \text{ mV m}^{-1} \text{ (Ans.)}$$

As the electrical length of a monopole aerial is increased the assumption of a linear current distribution can no longer be made. The current distribution becomes an increasingly large part of a complete sine wave, and when the electrical length is one wavelength one complete cycle is described. If the electrical length is less than $\lambda/4$ it is only necessary to determine the effective length of the monopole. If the length is $\lambda/4$ or more it will be necessary to consider the monopole as consisting of the cascade connection of a large number of current elements. Each current element produces an electric field due both to a direct and a ground-reflected wave, given by equation (7.19), at a distant point P. The total field strength at the distant point is then the phasor sum of the field strengths due to each current element. This will result in the addition, or cancellation (perhaps complete), at different angles in the vertical plane; a number of examples are shown by Fig. 7.7. The vertical plane radiation pattern changes only slowly with increase in the aerial height for heights up to about $\lambda/4$, and then, for heights between

Fig. 7.7 *Radiation patterns of monopole aerials of different heights*

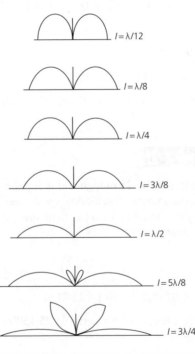

Fig. 7.8 *Current distribution on a monopole aerial*

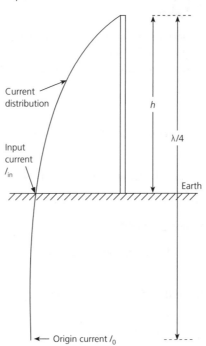

$\lambda/4$ and $\lambda/2$, becomes somewhat flatter in shape. The maximum radiation at ground level occurs when the electrical length of the aerial is $5\lambda/8$, although there is then some unwanted skywards radiation. If the electrical length is increased to more than $5\lambda/8$ the radiation of energy is concentrated in the direction of the sky. The radiation patterns differ from that of a current element because the distances from each part of the monopole to the distant point P may differ by an appreciable part of a wavelength. This will not affect the amplitude of the individual field strengths but it does introduce phase differences.

Effective length of a short monopole

When the electrical length of a monopole is short the current distribution on the aerial can be assumed to be a part of a cosinusoidal wave. As shown by Fig. 7.8 the current will be zero at the top of the aerial and increases to a maximum value I_0 at the origin which is at a distance $l = \lambda/4$ below the top of the aerial. Since the height of the aerial is less than $\lambda/4$ the origin is at a point situated $(l - h)$ below the surface of the earth. The current $I(y)$ at any point from the base of the aerial is given by

$$I(y) = I_0 \cos(2\pi y/\lambda) \qquad (7.23)$$

where y varies from $(l - h)$ to l.

EXAMPLE 7.3

A monopole aerial is 36 m in height and is supplied with an input current of 30 A peak at a frequency of 833 kHz. Calculate (a) the effective height of the aerial and (b) the field strength produced at ground level at a distance of 50 km.

Solution

At 833 kHz $\lambda = (3 \times 10^8)/(833 \times 10^3) = 360$ m. Hence $\lambda/4 = 90$ m. From equation (7.23),

$$I_{in} = 30 = I_0 \cos[(2\pi/360°)(90° - 36°)] = I_0 \cos 54°$$

Therefore, $I_0 = 30/(\cos 54°) = 51$ A. Hence

$$I(y) = 51 \cos(2\pi y/360°)$$

and the mean value of the aerial current is

$$I_{mean} = [51/(90° - 54°)] \int_{54°}^{90°} \cos(2\pi y/360°) \, dy$$

$$= 1.4167 \left[\frac{\sin(2\pi y/360°)}{(2\pi/360°)} \right]_{54°}^{90°}$$

$$= 81.17 \ (\sin 90° - \sin 54°)$$

$$= 15.5 \text{ A}$$

(a) Hence the effective length of the aerial is

$$(36 \times 15.5)/30 = 18.6 \text{ m } (Ans.)$$

(Note that the error introduced if the approximation $l_{eff} = l_{phy}/2 = 36/2 = 18$ m had been used is small.)

(b) From equation (7.19),

$$E = (120\pi \times 30 \times 18.6)/(\sqrt{2} \times 360 \times 50 \times 10^3) = 8 \text{ mV m}^{-1} (Ans.)$$

Top loading

An increase in the effective length of an aerial could be achieved if the mean aerial current were to be increased *without* a corresponding increase in the input current. This can only happen if the aerial current is prevented from falling to zero at the top of the aerial by the use of *top loading*. Top loading of a monopole aerial means that a horizontal system of conductors, which has a relatively large capacitance to earth, is fitted to the top of the aerial. The aerial current will flow in the top loading and so it will not fall to zero at the top of the radiating part of the aerial. Top loading increases the electrical length of an aerial without changing its physical length. The idea of top loading is

Fig. 7.9 *Top loading of a monopole aerial*

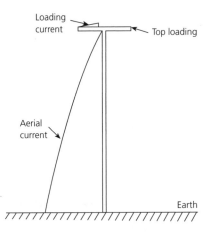

illustrated by Fig. 7.9. The top loading makes little, or no, contribution to the total field strength produced at a distant point because it is only a small electrical distance from its under-earth image. This image is of the opposite polarity to the top-loading conductors and hence it tends to cancel out any radiation from the top loading.

The effective length of a top-loaded monopole is calculated in a manner similar to that used before but the top loading must be taken into account. The total length of the aerial must now include the length of the top loading. Suppose, for example, that the aerial of Example 7.2 was fitted with a top-loading system in the form of a number of radially spaced conductors of length 5 m. Then the distance y would vary from $l = 90$ m to $(l - h) = 90 - 41 = 49$ m and the mean current I_{mean} would be 19.9 A.

λ/4 monopole

When the length of a monopole aerial is increased to $\lambda/4$, or more, the electrical distance between a current element in the actual aerial and the corresponding image current element leads to a phase difference between the field strengths produced at a distant point P, say. Consider Fig. 7.10, which shows a current element $I\,\mathrm{d}y$, distance y from the base of the aerial, which is radiating energy. The radiation from the image current element $I\,\mathrm{d}y$ has an extra distance $2y \cos \theta$ to travel before it reaches the point P. This extra distance produces a phase lag $\phi = (2\pi/\lambda)\,2y \cos \theta$; thus, referring to Fig. 7.11,

$$\cos (\phi/2) = (E/2)/E_d$$

$$E = 2E_d \cos(\phi/2)$$

Hence, the total field strength $\mathrm{d}E_T$ due to the two current elements is

$$\mathrm{d}E_T = 2E_d \cos(\phi/2) = 2E_d \cos[(2\pi/\lambda)y \cos \theta)]$$

Fig. 7.10 *Waves radiated by current elements in both the monopole aerial and its image*

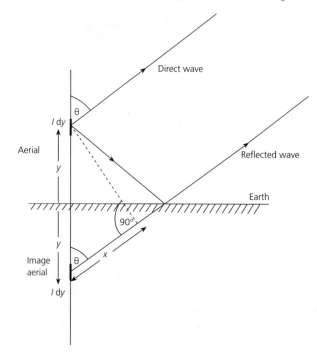

Fig. 7.11 *Phasor diagram of the field strengths at a distant point*

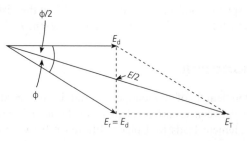

Where

$$E_d = (60\pi I \ dy \ \sin \theta)/\lambda D$$

The aerial current at distance y from the base of the aerial is

$$I(y) = I \cos\left(\frac{2\pi}{\lambda}y\right)$$

and hence

$$dE_T = \frac{120\pi I \sin \theta}{\lambda D} \cos\left(\frac{2\pi}{\lambda}y\right) \cos\left(\frac{2\pi}{\lambda}y \cos \theta\right)$$

The total field strength produced at the point is then

$$E_T = \frac{120\pi I \sin\theta}{\lambda D} \int_0^{\lambda/4} \left[\cos\left(\frac{2\pi}{\lambda}y\right)\cos\left(\frac{2\pi}{\lambda}y\cos\theta\right) \right] dy$$

$$= \frac{120\pi I \sin\theta}{2\lambda D} \int_0^{\lambda/4} \left[\cos\left(\frac{2\pi}{\lambda}y(1+\cos\theta)\right) + \cos\left(\frac{2\pi}{\lambda}y(1-\cos\theta)\right) \right] dy^{\dagger}$$

$$= \frac{60\pi I \sin\theta}{\lambda D} \left[\frac{\sin[(2\pi/\lambda)y(1+\cos\theta)]}{(2\pi/\lambda)(1+\cos\theta)} + \frac{\sin[(2\pi/\lambda)y(1-\cos\theta)]}{(2\pi/\lambda)(1-\cos\theta)} \right]_0^{\lambda/4}$$

$$= \frac{60\pi I \sin\theta}{\lambda D} \left[\frac{\sin[\pi/2 + (\pi/2)\cos\theta]}{(2\pi/\lambda)(1+\cos\theta)} + \frac{\sin[\pi/2 - (\pi/2)\cos\theta]}{(2\pi/\lambda)(1-\cos\theta)} \right]$$

$$= \frac{60\pi I \sin\theta}{\lambda D} \left[\frac{\sin(\pi/2)\cos[(\pi/2)\cos\theta]}{(2\pi/\lambda)(1+\cos\theta)} + \frac{\sin(\pi/2)\cos[(\pi/2)\cos\theta]}{(2\pi/\lambda)(1-\cos\theta)} \right]^{\dagger\ddagger}$$

$$= \frac{60\pi I \sin\theta}{\lambda D} \left[\frac{\cos[(\pi/2)\cos\theta]}{(2\pi/\lambda)(1+\cos\theta)} + \frac{\cos[(\pi/2)\cos\theta]}{(2\pi/\lambda)(1-\cos\theta)} \right]$$

$$= \frac{30 I \sin\theta}{D} \left[\frac{\cos[(\pi/2)\cos\theta]}{1+\cos\theta} + \frac{\cos[(\pi/2)\cos\theta]}{1-\cos\theta} \right]$$

$$= \frac{30 I \sin\theta}{D} \left[\frac{2\cos[(\pi/2)\cos\theta]}{1-\cos^2\theta} \right]$$

or

$$E_T = \frac{60 I}{D} \left[\frac{\cos[(\pi/2)\cos\theta]}{\sin\theta} \right] \tag{7.24}$$

The radiation resistance of a $\lambda/4$ monopole is approximately 37 Ω

A similar analysis for a $\lambda/2$ monopole (using $i = I \sin[(2\pi/\lambda)y]$) results in

$$E_T = \frac{60 I}{D} \left[\frac{\cos(\pi\cos\theta) + 1}{\sin\theta} \right] \tag{7.25}$$

VHF/UHF monopole aerial

At the higher end of the VHF band and in the UHF band a monopole aerial consists of a short metal rod that is mounted vertically on a metal surface such as the roof of a motor vehicle as shown by Fig. 7.12(a). At a frequency of 900 MHz, for example, $\lambda \approx 0.33$ m and hence the required length of rod is approximately 0.083 m. Such an aerial radiates, or receives, energy mainly in the horizontal plane and has a gain of about 1.5 or 1.76 dBi. Often such an aerial is retractable.

$\dagger$ $\cos A \cos B = \cos(A+B) + \cos(A-B)$, $\sin(A+B) = \sin A \cos B + \cos A \sin B$.
$\ddagger$ $\sin(-A) = -\sin A$, $\cos(-A) = \cos A$.

Fig. 7.12 *(a) VHF monopole aerial on the roof of a car, (b) UHF mobile telephone monopole aerial is coil loaded*

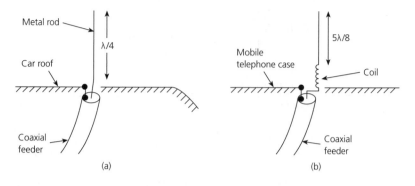

(a) (b)

Fig. 7.13 *Mobile telephone centre-fed dipole aerial*

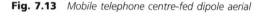
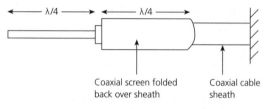

For hand-held equipment such as a mobile telephone 0.083 m would be excessively long, but then the necessary length of the rod could be reduced by the use of a series-connected inductance. *Coil loading* of a UHF monopole aerial is shown by Fig. 7.12(b). A mobile telephone cannot provide a good earth plane to provide a good image aerial and for this reason a λ/2 centre-fed aerial that does not need an earth plane is sometimes employed. Such an aerial is shown by Fig. 7.13; the screen of the coaxial cable is folded back over the plastic sheath for a distance of λ/4 and a λ/4 length of the inner conductor is exposed.

The λ/2 dipole

A dipole is a single conductor of length *l* that is centre fed as shown by Fig. 7.14(a). Nearly always the length is such that the dipole is resonant at the frequency of the input signal. This means that it is half a wavelength long and has the current distribution shown in Fig. 7.14(b). In practice, the dipole length is often made slightly less than λ/2 in order to achieve a purely resistive input impedance. At frequencies in the HF band, and particularly in the VHF and UHF bands, the physical dimensions of the λ/2 dipole make it the basic element of many types of aerial array.

The electric field set up by a λ/2 dipole at a distance *D* is given by equation (7.24). When θ = 90°, which defines the equatorial plane of the dipole, the radiation pattern is a circle (see Fig. 7.15(a)). In the plane of the aerial the radiation pattern is a figure-of-eight shape, as shown by Fig. 7.15(b). The *beamwidth* of the pattern, i.e. the angle subtended by the 3 dB points, is 129° − 51° = 78°.

Fig. 7.14 *(a) λ/2 dipole, (b) current distribution on a λ/2 dipole*

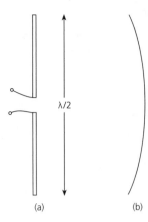

(a)   (b)

Fig. 7.15 *Radiation patterns of a λ/2 dipole: (a) equatorial plane and (b) meridian plane*

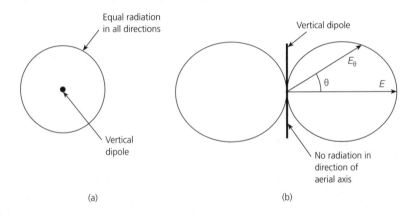

(a)   (b)

Effective length

The effective length l_{eff} of a λ/2 dipole is, from equation (7.16),

$$l_{eff} = (1/l) \int_{-\lambda/4}^{\lambda/4} [I \cos(2\pi y/\lambda)] \, dy$$

$$= (1/l)[(I\lambda/2\pi) \sin(2\pi/\lambda)y] \Big|_{-\lambda/4}^{\lambda/4} = \lambda/\pi \qquad (7.26)$$

Radiation resistance

If the effective length λ/π of a λ/2 dipole is substituted into equation (7.11), the value obtained for the radiation resistance will be 80 Ω. This figure is, however, incorrect. The correct value for the radiation resistance of a λ/2 dipole is 73.14 Ω.

EXAMPLE 7.4

Calculate the electric field strength produced in the equatorial plane of a $\lambda/2$ dipole at a distance of 20 km if the input current is 3 A r.m.s. Also calculate the power density of the wave at this point.

Solution

From equation (7.25),

$E = (60 \times 3)/20 = 9$ mV m^{-1} (*Ans.*)

Power density $= E^2/120\pi = 215$ nW m^{-1} (*Ans.*)

Alternatively, radiated power

$P_T = I^2 R_r = 9 \times 73.14 = 658.3$ W (*Ans.*)

and

power density $= (P_T G_T)/(4\pi D^2) = (658.3 \times 1.64)/(4\pi \times 400 \times 10^6)$
$= 215$ nW m^{-1} (*Ans.*)

Gain of an aerial

The *gain* of an aerial *either* indicates the extent to which the energy that it radiates is concentrated in a particular direction, *or* indicates the extent to which the aerial receives signals better from one direction than from all others. The gain of an aerial is defined relative to a reference aerial which is usually either an isotropic radiator or a $\lambda/2$ dipole. When the gain is quoted with reference to the isotropic radiator it is usually expressed in dBi. The gain of an aerial is the same whether the aerial is employed to transmit or to receive signals.

The two ways in which the gain of an aerial may be defined are:

1 The gain is the square of the ratio of the field strength produced at a point in the direction of maximum radiation to the field strength produced at the same point by the reference aerial, both aerials radiating the same power.
2 The gain is the ratio of the powers that the aerial, and the reference aerial, must radiate to set up the same field strength at a point in the direction of maximum radiation.

Isotropic radiator

The gain of an isotropic radiator is unity or 0 dBi.

Monopole aerial

From equations (7.4) and (7.21) the gain of a monopole is

$$G = \left(\frac{\sqrt{(90P_T)}}{D} \bigg/ \frac{\sqrt{(30P_T)}}{D} \right)^2 = 3 \quad \text{or} \quad 4.77 \text{ dBi}$$

λ/2 dipole

The power P_T radiated by a λ/2 dipole is equal to $73.14\ I^2$ and substituting I^2 into equation (7.24) gives

$$E = [60\sqrt{(P_T/73.14)}]/D \tag{7.27}$$

Therefore, the gain of a λ/2 dipole is

$$G = \left(\frac{60\sqrt{(P_T/73.14)}}{D} \bigg/ \frac{\sqrt{(30P_T)}}{D} \right)^2 = 1.64 \quad \text{or} \quad 2.15 \text{ dBi}$$

Effective isotropic radiated power

The effective isotropic radiated power (EIRP) of an aerial is the power which an isotropic radiator would have to radiate to produce the same field strength at a point in the direction of maximum radiation. Numerically, the EIRP is equal to the product of the total transmitted power P_T and the gain G_T of the aerial, i.e.

$$\text{EIRP} = G_T P_T \tag{7.28}$$

Using this concept, equation (7.4) can be modified to give the electric field strength produced by an aerial of gain G_T, i.e.

$$E = \sqrt{(30P_T G_T)}/D \tag{7.29}$$

EXAMPLE 7.5

Calculate the electric field strength at a distance of 20 km from a radio transmitter with an EIRP of 120 W.

Solution

$$E = \sqrt{(30 \times 120)}/20 = 3 \text{ mV m}^{-1} \ (Ans.)$$

Effective aperture of an aerial

The effective aperture A_e of an aerial is the imaginary cross-sectional area that would absorb the same power from an incident wave as does the aerial when it is matched to its load. If the incident radio wave has a power density of $P_d = E^2/120\pi$ W m^{-1}, then the

Fig. 7.16 *Determination of the effective aperture of a λ/2 dipole*

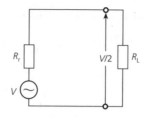

power P_R received by the aerial will be equal to $P_d A_e$. The gain G of an aerial is directly proportional to its effective aperture. Thus

$$G = A_e/(\text{effective aperture of isotropic radiator } A_{e(\text{iso})}) \tag{7.30}$$

λ/2 dipole

The voltage V induced into a λ/2 dipole by an incident radio wave is the product of the electric field strength and the effective length of the dipole. Thus $V = E\lambda/\pi$ V. The dipole has an input resistance that is equal to its radiation resistance of 73.14 Ω, and for the maximum transfer of power to the load, the load resistance must also be equal to 73.14 Ω. Then (see Fig. 7.16)

$$E^2 A_e/120\pi = V^2/4R_r = E^2\lambda^2/(4\pi^2 \times 73.14)$$

or

$$A_e = 30\lambda^2/73.14\pi = 0.13\lambda^2 \tag{7.31}$$

EXAMPLE 7.6

Calculate the effective aperture of a λ/2 dipole at a frequency of 100 MHz.

Solution

$\lambda = 3$ m. Therefore, $A_e = 0.13 \times 9 = 1.17$ m^2 (*Ans.*)

Alternatively,

$A_e = (9/4\pi) \times 1.64 = 1.17$ m^2 (*Ans.*)

Current element (short dipole)

Since the current flowing in the short dipole is assumed to be of uniform amplitude the voltage V induced into the aerial by an incident radio wave is equal to $E\,dl$. Therefore

$$E^2 A_e/120\pi = V^2/4R_r = (E\,dl)^2/[320\pi^2(dl/\lambda)^2]$$

or

$$A_e = 3\lambda^2/8\pi = 0.12\lambda^2 \qquad (7.32)$$

(Alternatively, $A_e = G\lambda^2/4\pi = 1.5\lambda^2/4\pi = 0.12\lambda^2$.)

Isotropic radiator

A current element has a gain of 1.5 relative to an isotropic radiator, and so

$$1.5 = A_{e(ce)}/A_{e(iso)} = 3\lambda^2/(8\pi\,A_{e(iso)})$$

or

$$A_{e(iso)} = \lambda^2/4\pi \qquad (7.33)$$

Power received by an aerial

The power P_R received by an aerial when it is positioned in a field of strength E V m^{-1} is

$$P_R = P_d A_e = (E^2\lambda^2 G_R)/(120\pi \times 4\pi) = (G_R/30)(E\lambda/4\pi)^2$$

From equation (7.29),

$$E = \sqrt{(30P_T G_T)}/D$$

and substituting this gives

$$P_R = G_T G_R P_T (\lambda/4\pi D)^2 \qquad (7.34)$$

Free-space attenuation

The free-space attenuation, also known as the *path loss*, accounts for the way in which the radio wave spreads out over an increasing area as it propagates away from the transmitting aerial. The free-space attenuation is given by the term in brackets in equation (7.34), i.e.

$$\text{free-space loss } L_p = (\lambda/4\pi D)^2 \qquad (7.35)$$

Using the free-space loss, the received power P_R can be written as

$$P_R = (\text{EIRP} \times G_R)/(\text{path loss}) \qquad (7.36)$$

or, using decibels,

$$P_R = \text{EIRP (dBW)} + G_R \text{ (dB)} - L_p \text{ (dB) dBW} \qquad (7.37)$$

The free-space loss

$$L_p = 20 \log_{10}(4\pi D/\lambda) = 22 + 20 \log_{10}(D/\lambda)$$
$$= 22 + 20 \log_{10} D - 20 \log_{10} \lambda \text{ dB} \qquad (7.38)$$

EXAMPLE 7.7

The transmitting aerial of a 600 MHz radio link has a gain of 26 dBi. The signal is received by an identical aerial that is 30 km away. Calculate the overall loss of the radio link.

Solution

Since 26 dB is a power ratio of approximately 308, then from equation (7.34),

$$P_R/P_T = 398^2 \times [(3 \times 10^8)/(4\pi \times 30 \times 10^3 \times 600 \times 10^6)]^2$$
$$= 2.79 \times 10^{-7}$$

Therefore,

link loss = 65.5 dB *(Ans.)*

Alternatively, from equation (7.38),

$$L_p = 22 + 20 \log_{10}(30 \times 10^3) - 20 \log_{10}(3/6)$$
$$= 22 + 89.5 - (-6) = 117.5 \text{ dB}$$

Thus overall loss = $117.5 - (2 \times 26) = 65.5$ dB *(Ans.)*

EXAMPLE 7.8

A $\lambda/4$ monopole aerial is supplied with a current of 30 A r.m.s. at 3 MHz. Calculate (a) the field strength produced at ground level at a point 50 km distant, and (b) the power received by an aerial of 10 dBi gain situated at that point.

Solution

(a) $\lambda = (3 \times 10^8)/(3 \times 10^6) = 100$ m and hence $\lambda/4 = 25$ m. Since the monopole aerial is $\lambda/4$ long the input current is at the origin and so $I = 30 \cos(2\pi y/100)$. The mean aerial current is

$[(1.2 \times 100)/2\pi][\sin(50\pi/100)] = 19.1$ A

Therefore, $l_{eff} = (19.1 \times 25)/30 = 15.9$ m. Substituting into equation (7.19),

$E = (120\pi \times 30 \times 15.9)/(100 \times 50 \times 10^3) = 36$ mV m^{-1} *(Ans.)*

(b) The receive aerial has a gain of 10 dBi = 10 times, so its effective aperture is

$A_e = 10 \times A_{e(iso)} = 10\lambda^2/4\pi = (10 \times 10^4)/4\pi = 7958$ m^2

The power density at the distant point P is $P_d = E^2/120\pi = 3.44 \times 10^{-6}$ W m^{-1} and therefore the received power is

$P_R = A_e P_d = 7958 \times 3.44 \times 10^{-6} = 27.36$ mW *(Ans.)*

Fig. 7.17 *Long-wire radiator*

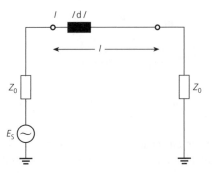

Fig. 7.18 *Calculation of the field strength produced by a long-wire raditator*

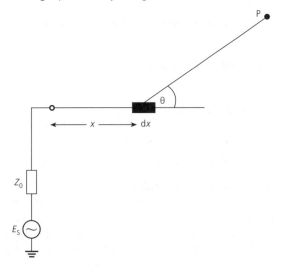

Long-wire radiator

Figure 7.17 shows the basic arrangement of a long-wire radiator. Essentially, it consists of a conductor, several wavelengths long at the frequencies of operation, which together with the earth forms a transmission line of characteristic impedance Z_0. At its sending end an RF source of e.m.f. E_S and impedance Z_0 supplies a current $I_S = E_S/2Z_0$. The attenuation of the line is negligibly small and so this current flows, with unchanged amplitude but varying phase, to the matched load. The length of line l can be considered to consist of the cascade connection of a large number of current elements. Each current element will radiate energy, the amplitude of which is at its maximum value in the equatorial plane and zero along the axis of the line. The total field strength produced at a distant point P is the phasor sum of the field strengths produced by each of the individual current elements.

Consider Fig. 7.18. The current at a distance x from the sending end of the line is $I_x = I_S e^{-j\beta x}$ and so it lags the sending-end current I_S by angle $\beta x = 2\pi x/\lambda$ rad. The current

Fig. 7.19 *Radiation patterns for different length long-wire radiators*

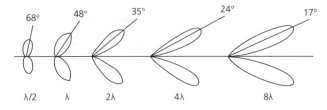

68° 48° 35° 24° 17°

λ/2 λ 2λ 4λ 8λ

element $I_x\,dx$ is closer to the distant point P by $x\cos\theta$ m and so the field strength dE produced by element $I_x\,dx$ lags the field strength due to the current element at the beginning of the line by angle $(2\pi x/\lambda)(1 - \cos\theta)$ rad. Now,

$$dE = (j60\pi\,I\,dx\sin\theta)/\lambda D$$

and hence the total electric field strength at the point P is

$$E = \int_0^l \{[j60\pi\sin\theta)/\lambda D][I_S e^{-(j2\pi x/\lambda)(1-\cos\theta)}]\}\,dx$$

$$= [(j60\pi I_s\sin\theta)/\lambda D]\left[\frac{e^{-(j2\pi x/\lambda)(1-\cos\theta)}}{(j2\pi x/\lambda)(1 - \cos\theta)}\right]_0^l$$

$$= (30I_s/D)[\sin\theta/(1 - \cos\theta)][e^{-(j2\pi l/\lambda)(1-\cos\theta)} - 1]$$

$$\text{or } E = [(60I_s/D)(\sin\theta/(1 - \cos\theta))][\sin((\pi l/\lambda)(1 - \cos\theta))]^\dagger \qquad (7.39)$$

The main lobes of the radiation pattern of a long-wire radiator for five different lengths are shown in Fig. 7.19. As the length of the wire increases the number of sidelobes increases also but these are not shown in the figure. When the length of the wire is between 4λ and 8λ there is a linear relationship between the angle of the main lobe and frequency. The long-wire radiator can be used as an aerial in its own right but, more often, it is a part of a rhombic aerial.

EXAMPLE 7.9

Calculate the ratio of the voltages induced into a long-wire radiator of 100 m length if the incident radio wave has a frequency of 15 MHz and the angle of incidence is (a) 17° and (b) 24°.

Solution

(a) From equation (7.39), with $\lambda = 20$ m,

$$\text{ratio} = \frac{[\sin 17°/(1 - \cos 17°)]\sin[(100\pi/20)(1 - \cos 17°)]}{[\sin 24°/(1 - \cos 24°)]\sin[(100\pi/20)(1 - \cos 24°)]}$$

$$= 0.92\ (Ans.)$$

---

† $e^{-jx} = \cos x - j\sin x$, $|e^{-jx} - 1| = \sqrt{[(\cos x - 1)^2 + \sin^2 x]} = \sqrt{[4\sin(x/2)]} = 2\sin(x/2)$.

Fig. 7.20 *Main lobe angle: variation with wavelength*

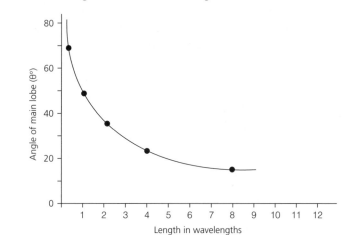

(b) Values of the lobe angle θ for different values of wire length, in wavelengths, can be obtained from equation (7.39) and are shown plotted in Fig. 7.20. The lobe angle varies, more or less linearly, from 24° at $l = 4\lambda$ to 17° at $l = 8\lambda$.

EXERCISES

7.1 Show that the radiation resistance of an earthed λ/4 vertical aerial is approximately 40 Ω. An aerial of this type is supplied with a current of 10 A r.m.s. at 4 MHz. Calculate (a) the effective height of the aerial, (b) the electric field strength produced at a point at ground level 30 km away, (c) the power received by an aerial of gain 12 dBi, and (d) the transmitted power.

7.2 Explain the meanings of the terms 'gain', 'effective aperture' and 'directivity' as applied to an aerial. Two aerials that operate at 600 MHz have effective apertures of 4 m and 2 m, respectively. Calculate the gain of each aerial with respect to (a) an isotropic radiator and (b) a λ/2 dipole.

7.3 What is meant by the terms the 'induction field' and the 'radiation field' of an aerial? At what distance from an aerial operating at 3 MHz are the two fields of equal amplitude? If, at a much greater distance, the radiation field has a magnetic field strength of 265×10^{-6} A m^{-1} what is (a) the electric field strength and (b) the power density at this point?

7.4 A power of 100 kW is radiated by an aerial whose effective length is 100 m. Calculate the field strength produced at a distance of 100 km if the frequency is 60 kHz.

7.5 Calculate the electric field strength at ground level at a point 10 km from a λ/2 monopole. The aerial is supplied with a 3 A r.m.s. current at a frequency of 10 MHz.

7.6 Explain what is meant by the effective height of an aerial. An earthed monopole has an effective height of 0.1 λ and it is supplied with an r.m.s. current of 100 A. Calculate the total radiated power and the effective radiated power. Also find the field strength at ground level 50 km distant.

Fig. 7.21

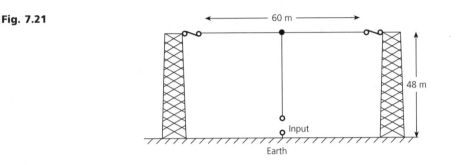

7.7 The transmitting aerial shown in Fig. 7.21 is supplied with current at 80 A peak and at frequency 666.66 kHz. Calculate (a) the effective height of the aerial and (b) the electric field strength produced at ground level 40 km away.

7.8 Show that the power received by an aerial of gain G_R is given by $P_R = P_T G_T G_R (\lambda/4\pi D)^2$. Calculate the total attenuation if $G_T = G_R = 30$ dBi, $D = 30$ km, and the frequency of operation is 600 MHz.

7.9 Calculate the radiation resistance of a λ/16 aerial. Determine its radiated power when the input current is 100 A r.m.s. If the loss resistance is 25 Ω calculate the efficiency of the aerial.

7.10 An aerial is 100 m in height and carries a current at 100 kHz whose amplitude decreases linearly from 200 A at the base to zero at the top. Calculate the effective height of the aerial when it is mounted upon perfectly conducting earth. Calculate the field strength produced at a distance of 20 km from the aerial.

7.11 A transmitting aerial has $G_R = 10$ dBi and $P_T = 1$ kW. Calculate (a) the EIRP, (b) the power density produced at a point 30 km distant, and (c) the power received by an aerial at that point that has a gain of 30 dBi. The frequency is 100 MHz.

7.12 (a) A radio transmitter has an output power of 10 W. The gain of the transmitting aerial is 28 dB. Calculate the EIRP in dBW.
 (b) Calculate the electric field strength produced at a distance of 10 km.
 (c) Calculate the magnetic field strength at the same point.

7.13 A radio link has a transmitted power of 40 W. If the gains of the transmitting aerial and receiving aerials are both 30 dB and the free-space loss is 85 dB calculate the received power in dBW.

7.14 Calculate the radiation resistance of a monopole 10 cm long at 200 MHz.

7.15 (a) Calculate the power radiated by a λ/16 aerial if the supplied current is $i = 20 \sin \omega t$ A. (b) Find the radiation resistance.

8 Aerials

After reading this chapter you should be able to:

(a) Calculate and plot the radiation patterns of arrays of dipoles.
(b) Use the principle of pattern multiplication.
(c) Understand the action of a reflecting surface on the radiation pattern of an aerial and apply this (i) to obtain the height factor of an aerial, and (ii) to the action of a corner reflector.
(d) Explain the meaning of the term beamwidth and know its importance.
(e) Determine the effect of mutual impedance on the gain of an aerial.
(f) Explain the operation of a rhombic aerial.
(g) Explain the operation of a log-periodic aerial.
(h) Explain the operation of a Yagi aerial.
(i) Discuss the differences between a notch aerial and a slot aerial.
(j) Compare the aerials used with mobile radio systems such as the loop, rod and helical aerials.
(k) Explain the principle of operation of a parabolic dish aerial and calculate its gain and beamwidth.
(l) Discuss the different feed arrangements employed for dish aerials.

For radio communication between two points, high-gain directive aerials are desirable for both transmission and reception. In the HF band the rhombic aerial was widely employed for many years but it has now been superseded, for all but a few special applications, by the log-periodic aerial. The log-periodic aerial can provide an equal, or superior, performance to the rhombic aerial in terms of both gain and bandwidth for a smaller physical size and cost. All HF radio links employ sky-wave propagation via the ionosphere, and for the best results the aerial must be selected to suit the existing propagation conditions at any given time. In particular, for reliable communications to be maintained, an HF system needs to be flexible in its choice of frequency, which means that both the transmitting aerial and the receiving aerial must be wideband. Nowadays, the selection of frequency and elevation angle is made easier and quicker by the use of computer control at the transmitter.

Omni-directional HF transmitting aerials are required for some purposes, and in the past were mainly vertical whip aerials. Such aerials have a fairly low gain and have an inadequate performance at high angles of elevation, and some modern systems use a vertical stack of loop aerials fed in a log-periodic manner. In the VHF and UHF bands the dimensions of a λ/2 dipole are small enough for linear arrays of dipoles to be the predominant type of aerial. Alternative aerials that are also often employed are the corner reflector, the Yagi and the log-periodic. For omni-directional radiation of energy a vertically stacked sleeve dipole is often used. Vehicle radio systems and mobile telephones normally use either the whip (rod) aerial or the helical aerial and the base station often employs a stack of folded dipoles. Aircraft often employ the notch aerial. In the SHF band parabolic dish aerials are most often employed for terrestrial radio-relay and communications satellite systems.

Two-dipole array

A λ/2 dipole has a gain of 2.16 dBi, a circular equatorial plane radiation pattern, and a figure-of-eight radiation pattern in the meridian plane. For many applications such a gain and directivity are inadequate, so two, or more, dipoles can be used in an array to obtain increased gain and directivity. A variety of radiation patterns can be obtained by varying one or more of (a) the number of dipoles used, (b) the spacing between the dipoles, and (c) the amplitudes and relative phases of the dipole currents. The radiation pattern and the gain of an aerial may be affected by mutual impedances between the dipoles in an array, but this factor will not be considered until p. 222. In the past arrays of dipoles were often employed as HF aerials, but today their main applications are in the VHF and the UHF bands.

Vertical dipoles

Horizontal plane radiation pattern

Equal-phase, equal-amplitude aerial currents

Figure 8.1 shows two vertical λ/2 dipoles mounted in the same horizontal plane and spaced apart by a distance of d m. If the dipoles are supplied with equal-amplitude, in-phase currents, both dipoles will radiate energy equally well in all directions in the horizontal plane. The total field strength at any point in this plane will be equal to the phasor sum of the individual field strengths produced by each aerial. If the distance to a distant point P is very much larger than the dipole spacing d these individual field strengths will be of equal amplitude but in most angular directions will be out of phase with one another. The remote point marked as O is equidistant from both dipoles and so at this point the fields produced by the two dipoles are in phase and will add algebraically. In most directions, however, the energy radiated by dipole A must travel an extra distance to reach the point P than the energy radiated by dipole B; this extra distance is equal to $d \cos \theta$. Therefore, the field strength due to dipole A will lag the field strength due to dipole B by an angle

$\phi = (2\pi d/\lambda) \cos \theta$ rad

The phasor diagram of the field strengths at the point P is shown by Fig. 8.2. From this figure, the total field strength E_T at point P is equal to

$$E_T = 2E \cos(\phi/2) = 2E \cos[(\pi d \cos \theta)/\lambda] \qquad (8.1)$$

Fig. 8.1 *Two-dipole array*

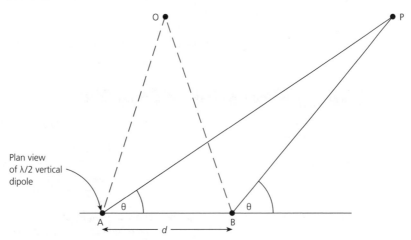

Fig. 8.2 *Phasor diagram of the field strengths at a distant point*

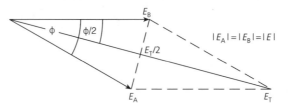

If either $\lambda/2$ dipole on its own was supplied with a power of P W the field strength produced at the point P would be $E_0 = 60I/D$ V m^{-1}.

If the same power is supplied to the two-dipole array each dipole will receive a power of $P/2$ W and so will produce a field strength of $E_0/\sqrt{2}$ V m^{-1} at the point P.

Hence, the total field strength at the point P is

$$E_T = (2E_0/\sqrt{2}) \cos[(\pi d \cos \theta)/\lambda]$$
$$= \sqrt{2}E_0 \cos[(\pi d \cos \theta)/\lambda)] \qquad (8.2)$$

The gain of the array, relative to a $\lambda/2$ dipole, is $20 \log_{10} \sqrt{2} = 3$ dB and relative to an isotropic radiator is 5.15 dBi.

The *array factor* is the term $\sqrt{2} \cos[(\pi d \cos \theta)/\lambda]$.

EXAMPLE 8.1

Calculate and plot the horizontal radiation pattern of two vertical $\lambda/2$ dipoles which are $\lambda/4$ apart and supplied with equal-amplitude, in-phase currents.

Solution

$$\phi = (2\pi/\lambda)(\lambda/4) \cos \theta = (\pi/2) \cos \theta$$

Hence the array factor is $\sqrt{2} \cos[(\pi/4) \cos \theta]$. It is usually sufficient to calculate the resultant field strength at $30°$ intervals over the range $0°$ to $180°$. This has been done to produce the tabulated values given in Table 8.1.

Using the figures given in the final row of Table 8.1 the radiation pattern for the array has been plotted and is shown in Fig. 8.3(a).

Table 8.1 *Two-dipole array, $\lambda/4$ spacing, $\alpha = 0°$*

θ	$0°$	$30°$	$60°$	$90°$	$120°$	$150°$	$180°$
$\cos \theta$	1	0.866	0.5	0	-0.5	-0.866	-1
$45° \cos \theta$	$45°$	$39°$	$22.5°$	$0°$	$22.5°$	$39°$	$45°$
$\cos(45° \cos \theta)$	1	1.1	1.3	1.41	1.3	1.1	1

Fig. 8.3 *Radiation pattern of a two-dipole array with $\lambda/4$ dipole spacing and (a) equal amplitude in-phase currents, (b) and (c) equal amplitude 90° out-of-phase currents*

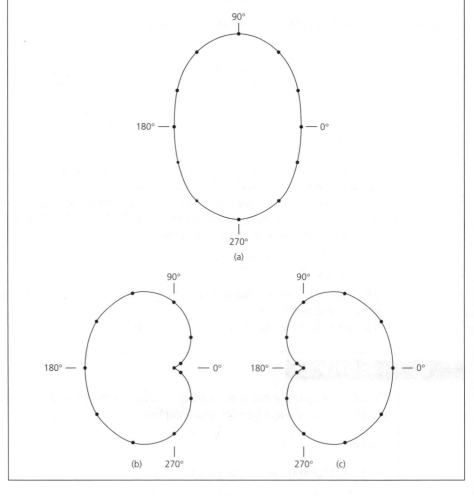

Equal-amplitude, out-of-phase aerial currents

When the currents in the two dipoles are of equal amplitude but there is a phase difference α between them the radiation pattern of the two-dipole array will be altered. The angle α must be added to angle ϕ to obtain a new phase difference $\Psi = \phi - \alpha$ radians if the phase of I_A leads I_B, or $\Psi = \phi + \alpha$ if the phase of I_B leads I_A. Very often, the value of α is made equal to the distance between the dipoles. If, for example, the dipole spacing is $\lambda/4$, α will often be equal to $90°$.

EXAMPLE 8.2

Calculate and plot the horizontal plane radiation pattern for two vertical $\lambda/2$ dipoles that are $\lambda/4$ apart and are fed with equal-amplitude currents that are $90°$ out of phase.

Solution

If I_B leads I_A,

$$\Psi = (2\pi/\lambda)(\lambda/4) \cos \theta + 90° = 90°(1 + \cos \theta)$$

and hence the array factor is $\sqrt{2} \cos[45°(1 + \cos \theta)]$. The results are tabulated in Table 8.2. The radiation pattern is shown in Fig. 8.3(b).
    Conversely, if I_A leads I_B,

$$\Psi = 90°(\cos \theta - 1)$$

and the array factor is equal to $\sqrt{2} \cos[45°(\cos \theta - 1)]$. The results are presented in Table 8.3 and the radiation pattern is shown plotted by Fig. 8.3(c).

Table 8.2 *Two-dipole array, $\lambda/4$ spacing, $\alpha = 90°$*

θ	0°	30°	60°	90°	120°	150°	180°
$1 + \cos \theta$	2	1.866	1.5	1	0.5	0.134	0
$45°(1 + \cos \theta)$	90°	84°	67.5°	45°	22.5°	6°	0°
Array factor	0	0.15	0.54	1.0	1.31	1.41	1.41

Table 8.3 *Two-dipole array, $\lambda/4$ spacing, $\alpha = -90°$*

θ	0°	30°	60°	90°	120°	150°	180°
$\cos \theta - 1$	0	-0.134	-0.5	-1.0	-1.5	-1.866	-2
$45°(\cos \theta - 1)$	0°	-6°	-22.5°	-45°	-67.5°	-84°	-90°
Array factor	1.41	1.41	1.31	1.0	0.54	0.15	0

Fig. 8.4 *(a) Phasor diagram of unequal amplitude field strengths, (b) simplified version of (a)*

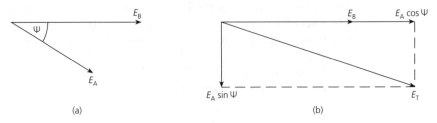

(a)   (b)

Aerial currents of different amplitudes

The currents supplied to the two dipoles may not always be of equal amplitude. Figure 8.4(a) shows the phasor diagram of the field strengths at the distant point P when $|I_B| > |I_A|$. Taking E_B as the reference phasor and resolving E_A into its horizontal and vertical components gives the phasor diagram shown in Fig. 8.4(b). From this diagram the total field strength E_T is

$$E_T = \sqrt{[(E_B + E_A \cos \Psi)^2 + E_A^2 \sin^2 \Psi]}$$
$$= \sqrt{(E_B^2 + 2E_A E_B \cos \Psi + E_A^2 \cos^2 \Psi + E_A^2 \sin^2 \Psi)}$$

or

$$E_T = \sqrt{(E_A^2 + E_B^2 + 2E_A E_B \cos \Psi)} \qquad (8.3)$$

Note that if $E_A = E_B = E$,

$$E_T = \sqrt{[2E^2(1 + \cos \Psi)]} = \sqrt{2}E\sqrt{(1 + \cos \Psi)}$$
$$= \sqrt{2}E\sqrt{(2 \cos^2 \Psi/2)} = 2E \cos \Psi/2$$

as before.

Vertical plane radiation pattern

The vertical plane radiation pattern of two vertical $\lambda/2$ dipoles mounted in the same horizontal plane is obtained by multiplying the array factor by equation (7.24), i.e.

$$E_T = [\sqrt{2}E \cos(\Psi/2)][(\cos(\pi/2) \cos \theta)/\sin \theta] \qquad (8.4)$$

Colinear vertical dipoles

Two colinear vertical dipoles (see Fig. 8.5) have a circular radiation pattern in the horizontal plane since, quite clearly, in this plane the energy radiated from each dipole does not combine with the energy radiated by the other. In the vertical plane the radiation pattern is given by the product of the array factor and the dipole's meridian plane pattern, i.e. by equation (8.4).

Dipole in front of a reflecting plane

If a $\lambda/2$ dipole is mounted in front of a reflecting plane the image of the dipole will act as though it were the second dipole in a two-dipole array. The polarity of the image dipole depends upon the orientation of the physical dipole and Fig. 8.6 shows the two

Fig. 8.5 *Co-linear dipoles*

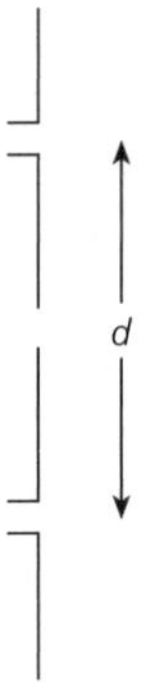

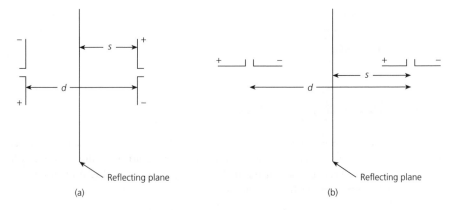

Fig. 8.6 *Dipole mounted in front of a reflecting surface (a) parallel to, and (b) normal to the plane*

most common cases. When, in Fig. 8.6(a), the dipole is mounted parallel to the reflecting plane the image dipole has the opposite polarity to the driven dipole. Conversely if, in Fig. 8.6(b), the dipole is mounted normal to the reflecting plane, both the dipole and its image have the same polarity. The apparent spacing *d* between the two 'dipoles' is twice the distance *S* between the dipole and the reflecting plane.

One application of this principle is the *corner reflector*. A λ/2 dipole is placed in a position parallel to the intersection of two reflecting planes as shown by Fig. 8.7(a). The reflecting planes are made of either solid metal or wire mesh, or perhaps a system of conductors spaced apart at 0.1λ or less, and usually the planes are at an angle of either 90° or 60° to one another. Each plane must be at least one wavelength long in each direction, i.e. $l \geq \lambda$. The spacing of the λ/2 dipole from the intersection of the planes is somewhere between 0.3λ and 0.5λ with the latter distance being the most common. If the plane angle θ is assumed to be 90°, Fig. 8.7(b) shows that reflections from the corner reflector produce image dipoles A, B and C; image A has the same polarity as the actual dipole D, while both images B and C have the opposite polarity. Effectively, therefore, the corner reflector gives a four-dipole array with two dipoles in each of two planes. The way in which the array factor of such an array can be calculated is discussed on p. 219.

Fig. 8.7 *(a) Corner reflector and (b) image aerials produced by the corner reflector*

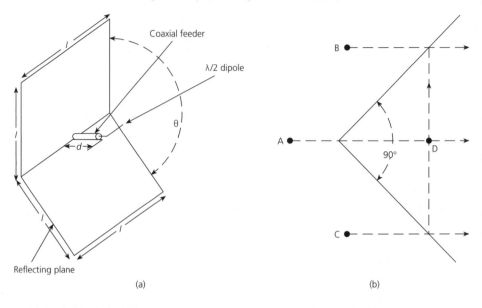

(a)   (b)

Three-dipole array

An increase in both the gain and the directivity of the two-aerial array can be obtained if a third dipole is added to form a three-dipole array. If the centre dipole B is taken to be the reference, then at the distant point P the E field due to dipole A will lag the E field due to aerial B by an angle

$$\Psi = (2\pi d/\lambda) \cos \theta \pm \alpha$$

while the E field produced by dipole C at P will lead the E field due to dipole B by angle

$$\Psi' = (2\pi d/\lambda) \cos \theta \pm \beta$$

where α and β are the phase of the currents in dipoles A and C respectively relative to the current in dipole B.

EXAMPLE 8.3

In a three-dipole array the dipole spacing is $\lambda/2$ and the dipole currents are $2I\angle 0°$ for the centre dipole and $I\angle 180°$ for both the outer dipoles. Determine the expression for the radiation pattern of the aerial.

Solution

$$\phi = (2\pi/\lambda)(\lambda/2) \cos \theta = \pi \cos \theta$$

$$\Psi = \pi - \pi \cos \theta \quad \text{and} \quad \Psi' = \pi + \pi \cos \theta$$

Fig. 8.8 *(a) Phasor diagram of a three-dipole array, and (b) simplified version of (a)*

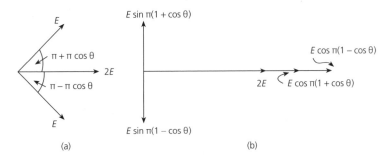

(a) (b)

The phasor diagram of the field strengths at a distant point P is given by Fig. 8.8(a). The diagram can be simplified by resolving the two smaller phasors into their horizontal and vertical components as shown by Fig. 8.8(b). From Fig. 8.8(b), the total field strength is

$$E_T = 2E + E \cos[\pi(1 + \cos\theta)] + E \cos[\pi(1 - \cos\theta)]$$
$$= 2E[1 - \cos(\pi\cos\theta)] = 4E \sin^2[(\pi/2)\cos\theta]$$

or

$$E_T = (4/\sqrt{3})E_0 \sin^2[(\pi/2)\cos\theta] \ (Ans.)$$

Broadside array

A broadside array consists of a number n of $\lambda/2$ dipoles equally spaced in one line and carrying equal-amplitude, in-phase currents. If the total power supplied to the array is P_T W, each dipole will be fed with P_T/n W and will produce a field strength of $E_0/\sqrt{n}$ at the distant point P.

Suppose, for example, that the number n of dipoles is 5, as in Fig. 8.9. The radiation from dipole A has a further distance $d \cos\theta$ to travel in order to reach the distant point P than has the radiation from dipole B. The field strength due to aerial A will therefore lag the field strength due to dipole B by angle

$$\phi = (2\pi d/\lambda) \cos\theta \text{ rad}$$

In a similar manner, the field strength E_B produced by dipole B lags the field strength E_C produced by dipole C, E_C lags E_D, and E_D lags E_E, all by the same angle ϕ. Figure 8.10(a) shows the phasor diagram of the field strengths at the distant point P.

If a line is drawn normal to the centre of each phasor the lines will meet at the point marked as C. Lines then drawn from point C to the ends of each phasor subtend the angle ϕ (see Fig. 8.10(b)). The total field strength E_T is represented by the phasor that goes from the base of phasor E_E to the tip of phasor E_A as shown by Fig. 8.10(c).

Fig. 8.9 *Broadside array*

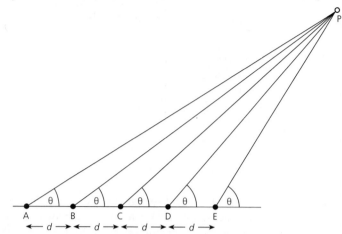

Fig. 8.10 *Phasor diagrams of the field strengths produced by a broadside array*

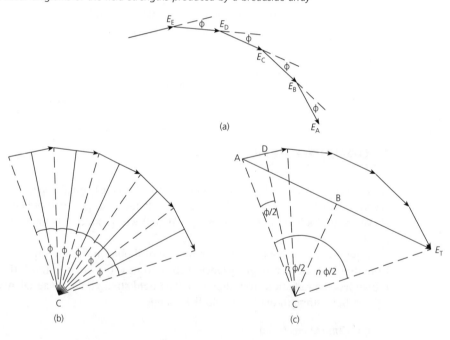

(a)

(b)

(c)

From Fig. 8.10(c),

$$E_T = 2AC \sin(n\phi/2)$$

To find the value of the length AC, consider the triangle ACD. From this,

$$\sin(\phi/2) = (E/2)/AC \quad \text{or} \quad AC = (E/2)/\sin(\phi/2)$$

Therefore,

$$E_T = [E \sin(n\phi/2)]/\sin(\phi/2) \tag{8.5}$$

This equation can be written as

$$E_T = [(E_0/\sqrt{n}) \sin(n\phi/2)]/\sin(\phi/2)$$
$$= [E_0\sqrt{n} \sin(n\phi/2)]/[n \sin(\phi/2)] \qquad (8.6)$$

When the angle θ is very nearly equal to 90°, cos θ, and hence ϕ, is small. Then

$$[\sqrt{n} \sin(n\phi/2)]/[n \sin(\phi/2)] \approx [\sqrt{n}\,n\phi/2]/[n\phi/2] = \sqrt{n}$$

and the gain of the broadside array is $(\sqrt{n})^2$ or n, i.e. the gain is equal to the number of dipoles in the array.

The radiation pattern of a broadside array has two main lobes in the plane perpendicular to the line of the array. Its exact shape is best determined by finding the angles at which maxima and minima occur.

EXAMPLE 8.4

A broadside array consists of six vertical $\lambda/2$ dipoles spaced $\lambda/2$ apart, and energised by equal-amplitude, in-phase currents. Calculate and plot the horizontal plane radiation pattern of the aerial.

Solution

Here $n = 6$ and $\phi = (2\pi/\lambda)[(\lambda/2) \cos \theta] = \pi \cos \theta$, and so

$$E_T = [(E_0/\sqrt{6}) \sin(3\pi \cos \theta)]/[\sin(\pi/2) \cos \theta]$$

At $\theta \approx 90°$,

$$E_T = (E_0/\sqrt{6}) \times 6 = \sqrt{6}E_0$$

Nulls occur in the radiation pattern when the numerator of equation (8.6) is zero and the denominator is *not* zero, i.e. when $3\pi \cos \theta = \pi$, 2π, 3π, etc. Hence

(a) $\cos \theta = 1/3$, $\theta = \pm 70.5°$
(b) $\cos \theta = 2/3$, $\theta = \pm 48.2°$
(c) $\cos \theta = 1$, $\theta = 0°$.

The centre of each minor lobe occurs when $\sin(n\phi/2) = 1$, or $n\phi/2 = \pm(2k + 1)(\pi/2)$. Hence

$$\cos \theta = [\pm(2k + 1)\lambda]/2nd$$

In this case,

$$\cos \theta = [\pm(2k + 1)\lambda]/(2 \times 6 \times \lambda/2) = [\pm(2k + 1)]/6$$

(a) $k = 1$, $\theta = \cos^{-1}(\pm 1/2) = \pm 60°$;
(b) $k = 2$, $\theta = \cos^{-1}(\pm 5/6) = \pm 33.6°$;
(c) $k = 3$, $\theta = \cos^{-1}(\pm 7/6)$, which is, of course, not possible.

The radiation pattern is shown by Fig. 8.11.

Fig. 8.11 *Radiation pattern of a broadside array*

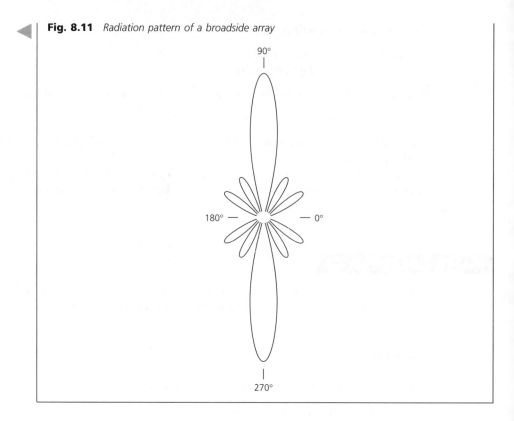

Beamwidth

The beamwidth of an aerial is the angle subtended by the 3 dB points on the major lobe(s) of the radiation pattern. Thus, in Fig. 8.12 the angle β is the beamwidth. The maximum field strength produced by a broadside array is

$$E_{T(max)} = \sqrt{n}\,E_0 = nE$$

Therefore,

$$E_T/E_{T(max)} = [\sin(n\phi/2)]/[n\,\sin(\phi/2)]$$

Fig. 8.12 *Beamwidth of a radiation pattern*

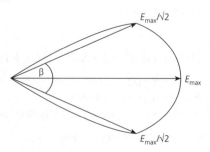

If the angle θ that gives $E_T = E_{T(max)}/\sqrt{2}$ is large, $\cos\theta$ will be small and then $\sin(\phi/2)$ is small. Therefore,

$$E_T/E_{T(max)} \approx [\sin(n\phi/2)]/[n\phi/2]$$

and this is equal to $1/\sqrt{2}$ when $n\phi/2 = 1.39$ rad. Hence

$$(n\pi d \cos\theta)/\lambda = 1.39 \quad \text{or} \quad \cos\theta = \sin(90° - \theta) = 1.39/n\pi d$$

Since θ is large, $\sin(90° - \theta) \approx \theta - \beta/2$, and so the beamwidth β is

$$\beta = 0.885\lambda/nd = (51\lambda/nd)° \tag{8.7}$$

In the case of the array given in Example 8.4,

$$\beta = 51\lambda/(6 \times \lambda/2) = 17°$$

The greater the number of $\lambda/2$ dipoles employed in an array the more directive the radiation pattern will become, although the number of small secondary lobes will also increase.

End-fire array

An end-fire array consists of a number n of $\lambda/2$ dipoles spaced $\lambda/4$ apart and fed with equal-amplitude currents but with a progressive phase difference equal to the spacing, i.e.

$$\alpha = (2\pi/\lambda)(\lambda/4) = \pi/2 \text{ rad}$$

The same analysis as that used for the broadside array is applicable, but with $\Psi = \phi + \alpha$ replacing ϕ to give

$$E_T = [\sqrt{n}\, E_0 \sin(n\Psi/2)]/[n \sin(\Psi/2)] \tag{8.8}$$

EXAMPLE 8.5

Calculate and plot the radiation pattern of a six-dipole end-fire array.

Solution

$$\Psi = (2\pi/\lambda)(\lambda/4) \cos\theta + \pi/2 = (\pi/2)(1 + \cos\theta)$$

The maximum field strength $E_{T(max)}$ is $\sqrt{6}E_0$ and it occurs when $\Psi = 0$, i.e. when $(\pi/2)(1 + \cos\theta) = 0$, or $\theta = 180°$.
   Nulls in the radiation pattern occur when

$$\sin[(3\pi/2)(1 + \cos\theta)] = 0$$

or

$$(3\pi/2)(1 + \cos\theta) = k\pi$$

Fig. 8.13 *Radiation pattern of an end-five array*

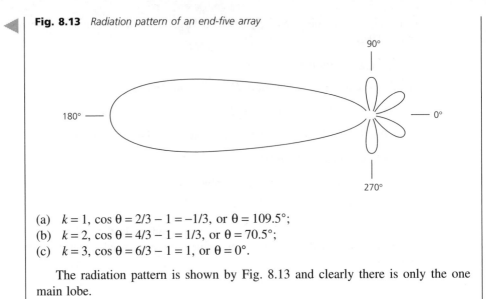

(a) $k = 1$, $\cos \theta = 2/3 - 1 = -1/3$, or $\theta = 109.5°$;
(b) $k = 2$, $\cos \theta = 4/3 - 1 = 1/3$, or $\theta = 70.5°$;
(c) $k = 3$, $\cos \theta = 6/3 - 1 = 1$, or $\theta = 0°$.

The radiation pattern is shown by Fig. 8.13 and clearly there is only the one main lobe.

Height factor

When an aerial is mounted above the earth, ground reflections will produce an image aerial beneath the earth as shown by Fig. 8.14. If the elements of the aerial are mounted

Fig. 8.14 *Aerial mounted above earth: (a) vertical aerial, (b) horizontal aerial*

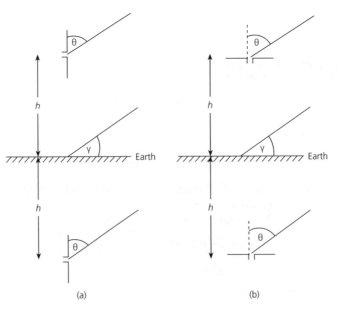

vertically the image aerial will have the same polarity as the actual aerial, but if the aerial elements are in the horizontal plane the image aerial will be of the opposite polarity.

An aerial and its image behave in the same way as a two-dipole array with a spacing equal to $2h$, where h is the height of the aerial above the earth.

Vertical aerial

The aerial and image currents are in phase with one another, and so the total field strength produced at a distant point P in the vertical plane is (from equation (8.1) with $d = 2h$)

$$E_T = 2E \cos[(2\pi h/\lambda) \cos \theta]$$

The angle θ is now the angle relative to the vertical line passing through both the aerial and its image. If the angle of elevation γ is used instead, which would be more convenient in practice, $\gamma = 90° - \theta$, and $\cos \theta = \cos(90° - \gamma) = \sin \gamma$. Therefore,

$$E_T = 2E \cos[(2\pi h \sin \gamma)/\lambda] \tag{8.9}$$

The *height factor* $H(\gamma)$ is

$$H(\gamma) = 2 \cos[(2\pi h \sin \gamma)/\lambda] \tag{8.10}$$

and it is the factor by which the free-space radiation pattern must be multiplied to take account of ground reflections.

Horizontal aerial

When the aerial is mounted horizontally the apparent current in the image aerial is in anti-phase with the current in the actual aerial. Hence

$$\begin{aligned} E_T &= 2E \cos[(2\pi h \sin \gamma)/\lambda + 90°] \\ &= 2E \sin[(2\pi h \sin \gamma)/\lambda] \end{aligned} \tag{8.11}$$

The angle of elevation γ of the main beam is the angle that makes

$$\sin[(2\pi h/\lambda) \sin \gamma] = 1$$

Then $(2\pi h/\lambda) \sin \gamma = \pi/2$, or

$$\gamma = \sin^{-1}[\lambda/4h] \tag{8.12}$$

EXAMPLE 8.6

A transmitting aerial operates at 20 MHz and is to have its maximum radiation in the vertical plane at an angle of elevation of 14°. Determine the height above ground at which the aerial should be mounted if it is (a) horizontally and (b) vertically mounted.

Solution

$$\lambda = (3 \times 10^8)/(20 \times 10^6) = 15 \text{ m}$$

(a) From equation (8.12), the maximum field strength is obtained when

$$\sin[(2\pi h/\lambda) \sin 14°] = 1$$

or

$$(2\pi h/\lambda) \sin 14° = \pi/2$$

Therefore,

$$h = 15/(4 \sin 14°) = 15.5 \text{ m } (Ans.)$$

(b) From equation (8.10), the maximum field strength occurs at the height where

$$\cos[(2\pi h/\lambda) \sin 14°] = -1$$

or

$$(2\pi h/\lambda) \sin 14° = \pi$$

Therefore,

$$h = 15/(2 \sin 14°) = 31 \text{ m } (Ans.)$$

Figure 8.15 shows the height factor $H(y)$ plotted for heights of $\lambda/4$, $\lambda/2$, $3\lambda/4$ and λ above the earth for both horizontal and vertical aerials. With a horizontal aerial there is zero radiation at ground level as well as at some angles of elevation.

Fig. 8.15 *Height factor for (a) vertical and (b) horizontal aerials*

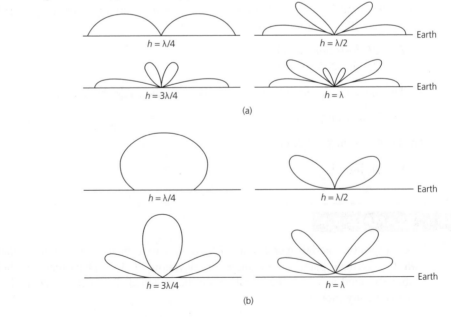

Fig. 8.16 *Showing the planes xz, xy and yz of an aerial*

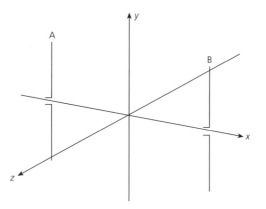

Pattern multiplication

The use of *pattern multiplication* to obtain the radiation pattern of a two-dipole array has already been touched upon (p. 208), but it was not specifically labelled as such. The radiation pattern of a two-dipole array can be drawn for each of the three planes shown in Fig. 8.16.

- In the plane xz, i.e. the equatorial plane, the array factor is $\sqrt{2} \cos[(\pi/4) \cos \theta]$. When $\theta = 0°$ this gives $\sqrt{2} \cos(\pi/4) = 1$, and when $\theta = 90°$ it gives $\sqrt{2} \cos 0° = \sqrt{2}$ (see Fig. 8.17(ai)). The radiation pattern of a single dipole is a circle (Fig. 8.17(aii)), and the overall radiation pattern in this plane is the product of (ai) and (aii) and this is shown by Fig. 8.17(aiii).
- In the plane xy, the meridian plane, the array factor is the same as for the equatorial plane, Fig. 8.17(bi). The dipole pattern is given by equation (7.24) and is shown by Fig. 8.17(bii). The overall radiation pattern is given by the product of these figures and is shown by Fig. 8.17(biii).
- In the plane yz, once again each dipole has a radiation pattern given by Fig. 8.17(bii) = Fig. 8.17(cii), but in the array factor equation the angle θ has only the value of 90°. Hence, the array factor is always equal to $\sqrt{2}$; see Fig. 8.17(ci). The overall radiation pattern is the product of Figs 8.17(ci) and (cii) and is shown by Fig. 8.17(ciii).

The principle of pattern multiplication can always be employed to determine the radiation patterns of complex aerial systems. Suppose, for example, that the radiation pattern of an array consisting of three rows of four $\lambda/2$ dipoles (Fig. 8.18) is to be determined. In each plane the overall radiation pattern is the product of (a) the pattern of an individual $\lambda/2$ dipole, (b) a four-dipole array, and (c) a three-dipole array.

Fig. 8.17 *Pattern multiplication*

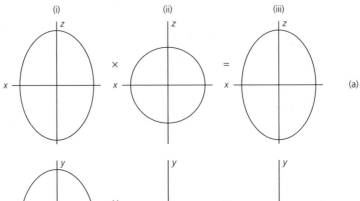
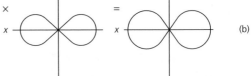
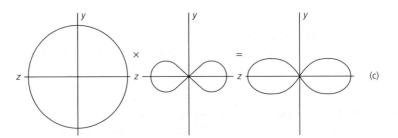

Fig. 8.18 *4 × 3 array*

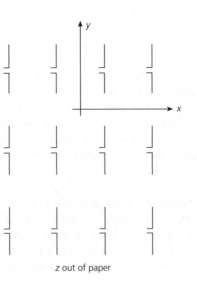

z out of paper

EXAMPLE 8.7

Calculate and plot the horizontal plane radiation pattern of the four vertical $\lambda/2$ dipole array shown in Fig. 8.19. The dipoles are fed with equal-amplitude, in-phase currents.

Fig. 8.19

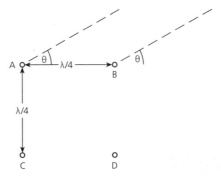

Solution

The radiation pattern due to dipoles A and B, and to dipoles C and D, is given by

$$E_T = \sqrt{2}E_0 \cos[(2\pi\lambda \cos\theta)/(4 \times 2\lambda)] = \sqrt{2}E_0 \cos[(\pi \cos\theta)/4]$$

Similarly, the radiation pattern due to the dipoles A and C, or B and D, is given by

$$E_T = \sqrt{2}E_0 \cos[(2\pi\lambda/8\lambda) \sin\theta] = \sqrt{2}E_0 \cos[(\pi \sin\theta)/4]$$

The overall radiation pattern is therefore given by

$$E_T = 2E_0^2 \cos[(\pi/4) \cos\theta] \cos[(\pi/4) \sin\theta]$$

Values for this equation for $\theta = 0°$ to $180°$ in $30°$ steps are given in Table 8.4. The radiation pattern of the array is shown in Fig. 8.20.

Table 8.4 *Four-dipole array*

θ	0°	30°	60°	90°	120°	150°	180°
45° cos θ	45°	39°	22.5°	0°	−22.5°	−39°	−45°
45° sin θ	0°	22.5°	39°	45°	39°	22.5°	0°
√2 cos(45° cos θ)	1.0	1.1	1.31	1.41	1.31	1.1	1.0
√2 cos(45° sin θ)	1.41	1.31	1.1	1.0	1.1	1.31	1.41
Overall	1.41	1.44	1.44	1.41	1.44	1.44	1.41

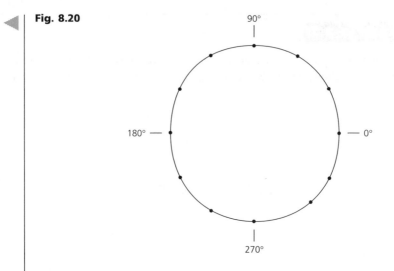

Fig. 8.20

EXAMPLE 8.8

A dipole array is receiving a strong interference signal 50° from the centre of the main lobe of its radiation pattern. To eliminate this interference another array is to be used to position a null at 50°. Determine the necessary separation of the two arrays.

Solution

The principle of pattern multiplication states that if the two-dipole array factor has a null at 50° then the overall radiation pattern will also have this null. Hence

$$\cos[(\pi d/\lambda) \cos 50°] = 0$$

or

$$(0.643\pi d)/\lambda = \pi/2$$

and

$$d = \lambda/(2 \times 0.643) = 0.78\lambda \ (Ans.)$$

Mutual impedances between dipoles

In the treatment so far of dipole arrays it has been assumed that there was zero inter-action between the dipoles. This assumption is not correct if the spacing between the dipoles is small. Each dipole that carries a current will induce a voltage into every other nearby dipole and this means that each pair of dipoles has a mutual impedance between them. The magnitude and phase of each mutual impedance is determined by the length and the diameter of the two dipoles and by their spacing. When a current flows in a dipole the e.m.f. it induces into another dipole in the array tends to oppose the voltage

Fig. 8.21 *Mutual impedances between dipoles*

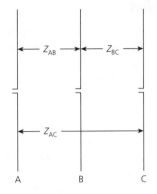

that is applied to that dipole. The voltage applied to a dipole must therefore be equal to the sum of (a) the voltage needed to produce the dipole current if there was zero mutual impedance and (b) the voltages necessary to balance the e.m.f.s induced into the dipole by currents flowing in the other dipoles. Consider, as an example, the three-dipole array shown in Fig. 8.21. For this array the voltage equations are

$$V_A = I_A Z_{AA} + I_B Z_{AB} + I_C Z_{AC}$$
$$V_B = I_B Z_{BB} + I_A Z_{AB} + I_C Z_{BC}$$
$$V_C = I_C Z_{CC} + I_A Z_{AC} + I_B Z_{BC} \qquad (8.13)$$

The input impedance of a dipole is the ratio (input voltage)/(input current); hence

$$Z_A = V_A/I_A = Z_{AA} + Z_{AB} I_B/I_A + Z_{AC} I_C/I_A$$
$$Z_B = V_B/I_B = Z_{BB} + Z_{AB} I_A/I_B + Z_{BC} I_C/I_B$$
$$Z_C = V_C/I_C = Z_{CC} + Z_{AC} I_A/I_C + Z_{BC} I_B/I_C \qquad (8.14)$$

The self-impedance, Z_{AA}, Z_{BB}, Z_{CC}, of a dipole is equal to its radiation resistance, which, if the dipole is slightly shorter than $\lambda/2$, is 73.14 Ω.

If the dipoles are fed with equal-amplitude, in-phase currents, as for a broadside array, then

$$I_A = I_B = I_C \quad \text{and} \quad Z_A = Z_{AA} + Z_{AB} + Z_{AC}$$

If the dipoles are spaced $\lambda/4$ apart and the currents have a progressive phase difference of 90°, as for an end-fire array, then

$$I_B = jI_A \quad \text{and} \quad I_C = jI_B = j^2 I_A = -I_A$$

and, for example,

$$Z_A = Z_{AA} + jZ_{AB} - Z_{AC}$$

The power radiated by each dipole is equal to the square of the dipole current times the real part of the dipole impedance. Thus, the power P_A radiated by dipole A is

$$P_A = I_A^2 \times (\text{real part of } Z_A)$$

EXAMPLE 8.9

Two vertical $\lambda/2$ dipoles spaced $\lambda/4$ apart are supplied with equal-amplitude currents having a phase difference of 90°. Each dipole has a radiation resistance of 73 Ω and their mutual impedance is $40 - j30$ Ω. Calculate (a) the radiated power and (b) the gain of the array in dBi, if the dipole currents are both 100 mA.

Solution

(a) $I_A = 100$ mA, $I_B = j100$ mA
$Z_A = 73 + (40 - j30) \times (j100/100) = 103 + j40$ Ω
$P_A = (100 \times 10^{-3})^2 \times 103 = 1.03$ W
$Z_B = 73 + (40 - j30) \times (-j100/100) = 43 - j40$ Ω
$P_B = (100 \times 10^{-3})^2 \times 43 = 0.43$ W
The total radiated power is

$$P_A + P_B = 1.46 \text{ W } (Ans.)$$

(b) In the end-fire direction the electric field strength is $2E$, where E is the field strength produced by either dipole. If the total power had been supplied to one dipole only its current would have been $\sqrt{(1.46/73)} = 141.4$ mA, giving a field strength of $(141.4/100) \times E$. Therefore, the gain of the aerial, relative to a $\lambda/2$ dipole, is

$$G = 20 \log_{10}[(2E \times 100)/(141.4E)] = 3.02 \text{ dB}$$

Therefore,

$$\text{gain} = 3.02 + 2.16 = 5.18 \text{ dBi } (Ans.)$$

EXAMPLE 8.10

Determine the gain, relative to a $\lambda/2$ dipole, of a four-dipole broadside array that uses a dipole spacing of $\lambda/4$. The mutual impedances between the dipoles are $Z_{AB} = Z_{BC} = Z_{CD} = -12 + j30$ Ω, $Z_{AC} = Z_{BD} = 4 + j20$ Ω and $Z_{AD} = -2 - j12$ Ω. Each dipole has a radiation resistance of 73 Ω.

Solution

The aerial currents are of equal amplitude and phase. Hence,

$$Z_A = 73 + (-12 + j30) + (4 + j20) + (-2 - j12)$$

The real part of Z_A is

$$73 - 12 + 4 - 2 = 63 \text{ } \Omega$$

and so the radiated power is $P_A = 63I^2$ W. Also,

$$Z_B = 73 + (-12 + j30) + (-12 + j30) + (4 + j20)$$

giving a real part of 53 Ω. The power radiated by dipole B is $P_B = 53I^2$ W.

$$Z_C = 73 + (4 + j20) + (-12 + j30) + (-12 + j30)$$

and the radiated power is $P_C = 53I^2$ W. Lastly,

$$Z_D = Z_A = 63 + j38 \ \Omega$$

and hence the radiated power $P_D = 63I^2$ W. The total radiated power P_T is

$$P_T = P_A + P_B + P_C + P_D = 232I^2 \ \text{W}$$

If this power were radiated by one dipole only, its current would have to be $\sqrt{[(232I^2)/73]} = 1.783I$. Therefore,

$$\text{gain} = 20 \ \log_{10}[4/1.783] = 7.02 \ \text{dB} \ (Ans.)$$

If the mutual impedances had been ignored the gain of the array would have been

$$20 \ \log_{10} \sqrt{4} = 6.02 \ \text{dB}$$

It should be noted that when the dipoles are supplied with in-phase currents the power radiated by each dipole can be obtained by taking only the resistive part of each mutual impedance.

The rhombic aerial

A long-wire radiator (p. 199) produces a radiation pattern that has one main lobe and a number of small sidelobes. The main lobe is at an angle θ to the wire axis and is a function of the electrical length of the wire. The rhombic aerial uses four long-wire radiators to form, in the horizontal plane, a rhombus shape as shown by Fig. 8.22. The *tilt angle* β is chosen to ensure that (a) the lobes marked as X point in opposite directions so that their radiated energies cancel out, and (b) the lobes marked as Y point

Fig. 8.22 *Rhombic aerial*

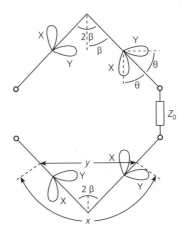

in the same direction so that their radiations are additive. For this to occur two things are necessary:

1   The distance x from the mid-point of one wire to the mid-point of the next must be $\lambda/2$ longer than the direct distance y between these two points.
2   The tilt angle β should be equal to $90° - \theta$. Since the lobe angle varies with frequency the choice of the tilt angle must be a compromise and it is generally calculated at the geometric mean of the two extreme operating frequencies.

The gain of a rhombic aerial is a function of the length of each wire, the tilt angle and the angle of elevation. The higher the gain that is required, the smaller must be the angle of elevation, but, fortunately, this is a favourable situation for long-distance routes. Typically, a rhombic aerial will operate over a 2:1 frequency ratio, e.g. 7–14 MHz, with a gain that varies from about 3 dB to about 15 dB. Since the HF band covers a frequency ratio of about 4:1, three, or four, rhombic aerials would be needed to give complete coverage of the band. Although the rhombic aerial was very widely employed in the past it has now been superseded for most applications by the log-periodic aerial. The log-periodic HF aerial can provide a wider bandwidth than can the rhombic aerial and it is physically smaller.

The log-periodic aerial

The log-periodic aerial (LPA) is a type of aerial whose radiation pattern and gain change vary little over a wide frequency band. The bandwidth of the aerial is restricted only by the physical size of the elements at the low-frequency end of the aerial, and by the accuracy of the construction at the upper frequency end. Several different forms of LPA exist and one of the most common consists of the tapered dipole array that is shown by Fig. 8.23. Moving along the aerial from the feed point, both the length of each dipole and the spacing between adjacent dipoles increase by a constant ratio. This ratio τ is known as the *scale factor* of the aerial:

$$\tau = l_2/l_1 = l_3/l_2 = \ldots = l_n/l_{n-1} \tag{8.15}$$

This means, of course, that $l_2 = l_1\tau$, $l_3 = l_2\tau = l_1\tau^2$, and so on up to $l_n = l_1\tau^{n-1}$. The aerial is fed, not at the origin, but at a point distance $d_1 = d_2/\tau$ to the left of the first dipole. The distance d_0 from the origin to the first dipole is then equal to $d_1/(1 - 1/\tau)$. The *characteristic angle* α is, from Fig. 8.24, obtained from

$$\tan \alpha = l_1/d_0 = l_2/(d_0 + d_1), \text{ etc.} \tag{8.16}$$

The *space factor* σ is the name given to $\tan \alpha$.

At any frequency within the operating bandwidth of the aerial only three, or perhaps four, of the dipoles are at, or near, the resonant length of $\lambda/2$. Only these dipoles will radiate appreciable power and they are said to be in the *active region*. The active region forms a radiation centre whose dimensions, in wavelengths, are both constant and independent of frequency. All other dipoles, which are either much longer or much shorter than $\lambda/2$, will radiate little, if any, energy.

As the frequency of the current supplied to the LPA is varied the position of the active region will move back and forth along the array. The result is that both the gain

Fig. 8.23 *Log-periodic aerial*

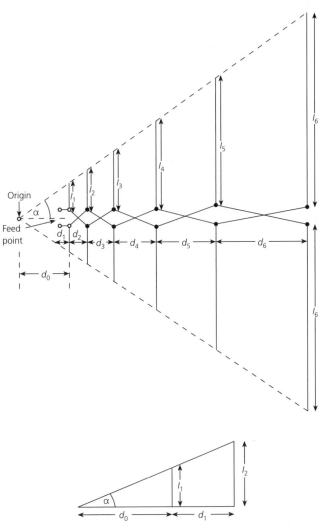

Fig. 8.24

and the radiation pattern of the LPA remain approximately constant with frequency. The highest, and the lowest, operating frequencies coincide with those wavelengths which make the shortest, and the longest, dipoles $\lambda/2$ in length. The difference in length may easily be as much as 10:1 and the length ratio gives the corresponding aerial bandwidth. Thus the maximum frequency is $f_{max} = c/\lambda_{min} = c/4l_1$, and the minimum frequency is $f_{min} = c/\lambda_{max} = c/4l_n$. The practical bandwidth obtained is somewhat less than $f_{max} - f_{min}$ because otherwise the active region would sometimes move right off the array.

The dipoles in an LPA are always transposed along the line of the array and the dipole currents are fed in at the smaller-dimensioned dipole end of the array to ensure an end-fire radiation pattern in the direction of the origin. Figure 8.25 shows typical radiation patterns for both the horizontal and the vertical planes at two different

Fig. 8.25 *Radiation patterns of a log-periodic aerial, (a) horizontal plane and (b) vertical plane*

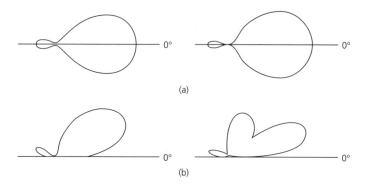

(a)

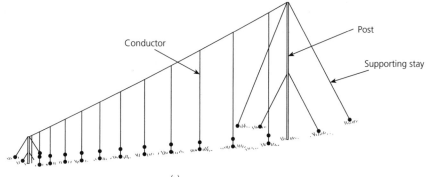

(b)

Fig. 8.26 *(a) Vertically-polarized LPA, (b) horizontally-polarized LPA*

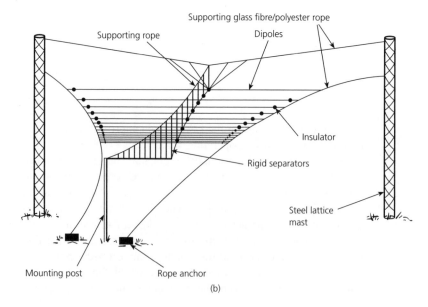

Table 8.5 LPA data

Bandwidth (MHz)	4 to 28	
Number of dipoles	17	46
α	18°	10°
τ	0.85	0.95
Angle of elevation	25°	25°
Beamwidth: vertical	45°	25°
horizontal	60°	150°
Gain (dBi)	12	15

frequencies. The radiation pattern has a wide main lobe and is clearly not very directive (less so than a rhombic aerial), but it does have small sidelobes.

A horizontally polarised LPA may be used in various configurations, either supported from a tower or suspended from masts. Figure 8.26 shows two practical HF log-periodic aerials; the vertically polarized version in (a) has a very low angle of elevation and this makes it suitable only for long-distance radio links. The aerial gain is reduced because the ground in the vicinity of the aerial is not of zero resistance. Because of their larger gain most HF LPAs are horizontally polarised. The aerial cannot be mounted at a fixed physical height above the ground because its electrical height would then vary with frequency. This is why horizontally polarised LPAs are constructed so that they slope relative to the ground to ensure that each dipole is at the same electrical height above earth. Figure 8.26(b) shows a typical example. Typically, an HF LPA can operate over most of the HF band with a gain of between 10 and 15 dBi, depending on the number of dipoles. Table 8.5 gives two sets of typical data for LPAs.

Log-periodic aerials are widely employed for various services in the HF band. They are particularly useful when a wide horizontal plane beamwidth is wanted, when a high elevation angle is needed, or when site area is a problem. An increased gain can be obtained if two LPAs are used in a broadside array. If a number of areas at different azimuth angles are to be served a rotatable LPA is often used. The log-periodic aerial is also often used in both the VHF and the UHF bands and Fig. 8.27 shows a typical example of this type.

The Yagi aerial

The equatorial and meridian plane radiation patterns of a $\lambda/2$ dipole, shown in Figs 7.15(a) and (b), are not directive enough for many applications. An increase in both the gain and the directivity can be obtained by the addition of one, or more, *parasitic elements*. A parasitic element is one that is not directly supplied with an exciting current and that is coupled by mutual impedance to the driven $\lambda/2$ dipole. If the parasitic element is longer than $\lambda/2$ and is mounted behind the dipole, relative to the required direction of maximum radiation, it is known as a *reflector*. Conversely, if the parasitic element is shorter than $\lambda/2$ and is mounted in front of the dipole, it is known as a *director*. A Yagi aerial consists of a $\lambda/2$ dipole, a reflector, and one, or more, directors.

Fig. 8.27 *VHF/UHF log-periodic aerial*

Fig. 8.28 *(a) Dipole with reflector, (b) dipole with one director*

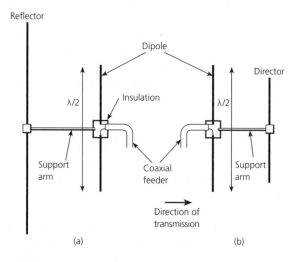

Figures 8.28(a) and (b) show, respectively, a λ/2 dipole with one reflector, or with one director. A parasitic element can be directly fixed onto a common metal support since its mid-point is a voltage node.

The spacing between the λ/2 dipole and each of the parasitic elements is small enough for mutual impedances to exist between them. When a current is supplied to the dipole and causes it to radiate energy an e.m.f. will be induced into each parasitic element. This e.m.f. will make a current flow in the element so that the parasitic element accepts power from the dipole and then reradiates it. The phase relationships between the energy radiated by the λ/2 dipole and the energy radiated by each parasitic element depend upon both the element spacing and the phase of the current in each element. In turn, the phase of the current in an element is determined by the electrical length of that element. The element spacings and lengths are chosen to give the maximum radiation in the wanted direction and minimum radiation in all other directions.

Fig. 8.29 *Reactance-electrical length curves for a dipole*

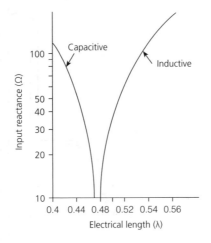

A director increases the radiated field on its side of the dipole while a reflector concentrates the radiated field in the opposite side of the dipole. Since a reflector is longer than $\lambda/2$ in length it has an inductive input reactance, while, conversely, a director has an input capacitive reactance. Values of reactance for different lengths of element are shown by Fig. 8.29: note that when the length is $\lambda/2$ the input reactance of the dipole is $+\text{j}43\ \Omega$.

Consider a $\lambda/2$ dipole with a reflector. Zero voltage is applied to the reflector and hence equation (8.13) becomes

$$V_D = I_D Z_{DD} + I_R Z_{DR} \tag{8.17}$$

$$0 = I_D Z_{DR} + I_R Z_{RR} \tag{8.18}$$

From equation (8.18), $I_R = -I_D Z_{DR}/Z_{RR}$, and hence

$$V_D = I_D[Z_{DD} - Z_{DR}^2/Z_{RR}]$$

or

$$Z_D = V_D/I_D = Z_{DD} - Z_{DR}^2/Z_{RR} \tag{8.19}$$

If typical values for Z_{DD}, Z_{RR} and Z_{DR} are inserted into equation (8.19) it will be found that the input impedance of the dipole has been considerably reduced. This reduction, which is accentuated if one or more directors are added, may lead to difficulties in matching the aerial to the coaxial feeder. To overcome this difficulty a *folded dipole* is often used since it has an impedance of about 300 Ω. Figure 8.30 shows a folded dipole. A stack of folded dipoles is often used as the aerial for the base stations in a mobile radio system.

Fig. 8.30 *Folded dipole*

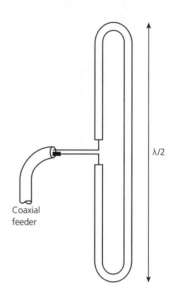

Coaxial
feeder

λ/2

EXAMPLE 8.11

An aerial consists of a λ/2 dipole of $73 + j0$ Ω impedance and a parasitic element whose impedance is $73 + j68$ Ω. If the mutual impedance between the dipole and the parasitic element is $65 + j0$ Ω, calculate (a) the input impedance and (b) the front-to-back ratio of the aerial. The dipole–reflector spacing is 0.13λ.

Solution

(a) From equation (8.19)

$$Z_D = 73 - 65^2/(73 + j68) = 42 + j29 \text{ Ω } (Ans.)$$

(b) $I_R = -I_D Z_{DR}/Z_{RR}$, and therefore

$$I_R/I_D = -65/(73 + j68) = 0.65\angle 137°$$

In the direction from the reflector to the dipole there is a phase difference of $137° - 360° \times 0.13 = 90°$ and hence the field strength is proportional to $\sqrt{(1^2 + 0.65^2)} = 1.194$. In the opposite direction, i.e. from the dipole to the reflector, the phase difference is $137° + 360° \times 0.13 = 180°$. Hence, the field strength in this direction is proportional to $1 - 0.65 = 0.35$. Therefore,

front-to-back ratio $= 20 \log_{10}[1.194/0.35] = 10.66$ dB (*Ans.*)

The addition of more directors will increase the gain of the Yagi aerial, and Fig. 8.31 shows the relationship between the number of directors and the gain. The element spacing is most critical for the dipole and the reflector, and for the dipole and the first director; the former should normally be somewhere in the range 0.17λ to 0.2λ.

Fig. 8.31 *Gain of a Yagi aerial plotted against number of directors*

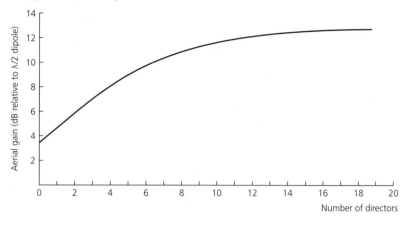

The director spacings are usually chosen to be in the range 0.15λ to 0.4λ; however, a large number of other combinations of lengths/spacings are equally likely to be used.

The notch aerial

The *notch aerial* is often employed for HF, and less often VHF, communications with aircraft. If a metal rod is positioned in an electromagnetic field so that it lies in the same direction as the electric field it will have an e.m.f. induced into it. This e.m.f. will give rise to a current in the rod whose magnitude and phase are determined by the electrical length of the rod. If the diameter of the rod is much smaller than the wavelength of the signal the current will fall to zero at each end of the rod and will have a uniform distribution around the circumference of the rod. With increase in frequency the rod diameter becomes a noticeable fraction of the signal wavelength and this has two effects: (a) the rod current no longer falls to zero at each end of the rod, and (b) the current distribution across the rod cross-section is no longer uniform.

If a short cut, or *notch*, is made in one edge of a relatively large metal sheet RF energy can be taken from an incident electromagnetic field. The basic notch aerial is shown by Fig. 8.32. The notch has a length h and a width w and a radiation resistance

Fig. 8.32 *Basic notch aerial*

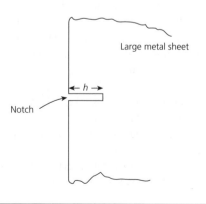

Fig. 8.33 *Notch aerial with coaxial cable feeder (a) principle and (b) basic construction*

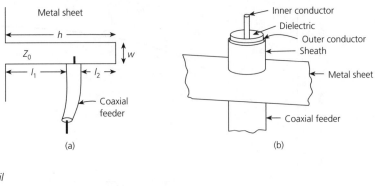

(a)   (b)

Fig. 8.34 *Aerofoil*

Fig. 8.35 *Two practical notch aerials*

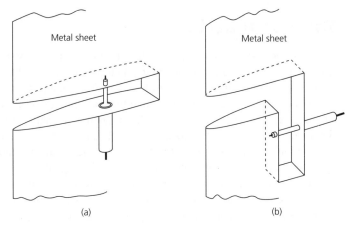

(a)   (b)

somewhere in the region of 300 to 10 000 Ω, the actual value depending upon the ratio h/λ. For example, when $h/\lambda \approx 1/4$, $R_r \approx 400\ \Omega$. The impedance of the notch varies along its length and this means that the notch aerial can be matched to a 50 Ω coaxial feeder by connecting the feeder at the point where the conductance is 0.02 S. Figure 8.33(a) shows a notch aerial and its coaxial feeder. The feeder is connected to a point l_1 from the mouth of the notch and distance l_2 from the notch end. Clearly, $l_1 + l_2 = h$. Figure 8.33(b) shows the coaxial feeder-to-notch connection in more detail.

A notch does not have to be cut in a flat sheet of metal; in an aircraft the metal screen is usually an aerofoil like Fig. 8.34 and its varying dimensions result in the impedance of the notch varying along its length. The varying impedance makes it easier to match a coaxial feeder to the aerial. Two practical examples of notch aerials are shown in Figs 8.35(a) and (b).

The radiation pattern of a notch aerial is the same as that of a loop aerial that has the same perimeter and hence a small notch has a very nearly circular radiation pattern. A notch aerial cut in the leading edge of an aircraft wing has a similar radiation pattern to a long wire radiator. It can be modified to give a dipole-like pattern if required, by using a parasitic notch which acts rather like a parasitic element in a Yagi aerial.

The slot aerial

Figure 8.36 shows a narrow slot cut in a relatively large sheet of metal that has a co-axial feeder connected across its narrow dimension. If an RF signal is applied to the coaxial feeder the slot will act as an aerial. The voltage in the slot has its maximum value in the middle and is zero at each end. The *slot aerial* will not radiate at all in the plane of the metal sheet, but in the equatorial plane the radiated electric field has very nearly the same radiation pattern as the $\lambda/2$ dipole that would just fit into the slot, but with the electric and magnetic fields interchanged. The input impedance of the slot aerial is $Z_S = (60\pi)^2/Z_D$, where Z_D is the impedance of the $\lambda/2$ dipole. Hence $Z_S = (60\pi)^2/73.14 \approx 486\ \Omega$.

If one side of the slot is enclosed in a conducting box that forms a cavity behind the slot, then the radiation from the other side of the slot is increased twofold. The input impedance of a cavity-backed slot is high and this provides problems in matching to a coaxial feeder. The impedance can be reduced if the slot is folded as shown by Fig. 8.37. If the two sides of the slot are of equal dimension the impedance step-down is 1:4, but it is possible to obtain other step-down ratios by using different width sides to the folded slot.

A slotted cylinder aerial is shown by Fig. 8.38(a). When the diameter of the cylinder is about 0.1λ the radiation pattern in the horizontal plane is more or less circular and the pattern changes only slightly with increase in the cylinder diameter. To obtain better directivity a dipole can be used in conjunction with the slot as shown by Fig. 8.38(b). The dipole should be mounted approximately 30° from the slot as shown by Fig. 8.38(c).

An increase in gain can be obtained by the use of an array of slots, as in Fig. 8.39. The slots are positioned λ apart and are typically about $3\lambda/4$ in length and 0.04λ wide. The gain of the slotted array, relative to a $\lambda/2$ dipole, is equal to the number of slots.

Fig. 8.36 *Slot aerial*

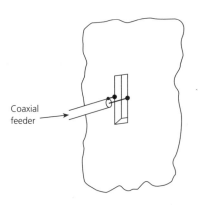

Coaxial feeder

Fig. 8.37 *Folded slot aerial*

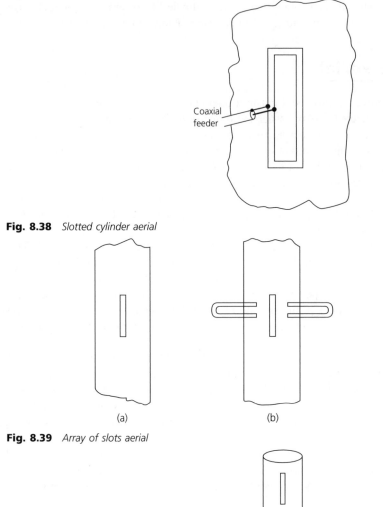

Fig. 8.38 *Slotted cylinder aerial*

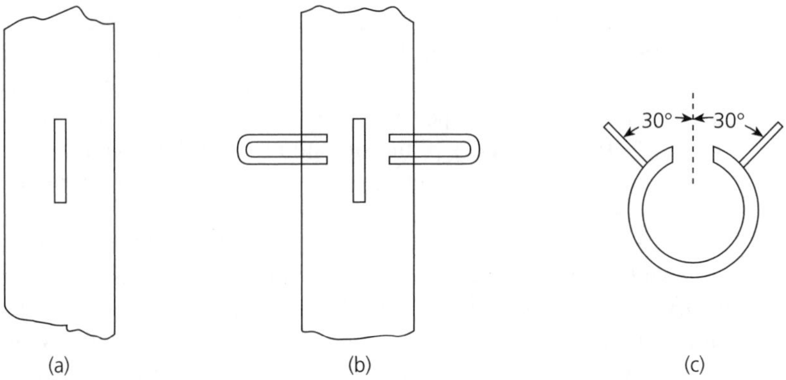

(a)   (b)   (c)

Fig. 8.39 *Array of slots aerial*

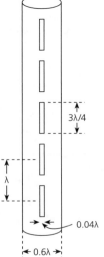

Fig. 8.40 *Alternative form of slot aerial*

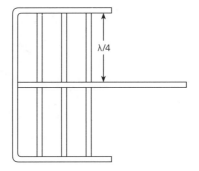

Some VHF slot aerials are constructed in a different way: the slot aerial shown by Fig. 8.40 consists of three λ/2 dipoles connected in parallel with one another and with their ends linked by a conductor. Four aerials of this type can be mounted around a mast to produce an omni-directional radiation pattern.

The whip or rod aerial

The aerial used with a mobile radio receiver, be it a mobile telephone or an in-car transceiver, should have an omni-directional radiation pattern in the horizontal plane. The simplest aerial with such a radiation pattern is the whip or rod aerial. This is a VHF/UHF monopole aerial that is mounted on a conducting plane (p. 191). The aerial may merely consist of a single straight wire that protrudes from a printed circuit board (PCB) or may be a metal trace built into the PCB, but more often it is a metal rod that protrudes from the earth plane. The earth plane may be the case of the mobile telephone or the roof, or other part of the body, of a motor vehicle.

The helical aerial

The helical aerial has more compact dimensions than the rod aerial and is often used instead of a rod as the aerial for a mobile receiver. A helical aerial consists of a copper-wire helix that is fed at one end by a coaxial cable, as in Fig. 8.41(a). The inner conductor of the coaxial cable is connected to the helix and the outer conductor is connected to an earth plane which is either solid metal or a metal mesh.

Fig. 8.41 *(a) Helical aerial, (b) relationship between pitch, turn length and helix circumference*

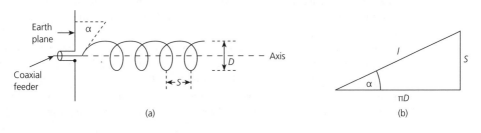

Fig. 8.42 *Operation of a helical aerial*

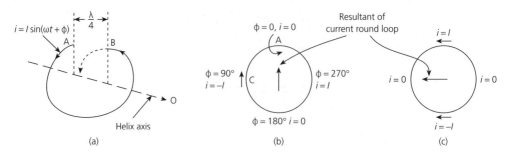

(a) (b) (c)

Fig. 8.43 *Radiation patterns for helical aerial (a) axial mode, (b) normal mode*

(a) (b)

Figure 8.42(a) shows a wire helix having a pitch S of $\lambda/4$ and a turn length l of $5\lambda/4$. Figure 8.42(b) shows a single turn in the helix that is carrying a sinusoidal current $i = I \sin \omega t$ A. The current enters the turn at point A and leaves at point B after travelling a distance of $5\lambda/4$; hence the current at B lags the current at A by $5\pi/2$ radians. The direct wave travelling from A to B in the direction of the helix to O is delayed by $\pi/2$ radians because the direct distance A to B is $\lambda/4$. The phase difference between the two waves is 2π rad and so they appear to be in phase to a distant observer at point O. Similarly, the waves from each turn of the helix all add in phase but this is not the case off the O axis where the total signal is weaker.

To an observer at O the helix looks like a single loop of wire with a circumference of λ as shown by Fig. 8.42(b). At time $t = 0$ the current at point A is $i = I \sin 0 = O$. At point C, the phase ϕ is delayed by $\pi/2$ rad so that the current is $i = I \sin(-\pi/2) = -I$, and so on around the loop. The resultant current is as shown. At the instant when $\omega t = \pi/2$ rad the resultant current has rotated by $\pi/2$ rad as shown by Fig. 8.42(c). The resultant current phasor rotates once for each cycle of the feed current and this means that the helix radiates a circularly polarised wave. The radiation pattern of the aerial when in its axial mode has a bandwidth that is typically ±20% of centre frequency and a beamwidth in the region of 90°.

Small helical aerials operate in the *normal mode* and large helical aerials operate in the *axial mode*; normal refers to the direction of the radiation pattern being perpendicular to the axis of the aerial, and axial has a radiation pattern that points along the axis of the helix. The radiation patterns for the two modes are given in Fig. 8.43; the polarisation is circular for the axial mode and elliptical for the normal mode.

The length L of the axis is equal to the product of the number of turns N and the pitch S; α is the pitch angle and D the diameter of the helix. Each turn is of length l and when one turn is unrolled on a flat surface the triangle in Fig. 8.41(b) shows the relationship between l, S and D. From the triangle,

$$l = \pi D/\cos \alpha \qquad S = l \sin \alpha = (\pi D \sin \alpha)/\cos \alpha$$

and hence

$$S/\lambda = (\pi D \tan \alpha)/\lambda \qquad\qquad (8.20)$$

For operation in the axial mode, which is usual for all except the small aerials used with hand-held equipment like mobile telephones, $0.75 < \pi D/\lambda < 1.33$. In practice, usually $\pi D/\lambda \approx 1$ when $S/\lambda = \tan \alpha$.

EXAMPLE 8.12

A helical aerial with six turns in a 0.1 m long helix of diameter 10 cm operates at 2 GHz. Calculate (a) the turn spacing and (b) the pitch angle.

Solution

(a) $S = L/N = 0.1/6 = 0.167$ m (*Ans.*)
(b) $\alpha = \tan^{-1}(0.167/0.1\pi) = 28°$ (*Ans.*)

The loop aerial

A loop aerial is merely a length of conductor that has been bent into an almost closed contour with its input terminals at the gap in the conductor. Provided the area of the loop is small, a maximum of about $0.01\lambda^2$, the shape of the loop is unimportant. This allows the aerial to be formed from a length of PCB track and the loop aerial is therefore often used in mobile telephones. Figure 8.44 shows a typical PCB loop aerial. The loop area is made as large as possible and then the aerial is tuned to resonance at the required operating frequency by a capacitor. Larger loop aerials may have either a square or a circular cross-section and may have a ferrite core to improve reception of radio waves.

Fig. 8.44 *PCB loop aerial*

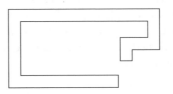

Fig. 8.45 *Principle of a parabolic dish aerial*

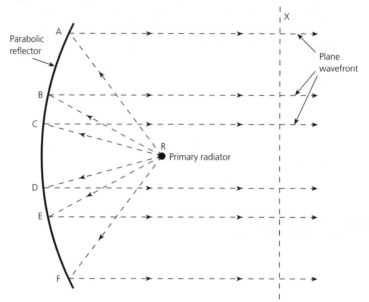

The parabolic dish aerial

For point-to-point radio links in the upper part of the UHF band and in the SHF band the main requirement is for high directivity and gain, and usually the *parabolic dish* aerial is employed. The parabolic dish aerial is essentially a large metal dish that is illuminated by an RF source with a spherical wavefront, and which converts the incident radiation into a narrow-beam radio wave with a plane wavefront. It is necessary to control the amplitude of the dish illumination from its centre to its edge both to maximise the aerial gain and to minimise losses. The *illumination efficiency* η is 100 times the ratio of the on-axis directivity for a given illumination to the directivity produced by a uniform illumination with the same total radiated power. This means that a uniformly illuminated dish has an illumination efficiency of 100%.

The basic concept of a dish aerial is illustrated by Fig. 8.45. The focal point of the dish is the point at which incident parallel waves that have been reflected by the dish converge. The feed point is placed at the focal point of the dish; energy is radiated from the feed point with a spherical wavefront and is directed onto the dish. The geometry of the dish is such that the distance from the focal point to the dish and then to an arbitrary plane X on the other side of the focal point is a constant, *regardless* of which point on the surface of the dish is considered. Thus, the distance RAX = distance RBX = RCX = RDX = RFX. This ensures that the spherical wavefront produced by the feed is converted into a plane wavefront at the plane X. The reflected waves are all in parallel with one another and form a highly directive radio wave.

The effective aperture A_e of the dish is, for an illumination efficiency of 100%, equal to the geometric aperture, i.e.

$$A_e = \pi(D/2)^2 \qquad (8.21)$$

where D is the diameter of the dish. The gain G of the aerial, with respect to an isotropic radiator, is, from equation (8.21),

$$G = [\pi(D/2)^2]/(\lambda^2/4\pi)$$
$$= \pi^2 D^2/\lambda^2 \qquad (8.22)$$

or, relative to a $\lambda/2$ dipole,

$$G = [\pi(D/2)^2]/(0.13\lambda^2)$$
$$= 6(D/\lambda)^2 \qquad (8.23)$$

The sidelobes in the radiation pattern are mainly caused by the position of the primary radiator and its supports blocking some of the radiated signal energy. The effective gain of the aerial is reduced by the illumination efficiency which is typically about 50%. Then the effective gain of a parabolic dish aerial relative to an isotropic radiator is

$$G \approx 0.5\pi^2 D^2/\lambda^2$$
$$= 0.5\pi^2 D^2 (f \times 10^9)^2/(3 \times 10^8)^2$$
$$\approx 55 f^2 D^2 \qquad (8.24)$$

where f is in GHz.

Clearly, for a dish aerial to have a high gain its diameter must be several times greater than the signal wavelength. This is the reason why the dish aerial is only employed in the UHF and SHF bands. The radiation pattern of a dish aerial is highly directive with a very narrow main lobe in the direction of the dish axis. Consequently, the usual way of drawing the radiation pattern gives insufficient detail. Normally, therefore, the radiation pattern is drawn using Cartesian co-ordinates in the manner shown by Fig. 8.46.

The beamwidth of a dish aerial is approximately given by

$$\text{beamwidth} = (70\lambda/D)^\circ \qquad (8.25)$$

where D and λ are both in metres.

Fig. 8.46 *Radiation pattern of a parabolic dish aerial*

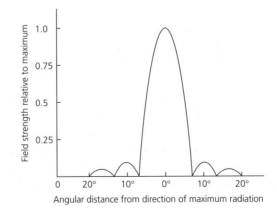

Fig. 8.47 *Side lobe specification for an earth station aerial*

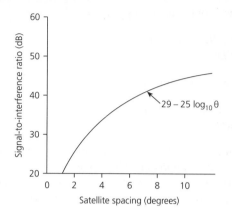

Sidelobes

The radiated power contained in the sidelobes of the aerial's radiation pattern is power that is radiated in unwanted directions where it may well interfere with other systems. The net efficiency of a dish aerial can be increased if the total energy in the sidelobes is minimised. For the ground aerial of a communications satellite system the sidelobe performance, in the direction of the geometric arc, is specified by such bodies as the ITU-R, INTELSAT and EUTELSAT: 90%, or more of the sidelobes are required to lie under the envelope defined by $29 - 25 \log_{10} \theta$, where θ is the sidelobe angle in degrees. This relationship gives the signal-to-noise ratio in decibels for various satellite spacings shown by the graph of Fig. 8.47. The design of a ground-station aerial must reduce the sidelobe level to the defined figure.

There are a number of sources of sidelobe energy produced by a dish aerial. These are:

- *Feed spillover* due to direct radiation from the feed, and/or (for a Cassegrain or Gregorian aerial) direct radiation from the sub-reflector, spilling past the edge of the main reflector.
- *Blockage* in which the feed point, or the sub-reflector, blocks some of the energy reflected by the main reflector, thus producing a hole in the energy distribution of the aerial's aperture.
- *Reflector illumination*, where, if the main dish is uniformly illuminated, relatively large sidelobes are produced, particularly up to about 10° from the aerial's axis.

The sidelobe amplitude can be considerably reduced by tapering the amplitude distribution across the dish. If the amplitude distribution is varied from a maximum at the centre to zero at the edge of the dish the sidelobe level will be reduced. This reduction will, however, be paid for by a reduction in the illumination efficiency. The inverse distribution, i.e. varying illumination from a maximum at the edge of the dish to zero at the centre, is not employed since it both reduces the gain and increases the sidelobe level.

EXAMPLE 8.13

Calculate the gain in dBi of a dish aerial 5 m in diameter at (a) 4 GHz and (b) 10 GHz if the illumination efficiency is 60%. (c) The gain of an INTELSAT standard dish aerial is 60 dBi; calculate its diameter at 11 GHz if the illumination efficiency is 60%.

Solution

(a) $\lambda = 0.075$ m. Gain $= 10 \log_{10}[0.6(5\pi/0.075)^2] = 44.2$ dBi (*Ans.*)
(b) $\lambda = 0.03$ m. Gain $= 10 \log_{10}[0.6(5\pi/0.03)^2] = 52.2$ dBi (*Ans.*)
(c) $\lambda = 0.027$ m

$$60 \text{ dBi} = 10^6 = 0.6(\pi D/0.027)^2$$

or

$$D = \sqrt{123} \approx 11.1 \text{ m } (Ans.)$$

Feed arrangements

The feed point, or *primary radiator*, of a parabolic dish aerial is required to radiate RF energy towards the dish; ideally it ought to radiate all its energy towards the dish and not produce a *shadow*. Practical feeds, however, always obscure the wave reflected from the dish to some extent. The simplest form of primary feed is a $\lambda/2$ dipole with a reflector fed by a coaxial cable, or mounted at the end of a length of waveguide, to ensure that the radiation is directed onto the dish. At frequencies greater than a few gigahertz a waveguide feeder will be employed. Figure 8.48 shows a waveguide-fed $\lambda/2$ dipole feed radiator. The end of the waveguide is tapered to match the waveguide impedance to the impedance of the $\lambda/2$ dipole. The dipole is mounted on a conducting plate that is fixed at the centres of the two narrow sides of the waveguide to bisect the narrow wall dimension. Because the plate is perpendicular to the electric field it has little effect on the radiation. The electric field parallel to the narrow side is divided into

Fig. 8.48 *Waveguide feed for a dish aerial*

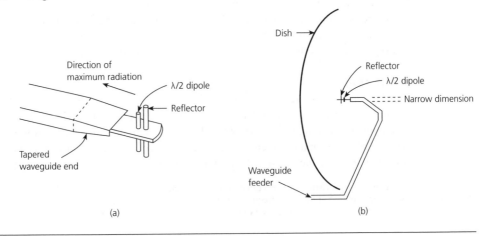

(a)

(b)

Fig. 8.49 *Dish aerials: (a) front feed, (b) Cassegrain, (c) Gregorian, and (d) offset*

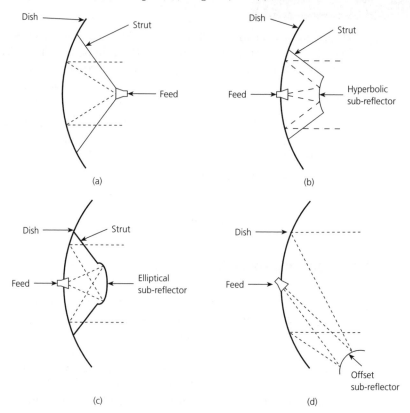

two equal parts by the conducting plate and these parts energise the two halves of the dipole in anti-phase. The reflector is provided to ensure that the maximum radiation from the dipole is directed towards the dish.

At higher frequencies it is usual to employ some kind of waveguide primary radiator and one example of this is the horn radiator. The horn radiator is just a length of waveguide whose open end is flared out into a horn shape.

There are four main ways in which the main reflecting dish can be illuminated by the feed: these are known, respectively, as *front feed* (or *focus*), *Cassegrain*, *Gregorian* and *offset feed*. The basic arrangement of each of these methods is shown in Fig. 8.49.

Front feed

Front feeding a dish aerial, shown by Fig. 8.49(a), is the simplest method of illuminating the main reflector. To reduce the sidelobes to an acceptable level the illumination efficiency is only about 55 to 60%. The feed and its supporting structure produce aperture blockage and this increases the sidelobe level. There may also be some reradiation from the struts, which will degrade the *cross-polarisation*[†] of the aerial. A horn front

---

[†] Communications satellite systems often employ identical frequency bands to carry different signals. Two signals are transmitted at the same frequency but one is horizontally polarised and the other is vertically polarised. The cross-polarisation isolation is a measure of the degree of crosstalk immunity between the two signals.

feed can give a good gain and an acceptable noise temperature and is often used with small aerials.

Cassegrain

The Cassegrain method of feeding a dish aerial, shown in Fig. 8.49(b), uses a sub-reflector to reflect the energy radiated by the primary feed onto the main reflector. The system has the advantages over the front-feed method in that the feed system is simpler and a shorter length of waveguide feeder is necessary. Although aperture blockage and strut reradiation are still a problem the Cassegrain aerial is commonly employed.

Gregorian

The Gregorian aerial, Fig. 8.49(c), is a variant of the Cassegrain aerial in which an elliptical sub-reflector is employed. This gives an increased illumination efficiency of about 76% and also improved cross-polarisation isolation.

Offset feed

Blockage of the transmitted beam may be avoided if the feed, or the sub-reflector, is mounted outside the area occupied by the main beam. Figure 8.49(d) shows an offset Cassegrain dish aerial. A front-feed, or a Gregorian, aerial can be similarly offset. The feed and the sub-reflector are mounted at the appropriate angles to the aerial axis to ensure that the main beam is directed along the axis. The overall size of the offset aerial is smaller, for a given gain at a given frequency, and the sidelobes are smaller, but depolarisation effects are increased.

EXERCISES

8.1 Two vertical $\lambda/2$ dipoles are in the same horizontal plane and spaced $\lambda/4$ apart. The dipoles are supplied with currents of $I\angle 0°$ and $I\angle 90°$ respectively. Calculate and plot the horizontal plane radiation pattern of the array.

8.2 An aerial array consists of four vertical $\lambda/2$ dipoles in the same horizontal plane spaced $\lambda/2$ apart. The currents fed to the aerials are of the same magnitude but have a progressive phase difference of 90°. Derive the expression for the horizontal plane radiation pattern of the array and show that maximum field strength occurs at 120° to the line of the array.

8.3 A Yagi aerial consists of a dipole of $73 + j0\ \Omega$ impedance and a parasitic element of $81 + j108\ \Omega$ impedance. The mutual impedance between the two elements is $40 - j30\ \Omega$. Calculate the ratio of the powers radiated in the directions dipole to parasitic and parasitic to dipole. Hence state whether the parasitic element is a reflector or a director. (Element spacing $= 0.25\lambda$.)

8.4 An aerial array consists of three $\lambda/2$ dipoles A, B and C that are fed with equal-amplitude, in-phase currents. Each dipole has a radiation resistance of $73\ \Omega$ and their mutual impedances are $Z_{AB} = Z_{BC} = -12.5 - j30\ \Omega$, $Z_{AC} = 5 + j17.5\ \Omega$. Calculate the gain of the array.

8.5 Draw the radiation pattern of an HF log-periodic aerial for both the horizontal and vertical planes. Why is the LPA generally preferred for long-distance radio HF systems? Draw a sketch of an LPA suitable for use at about 5 to 20 MHz. What is the effect on the main lobe of the radiation pattern of changing frequency?

8.6 Calculate the necessary aperture for a parabolic dish aerial to have a gain of 60 dBi at 5 GHz if the illumination efficiency is 60%.

What are the effects on the gain, the beamwidth and the sidelobe level of this aerial if the amplitude distribution across the dish aperture varies (a) uniformly, (b) from maximum at the edge to zero at the centre, or (c) from zero at the edge to maximum at the centre?

8.7 What is meant by the principle of pattern multiplication? An aerial array consists of 15 vertical $\lambda/2$ dipoles arranged in three rows of five dipoles. Derive an expression for the horizontal plane radiation pattern.

8.8 What is meant by the gain of a transmitting aerial? An aerial is operated at 11 GHz; calculate its effective aperture if its gain is 56 dBi. Explain what is meant by the term 'beamwidth' and calculate its value for this aerial. Why are sidelobes undesirable in (a) a transmitting aerial and (b) a receiving aerial?

8.9 Three vertical $\lambda/2$ dipoles are mounted 3λ apart in the same horizontal line and are fed with currents of $I_A = 0.251 \sin(\omega t - 90°)$, $I_B = I \sin \omega t$ and $I_C = 0.251 \sin(\omega t + 90°)$. Derive an expression for the field strength produced at a distant point.

8.10 A $\lambda/2$ dipole has an input impedance of $73.2 + j42.5\ \Omega$. Calculate the impedance of the equivalent slot aerial.

8.11 (a) Explain what is meant by saying that the gain of a $\lambda/2$ dipole is 2.16 dBi.
(b) An aerial has a gain of 30 dB relative to a $\lambda/2$ dipole and radiates a power of 1.8 W. Calculate the power density at a distance of 10 km in the direction of maximum radiation.
(c) The aerial in (b) has a beamwidth of 2.7°; find the power density produced at an angle of 1.35° to the direction of maximum radiation.

8.12 A dish aerial has a gain of 39 dB and a beamwidth of 3.75° at 6 GHz. Calculate the gain and beamwidth at 4.5 GHz.

8.13 Calculate the aperture required for a parabolic dish aerial to have a gain of 2500 at 5.2 GHz if the illumination efficiency is 70%.

8.14 (a) List the factors that reduce the gain of a dish aerial. Explain how the effects of each are reduced in the design of a dish aerial.
(b) Calculate the gain in dBi and the beamwidth of a dish aerial at 4 GHz if the aerial diameter is 4 m and the illumination efficiency is 72%.

9 Propagation of radio waves

After reading this chapter you should be able to:

(a) Explain what is meant by the ionosphere and know how its propagation conditions vary with both time and frequency.

(b) Explain what is meant by the troposphere and understand how abnormal conditions affect its propagation characteristics.

(c) Understand the use of the *k factor* in calculations of propagation paths using the troposphere.

(d) Explain how a radio wave may be propagated using the ground wave.

(e) Explain how a radio wave may be propagated using the sky wave.

(f) Explain the meanings and importance of the terms *critical frequency, maximum usable frequency, optimum working frequency* and *skip distance*.

(g) Calculate the values of the terms in (f) for both flat and curved earth.

(h) Understand the various forms of fading that may affect a radio link and explain some ways in which the effects of such fading may be overcome.

(i) Explain how a radio wave may be propagated using the space wave.

(j) Calculate the received power and the received field strength at the end of a space-wave radio link.

(k) State what is meant by a *Fresnel zone* and explain its importance in the planning of a space-wave radio link.

(l) Carry out calculations of received power and field strength for space-wave radio links.

(m) Discuss the use of scatter propagation for communication over difficult terrain.

(n) Determine the power received at the end of a radio link that has been established via a communications satellite.

The RF energy radiated by a transmitting aerial in the direction(s) determined by its radiation pattern will travel through the atmosphere and arrive at the distant aerial by one or more different modes of propagation. These modes are the *ground wave*, the *sky wave*, the *space wave*, *tropospheric scatter* and propagation via a *communications satellite*. The RF spectrum has been divided into a number of frequency bands which are listed in Table 9.1. When the transmitting aerial is mounted on the surface of the earth propagation will mainly be by means of the ground wave. There will also be some sky-wave radiation which may, or may not, be returned to earth. The ground wave is used in the VLF and LF bands for long-distance, narrow-bandwidth communications, and in the

Table 9.1 Frequency bands

Frequency band	Classification	Abbreviation
10–30 kHz	very low frequency	VLF
30–300 kHz	low frequency	LF
0.3–3 MHz	medium frequency	MF
3–30 MHz	high frequency	HF
30–300 MHz	very high frequency	VHF
0.3–3 GHz	ultra high frequency	UHF
3–30 GHz	super high frequency	SHF

MF band for shorter-distance sound broadcast signals. In the VLF band the received signal at long distances from the transmitter is extremely stable and shows very little change over a day, or even seasonally. The main disadvantage of the VLF band is its very limited bandwidth and the large physical structures that are necessary for the transmitting aerials. The range of the ground wave is not quite as large for signals in the LF and the MF bands since wave attenuation increases with frequency; the daytime range is typically a few hundred kilometres at the lower end of the MF band to about 100 km at the upper end of the MF band. The night-time range may well be some thousands of kilometres because propagation can then take place via the ionosphere using the sky wave. In the LF and MF bands the received field strength is usually given in dBμ, i.e. dB relative to $1 \ \mu V \ m^{-1}$.

At higher frequencies the transmitting aerial can be mounted above the earth, perhaps by several wavelengths, and then propagation is mainly by either the sky wave or the space wave. The sky wave is mainly employed for long-distance telephony links in the HF band but also for some sound broadcast services. HF radio is still employed for ship-to-shore communications even though a communications satellite system known as INMARSAT is available. HF radio is also used by the military, mainly as a back-up for satellite systems but also as a primary link. The space wave is employed for various services in the VHF, UHF and SHF bands, such as radio-relay systems and land, sea and air mobile systems. The UHF band is also utilised for television broadcast signals. The applications for tropospheric scatter propagation are limited to some beyond-the-horizon radio systems where considerable terrain difficulties, such as mountains, jungle and ocean, exist. Finally, communications satellite systems are employed to carry wideband telephony and television systems over long distances and for various other services.

The ionosphere

Ultraviolet, and other, radiation from the sun ionises large numbers of the atoms which make up gas molecules in the upper atmosphere. This ionisation causes the earth to be surrounded by a belt of ionised gases which is known as the *ionosphere*. The height of the ionosphere above the surface of the earth varies considerably but it is normally

Fig. 9.1 *Ionospheric layers (a) in the daytime and (b) at night*

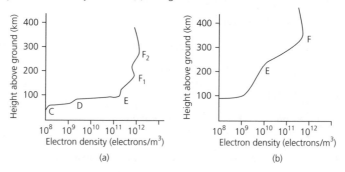

somewhere within the limits of 50 to 400 km. Within the ionosphere the density of the free electrons is much higher than it is at heights either above or below the ionosphere. Below the ionosphere there are two other regions: the *troposphere*, from ground level to about 10 km above the ground; and the *stratosphere*, from about 10 km to the lower edge of the ionosphere.

The electron density, measured by the number of free electrons per cubic metre, within the ionosphere is not a constant quantity. During the daytime the ionosphere contains four distinct regions, or layers, within which the electron density exhibits a maximum value. These four layers are known as the D, E, F_1 and F_2 layers, in order of their increasing height above ground. There is also a fifth layer, labelled C, below the D layer, but it plays no part in radio communications. The heights of the four layers above the ground vary daily, seasonally, and with the 11 year variations in the 22 year sun-spot cycle. Approximate heights, for both daytime and night-time, are shown by Figs 9.1(a) and (b), respectively. In the daytime the D layer has a much lower electron density than the other layers, and during the night it disappears completely. The E layer becomes weaker at night but it does not normally disappear. In the daytime the F_1 layer is at a height of about 200 km but the height of the F_2 layer varies considerably. Typically, the F_2 layer is at about 250 to 350 km above the earth in the winter, and between 300 and 400 km high in the summer.

Refractive index of the ionosphere

As a radio wave propagates through the ionosphere its electric field will exert a force upon the free electrons which causes them to move. If the free electron density is N electrons per m^3, each free electron has a charge of e C, and the field strength of the radio wave is $E \sin \omega t$ rad, then the force exerted upon each free electron is $F = eE \sin \omega t$ N. Each electron is given an acceleration of

$$F/m = (eE \sin \omega t)/m \qquad (9.1)$$

where m is the mass of an electron.

The consequent velocity v of an electron is obtained by integrating its acceleration with respect to time; hence

$$v = (-eE \cos \omega t)/\omega m \text{ m s}^{-1} \qquad (9.2)$$

The current represented by this movement of electrons is

$$i = Ne(-eE \cos \omega t)/\omega m = (-Ne^2 E \cos \omega t)/\omega m \text{ A m}^{-2}$$

The current that flows in a dielectric of unity relative permittivity is

$$i = \varepsilon_0 dE/dt = \varepsilon_0 \omega E \cos \omega t \text{ A m}^{-2}$$

and so the total current flow is

$$i = \varepsilon_0 \omega E \cos \omega t - (Ne^2 E \cos \omega t)/\omega m$$
$$= \varepsilon_0 [1 - (Ne^2/\omega^2 m \varepsilon_0)] \omega E \cos \omega t \tag{9.3}$$

From this, the relative permittivity ε_R of an ionospheric layer is

$$\varepsilon_R = 1 - Ne^2/(\omega^2 m \varepsilon_0) \tag{9.4}$$

Substituting the values for the charge and the mass of an electron into equation (9.4) gives

$$\varepsilon_R = 81N/f^2 \tag{9.5}$$

This means that the relative permittivity of an ionospheric layer is smaller than that of free space.

The refractive index n of a layer is equal to the square root of its relative permittivity, and hence

$$\text{Refractive index } n = \sqrt{(1 - 81N/f^2)} \tag{9.6}$$

Also, of course, the refractive index is equal to the ratio (sine of angle of incidence)/(sine of angle of refraction).

Behaviour of the ionosphere at different frequencies

The effect of the ionosphere on an incident radio wave is very much a function of frequency. In the VLF and LF bands the ionosphere has a high conductivity and it *reflects*, with very little loss, any radio wave that is incident upon its lower edge. In the MF band the D layer acts like a lossy medium whose attenuation reaches its maximum value at the *gyro-frequency* of 1.4 MHz. Signals in the MF band are absorbed by the D layer and are not returned to earth. At frequencies in the HF band the E and F layers *refract* radio waves and, if conditions are correct, return the wave to earth. The D layer has little, if any, refractive effect. Signals in the VHF, UHF and SHF bands normally pass straight through the ionosphere but may have their polarisation rotated.

Ionospheric variations

The intensity of the ultraviolet, and other, radiation from the sun that enters the earth's atmosphere is continually fluctuating. Both regular and irregular variations occur. The regular variations occur for two reasons: (a) the intensity of the sun's radiation varies with both the time of the day and the month in the year; and (b) sun spots occur at the sun's surface which produce 11 year fluctuations in its radiation that affect the ionosphere. The sun-spot cycle has an average periodicity of 22 years.

Irregular ionospheric disturbances are also experienced. Solar flares emit large amounts of radiation from the sun that produce a large increase in the ionisation of the D layer. This may cause the D layer to absorb all HF signals, giving a complete blackout for anything up to about two hours. Sometimes, ionospheric storms occur; this is the name given to irregular fluctuations in the conductivity of the ionosphere which cause rapid fading, particularly at the higher frequencies. Ionospheric storms tend to occur at intervals of 27 days.

Sporadic E consists of a cloud of drifting electrons which suddenly, and unpredictably, appears within the E layer. The electron cloud has a much higher electron density than is usual and is therefore able to return to the earth waves that normally pass straight through the ionosphere. When sporadic E is present, the maximum usable frequency (p. 258) of a returned wave may be, typically, some 20–40 MHz, although even higher figures sometimes occur. Sporadic E is more likely to occur in the summer than in the winter.

Gyro-frequency

The attenuation of the ionosphere reaches its maximum value at the gyro-frequency of 1.4 MHz because of the effect of the magnetic field of the earth on electrons in an ionospheric layer. Free electrons in the layer are subject to forces exerted by both the electric field of the radio wave and the magnetic field of the earth. The combined effects of these two forces cause electrons to follow a spiral path whose magnitude is largest at 1.4 MHz. As an electron follows this path it extracts energy from the radio wave and this energy is lost to the wave and hence attenuates the wave.

Faraday rotation

The ionosphere has an effect on signals in the UHF and SHF bands known as *Faraday rotation*. Faraday rotation is caused by anisotropy in the ionosphere which results in the rotation of the plane of polarisation of a linearly polarised radio wave. The angle of rotation is proportional to the orientation and direction of the signal path relative to the magnetic field of the earth. Typically the rotation is about 3° at 4 GHz. The use of circular polarisation avoids this effect.

The troposphere

The International Telecommunications Union ITU-T has adopted the following expression for the refractive index n of the troposphere:

$$n = 1 + (77.6/T)[p + (4810e/T)] \times 10^{-6} \tag{9.7}$$

where T is the temperature in K, and e and p are the water vapour and atmospheric pressures in mbar. Since all three parameters are functions of height equation (9.7) can be written in the form

$$n(h) = 1 + ae^{-bh} \tag{9.8}$$

Fig. 9.2 *Variation of refractivity with height*

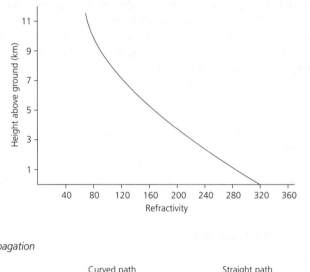

Fig. 9.3 *Space-wave propagation*

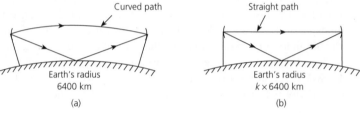

where *a* and *b* are constants, e is the base of natural logarithms, i.e. e = 2.7183, and *h* is the height above the ground in km. If $a = 315 \times 10^{-6}$ and $b = 0.136$ (which refer to the ITU-T *average atmosphere*), the ITU-T reference refractive index is obtained. The refractive index, calculated from equation (9.8), gives most inconvenient numbers, e.g. at $h = 1$ km, $n = 1.000\ 27$, and at $h = 2$ km, $n = 1.000\ 24$. To obtain more convenient numbers it is customary to use the *refractivity index N* of the troposphere instead. This is merely $N = (n - 1) \times 10^{6}$; thus for $h = 1$ km the refractivity is equal to 270. The variation of the refractivity with increase in height above the ground is shown by Fig. 9.2.

k *factor*

Since the refractive index falls with increase in height a radio wave will follow a curved path through the troposphere. Provided the wave is launched in a horizontal plane the radius of curvature of the path is $-\mathrm{d}h/\mathrm{d}n$. In the British Isles, at a height of about 1 km, *n* is normally about 40 parts in 10^{6} lower than at ground level (see Fig. 9.2); hence $-\mathrm{d}h/\mathrm{d}n = 2.5 \times 10^{-7}$ m. The radius of the earth is 6400 km and so the radius of curvature of the radio path is 25 000/6400 = 3.9 times the radius of the earth. When a radio link is planned it is convenient to consider that the radius of the earth is *k* times its actual value and that the space wave travels in a straight line (see Fig. 9.3). Under normal atmospheric conditions $k = 4/3$, giving an effective earth radius of $(4 \times 6400)/3 \approx 8500$ km. If the distance between the two aerials is not too great the earth between them may be assumed to be flat. Little error is then introduced into any calculations and, if required, a correction factor can be used. Departures from normal atmospheric conditions are not usually large enough to give significant fading on a line-of-sight radio path. Sometimes, however, abnormal conditions do arise that noticeably affect space-wave propagation.

Under normal atmospheric conditions the free-space loss is given by $L_p = 20 \log_{10}(4\pi D/\lambda)$ dB. Abnormal atmospheric conditions can occur which may lead to extra losses of tens of decibels. Usually the departure from normal conditions is insufficient to cause appreciable fading. The various kinds of abnormal conditions that may occur are as follows.

Temperature inversion

A *temperature* inversion occurs when the temperature of the atmosphere increases with increase in height above the ground. In the early part of a sunny day cloudless skies may result in the air temperature being higher than the ground temperature, contrary to the normal state of affairs. Such a temperature inversion means that the refractive index of the troposphere would decrease with height more rapidly than usual for up to about 100 m above the earth. Temperature inversions also occur because of the following.

Subsidence

A mass of warm air may be further heated by compression and then rises to a greater height, while cooler air falls to a lower height to replace it.

Dynamic

A mass of warm air may move on top of a mass of cold air.

Nocturnal

The air at the surface of the earth is rapidly cooled after sunset.

Cloud layer

The sun's rays may be reflected from the upper surface of a cloud and heat up the air above the cloud.

Water vapour

For normal atmospheric conditions the humidity of the atmosphere falls gradually with increase in height, but sometimes an abrupt change in the humidity gradient may occur. This is most likely to happen above the sea during hot weather and it often occurs to the leeward of land as warm air moves from the land out over the sea.

Super-refraction

A temperature inversion and/or a non-standard water vapour gradient will produce non-standard refraction of the space wave. This may be either *super-refraction* or *sub-refraction*. When the refractive index of the troposphere decreases with height more rapidly than usual the wave is bent towards the earth to a greater extent than normal and

Fig. 9.4 *(a) Super-refraction (b) ducting and (c) sub-refraction of a space wave*

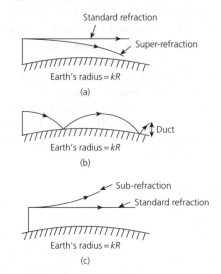

a *duct* is formed. Super-refraction is shown by Fig. 9.4(a). The wave may be reflected from the earth, again super-refracted, again reflected and so on to produce the *ducting* shown in Fig. 9.4(b). Ducting occurs when two layers of air with temperature inversions exist at different heights. When a duct is present the space wave may propagate for distances well beyond the radio horizon, up to about 4000 km in some cases. Sometimes an elevated duct may appear at a height of a kilometre or so above the ground.

Sub-refraction

Sub-refraction of a space wave occurs when the refractive index of the troposphere decreases with height at a smaller rate than normally; this situation is mainly caused by cold-water fog. When sub-refraction is present the space wave is refracted to a lesser extent than normal, and if the k factor of 4/3 has been employed in the design of the link, the wave will appear to be bent upwards as shown by Fig. 9.4(c).

Ground-wave propagation

At very low and low frequencies the transmitting aerial is an electrically short monopole which radiates energy in the form of a ground wave that must be vertically polarised. The ground wave is able to follow the undulations of the surface of the earth because of the bending effect of diffraction.[†] As the ground wave travels around the curvature of the earth, its magnetic field cuts the conductance of the earth and induces e.m.f.s into it. In turn, these induced e.m.f.s cause currents to flow into the earth which dissipate I^2R power in the earth's conductance. This power can only be supplied by the radio wave and so there is a continuous flow of energy from the wave into the ground. This results

---

[†] Diffraction is a phenomenon which occurs with all wave motion. It causes a radio wave to bend around any obstacle it passes. For the ground wave the earth itself is the obstacle.

Fig. 9.5 *Ground wave propagation*

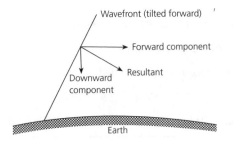

in the wavefront having two components of velocity, one in the forward direction and one downwards normal to the earth. This is shown by Fig. 9.5: the resultant velocity of the wave is the phasor sum of the two components and its direction makes the wavefront tilt forwards. Since the downward component of velocity is always normal to the surface of the earth the wave is able to follow the undulations of the ground.

The wave is attenuated as it travels for two reasons. First, the wavefront diverges as it travels so that the field strength is inversely proportional to distance (the free-space loss) and, second, power is taken from the wave to supply the ground losses. The calculation of the ground power losses is complex and depends upon such factors as the frequency of the wave, and the conductivity and permittivity of the earth. The attenuation is at its smallest when the earth's surface is wet, e.g. seas and oceans, and at its largest when the surface of the earth is dry, e.g. desert. The attenuation is expressed by an attenuation factor K whose value can be approximately predicted from published graphs. Thus, the electric field strength E_D at a distance D kilometres from the transmitting aerial is given by

$$E_D = KE_1/D \text{ V m}^{-1} \tag{9.9}$$

where E_1 is the electric field strength 1 km from the transmitting aerial and is equal to $300V\sqrt{P_T}$ (p. 185), where P_T is the transmitted power in kW. Hence, if the distance D is expressed in kilometres,

$$E_D = (K300\sqrt{P_T})/D \text{ mV m}^{-1} \tag{9.10}$$

At low and medium frequencies the attenuation factor K is inversely proportional to the square of the frequency. Hence the attenuation of the wave increases rapidly with increase in frequency. At frequencies in the HF band, and above, the attenuation factor reduces the amplitude of the ground wave to a negligible value even over quite small distances.

EXAMPLE 9.1

A radio transmitter is to produce, using the ground wave, a field strength of 5 mV m^{-1} at a distance of 200 km. (a) If the attenuation factor is 0.2 calculate the necessary radiated power. (b) What would be the field strength if the frequency of the transmitted signal were to be doubled? (c) Quote the answer to part (b) in dBμ.

(a) $E_{200} = 5 = (0.2 \times 300\sqrt{P_T})/200$, or

$P_T = 278$ kW (*Ans.*)

(b) If the frequency is doubled

$E_{200} = 1.25$ mV m^{-1} (*Ans.*)

(c) $E_{200} = 20 \log_{10}[(1.25 \times 10^{-3})/(1 \times 10^{-6}) \approx 62$ dBμ (*Ans.*)

At frequencies in the MF band the maximum field strength at ground level is obtained when the height of the transmitting aerial is $5\lambda/8$. There is then appreciable radiation into the sky (p. 186). During the daytime, the sky wave is completely absorbed by the D layer and does not return to the earth. During the night, however, the D layer disappears and then the sky wave will be returned to earth via either the E or the F layer. The two cases of interest are illustrated by Figs 9.6(a) and (b). In the first case, a transmitted signal is received at a distant location by means of both the ground wave and the sky wave. The total field strength at this point is the phasor sum of the individual field strengths and this will vary because of fluctuations in the length of the ionospheric path. This means that the received signal will be prone to fading. In the second case, two different signals, radiated at the same frequency by different transmitters, are received together at a point. The quality of the received wanted signal will be impaired and its reception may be so poor that it is unusable. This is, of course, the effect that makes the night-time reception of medium-wave broadcast signals in Europe of such poor quality.

Fig. 9.6 *MF transmissions at night*

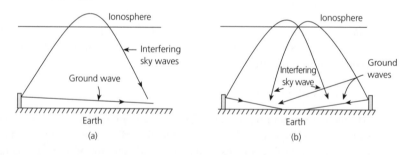

Sky-wave propagation

The basic principle of a radio link operating in the HF band is illustrated by Fig. 9.7. The sky wave is directed into the ionosphere where it is continuously refracted. If, before it reaches the top of the F_2 layer, it has been refracted to the extent that the angle of refraction is 90° then the wave will be returned to earth. The intrinsic instability of the ionosphere causes the length of a sky-wave path to vary continuously in a random manner, and considerable fading may take place. Particularly difficult in this respect are

Fig. 9.7 *Sky-wave propagation*

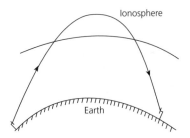

Fig. 9.8 *Showing the effect on a sky wave of (a) the angle of incidence, and (b) frequency*

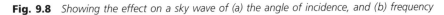

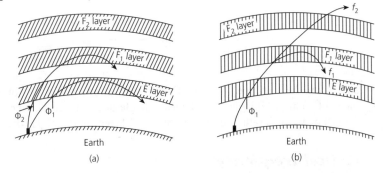

(a) (b)

the periods around dawn and around dusk when the electron densities in the ionosphere change more rapidly than at other times.

The potential unreliability of an HF radio link has meant that HF radio has, in the past, lost considerable ground to both communications satellite and terrestrial radio-relay systems. Nowadays, however, the relative cheapness of HF radio systems plus the introduction of various technical innovations, such as diversity, frequency synthesis and new modulation techniques, have revived interest in HF technology. Congestion in the HF band has been partially alleviated by an increased use of SSB/ISB transmissions.

A radio wave that enters the E layer with an angle of incidence ϕ_i will continuously be refracted away from the normal. If the values of the electron density N and the frequency f are such that $\sin \phi_i = \sqrt{(1 - 81N/f^2)}$ then, since the refractive index $n = (\sin \phi_i)/(\sin \phi_r)$, $\sin \phi_r$ must be equal to unity. Then $\phi_r = 90°$ and the wave must then be travelling in a horizontal direction. Any further refraction of the wave will return it back to earth. If no part of the E layer has an electron density large enough for the $\sin \phi_r = 1$ relationship to be satisfied, the sky wave will not be returned to earth but will escape from the top of the layer. The wave will then be incident on the F_1 (or, at night, the F) layer with an increased angle of incidence and it will here be further refracted and may perhaps be returned to earth by this layer. If not, the wave will leave the top of the F_1 layer and pass on to the F_2 layer with an even larger angle of incidence and now it may be returned to earth. If the wave is not returned by the F_2 layer it will escape from the earth. This concept is illustrated by Figs 9.8(a) and (b).

In Fig. 9.8(a) a wave entering the E layer with an angle of incidence ϕ_1 is returned to earth, but another signal, at the same frequency, which is incident on the E layer with a smaller angle of incidence ϕ_2 is not returned. This second wave travels on to the F_1 layer

Fig. 9.9 *Virtual height of a layer*

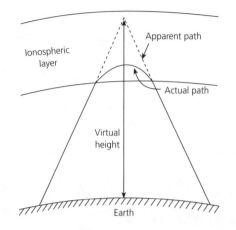

and is from here returned to earth. Figure 9.8(b) shows two waves of frequencies f_1 and f_2 incident upon the E layer with the same angle of incidence ϕ_1, where $f_2 > f_1$. The lower-frequency wave is returned to earth by the F_1 layer but the higher-frequency wave is not.

Critical frequency

The critical frequency f_{crit} of an ionospheric layer is the highest frequency that can be radiated upwards with an angle of incidence ϕ_i of zero and be returned to earth. This will be the frequency of the wave that travels up to the top of the layer, where the electron density is at its highest value, before it is refracted to the extent that ϕ_r becomes equal to 90°. From equation (9.6),

$$\sin 0° = 0 = \surd(1 - 81 N_{max}/f^2_{crit})$$

or

$$f_{crit} = 9\surd N_{max} \tag{9.11}$$

Each of the ionospheric layers will have its own value of critical frequency. From the ground it appears as though the wave has travelled in a straight line, has been reflected by the ionosphere, and has then returned to earth from the point of reflection in another straight-line path. The *virtual height* of a layer is the height at which this apparent reflection takes place (see Fig. 9.9).

Maximum usable frequency

The maximum usable frequency (MUF) of a layer is the highest frequency that can be employed for a sky-wave path between two points on the earth's surface. For a wave to be returned to earth $\sin \phi_r = 1$, and so

$$\sin \phi_i = \surd(1 - f^2_{crit}/f^2_{max})$$
$$1 - \sin^2 \phi_i = f^2_{crit}/f^2_{max}$$

or

$$f_{max} = \text{MUF} = f_{crit}/\cos \phi_i = f_{crit} \sec \phi_i \qquad (9.12)$$

Since the electron density of each layer is subject to continuous fluctuations, some regular and predictable and others not, the MUF is not a constant figure. The MUF of a sky-wave path between two points on the earth's surface will vary throughout the day, and graphs of the forecast MUF for various routes are commercially available.

Optimum working frequency

Because of the instability of the ionosphere, operating a radio link at a frequency equal to the MUF would not give a reliable system. It is customary to work an HF route at a frequency of about 80% of the MUF; this lower frequency is known either as the *optimum working frequency* (OWF) or as the *optimum traffic frequency.*

Since the MUF is not of constant value it will be necessary to change the frequency of a sky-wave link as, and when, the propagation conditions alter. Usually, an HF radio transmitter is allocated (although not exclusively) several different frequencies, and any one of them may be in use at a given time. When the propagation conditions are severe it may become necessary to use two or more frequencies simultaneously and, perhaps, even retransmit the message later when conditions have improved.

EXAMPLE 9.2

An ionospheric layer has a maximum electron density of 6×10^{11} electrons/m^3. Calculate (a) the critical frequency, (b) the MUF when the angle of incidence is 50°, and (c) the OWF.

Solution

(a) $f_{crit} = 9\sqrt{(6 \times 10^{11})} = 6.971$ MHz (*Ans.*)
(b) MUF $= 6.971/\cos 50° = 10.85$ MHz (*Ans.*)
(c) OWF $\approx 0.8 \times 10.85 = 8.68$ MHz (*Ans.*)

EXAMPLE 9.3

The virtual height of a layer is 110 km and its critical frequency is 4 MHz. Calculate the MUF for two points on the surface of the earth that are 600 km apart if (a) the earth is assumed to he flat, and (b) the radius of the earth is 6400 km.

Solution

(a) From Fig. 9.10(a),

$$\phi = \tan^{-1}(300/110) = 70°$$

Fig. 9.10

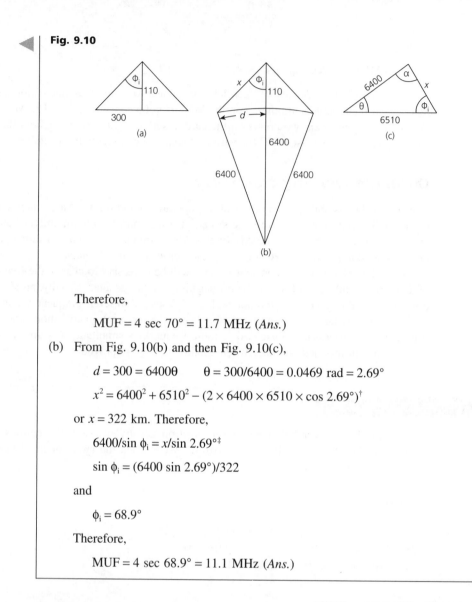

Therefore,

MUF = 4 sec 70° = 11.7 MHz (*Ans.*)

(b) From Fig. 9.10(b) and then Fig. 9.10(c),

$d = 300 = 6400\theta$ $\theta = 300/6400 = 0.0469$ rad = 2.69°

$x^2 = 6400^2 + 6510^2 - (2 \times 6400 \times 6510 \times \cos 2.69°)^†$

or $x = 322$ km. Therefore,

$6400/\sin \phi_i = x/\sin 2.69°^‡$

$\sin \phi_i = (6400 \sin 2.69°)/322$

and

$\phi_i = 68.9°$

Therefore,

MUF = 4 sec 68.9° = 11.1 MHz (*Ans.*)

Maximum value of ϕ_i

The angle of incidence ϕ_i with which a sky wave enters the ionosphere cannot be increased without limit. The maximum possible value $\phi_{i(max)}$ occurs when the transmitted wave is tangential to the earth's surface, as shown by Fig. 9.11. Here R is the radius of the earth, approximately 6400 km, and h is the virtual height of a layer. From the figure,

$\phi_{i(max)} = \sin^{-1}[R/(R + h)]$ (9.13)

† Using the cosine rule.
‡ Using the sine rule.

Fig. 9.11 *Maximum value of* ϕ_i

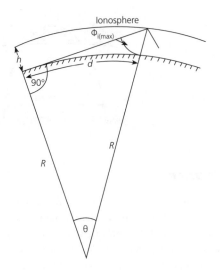

Also,

$$\theta = 180° - (90° + \phi_{i(max)}) = 90° - \sin^{-1}[R/(R + h)] = \cos^{-1}[R/(R + h)]$$

Therefore, the maximum ground range is

$$2d = 2R\theta = 2R\cos^{-1}[R/(R+ h)] \qquad\qquad (9.14)$$

The maximum distance of a sky-wave link using the E layer is about 4000 km; longer distances are possible using the F layer(s). If a path length approaching, or exceeding, the maximum range is wanted a multi-hop path will be necessary.

EXAMPLE 9.4

At a particular time of day the E layer contains a maximum 1.5×10^{11} electrons/m³ and is at a virtual height of 150 km. Calculate the MUF and the maximum single-hop range.

Solution

$$f_{crit} = 9\sqrt{(1.5 \times 10^{11})} = 3.49 \text{ MHz}$$

$$\sin \phi_{i(max)} = \sin^{-1}(6400/6550) = 77.7°$$

Therefore,

$$MUF = 3.49 \sec 77.7° = 16.4 \text{ MHz } (Ans.)$$

The maximum ground range is

$$2 \times 6400 \times \cos^{-1}(6400/6550) = 2745 \text{ km } (Ans.)$$

Fig. 9.12 *Skip distance*

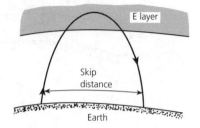

Skip distance

There is a maximum usable frequency for any distance from the transmitter and this distance is also the minimum distance at which that frequency can be transmitted using a sky-wave path. This minimum distance is called the *skip distance* or the *dead zone*. For a wave to be (apparently) reflected at the virtual height of the layer the angle of incidence should be such that $\sin \phi_i > \sqrt{(1 - 81N_{max}/f^2)}$. Skip distance is illustrated by Fig. 9.12.

EXAMPLE 9.5

Determine the skip distance for a 10 MHz sky-wave link that uses an ionospheric layer at a virtual height of 150 km that has a maximum electron density of 8×10^{11} electrons/m^3.

Solution

$$\sin \phi_i = \sqrt{[1 - (81 \times 8 \times 10^{11})/(10 \times 10^6)^2]} = 0.593 \quad \text{and} \quad \phi_i = 36.4°$$

The skip distance is

$$300 \tan 36.4° = 221.2 \text{ km } (Ans.)$$

Multi-hop links

The maximum distances over which communication can be established using a sky-wave path are; (a) using the E layer, 2000 km; (b) using the F_1 layer, 3400 km; and (c) using the F_2 layer, 4000 km. If transmission over a longer distance is required it becomes necessary to use two or three hops. Figure 9.13 shows a two-hop link; the sky-wave is radiated upwards into the ionosphere by the transmitting aerial and returned to earth at some distance away. The downward wave is then reflected by the earth and returned to the ionosphere for further refraction before it returns to earth at some still further point. The overall MUF of a multi-hop link is equal to the lowest MUF of the individual MUFs. A two-hop link can cover a distance of between 4000 and 7000 km and a three-hop link can cover a distance from 7000 to 12 800 km. Each reflection from

Fig. 9.13 *Multi-hop transmission of a sky wave*

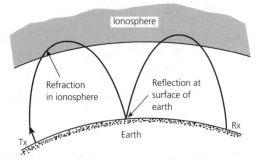

the earth introduces more losses and hence the number of hops employed is limited to three and more usually two.

Fading

General fading

General fading, in which the complete signal fades to the same extent, is produced by fluctuations in the attenuation of the ionosphere. A complete fade-out of an HF signal can occur because of its complete absorption by the D layer. This kind of fade only occurs in the daytime and is caused by solar flares. A complete fade-out may last for a few minutes or several hours. Unless there is a complete fade-out of the signal the effects of general fading can be overcome by the use of automatic gain control in the radio receiver. Ionospheric storms can cause the MUF of a link to alter and result in fading.

Polarisation

The magnetic field of the earth can cause a propagating radio wave to split into two parts with different polarisations. The two components can then interfere with one another to produce an elliptically polarised wave, an effect known as Faraday rotation. Since HF aerials are either horizontally, or vertically, mounted the received voltage is reduced and fades of a few seconds' duration may be experienced.

Selective fading

Selective fading occurs when the signal picked up by the receiving aerial has arrived via two or more different paths (see Fig. 9.14). The total field strength at the aerial is the phasor sum of the field strengths produced by each signal. The phase difference between the signals arriving via the two separate paths is equal to $2\pi/\lambda$ times the difference between the lengths of the two paths. If this difference should vary, owing to fluctuations in the ionosphere, the two signals will come into and out of phase with one another repeatedly. This means that the total field strength will also vary in a frequency-dependent manner (because of the $1/\lambda$ term) and hence the different frequency components of a complex signal may fade to different extents.

Fig. 9.14 *Selective fading*

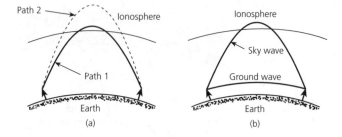

(a)   (b)

There are a number of ways in which selective fading may be combated. These include:

- The use of a highly directive transmitting aerial so that the number of possible propagation paths is minimised.
- Operation at a frequency as near to the MUF as possible.
- The use of SSB/ISB signals.
- Lincompex.
- The use of space and/or frequency diversity.

EXAMPLE 9.6

The signals received by an aerial arrive over two different paths, one of which is 75 km longer than the other. At the carrier frequency the two signals cancel out. If the carrier is amplitude modulated, at what side frequencies will cancellation occur?

Solution

For the two signals to cancel out $2\pi d/\lambda = n\pi$, where d is the path-length difference and n is an odd integer. Therefore, $2d/\lambda = n$, $2d = n\lambda = nc/f$, and

$$f = (3n \times 10^8)/(2 \times 65 \times 10^3) = 2n \text{ kHz}$$

Hence, the side frequencies that cancel out are

$$f_c \pm 2000 \text{ Hz}, f_c \pm 6000 \text{ Hz, etc. } (Ans.)$$

Frequency diversity

Signals at different frequencies received by the same aerial very rarely fade simultaneously. This fact is used as the basis of a frequency-diversity system. A single aerial is connected to a number of radio receivers, each of which is tuned to a different frequency, whose outputs are connected in parallel. The receiver circuitry is so arranged that the receiver that is instantaneously receiving the strongest input signal will provide the output signal. The obvious disadvantage of frequency diversity is its use of two or more frequencies to transmit the same information. The frequencies are usually separated from one another by 2 to 4%.

Space diversity

Signals at the same frequency that are received by two aerials sited several wavelengths apart rarely fade simultaneously. In a space-diversity system two or three (but rarely more) aerials are sited some distance apart and are connected to two or three radio receivers. Each receiver is tuned to the same frequency and has a common output. As with frequency diversity the circuitry is arranged so that the receiver that is receiving the strongest signal supplies the output. The disadvantage of space diversity is the need for more than one aerial and the large site area required.

EXAMPLE 9.7

At the distant end of an 8 MHz sky-wave radio link signals are received via two paths that are at angles of 12° and 24° to the ground. Calculate the optimum distance between the aerials in a two-aerial space-diversity system.

Solution

Consider Fig. 9.15. The wavefront of signal 1 arrives first at aerial A and then at aerial B, so that the signal at B lags the signal at A by angle

$$\phi_1 = (2\pi d/\lambda) \cos 12° \text{ rad}$$

Similarly, for signal 2 the phase difference between the signals at aerials A and B is

$$\phi_2 = (2\pi d/\lambda) \cos 24° \text{ rad}$$

For the optimum space diversity the difference between the two phase angles should be equal to π radians. Therefore

$$(2\pi d/\lambda)(\cos 12° - \cos 24°) = \pi$$

and

$$d = (3 \times 10^8)/[8 \times 10^6 \times 2(\cos 12° - \cos 24°)]$$
$$= 290 \text{ m } (Ans.)$$

Fig. 9.15

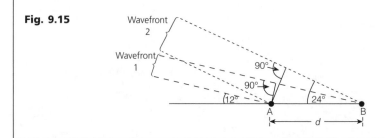

Fade margin

To allow for likely fading an HF radio system is designed with a *fade margin*. The fade margin is an additional nominal loss that is added to the free-space path loss.

Space-wave propagation

At frequencies in the VHF, UHF and SHF bands the main mode of propagation between two points on the surface of the earth is the *space wave*. Since the wavelength of the signal is small, both the transmitting and the receiving aerials can be mounted at a height of several wavelengths above ground. Figure 9.16 illustrates the principle of space-wave propagation. A radio wave travelling in the troposphere follows a slightly curved path because of tropospheric refraction, and this results in the radio horizon being approximately 15% more distant than the optical horizon. At distances less than the optical horizon reception is by means both of a direct wave and of a ground-reflected wave, but at greater distances, up to the radio horizon, only the direct wave is received. Some signals are also received at distances greater than the radio horizon because some diffraction takes place. To allow the radio wave to follow an assumed straight-line path through the troposphere the radius of the earth is increased (on paper!) by the ratio that known as the *k* factor. For normal propagation conditions the *k* factor is equal to 4/3.

Reflection of a radio wave occurs whenever the wave is incident upon the junction of the atmosphere and the ground, or a building, tree, etc., and some, or all, of the incident power does not penetrate the ground. When the ground is perfectly flat at the point of reflection the angle of reflection is equal to the angle of incidence. The ratio (reflected wave)/(incident wave) is known as the *reflection coefficient* ρ.

Figure 9.17 shows how, typically, the magnitude of the reflection coefficient | ρ | of the ground may vary with the angle of incidence for both horizontally polarised and vertically polarised waves. For a horizontally polarised wave | ρ | is always equal to unity, but for a vertically polarised wave | ρ | varies considerably with the angle of incidence. The angle of the reflection coefficient ∠ρ is always 180° for a horizontally polarised wave, but for a vertically polarised wave ∠ρ varies from about 180° to about 10° as the angle of incidence is increased from zero. In practice, the angle of incidence is always small (and it is often called the *grazing angle*) and little error results if ∠ρ is assumed to be 180°. With mobile telephone systems the distances are always small, less than 20 km, and the grazing angle is typically 0.6° to 6°.

If the ground at the point of reflection is curved and not flat the angles of reflection and incidence will not be the same. Reflection also occurs when a radio wave is incident

Fig. 9.16 *Space-wave propagation*

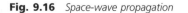
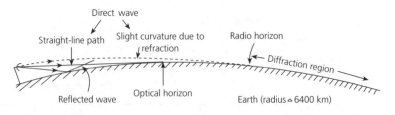

Fig. 9.17 *Reflection coefficient of the earth*

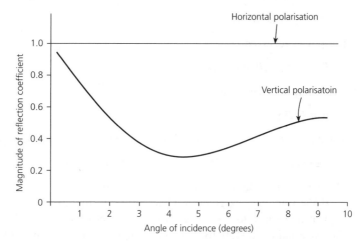

upon an irregular, or rough, surface but now the reflected wave is scattered in a number of different directions and this has the effect of reducing the signal power in the wanted direction.

Horizontal versus vertical polarisation

The relative merits of using horizontal, or vertical, polarisation are as follows. The total field strength at the receiving aerial is the resultant of the field strengths due to several components, including direct and reflected waves as well as some diffracted energy. A wave that has been diffracted over a treeless hill will suffer less attenuation if it is vertically polarised. Conversely, if the hill is tree covered a vertically polarised wave will be scattered to a greater extent and will thus suffer the greater attenuation. Reflected signals arrive at the receiving aerial after reflection from the earth in front of the aerial, and from objects either side of the radio path. Reflecting objects in the vertical plane, such as hills, will produce a stronger reflected signal if the wave is vertically polarised.

In general, it is found that vertical polarisation gives a larger received field strength at low heights above the ground but the probability of fading is greater. In hilly and/or wooded areas horizontal polarisation is probably the better choice but vertical polarisation is preferred for links that pass over flat countryside. For horizontal polarisation the received field strength tends to fall to zero at heights below about 4 m. This does not matter for point-to-point links since the receiving aerial is always mounted at greater heights than that, but it does mean that mobile land systems must employ vertical polarisation.

Received power

Line-of-sight radio links are engineered using the free-space loss concept. This (p. 197) is the basic transmission loss between isotropic radiators situated at each end of the radio path; it is defined as the ratio (transmitted power)/(received power).

The power density P_d received at a distance D m from the transmitting aerial is

$$P_d = P_T/4\pi D^2 \text{ W m}^{-2}$$

The power received is

$$P_R = P_d A_e = (P_T/4\pi D^2)(\lambda^2/4\pi) = P_T\lambda^2/(4\pi D)^2$$

Therefore, the free-space loss is

$$[(4\pi D)/\lambda]^2 \tag{9.15}$$

It is customary in radio-relay link calculations to write the free-space loss in the form

$$\text{free-space loss} = 32.45 + 20 \log_{10} D + 20 \log_{10} f \text{ dB} \tag{9.16}$$

where D is in km and f is the frequency in MHz.

If the frequency is given in GHz add 60 to the constant term to obtain 92.45 dB. Typical free-space losses are: microwave radio-relay system, 90–120 dB; mobile telephone/car radio, 40–130 dB; communications satellite system, 190–200 dB; and ground-to-aircraft, 40–160 dB.

EXAMPLE 9.8

Determine the free-space loss of a radio link that is 30 km in length and operates at (a) 580 MHz and (b) 6.4 GHz. (c) Calculate the received power for the 6.4 GHz link if the transmitted power is 5 W, the gains of the aerials are $G_T = 34$ dB and $G_R = 30$ dB, and the waveguide feeders have 3.8 dB loss at the transmitter and 3 dB loss at the receiver.

Solution

(a) The free-space loss is

$$32.45 + 20 \log_{10} 30 + 20 \log_{10} 580 = 32.45 + 29.54 + 55.27 = 117.3 \text{ dB } (Ans.)$$

(b) The free-space loss is

$$92.45 + 29.54 + 20 \log_{10} 6.4 = 138.1 \text{ dB } (Ans.)$$

(c) EIRP $= 10 \log_{10} 5 - 3.8 + 34 = 37.2$ dB

$$P_d = 37.2 - 138.1 = -100.9 \text{ dBW m}^{-2}$$

$$P_R = -100.9 - 3 + 30 = -73.9 \text{ dBW } (Ans.)$$

Received field strength

Figure 9.18 shows a line-of-sight radio link in which radio signals are transmitted using both a direct wave and a ground-reflected wave. The figure assumes that the k factor is 4/3 so that the radio wave travels in a straight-line path and the earth can be taken as

Fig. 9.18 *A line-of-sight radio link*

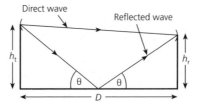

Fig. 9.19 *Phasor diagrams of the received field strength in a line-of-sight radio link*

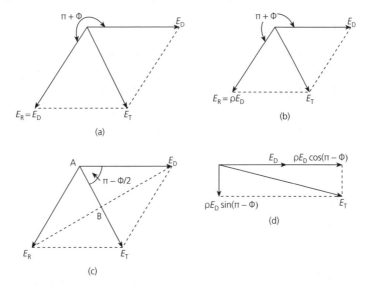

being flat. Two aerials, one at height h_t above ground and the other at height h_r, are D km apart. The total field strength produced at the receiving aerial is the phasor sum of the individual field strengths produced by the direct wave and by the reflected wave. The magnitudes of these waves are inversely proportional to the distance they have travelled. Since the extra length of the reflected path is negligible compared with the distance D between the two aerials, any difference in amplitude due to this factor is negligibly small. Hence if $|\rho| = 1$, $|E_D| = |E_R| = E_1/D$; if $|\rho| \neq 1$, then $|E_R| = |\rho| |E_1/D$.

The amplitude of the resultant field strength will be a function of the phase difference between the direct and the reflected waves. This phase difference exists because of the angle of the ground-reflection coefficient and because of the difference in the direct and reflected path lengths. For small grazing angles the phase change upon reflection is approximately constant at 180°. The phase difference ϕ due to the path-length difference is $\phi = 2\pi/\lambda$ times that difference. The phasor diagram of the field strengths at the receive aerial is shown by Figs 9.19(a) and (b). Consider Fig. 9.19(a) in which $|\rho| = 1$ so that $|E_D| = |E_R|$; this figure has been redrawn in Fig. 9.19(c) from which

$$AB = E_D \cos[(\pi - \phi)/2] = E_D \sin[\phi/2]$$

Fig. 9.20 *Calculation of the angle ɸ*

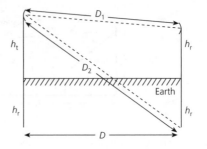

and

$$E_T = 2AB = 2E_D \sin(\phi/2) = (2E_1/D) \sin(\phi/2) \tag{9.17}$$

Figure 9.19(b) is the phasor diagram when $|E_D| \neq |E_R|$; resolving E_R into its horizontal and vertical components gives the diagram shown in Fig. 9.19(d). From this figure

$$E_T = \sqrt{\{[E_D + |\rho| E_D \cos(\pi - \phi)]^2 + |\rho|^2 E_D^2 \sin^2(\pi - \phi)\}}$$
$$= E_D\sqrt{[1 + |\rho|^2 + 2|\rho| \cos(\pi - \phi)]}$$

or

$$E_T = (E_1/D)\sqrt{[1 + |\rho|^2 - 2|\rho| \cos \phi]} \tag{9.18}$$

If $|\rho| = 1$,

$$E_T = (E_1/D)\sqrt{[2(1 - \cos \phi)]} = (E_1/D)\sqrt{[4 \sin^2(\phi/2)]}$$
$$= (2E_1/D) \sin(\phi/2)$$

as before.

It is now necessary to determine the angle ϕ. Figure 9.20 is an extension of Fig. 9.19. From this figure

$$D_1^2 = D^2 + (h_t - h_r)^2 \approx D + (h_t - h_r)^2/2D$$
$$D_2^2 = D^2 + (h_t + h_r)^2 \approx D + (h_t + h_r)^2/2D$$

The difference between the lengths of the direct and the reflected paths is

$$D_2 - D_1 = [(h_t + h_r)^2 - (h_t - h_r)^2]/2D = 2h_t h_r/D$$

and hence the phase angle ϕ is

$$\phi = (2\pi/\lambda)(2h_t h_r/D) = (4\pi h_t h_r)/\lambda D$$

Therefore, from equation (9.17),

$$E_T = (2E_1/D) \sin[(2\pi h_t h_r)/\lambda D] \tag{9.19}$$

At a fixed distance from the transmitting aerial the received field strength goes through successive maxima and minima as the height h_r above ground is increased. This is shown by Fig. 9.21. In practice, the reflection coefficient of the earth at frequencies in the UHF and higher bands is never exactly equal to $1\angle180°$ because of surface

Fig. 9.21 *Variation of field strength with height above ground at the receive end of a line-of-sight radio link*

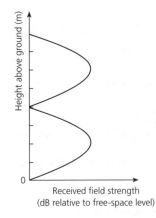

Height above ground (m)

0

Received field strength
(dB relative to free-space level)

Fig. 9.22 *Typical height-field strength characteristics. Reflecting surface (a) at mid-path, (b) near the transmit aerial, and (c) near the receive aerial*

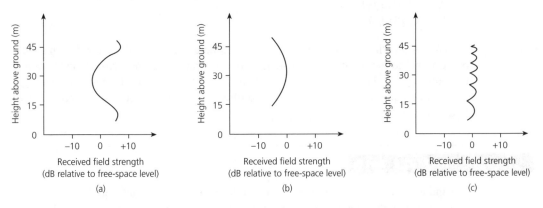

roughness and the minima do not quite reach zero. If the height of the receiving aerial is fixed the field strength will vary with the wavelength of the received signal. Three examples of height versus field strength for a reflection coefficient of 0.5 are plotted in Fig. 9.22. In Fig. 9.22(a) the reflecting surface is at the mid-path point and the received signal strength varies by approximately ±5 dB either side of the free-space value. When the reflecting surface is near the receiving aerial as in Fig. 9.22(b) the plot shows only one maximum. When the reflecting surface is near the transmitting aerial, Fig. 9.22(c), rapid fluctuations in the received signal level occur with a maximum of about ±3 dB.

EXAMPLE 9.9

An aerial is mounted 250 m above flat earth. Determine the minimum height at which the receiving aerial should be mounted if it is to receive the maximum field strength. The distance between the aerials is 22 km and the frequency is 600 MHz.

Solution

From equation (9.19) the maximum field strength is obtained when

$(2\pi h_t h_r)/\lambda D = n\pi/2$

where n is an odd integer, or

$h_r = n\lambda D/4h_t$

The minimum aerial height occurs when $n = 1$ and therefore

$h_r = (3 \times 10^8 \times 22 \times 10^3)/(600 \times 10^6 \times 250 \times 4) = 11$ m (*Ans.*)

The distance D between the two aerials is always much larger than the heights h_t and h_r of the transmitting and receiving aerials. This means that the term $2\pi h_t h_r/\lambda D$ represents a small angle and so equation (9.19) can be written as

$$E_T \approx (2E_1/D)(2\pi h_t h_r/\lambda D)$$
$$= (4\pi E_1 h_t h_r)/\lambda D^2 \qquad\qquad (9.20)$$

This means that the field strength at a fixed height h_r above the ground is inversely proportional to the square of the distance from the transmitter, and directly proportional to frequency. As the distance is increased and nears the optical horizon the field strength tends to be equal to that produced by the direct wave alone and to be independent of frequency.

EXAMPLE 9.10

A mobile radio receiver with an aerial of 3 dB gain is 8 km distant from a base station aerial. (a) If the electric field strength 1 km from the base station is 2 mV m^{-1} calculate the field strength at the mobile receiver. The frequency is 900 MHz and the aerial heights are $h_t = 48$ m and $h_r = 1.4$ m. (b) Calculate the received power.

Solution

(a) $\lambda = 1/3$ m, $2\pi h_t h_r/\lambda D \approx 0.158$ rad and sin $0.158 \approx 0.158$, so that equation (9.20) can be employed:

$$E_8 = (2 \times 10^{-3} \times 4\pi \times 48 \times 1.4 \times 3)/(8 \times 10^3)^2 = 79.2 \ \mu V \ m^{-1} \ (\textit{Ans.})$$

(b) As 3 dB = 2,

$$P_R = A_e P_d = G_R A_{e(iso)}(E^2/120\pi)$$
$$= (2\lambda^2/4\pi)[(79.2 \times 10^{-6})^2/(120\pi)]$$
$$= 0.294 \ pW = -125.3 \ dBW \ (\textit{Ans.})$$

Curvature of the earth

The assumption made in deriving expressions for the received field strength, namely that the earth between the aerials is flat, is of course not true. The curvature of the earth reduces the difference between the path lengths of the direct and reflected waves and this reduces the total field strength at a distant point. At the same time the earth's curvature causes the reflected wave to be divergent and this effect makes the reflected field strength greater. The two effects tend to cancel and so the error implicit in assuming flat earth is small unless the length of the link is approaching the optical horizon. If the curvature of the earth is to be taken into account a *divergence factor F* must be introduced that allows for the wave to be reflected from a curved surface. The divergence factor is employed by multiplying it and the reflection coefficient together, i.e.

$$E_R = E_D(1 \pm |\rho| F) \tag{9.21}$$

Maximum distance between aerials

Because of the curvature of the earth there is a maximum distance from the transmitting aerial at which the receiving aerial can be sited and still be able to receive the direct wave. This distance is known as the radio horizon. It is shown in Fig. 9.23 in which the effective radius of the earth is $kR = 8500$ km, h_t and h_r are the heights of the transmitting and receiving aerials, and D_1 and D_2 are the distances from each aerial to the point of grazing incidence. At this point the direct wave is tangential to the surface of the earth (when there will not be a reflected wave). From the figure,

$$(h_t + kR)^2 = D_1^2 + (kR)^2$$

or

$$D_1 \approx \sqrt{(2h_t kR)}$$

Similarly, $D_2 \approx \sqrt{(2h_r kR)}$.

The maximum distance D_{max} between the aerials is

$$D_{max} = D_1 + D_2 = \sqrt{(2h_t kR)} + \sqrt{(2h_r kR)} \tag{9.22}$$

If the heights of the two aerials are measured in m and the distance D is in km,

$$D_{max} = \sqrt{[(2h_t/1000) \times 8500]} + \sqrt{[(2h_r/1000) \times 8500]}$$
$$= 4.13(\sqrt{h_t} + \sqrt{h_r}) \tag{9.23}$$

Fig. 9.23 *Maximum distance between two aerials*

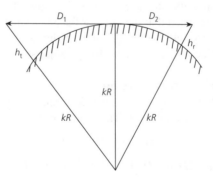

Fig. 9.24 *The first, second and third Fresnel zones*

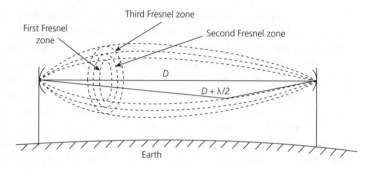

Fresnel zones

For a good, reliable signal to be received by an aerial there must be adequate clearance between the direct path and any obstacles. The necessary clearance is usually expressed in terms of *Fresnel zones*. A Fresnel zone is the locus of the points from which the sum of the distances to the transmitting and receiving aerials is equal to the direct distance between the aerials plus an integral number of half-wavelengths.

The first Fresnel zone is the locus of the points from which the sum of the distances to each aerial is $\lambda/2$ longer than the direct path between the aerials. Since the ground-reflected wave experiences approximately $180°$ phase change upon any reflection that takes place at a point on the first Fresnel zone, it results in a signal which, at the receiving aerial, is in phase with the direct wave. The second Fresnel zone is the locus of the points from which the sum of the distances to each aerial is λ longer than the direct path between the aerials. Reflection from a point on this zone will produce a signal which, at the receiving aerial, is in anti-phase with the wanted signal. In similar fashion, the third, fifth, etc., Fresnel zones produce in-phase signals, and the fourth, sixth, etc., Fresnel zones produce anti-phase signals. The first, second and third Fresnel zones are shown by Fig. 9.24.

The design of a line-of-sight radio link involves a choice of the Fresnel zone clearance deemed to be necessary since, if the direct path is too near the surface of the earth, extra diffraction losses must be expected. To avoid this the clearance above ground of the direct ray should be equal to about 0.6 times the radius of the first Fresnel zone. Account must also be taken of possible sub-refraction effects, when the atmospheric conditions are such that the k factor becomes smaller than unity. In the British Isles the k factor rarely falls below 0.7 and so this is the value that is generally used in link design. Reflections from more distant objects tend to cancel out.

Radius of a Fresnel zone

In Fig. 9.25 the distance T–A–R is $\lambda/2$ longer than the distance T–R so that the point A is on the first Fresnel zone. The radius of this zone is r and hence

$$(D_1^2 + r^2) = (D_2^2 + r^2) = D_1 + D_2 + \lambda/2$$

$$D_1[1 + r^2/(2D_1^2)] + D_2[1 + r^2/(2D_2^2)] = D_1 + D_2 + \lambda/2$$

Fig. 9.25 *Calculation of the radius of the first Fresnel zone*

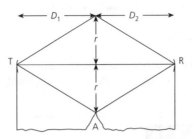

or

$$r = \sqrt{[(D_1 D_2 \lambda)/(D_1 + D_2)]}$$ (9.24)

The radius of any of the higher-order Fresnel zones is simply found by multiplying equation (9.24) by $\sqrt{n}$.

EXAMPLE 9.11

A 3 GHz radio link has transmitting and receiving aerials at equal heights above the ground, and is 36 km long. There is a 30 m high obstacle mid-way between the two aerials. Determine the minimum height at which the aerials ought to be mounted for the radio path to be unobstructed. Assume the k factor to be 0.7.

Solution

The minimum height of the two aerials must be equal to $h_1 + h_2 + h_3$, where h_1 is the height for grazing incidence, h_2 is the height of the obstacle, and h_3 is 0.6 times the radius of the first Fresnel zone.
   Here $\lambda = 0.1$ m. From equation (9.23),

$$18 \times 10^3 = \sqrt{(2h_1 \times 0.7 \times 6400 \times 10^3)}$$

or

$$h_1 = 36.16 \text{ m} \quad \text{and} \quad h_2 = 30 \text{ m}$$

From equation (9.24),

$$h_3 = 0.6\sqrt{[(0.1 \times 18 \times 10^3)/2]} = 18 \text{ m}$$

Therefore the minimum aerial height is

$$h = 36.16 + 30 + 18 = 84.16 \text{ m } (\textit{Ans.})$$

If the two aerials are not at equal heights and/or the obstacle is not at mid-path the problem is more complex. It is best approached by assuming the earth between the aerials to be flat and then increasing the effective height of the obstacles by the amount

---

necessary to account for the curvature of the earth. The effective increase in height h_{inc} of the obstacle is given by equation (9.25):

$$h_{inc} = D_1 D_2 / 2kR \qquad (9.25)$$

where D_1 is the distance from the transmitting aerial to the obstacle and D_2 is the distance from the obstacle to the receiving aerial.

EXAMPLE 9.12

A 3GHz signal is transmitted from an aerial 50 m high towards a receiving aerial that is 39 km away. An obstacle 50 m high is 25 m from the transmitter. Calculate the necessary minimum height of the receiving aerial. Assume the k factor to be 0.7 and allow a clearance equal to 0.6 times the radius of the first Fresnel zone.

Solution

When flat earth is assumed the obstacle must be given an effective height of

$$(25 \times 14 \times 10^6)/(2 \times 0.7 \times 6400 \times 10^3) = 39 \text{ m} + 50 \text{ m} = 89 \text{ m} \quad (\lambda = 0.1 \text{ m})$$

The first Fresnel zone clearance is

$$0.6\sqrt{[(0.1 \times 25 \times 14 \times 10^6)/(39 \times 10^3)]} = 18 \text{ m}$$

From Fig. 9.26

$$\tan \theta = [(89 + 18) - 80]/(25 \times 10^3) = (h_r - 80)/(39 \times 10^3)$$

or

$$h_r = 122 \text{ m} \; (Ans.)$$

Fig. 9.26

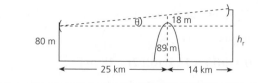

In the planning of a space-wave radio link a *path profile* is drawn on flat earth. The path profile has the heights of the principal hills modified to allow for curved earth ($k = 0.7$). A first Fresnel zone clearance of 0.577 at the design frequency is used to draw a straight line to represent the radio path between the transmitting and receiving stations. A typical path profile is shown by Fig. 9.27.

Fig. 9.27 *Typical path profile*

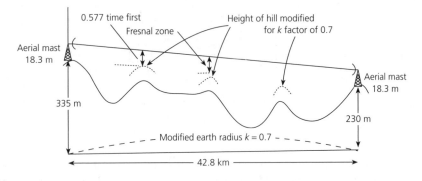

Fig. 9.28 *(a) Diffraction of radio wave, (b) Calculation of diffraction angle*

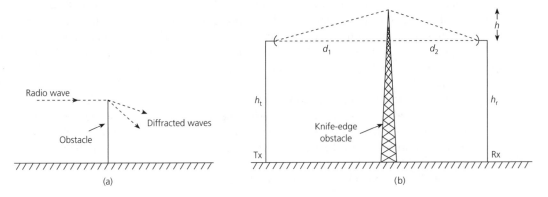

Height diversity

If the radio path crosses over a wide stretch of water, such as a tidal estuary, or the sea, the geometry of the link may vary with the tide. It is often necessary to employ some form of diversity reception in order to obtain a reliable system. To economise on the use of the frequency spectrum it is usual to employ *height diversity* in which two receiving aerials are used, one mounted above the other. For optimum results the lower aerial should be mounted at a height corresponding to the first maximum in the field strength/height characteristic (Fig. 9.21) and the other aerial mounted at the height of the null immediately above.

Diffraction

When a radio wave passes near to an obstacle whose dimensions are of the same order as the signal wavelength the wave will be *diffracted*. Diffraction allows a radio wave to appear at points behind an obstacle where straight-line ray theory predicts that there should be zero signal. The diffracted signal has a greater loss than the free-space loss. The diffraction loss increases with increase in frequency except for grazing incidence when the loss is independent of frequency and approximately 6 dB. Figure 9.28(a)

Fig. 9.29

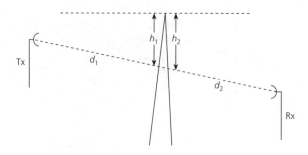

shows diffraction at the edge of an obstacle; it can be seen that the radio wave is bent around the obstacle. Diffraction allows a radio signal to propagate beyond the horizon and behind obstacles such as a hill or a building. The field strength of the diffracted signal falls with distance travelled into the shadowed area but it can provide a useful signal. This is not very important with line-of-sight radio systems which are engineered to avoid obstacles but it is very important with mobile systems. A mobile radio receiver is continually on the move and is often in places that are not in the line of sight of the base station aerial and then reception depends upon a combination of reflected and diffracted signals.

The simplest case of diffraction occurs when the obstacle may be represented by a single knife-edge as shown by Fig. 9.28(b). The wave that reaches the radio receiver by means of diffraction has travelled a longer distance than it would have if a direct path existed. From Fig. 9.28 the length of the direct path is $d_1 + d_2$, and the length of the diffracted path is $\sqrt{(d_1^2 + h^2)} + \sqrt{(d_2^2 + h^2)}$.

The difference between the two path lengths is

$$
\begin{aligned}
\text{difference} &= \sqrt{(d_1^2 + h^2)} + \sqrt{(d_2^2 + h^2)} - (d_1 + d_2) \\
&= d_1\sqrt{[1 + (h/d_1)^2]} + d_2\sqrt{[1 + (h/d_2)^2]} - (d_1 + d_2) \\
&= d_1 + d_1 h^2/2d_1^2 + d_2 + d_2 h^2/2d_2^2 - (d_1 + d_2) \\
&= h^2/2d_1 + h^2/2d_2 = (h^2/2)[(d_1 + d_2)/d_1 d_2]
\end{aligned}
\tag{9.26}
$$

which produces a phase change ϕ of

$$
\phi = (2\pi h^2/2\lambda)[(d_1 + d_2)/d_1 d_2]
\tag{9.27}
$$

This means that ϕ is a function of both the height and position of the obstacle relative to the transmitting and receiving aerials. If $h_t \neq h_r$ strictly the height h either side of the obstacle ought to be considered; see Fig. 9.29.

In a mobile radio system radio waves may arrive at the receiver after following a variety of different paths. These paths may include (a) the direct path, (b) reflections from various buildings, and (c) diffraction from various obstacles. Any of these paths may, or may not, exist in a particular case; for mobile reception within an urban area it is quite likely that a direct path may be non-existent. Figure 9.30 shows a typical example of the various paths that a radio signal transmitted by a base station may follow to provide service to a mobile receiver.

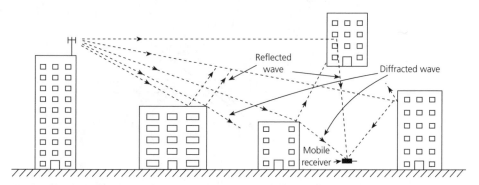

Space-wave fading

As in the HF band fading may be either general or selective. Fading caused by varying attenuation is usually general while fading caused by multi-path propagation is selective.

General

The attenuation of a VHF/UHF/SHF terrestrial or satellite radio signal is mainly caused by rainfall. Heavy rain causes fluctuations in the attenuation of the radio path as the intensity of the rainfall varies. Unusual weather conditions may vary the propagation characteristics of a link to such an extent that the radio wave no longer clears an obstacle. If the path passes over a wide expanse of water surface fog may make the direct radio wave descend to water level where it will be reflected and probably miss the receiving aerial.

Selective

Selective fading occurs whenever two or more paths exist between the transmitting and receiving aerials, one direct and the other(s) reflected from the earth and/or some obstacle. A 40 km link, for example, with aerials at heights of 500 m and 60 m, and one reflection will have a path-length difference of 1.5 m. The reflected signal will arrive at the receiver $1.5/(3 \times 10^8) = 5$ ns after the direct wave arrived. This time delay is equivalent to a frequency of 200 MHz, which means that the two waves will move into, and out of, phase to add or subtract algebraically every 200 MHz.

Scatter propagation

A tropospheric scatter radio link operates with its distant terminal well beyond the radio horizon. A large amount of RF energy is radiated by a highly directive aerial towards the horizon. A very small proportion of the radiated energy is *forward scattered* by the troposphere and is directed downwards towards the receiving aerial. Most of the

Fig. 9.31 *Tropospheric scatter link*

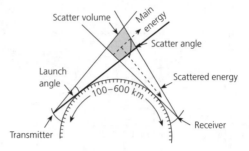

transmitted energy continues upwards, passes through the ionosphere and is radiated into space. Figure 9.31 shows the path geometry of a tropospheric scatter radio link. The solid angles formed by the narrow radiation patterns of the two aerials intercept one another to form a common volume that is known as the *scatter volume*. The scatter volume is typically only 1 or 2 km above the earth and it is here that the useful energy is returned to earth. Both the transmitter *launch angle* and the *scatter angle* should be small, usually less than about 4°.

Tropospheric scatter propagation is possible at most frequencies higher than 500 MHz, but it is employed mostly at frequencies in the region of 900 MHz, 2 GHz and 5 GHz. It provides a bandwidth of several megahertz and is employed to carry wideband telephony systems, with between 38 and 132 channels. The main application for a tropospheric scatter system is for communication over hostile terrain, such as sea or mountains, where a communications satellite system would not be economically viable. It is the principal broadband communication technology employed for communication between the mainland and the North Sea oil rigs; these operate at 2.25 GHz with a transmitted power of 1 kW.

The path attenuation between transmitter and receiver is much greater than the free-space attenuation by an *over-the-horizon loss*, or *scatter loss*. The scatter loss accounts for the fact that only a small fraction of the transmitted power arrives at the receiving aerial. Since this loss is high, typically 70 dB or more, a tropospheric scatter system must be provided with high-power transmitters, high-gain aerials and low-noise-factor, highly sensitive radio receivers. The received signal is further reduced by the *aperture-to-coupling loss*. This loss expresses the reduction in the gain of a parabolic dish aerial when it receives a scattered signal and is typically about 10 dB; it occurs because the received signal is made up of a large number of components bearing a random phase and amplitude relationship to one another. The scatter loss is continually varying and this leads to substantial fading of the received signal. To counter this some kind of diversity reception is usual and perhaps the most commonly employed is *quadruple space diversity*. This involves the use of four aerials, two at each end of a route. The two transmitting aerials radiate energy simultaneously with their signals polarised at right angles to one another. The two receiving aerials pick up signals in both the horizontal and vertical planes and feed receivers whose outputs are commoned.

EXAMPLE 9.13

A 200 km tropospheric scatter system operates at 2 GHz with a transmitted power of 1 kW and receiver noise factor of 5 dB. The system uses frequency modulation with a maximum modulating frequency of l00 kHz and a deviation ratio of 4.5. Calculate the dimensions of the identical transmitting and receiving aerials required to give an output signal-to-noise ratio of 60 dB. The over-the-horizon loss is 70 dB and the aerial noise temperature is 290 K. Assume the aerial to have an illumination efficiency of 60% and an aperture-to-medium loss of 9 dB.

Solution

The frequency deviation of the signal is $4.5 \times 100 = 450$ kHz. Hence the required bandwidth is $2(450 + 100) \times 10^3 = 1.1$ MHz. Deviation ratio $D = 4.5$. Then

$$60 \text{ dB} = P_R \text{ dBW} + 20 \log_{10}(D\sqrt{3}) - kTB \text{ dBW} - F \text{ dB}$$
$$= P_R \text{ dBW} + 20 \log_{10}(4.5\sqrt{3}) \text{ dB} - (-143.6) \text{ dBW} - 5 \text{ dB}$$
$$= P_R \text{ dBW} + 156.44 \text{ dBW}$$

and

$$P_R = -96.44 \text{ dBW} = 2.27 \times 10^{-10} \text{ W}$$

Therefore,

$$2.27 \times 10^{-10} = G_T G_R \times 1000[(3 \times 10^8)/(2 \times 10^9 \times 4\pi \times 200 \times 10^3)]^2 \times 10^{-7} \times 0.125$$

$$G_T G_R = (2.27 \times 10^{-10})/(4.45 \times 10^{-20}) = 5.101 \times 10^9$$

$$G_T = G_R = 71\,422 \quad \text{or} \quad 48.5 \text{ dB}$$

and so

$$71\,422 = 0.6(\pi D/\lambda)^2 = 0.6(\pi D/0.15)^2$$

or

$$D \approx 16.5 \text{ m } (Ans.)$$

Propagation via a communications satellite

The power received by the ground station of a communications satellite link can be determined using the free-space loss expression $(4\pi D/\lambda)^2$. This relationship can be alternatively expressed as

$$P_R = \text{(effective radiated power} \times \text{gain of receiving aerial)/} \text{(transmission loss)} \tag{9.28}$$

The received power is often referred to as the carrier power. In practice, further losses are experienced because of climatic conditions such as rain and snow.

EXAMPLE 9.14

A communications satellite is 40 000 km from a point on the surface of the earth and transmits a power of 2 W from an aerial of 20 dB gain. Calculate the power received at the earth station by an aerial of effective aperture 10 m if the frequency is 11 GHz.

Solution

Method (a):

$$\lambda = (3 \times 10^8)/(11 \times 10^9) = 0.027 \text{ m}$$

The flux density at the receiving aerial is

$$P_a = P_T G_T/4\pi D^2 = (2 \times 100)/[4\pi(40 \times 10^6)^2] = 9.95 \times 10^{-15} \text{ W m}^{-1}$$

The received power P_R is

$$P_R = P_a A_e = 9.95 \times 10^{-15} \times 10 = 9.95 \times 10^{-14} \text{ W } (Ans.)$$

Method (b):

$$\text{Transmission loss} = [(4\pi \times 40 \times 10^6)/0.027]^2 = 3.466 \times 10^{20}$$

$$\text{Gain of the receiving aerial} = 4\pi A_e/\lambda^2 = (4\pi \times 10)/0.027^2 = 172\ 378$$

Therefore,

$$\text{received power} = (2 \times 100 \times 172\ 378)/(3.466 \times 10^{20})$$
$$= 9.95 \times 10^{-14} \text{ W } (Ans.)$$

EXERCISES

9.1 A 2 GHz radio link operates over a 48 km stretch of sea with aerials mounted at equal heights. Calculate the necessary heights of the aerials if the k factor is 0.65 and the direct wave is to clear the sea by a distance equal to 0.577 times the first Fresnel zone. If a second aerial is fitted to give height diversity, calculate its height also.

9.2 An ionospheric layer has a maximum electron density of 1.6×10^{11} electrons/m^3 and is at a virtual height of 162 km. Calculate its MUF if the radius of the earth is 6400 km and the sky-wave link is 2000 km long.

9.3 At a distance of 1 km from a 1 MHz radio transmitter the daytime field strength is 200 mV m^{-1}. Calculate the field strength 110 km from the transmitter if the ground-wave attenuation is 9 dB greater than the free-space loss. Also calculate the field strength at the same point during the night when there is also a sky wave received. Assume the sky wave to be reflected from a height of 120 km and that the earth is flat.

9.4 Explain how the field strength of a UHF transmitter varies with the distance from the transmitter.

Calculate the maximum range for a UHF radio link if the transmitting aerial is at a height of 110 m and the receiving aerial height is 60 m. Take the radius of the earth as 6400 km.

9.5 A transmitting aerial has a gain of 6 dBi and is mounted 180 m above flat earth. The transmitted power is 5 W at 50 MHz and the 16 m high receiving aerial is 18 km distant. Calculate the total field strength at the receiving aerial if the reflection coefficient of the earth is −0.8.

9.6 A communications satellite is in orbit 35 800 km above an earth station. The down path from satellite to earth station operates at 4 GHz. At the earth station the receiver has an effective input noise temperature of 60 K and a bandwidth of 30 MHz, the parabolic dish aerial has a gain of 60 dBi, and the aerial noise temperature is 40 K. If the EIRP of the satellite is 30 dBW, calculate the carrier-to-noise ratio of the receiver.

9.7 A communications satellite link has the following data: operating frequency 6 GHz, gain of satellite aerial 6 dBi, gain of earth station aerial 50 dBi, noise temperature of earth station aerial 290 K, noise factor of receiver 3 dB, bandwidth of receiver 20 MHz, and link length 36 000 km.

   The carrier-to-noise ratio at the earth station is to be 30 dB. Calculate (a) the minimum signal power density at the earth station receiving aerial, (b) the minimum field strength at the receiving aerial, and (c) the minimum power that must be transmitted by the satellite.

9.8 Discuss how the propagation of HF radio waves is affected by sun-spots. The maximum electron density in the ionospheric layer is 1.6×10^{11} electrons/m^3 and occurs at a height of 162 km. Calculate the skip distance if the radius of the earth is 6400 km and the MUF is 5.6 MHz.

9.9 Explain briefly the way in which a tropospheric scatter system works. A 2.5 GHz tropospheric scatter system has its terminals 200 km apart and uses parabolic dish aerials whose diameters are both 6.1 m. If the transmitted power is 20 kW and the over-the-horizon loss is 62 dB calculate the signal power supplied to the receiver.

9.10 What is meant by the term Fresnel zone and what is the use of this zone in radio communications? A 600 MHz signal is transmitted from a 75 m high aerial towards the receiving aerial 30 km away. There is a 42 m high obstacle 20 m from the transmitter which must be cleared by the direct ray by a distance equal to 0.577 times the radius of the first Fresnel zone. Assuming the k factor to be 0.7, determine the minimum height for the receiving aerial.

9.11 (a) What is meant by the refractivity value of the atmosphere? (b) If the refractive index is 1.000 32 determine the refractivity.

9.12 (a) List the applications of HF radio using sky-wave propagation. (b) State the two main disadvantages of HF radio.

9.13 (a) Explain why a space-wave path must be kept clear of any obstacles.
   (b) What is the least clearance required?
   (c) Calculate the free-space loss for a 7 GHz, 40 km path.

9.14 (a) List the causes of fading in a UHF radio link. (b) A radio transmitter sends an output power of 5 W into a waveguide feeder of 2.6 dB loss. If the gain of the transmitting aerial is 32 dB calculate the EIRP.

9.15 A 7 GHz, 30 km radio link has identical transmitting and receiving aerials with 32 dB gain and waveguide feeder losses of 2.5 dB. The transmitted power is 2 W. Calculate the received power.

9.16 (a) Calculate the free-space loss of a 1 km, 450 MHz mobile radio link.
   (b) If the required signal-to-noise ratio is 22 dB and the total noise level at the receiver is −120 dBm calculate the required transmitted power. (Both aerials have a gain of 0 dB.)
   (c) Discuss how reflections and/or diffraction on the radio path between the base station and the mobile may alter the answer to (b).

9.17 Explain (a) the principle of ground wave propagation and (b) why a ground wave cannot be horizontally polarised.

9.18 (a) Explain what is meant by (i) power density, (ii) received power, (iii) electric field strength.
   (b) Calculate the power density at a distance of 25 km if the transmitted power is 1 kW.
   (c) Calculate the electric field strength at the same point.
   (d) Calculate (b) using (c).

9.19 A 10 km radio link operates at 900 MHz. The transmitted power is 20 W and the aerial gains are $G_T = 3$ dB and $G_R = 4$ dB. Calculate (a) the received power and (b) the input voltage to the radio receiver. Assume the radio receiver to have a matched input resistance of 50 Ω.

10 Radio circuits

After reading this chapter you should be able to:

(a) Describe the operation of a Class C RF amplifier and understand why it is often employed in radio transmitters.

(b) Explain that a Class C RF amplifier can be modified to work as an amplitude modulator.

(c) Explain that any non-linear device can be used as an amplitude modulator and state the two kinds of non-linearity that are employed.

(d) Explain the action of a balanced modulator.

(e) Understand the need for amplitude demodulation and discuss the various types of demodulator that are available.

(f) Explain the operation of a diode detector.

(g) Calculate the efficiency and the maximum load capacitance of a diode detector.

(h) Explain the operation of a product detector.

(i) State that frequency modulators are either direct or indirect and support the use of the indirect method mathematically.

(j) Explain the operation of a reactance frequency modulator.

(k) Explain the action of a varactor diode frequency modulator.

(l) Explain the operation of a phase modulator.

(m) Compare and contrast the various kinds of FM detector.

(n) Explain the action of a quadrature detector.

(o) Explain the operation of a PLL detector.

(p) Explain the need for frequency synthesis and discuss the operation of a frequency synthesiser.

(q) Understand DDFS.

(r) Explain how a mixer can work as either a down-converter or an up-converter and compare the various types of mixer.

(s) Explain the need for a squelch circuit in a radio receiver and explain the operation of a squelch circuit.

Radio receivers and transmitters employ a number of circuits that are peculiar to radio and the more commonly used of these will be discussed in this chapter. Circuits that are commonly employed in electronic engineering, such as audio amplifiers, small-signal RF amplifiers, oscillators and power supplies, are not discussed. RF amplifiers are required to have a low noise factor, high gain, low intermodulation and harmonic distortion; the amplifiers used in sound broadcast receivers are usually required to have some selectivity as well and, in particular, be able to reject the *image channel signal* (p. 343). Often RF amplifiers are provided inside ICs that contain a number of other circuits as well, such as oscillators, mixers and detectors. Low-noise amplifiers (LNAs) which are used in the UHF band are provided in microwave ICs (MMICs) that include one RF transistor and need only input and output coupling capacitors to provide, typically, a gain of 20 dB, a noise factor of less than 3 dB over a bandwidth of from 0 Hz to 3 GHz. Intermediate-frequency (IF) amplifiers, other than those in cheap sound broadcast receivers, are usually in IC packages that also include circuits such as automatic gain control, mixer and quadrature detection.

Class C RF amplifiers

In an RF amplifier that is operated under Class C conditions the transistor is biased beyond cut-off. When the signal applied to the base–emitter circuit of the transistor is large enough to take the base positive with respect to the emitter by about 0.7 V, the transistor will conduct. Figure 10.1 illustrates Class C bias in which the collector current of the transistor flows in a series of narrow pulses whose duration is less than 180°. The basic circuit of a Class C RF amplifier is shown in Fig. 10.2. The inductor in the collector tuned circuit is often tapped as shown so that the transistor works into its optimum load resistance. The RF choke L_1 is necessary to prevent RF currents passing into the power supply. When a signal voltage whose positive peak value is large enough to take the base–emitter voltage V_{BE} positive is applied to the circuit, the transistor will conduct current only at the positive peaks of the signal waveform. This means that the collector current is far from sinusoidal but if the collector circuit is tuned to be resonant at the signal frequency a sinusoidal voltage will appear across it. The peak voltage of the output waveform is directly proportional to the collector supply voltage V_{CC}.

Fig. 10.1 *Class C bias* **Fig. 10.2** *Class C RF amplifier*

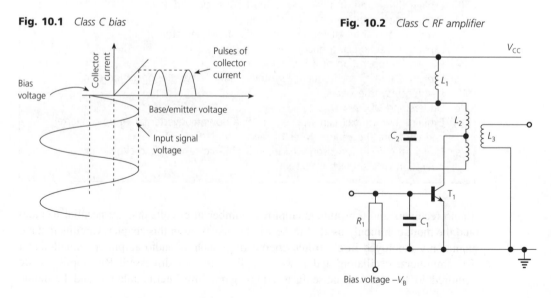

Aim: To investigate Class C bias of a transistor and the basic Class C RF amplifier.
Components and equipment: Capacitors, two 1 μF and one nF (value to be calculated); μH inductor (value to be calculated); 1 kΩ, 3 kΩ and 100 kΩ resistors; transistor (able to work at 50 kHz). Two power supplies. CRO and oscillator.
Breadboard.
Procedure:

(a) Build the circuit given in Fig. 10.3(a).
(b) Connect the oscillator to the input terminals of the circuit and set it to 0 V at 50 kHz. Connect the CRO across the 3 kΩ collector resistor. Set the collector supply voltage V_{CC} to 15 V.
(c) Increase the oscillator voltage in a number of suitable steps and each time note the output waveform displayed by the CRO. State the input signal voltage at which the transistor started to conduct. Note the effect of continually increasing the signal voltage and explain what happens.
(d) Modify the circuit as shown by Fig. 10.3(b). Try, in turn, different values of bias voltage V_B from 0 to 6 V. What happens as the input signal voltage is increased from 0 V? Explain.
(e) Revert to $V_B = 3$ V and $V_{in} = 4$ V and reduce the collector supply voltage to zero. Then increase V_{CC} in 2 V steps up to 20 V and at each step note the waveform displayed by the CRO. State whether the amplitudes of the collector current pulses are directly proportional to V_{CC}.
(f) Remove the 3 kΩ resistor from the circuit and replace it with a parallel LC circuit; see Fig. 10.3(c). Calculate suitable values for L and C for the parallel circuit to be resonant at 50 kHz, e.g. $C = 22$ nF and $L \approx 460$ μH as shown. Make $V_{CC} = 12$ V and with the input signal voltage at 4 V/50 kHz and $V_B = 3$ V note the waveform displayed by the CRO. Measure its peak voltage.
(g) Vary V_{CC} and note whether the amplitude of the output waveform varies in direct proportion to V_{CC}.
(h) Suggest an application for the last effect and say why Class C amplifiers are used in radio transmitters.

Fig. 10.3

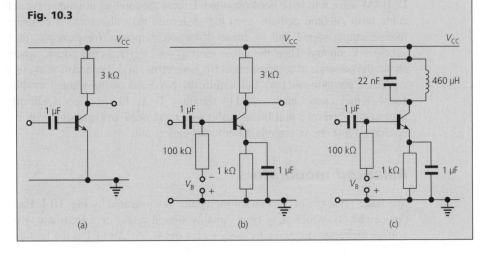

(a)   (b)   (c)

Amplitude modulators

Probably the most commonly employed method of generating a DSBAM wave in a radio transmitter is the anode-, or collector-modulated Class C RF tuned amplifier. While most AM transmitters employ transistor Class power amplifiers, some high-power transmitters with transmitted powers in the kilowatt range still employ the thermionic valve (usually a tetrode). The collector, or anode, current of a Class C RF amplifier is directly proportional to the collector, or anode, supply voltage. Hence, if the collector (anode) supply voltage can be varied by the modulating signal an AM wave will be produced.

Other DSB modulators utilise the non-linear relationship between the applied voltage and the resulting current of many electronic devices.

Non-linear amplitude modulators

Essentially, there are two types of non-linear characteristic: (a) those in which the characteristic is continuous and can be described by a power series of the form $i = av + bv^2 + cv^3 + \ldots$, and (b) those in which the device acts as an electronic switch (this means that the carrier voltage must be large enough to turn the non-linear device ON and OFF).

If a carrier wave $V_c \sin \omega_c t$ and a modulating signal $V_m(t)$ are applied in series to a non-linear device and the carrier voltage is not large enough to switch the device, then the current flowing will be given by

$$i = a[V_c \sin \omega_c t + V_m(t)] + b[V_c \sin \omega_c t + V_m(t)]^2 + c[V_c \sin \omega_c t + V_m(t)]^3 \ldots$$

The squared term will produce

$$i = bV_c^2 \sin^2 \omega_c t + bV_m^2(t) + 2bV_m(t)V_c \sin \omega_c t$$

and if a filter can be employed to pass only the terms $aV_c \sin \omega_c t + 2bV_m(t)V_c \sin \omega_c t$, a DSBAM wave will have been obtained. Unless the total input voltage is fairly small the cubic term cv^3 (and perhaps even higher terms) may also make a contribution to the filtered output signal and so cause distortion. Suppose, for example, that $V_m(t) = V_1 \sin \omega_1 t + V_2 \sin \omega_2 t$. Then the cubic term gives $cV_m^2(t) \sin \omega_c t$ which, when expanded, shows the presence of components at frequencies ω_c, $\omega_c \pm 2\omega_1$ and $\omega_c \pm \omega_2$, $\omega_c \pm (\omega_1 \pm \omega_2)$.

These components may fall within the passband of the wanted modulating signal and then they cannot be removed by the filter. To avoid this effect it will often be found necessary to use two non-linear devices in a balanced arrangement, with respect to the carrier, so that the intermodulation terms cancel out.

Balanced modulators

The basic principle of a balanced modulator is illustrated by Fig. 10.4. Each non-linear device (NLD), which may be a suitably biased diode or a transistor, has a current–voltage characteristic given by $i = i_0 + av + bv^2 + \ldots$. An FET is the best device for this

Fig. 10.4 *Balanced modulator*

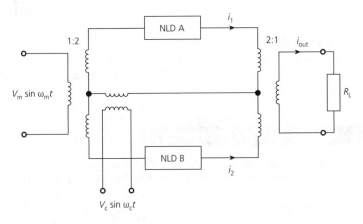

purpose since its mutual characteristic very nearly obeys a square law. Assuming identical square-law devices, the voltage applied to NLD A is

$$v_A = V_m \sin \omega_m t + V_c \sin \omega_c t$$

and the voltage applied to NLD B is

$$v_B = -V_m \sin \omega_m t + V_c \sin \omega_c t$$

Therefore,

$$i_1 = aV_m \sin \omega_m t + aV_c \sin \omega_c t + bV_m^2 \sin^2 \omega_m t + 2bV_m V_c \sin \omega_c t \sin \omega_m t + bV_c^2 \sin \omega_c t$$

$$i_2 = -aV_m \sin \omega_m t + aV_c \sin \omega_c t + bV_m^2 \sin^2 \omega_m t \\ - 2bV_m V_c \sin \omega_c t \sin \omega_m t + bV_c^2 \sin^2 \omega_c t$$

The output current i_{out} of the modulator is proportional to the difference between i_1 and i_2 and so it is equal to

$$i_{out} = 2(aV_m \sin \omega_m t + 2bV_m V_c \sin \omega_c t \sin \omega_m t)$$

The term at the modulating signal frequency can be removed by a filter, provided $\omega_c \gg \omega_m$, to leave the wanted DSBSC signal. A number of IC balanced modulators are available, such as the LM/MC 1496 and 1596, both of which are available from several manufacturers. An IC device will probably be used when it is required to avoid the use of a relatively bulky transformer and/or a conversion gain is wanted.

The switching-type DSB modulator includes one, or more, transistors that are turned ON and OFF by the carrier voltage and it effectively multiplies the modulating signal by a square wave whose amplitude is either ±1 V, or 0 V and 1 V. The Fourier series for a ±1 V square wave is

$$v = (4/\pi)[\sin \omega_c t + \tfrac{1}{3}\sin 3\omega_c t + \tfrac{1}{5}\sin 5\omega_c t + \dots] \qquad (10.1)$$

and for a square wave whose voltage is either 0 V or 1 V is

$$v = \tfrac{1}{2} + (2/\pi)[\sin \omega_c t + \tfrac{1}{3}\sin 3\omega_c t + \tfrac{1}{5}\sin 5\omega_c t + \dots] \qquad (10.2)$$

If the input signal is $V_B + V_m \sin \omega_m t$ then, in either case, the output voltage will be equal to $K \sin \omega_c t + K \sin \omega_c t \sin \omega_m t + \ldots$, which is the wanted DSBAM signal.

Diode balanced modulator

The most commonly employed form of discrete (not inside an IC) balanced modulator is the four-diode balanced, or ring, modulator whose operation was described in Chapter 4.

PRACTICAL EXERCISE 10.2

Aim: To investigate the operation of a diode ring modulator.
Components and equipment: Four signal diodes, e.g. 1N4148. Two centre-tapped transformers. Two signal generators. CRO. Breadboard.
Procedure:

(a) Build the diode balanced modulator whose circuit is shown in Fig. 10.5.
(b) Connect one signal generator to the modulating signal input terminals of the circuit and set it to 1 V at 2 kHz. Connect the other signal generator to the carrier input terminals and set it to 10 V at 50 kHz. Connect the CRO to the output terminals of the modulator and observe the output waveform.
(c) Vary the modulating signal frequency from 500 Hz to 3 kHz in 500 Hz steps and each time note the output waveform. What is the effect of changing the modulating signal frequency?
(d) With the modulating signal frequency at 3 kHz increase the modulating voltage in 2 V steps and note the effect on the output waveform. What happens when the modulating signal voltage becomes larger than the carrier voltage?
(e) Reduce the modulating signal voltage to 1 V and the carrier voltage to 5 V. Note the output waveform. Then increase the modulating signal voltage to 6 V and note any effect on the output waveform. Say which voltage is switching the diodes. Increase the modulating signal voltage to 8 V. What happens to the output waveform now?
(f) Probably the displayed output waveform has had a number of spikes which ought to be removed in a practical system. Why? Design a low-pass filter to remove those spikes; the filter could perhaps be merely a shunt capacitor or perhaps a constant-k low-pass filter.
(g) The circuit can also employed as a phase detector when the two input signals are at, or near, the same frequency. Set both signal generators to 2 V at 1 kHz

Fig. 10.5

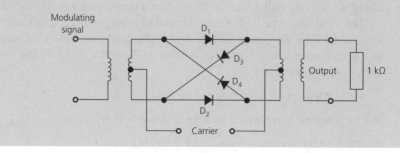

---

and connect a d.c. voltmeter across the output terminals. Observe the output waveform and measure the output voltage. Vary the frequency of one of the signal generators by a few hertz and note the effect on (i) the output waveform and (ii) the d.c. output voltage.

PRACTICAL EXERCISE 10.3

Aim: To investigate the operation of an IC balanced modulator.

Components and equipment: 1596 balanced modulator. Three 51 Ω, two 750 Ω, one 1 kΩ and two 3.9 kΩ resistors. One 50 kΩ variable resistor. Two 0.1 µF capacitors. Breadboard. CRO. Two power supplies. RF signal source. AF signal source.

Procedure:

(a) Build the circuit given in Fig. 10.6.

(b) Connect the RF signal source to the carrier input terminal of the circuit and set it to 0.6 V at 1 MHz. Connect the AF signal source to the modulating signal input terminal and set it to 0.3 V at 1 kHz.

(c) Use the CRO to observe and note the output waveform of the circuit. Note and explain the effect of varying the 50 kΩ variable resistor.

(d) With the 50 kΩ resistor at its optimum setting vary (i) the modulating signal frequency from 50 Hz to 5 kHz, and (ii) the modulating signal voltage from 0 to 0.6 V. Each time note the effect on the output waveform of the circuit.

(e) Overmodulate the circuit by increasing the modulating signal voltage to 1 V and note the effect on the output waveform.

Fig. 10.6

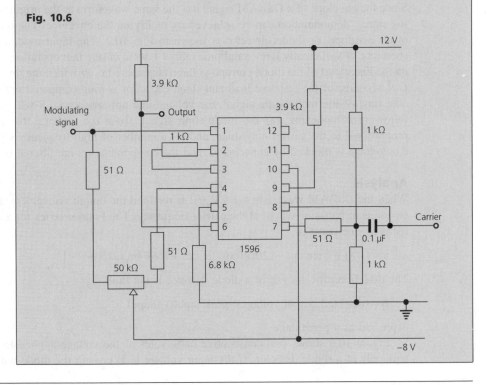

Fig. 10.7 *Diode detector*

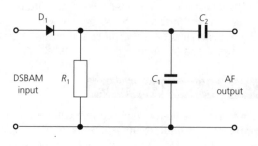

AM detectors

The methods used to detect, or demodulate, a DSBAM signal fall into one of three main classes: (a) non-coherent or *envelope detection*, (b) coherent or *synchronous detection*, and (c) *non-linear detection*. Phase-locked loop (PLL) demodulation is also possible for DSBAM but it does not have a good performance. The envelope or diode detector is the most commonly employed form of discrete component DSBAM demodulator because of its simplicity and cheapness. SSBSC/ISB signals are most often demodulated using a product detector.

Envelope detection

Since the envelope of a DSBAM signal has the same waveform as the original modulating signal, demodulation can be achieved by rectifying the envelope. The basic circuit of an envelope, or diode, detector is shown in Fig. 10.7. The input modulated signal should be of sufficiently large amplitude (about 1 V) to ensure that operation takes place on the linear part of the diode current–voltage characteristic. Provided the time constant, $C_1 R_1$ seconds, of the resistive load and shunt capacitor is long compared with the periodic time of the modulating signal, the voltage that appears across R will include the following components: (a) the modulating signal, (b) a d.c. voltage that is directly proportional to the carrier amplitude, and (c) a number of high-frequency signals. The d.c. voltage is blocked by capacitor C_2 and the components (c) are filtered off.

Analysis
When the DSBAM wave $[\sin \omega_c t + V_m(t)]$ is rectified the output voltage consists of the envelope of half-sine waves at the carrier frequency. The Fourier series for a half-wave rectified sine wave is

$$v = (1/\pi) + \tfrac{1}{2}\sin \omega_c t - (2/\pi)[(\cos 2\omega_c t)/3 + (\cos 4\omega_c t)/15 + \ldots] \tag{10.3}$$

The detection efficiency η of a diode detector is the ratio

$$\eta = (\text{detected output voltage})/(\text{peak input voltage}) \tag{10.4}$$

expressed as a percentage.

Figure 10.8 shows two consecutive half-cycles of the voltage applied to the input terminals of a diode detector. If the input voltage is $V_c \cos \omega_c t$ the diode will conduct

Fig. 10.8 *Action of the diode detector*

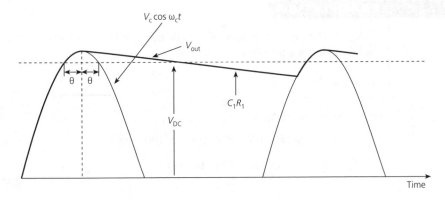

when $V_c \cos \omega_c t > V_{out}$; then $\omega_c t = \theta = \cos^{-1}(V_{out}/V_c)$, or $\cos \theta = V_{out}/V_c$. During the time period 2θ, the current that flows into the diode detector is

$$i = (V_c \cos \omega_c t - V_{out})/r$$

where r is the forward resistance of the diode. The average value of the diode current is

$$I_{DC} = (1/2\pi)\int_{-\pi}^{\pi} i \ d\omega_c t = (1/2\pi)\int_{-\theta}^{\theta} i \ d\omega_c t = (1/\pi)\int_{0}^{\theta} i \ d\omega_c t$$

$$= (1/\pi r)(V_c \sin \theta - V_{out}\theta) = (V_c/\pi r)(\sin \theta - \theta \cos \theta)$$

Hence, the output voltage is

$$V_{out} = I_{DC}R_1 = (V_c R_1/\pi r)(\sin \theta - \theta \cos \theta)$$

and

$$\eta = V_{out}/V_c = \cos \theta = (R_1/\pi r)(\sin \theta - \theta \cos \theta)$$

Then, $(\pi r/R_1) = \tan \theta - \theta \approx \theta + \theta^3/3 - \theta = \theta^3/3$, or $\theta = (3\pi r/R_1)^{1/3}$, and

$$\eta = \cos(3\pi r/R_1)^{1/3} \times 100\%$$
$$\approx [1 - \tfrac{1}{2}(3\pi r/R_1)^{2/3}] \times 100\% \tag{10.5}$$

For a low-voltage input signal the forward resistance of the diode is not constant and so the efficiency of the diode detector will vary. For voltages in excess of about 1 V the efficiency is constant at (usually) 90% or more.

The input resistance of a diode detector is related to its detection efficiency. The diode conducts only when the input voltage is at, or near, its peak positive value. Hence the average input power is

$$P_{IN} = V_c I_{DC} = \eta V_c^2/R_1 = (V_c/\sqrt{2})^2 \times (1/R_{IN}).$$

Therefore,

$$R_{IN} = R_1/2\eta \tag{10.6}$$

In many radio receivers the reactive part of the detector low-pass filter is connected via a buffer amplifier so that the load seen by the diode detector is always resistive.

EXAMPLE 10.1

Calculate the input resistance of a diode detector that has a load resistance of 8 kΩ and a diode forward resistance of 100 Ω.

Solution

From equation (10.5),

$$\eta = [1 - 0.5(3\pi \times 100)/(8 \times 10^3)^{2/3}] \times 100 = 88\%$$

$$R_{IN} = 8000/(2 \times 0.88) = 4545 \ \Omega \ (Ans.)$$

Clipping caused by incorrect time constant

The diode detector shunt capacitor C_1 must be able to discharge rapidly enough for the voltage across it to follow the modulation envelope. This is most difficult when the envelope is decreasing in amplitude; see Fig. 10.9. If the time constant C_1R_1 is too long, relative to the periodic time of the modulating signal, the capacitor voltage will not be able to follow the troughs of the modulation envelope; this is shown by the dashed line in Fig. 10.9.

As the capacitor C_1 discharges through R_1 its voltage is $v = V_c e^{-t/CR}$, where V_c is its initial peak value which is equal to the peak input voltage (minus the diode voltage drop). The rate at which the capacitor voltage v falls is given by $-dv/dt = v/C_1R_1$. For v to follow the modulation envelope without distortion

$$v/C_1R_1 \geq d[V_c(1 + m \sin \omega_m t)]/dt \geq -m\omega_m V_c \cos \omega_m t \ \text{V s}^{-1}$$

Thus,

$$V_c(1 + m \sin \omega_m t) \geq -m\omega_m V_c \cos \omega_m t$$

Fig. 10.9 *Output voltage of a diode detector showing the effect of an incorrect time constant*

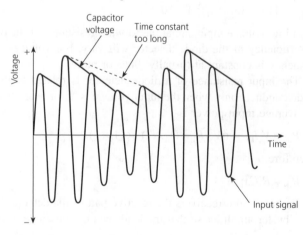

or

$$-(1/C_1R_1) \geq (m\omega_m V_c \cos \omega_m t)/V_c(1 + m \sin \omega_m t) \qquad (10.7)$$

This inequality is most difficult to satisfy when its right-hand side has its maximum negative value. Differentiating and equating to zero gives $\sin \omega_m t = -m$. Therefore, $\cos \omega_m t = -\sqrt{(1 - m^2)}$, and substituting into inequality (10.7) gives

$$-(1/C_1R_1) \geq [-m\omega_m\sqrt{(1 - m^2)}]/(1 - m^2) = -m\omega_m/\sqrt{(1 - m^2)}$$

and

$$C_1R_1 \leq \sqrt{(1 - m^2)}/m\omega_m \qquad (10.8)$$

The time constant must be long compared with the periodic time of the carrier but short compared with the periodic time of the highest frequency in the modulating signal. Sound broadcast radio receivers often use a time constant in the region of 20 μs.

EXAMPLE 10.2

A diode detector is to produce an audio output signal in the frequency band 100 to 4500 Hz. If the maximum modulation depth is 50% and the load resistor is 10 kΩ calculate the maximum possible value for the shunt capacitor.

Solution

From equation (10.8),

$$C_{1(max)} = [\sqrt{(1 - 0.25)}]/(0.5 \times 2\pi \times 4500 \times 10 \times 10^3) = 6.125 \text{ nF } (Ans.)$$

The diode detector has the advantage of simplicity but the disadvantages that: (a) at least 0.5 V is required for the diode to conduct and this means that a high IF gain is necessary; (b) if the input signal-to-noise ratio is low the output signal-to-noise ratio will fall more rapidly than the input signal-to-noise ratio (this is known as the threshold effect); and (c) it generates energy at harmonics of the intermediate frequency of the radio receiver.

PRACTICAL EXERCISE 10.4

Aim: To investigate the operation of a diode detector.
Components and equipment: One 1N4148 signal diode; one 22 kΩ resistor; one 10 kΩ variable resistor; and one 22 nF variable capacitor. Signal generator. CRO.
Procedure:

(a) Build the circuit shown in Fig. 10.10.
(b) Connect the signal generator to the input terminal of the circuit and connect the Y1 input of the CRO across the 22 kΩ resistor. Connect the Y2 input of the CRO to the output of the signal generator. Set the signal generator to

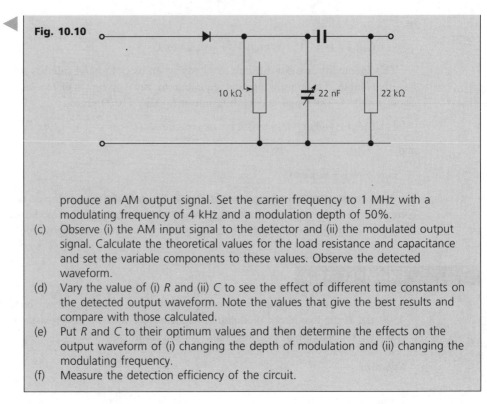

Fig. 10.10

10 kΩ   22 nF   22 kΩ

produce an AM output signal. Set the carrier frequency to 1 MHz with a modulating frequency of 4 kHz and a modulation depth of 50%.

(c) Observe (i) the AM input signal to the detector and (ii) the modulated output signal. Calculate the theoretical values for the load resistance and capacitance and set the variable components to these values. Observe the detected waveform.

(d) Vary the value of (i) R and (ii) C to see the effect of different time constants on the detected output waveform. Note the values that give the best results and compare with those calculated.

(e) Put R and C to their optimum values and then determine the effects on the output waveform of (i) changing the depth of modulation and (ii) changing the modulating frequency.

(f) Measure the detection efficiency of the circuit.

At frequencies in the VHF and UHF bands the types of diode employed include *point contact*, *backward*, and *Schottky barrier*. These are all devices in which the method of construction reduces charge storage effects. Radar receivers often employ diode detector packages that include matching to allow use over a very wide bandwidth.

Non-linear detectors

If a DSBAM signal is applied to a non-linear device detection will occur because of the v^2 term in the current–voltage characteristic. The non-linear device may well be the diode in an envelope detector when the input voltage is small. If the input voltage is $V_c(1 + m \sin \omega_m t) \sin \omega_c t$, the v^2 term will give

$$bV_c^2(1 + m \sin \omega_m t)^2 \sin^2 \omega_c t$$

Expanding this equation gives the term $bV_c^2 m \sin \omega_m t$, which is, of course, the wanted modulating signal. There are a number of other, unwanted, components at other frequencies also present and one of the most troublesome of these arises from the term $(bV_c^2/2)m^2 \sin^2 \omega_m t$. Expanding this term gives $(-bV_c^2/4)m^2 \cos 2\omega_m t$, which results in second-harmonic distortion and possible intermodulation.

The second-harmonic distortion is $(bV_c^2 m^2/4)/(bV_c^2 m)$, or $25m\%$. If, for example, $m = 30\%$, the percentage second-harmonic distortion will be 7.5%. This second-harmonic component and the other, higher-frequency components will probably be

Fig. 10.11 *(a) Product detector, (b) use of a hard limiter to obtain the carrier component*

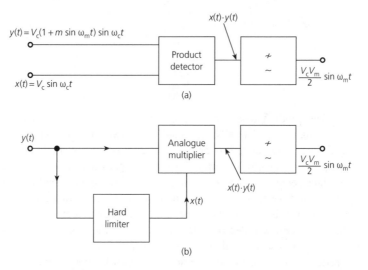

removed by a low-pass filter. More serious are the intermodulation products that are generated. Suppose that $V_m(t) = V_1 \sin \omega_1 t + V_2 \sin \omega_2 t$; then the squared term contains the component $bV_1V_2 \sin \omega_1 t \sin \omega_2 t$ which, upon expansion, shows the presence of components at frequencies $f_1 \pm f_2$. These intermodulation products will fall within the bandwidth occupied by the modulating signal and so they cannot be filtered out.

Product detector

A product detector multiplies together the DSBAM wave to be demodulated and the unmodulated carrier; it is therefore necessary that the original carrier, at the correct frequency, is available at the receiver. The output voltage of the detector is

$$v_{out} = V_c \sin \omega_c t \times V_c(1 + m \sin \omega_m t) \sin \omega_c t$$
$$= (V_c^2/2)(1 - \cos 2\omega_c t)(1 + m \sin \omega_m t)$$

and this term contains the term $(V_c V_m/2) \sin \omega_m t$. This is the wanted modulating signal so that detection has been achieved.

The block diagram of a product detector is given by Fig. 10.11(a). The carrier component must be extracted from the incoming DSBAM signal and one method of doing this is shown by Fig. 10.11(b). The DSBAM signal is hard limited to produce a square wave of frequency f_c. The two signals are applied to an analogue multiplier whose output contains the detected signal.

Another carrier extraction method employs a PLL; see Fig. 10.12. The phase detector has inputs of $V_c(1 + m \sin \omega_m t) \sin \omega_c t$ and the voltage generated by the voltage-controlled oscillator (VCO) and it generates an output voltage that is proportional to the phase difference between the two voltages. The output of the phase detector is fed, via a low-pass filter, to the control terminal of the VCO, causing it to change frequency in the direction which minimises the error. Once *lock* has been established the VCO frequency will be equal to the carrier frequency and this is also the output voltage of the circuit.

Fig. 10.12 *Carrier extraction by PLL*

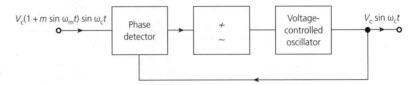

The product detector has a good performance but it needs a local oscillator and hence its use is generally restricted to SSBSC systems. The product detector is now in widespread use since it is particularly convenient for implementation in an IC. Usually, the product detector is within the same IC package as other radio receiver circuitry. The product detector offers the advantage that the input signal may be very small since its lower limit is set only by the wanted signal-to-noise ratio. This will allow the IF gain of a receiver to be up to 60 dB less than if a diode detector is used. The disadvantages are (a) the circuit will demodulate input noise if there is no signal and so a squelch circuit is really necessary, and (b) the d.c. output voltage is small and so a d.c. amplifier is needed to produce the automatic gain control (AGC) voltage. This is often on-chip; if not, an op-amp or an AGC generator chip can be used instead.

Frequency modulators

The *sensitivity* of a frequency modulator is equal to the ratio $f_d/V_{m(max)}$ kHz V^{-1}. Ideally, there should be no amplitude modulation of the carrier. Frequency modulators are classified as being either *direct* or *indirect* types: with direct modulation the carrier frequency is directly deviated by the modulating signal; with indirect modulation the modulating signal directly varies the instantaneous phase of the carrier, which means that a phase modulator must be employed. Figure 10.13 shows how an FM waveform can be produced using either direct or indirect modulation. In Fig. 10.13(a) the modulating signal is applied to a direct frequency modulator to produce an FM wave. When a phase modulator is used, Fig. 10.13(b), the modulating signal is first applied to an

Fig. 10.13 *(a) Direct and (b) indirect frequency modulation methods*

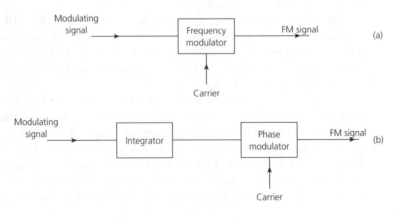

Fig. 10.14 *Principle of a frequency modulator*

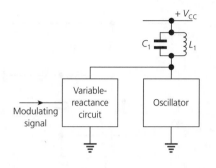

integrating circuit and the integrated modulating signal is applied to a phase modulator whose output is then an FM wave.

Direct frequency modulators

Figure 10.14 illustrates the basic principle upon which the majority of direct frequency modulators are based. The frequency of oscillation of an oscillator is determined by a parallel-tuned circuit whose total capacitance is provided by the parallel connection of a physical capacitor C_1 and a voltage-variable reactance. The modulating signal voltage is applied, usually together with a bias voltage, to the voltage-variable reactance to vary its capacitance. The change in capacitance will then alter the resonant frequency of the tuned circuit and so vary the frequency of oscillation. In this way the modulating signal voltage is able to modulate the carrier frequency. When the modulating signal voltage is zero the voltage-variable reactance has its average value C_e of capacitance and the oscillation frequency will be the unmodulated carrier frequency, i.e.

$$f_c \approx 1/\{2\pi\sqrt{[L_1(C_1 + C_e)]}\} = 1/[2\pi\sqrt{(L_1 C_T)}] \text{ Hz} \tag{10.9}$$

When the instantaneous value of the modulating signal voltage is V_m volts the total capacitance of the tuned circuit is varied by an amount δC_T. Then

$$f_c + \delta f_c = 1/\{2\pi\sqrt{[L_1(C_T + \delta C_T)]}\} \text{ Hz} \tag{10.10}$$

Dividing equation (10.10) by (10.9) gives

$$1 + \delta f_c/f_c = \sqrt{[C_T/(C_T + \delta C_T)]} = 1\sqrt{(1 + \delta C_T/C_T)} \tag{10.11}$$

Since $\delta C_T \ll C_T$ equation (10.11) can be written as

$$1 + \delta f_c/f_c \approx 1 - \delta C_T/2C_T$$

or

$$\delta f_c/f_c \approx -\delta C_T/2C_T \tag{10.12}$$

This means that a fractional increase in C_T will produce a fractional decrease in f_c which is approximately half as large.

Reactance frequency modulator

The circuit of a reactance frequency modulator that employs a bipolar transistor is shown in Fig. 10.15. R_1, R_2, R_3 and C_1 are bias and decoupling components, L_1 is an RF

Fig. 10.15 *Reactance frequency modulator*

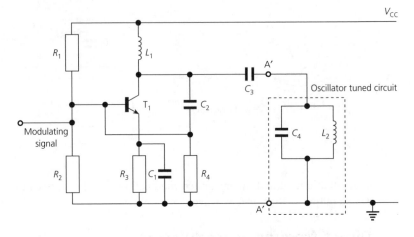

choke and C_3 is a d.c. block. The required reactance effect is provided by C_2 and R_4. The current i flowing in the series C_2R_4 circuit is

$$i = V_{ce}/(R_4 + 1/j\omega C_2)$$

and this current develops a voltage across R_4 of

$$V_{in} = (V_{ce}j\omega C_2R_4)/(1 + j\omega C_2R_4)$$

The collector current i_c of T_1 is equal to g_mV_{in} and so the output admittance Y_{out} of the modulator is

$$Y_{out} = i_c/V_{ce} = (j\omega g_m C_2R_4)/(1 + j\omega C_2R_4) \approx jg_m\omega C_2R_4 \qquad (10.13)$$

The circuit thus provides an effective capacitance of $C_e = g_m C_2R_4$ across the oscillator's tuned circuit that is directly proportional to the mutual conductance g_m of the transistor. Since g_m can be varied by applying the modulating signal to the input terminals of the circuit, frequency modulation of the carrier is achieved.

EXAMPLE 10.3

The reactance frequency modulator shown in Fig. 10.15 has $C_2 = 5$ pF and $R_4 = 1$ kΩ. The total tuned circuit capacitance when there is no input signal is 500 pF and the unmodulated carrier frequency is 1 MHz. Calculate the deviation of the carrier frequency when a modulating signal varies the mutual conductance of T_1 by 2 mS.

Solution

$$\delta C = 2 \times 10^{-3} \times 5 \times 10^{-12} \times 10^3 = 10 \text{ pF}$$

From equation (10.12),

$$\delta f_c = (-1 \times 10^6 \times 10)/(2 \times 500) = -10 \text{ kHz } (Ans.)$$

Fig. 10.16 *Varactor diode frequency modulator (a) basic circuit (b) crystal oscillator/modulator circuit*

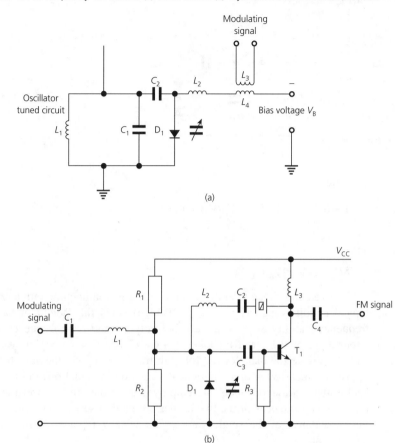

(a)

(b)

Varactor diode frequency modulator

The basic circuit of a varactor diode frequency modulator is shown in Fig. 10.16(a). The varactor (or voltage-variable) diode is connected in parallel with the tuned circuit $C_1 L_1$ of the oscillator that is to be frequency modulated. C_2 is a d.c. blocking component while L_2 is an RF choke. C_3 is a decoupling capacitor which may not be needed if the source of the bias voltage is of very low impedance. When the modulating signal voltage is zero the varactor diode is reverse biased by the bias voltage V_B volts and it then has a capacitance of $C_d = C_0/\sqrt{V_B}$ pF, where C_0 is the capacitance for zero applied voltage. The frequency of oscillation is then

$$f_c = 1/\{2\pi\sqrt{[L(C_1 + C_d)]}\} \text{ Hz} \tag{10.14}$$

When a modulating signal is applied to the circuit the reverse-bias voltage becomes $V_B + V_m \sin \omega_m t$ and

$$
\begin{aligned}
C_d + \delta C_d &= C_0/\sqrt{(V_B + V_m \sin \omega_m t)} \\
&= C_0/\{\sqrt{V_B} \sqrt{[1 + (V_m/V_B)]} \sin \omega_m t]\} \\
&= C_d/\sqrt{[1 + (V_m/V_B)} \sin \omega_m t]
\end{aligned}
$$

Fig. 10.17 *Improved varactor diode modulator*

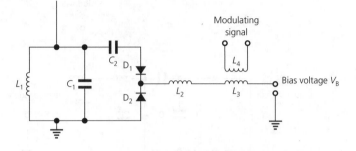

Therefore,

$$1 + \delta C_d/C_d = 1/\sqrt{[1 + (V_m/V_B) \sin \omega_m t]}$$
$$\approx 1 - (V_m/2V_B) \sin \omega_m t$$

and

$$\delta C_d = (-V_m/2V_B)C_d \sin \omega_m t \qquad (10.15)$$

The varactor diode modulator can be used in conjunction with a crystal oscillator, a typical circuit being given by Fig. 10.16(b) when the modulator has the same high-frequency stability as the oscillator but only a small peak frequency deviation. In this circuit L_1, L_2 and L_3 are RF chokes, C_1, C_2, C_3 and C_4 are coupling capacitors, while R_1 and R_2 provide the bias voltage for both transistor T_1 and the varactor diode D_1.

Better linearity, with a consequent reduction in signal distortion, is obtained if two back-to-back varactor diodes are employed as in the circuit shown by Fig. 10.17. The effective capacitances of the two diodes are now in series and so each must have *twice* the capacitance of the single varactor diode they replace. Again C_3 is a decoupling component.

EXAMPLE 10.4

The circuit of Fig. 10.17 is a part of a frequency modulator which operates at a centre frequency of 1 MHz. $L_1 = 100$ µH, $C_1 = 200$ pF and each varactor diode has $C_0 = 200$ pF. (a) Calculate the values of the bias voltage and the peak modulating voltage if the frequency deviation is 1 kHz. (b) Calculate the sensitivity of the modulator.

Solution

(a) The necessary tuning capacitance is equal to $1/(4\pi^2 \times 10^{12} \times 100 \times 10^{-6}) \approx 253$ pF and so the varactor diodes must contribute 53 pF. Each diode must therefore have a capacitance of 106 pF. This means that the reverse-bias voltage V_B must be

$$V_B = (200/106)^2 = 3.56 \text{ V } (Ans.)$$

When the carrier frequency is deviated by 1 kHz

$$(1 \times 10^3)/(1 \times 10^6) = \delta C_T/(2 \times 253 \times 10^{-12}) \quad \text{or} \quad \delta C_T = 0.5 \text{ pF}$$

and then C_T is either 253.5 pF or 252.5 pF. Each varactor diode must then have a capacitance of either 107 pF or 105 pF. Choosing the first value, $V_B - V_m = (200/107)^2 = 3.49$ V and the peak modulating voltage is

$$3.56 - 3.49 = 70 \text{ mV } (Ans.)$$

On the other half-cycle, $V_B + V_m = (200/105)^2 = 3.63$ V and the peak signal voltage is

$$3.63 - 3.56 = 70 \text{ mV } (Ans.)$$

(b) The sensitivity of the modulator is

$$1/(70 \times 10^{-3}) = 14.286 \text{ kHz V}^{-1} (Ans.)$$

The varactor diode and reactance frequency modulators produce NBFM signals because $\delta C_T \ll C_T$ and if wideband modulation is wanted some stages of frequency multiplication will be necessary.

Indirect frequency modulation

The inherent stability of the unmodulated carrier frequency when a direct modulator is used is often not good enough to meet modern standards. There are two ways in which this difficulty can be overcome: (a) direct frequency modulation with automatic frequency control applied to the transmitter; and (b) indirect frequency modulation of a very stable crystal oscillator.

The expressions for the instantaneous frequency and voltage of a sinusoidally modulated PM wave are given by equations (3.20) and (3.21), respectively. If the modulating signal $v_m = V_m \sin \omega_m t$ is integrated before it is applied to the phase modulator, to give $(V_m/\omega_m) \cos \omega_m t$, these equations become $f_i = f_c + k\phi_d \sin \omega_m t$ and $v_c = V_c \sin[\omega_c t + (k\phi_d/\omega_m) \cos \omega t]$. The frequency deviation is now proportional to the modulating signal voltage, and inversely proportional to the modulating signal frequency, the same as an FM wave. Hence, an FM wave can be obtained by integrating the modulating signal and then applying the integrated signal to a phase modulator; see Fig. 10.13(b).

Phase modulators

A PM wave can be generated using an AM balanced modulator and a carrier source that has both in-phase and quadrature outputs. Figure 10.18 shows the circuit of an Armstrong phase modulator. The balanced modulator has two inputs – the modulating signal and a 90° phase-shifted carrier voltage – and it generates the upper and lower sidebands of amplitude modulation but suppresses the carrier. Assuming the modulating signal to be of sinusoidal waveform, the output of the balanced modulator is $mV_c \cos \omega_c t \sin \omega_m t$. This signal is added to the non-phase-shifted carrier voltage to give an output of

$$V_{out} = V_c \sin \omega_c t + mV_c \cos \omega_c t \sin \omega_m t$$
$$= \sqrt{(V_c^2 + m^2 V_c^2 \sin^2 \omega_m t)} \sin(\omega_c t + \theta)$$

Fig. 10.18 *Armstrong phase modulator*

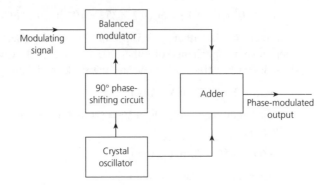

where $\theta = \tan^{-1}(m \sin \omega_m t)$. Hence,

$$V_{out} \approx V_c \sin(\omega_c t + m \sin \omega_m t)$$

which is of the same form as equation (3.22).

The carrier voltage can be produced by a stable crystal oscillator. The maximum modulation index that this circuit can give is only about 0.25 and so several stages of frequency multiplication will be necessary to obtain a wideband FM wave. If, for example, the modulation index is 0.25 and the required value is 5, frequency multiplication of 20 times is required. The crystal oscillator frequency should then, of course, be equal to f_c/N, where f_c is the wanted carrier frequency and N is the multiplication ratio.

EXAMPLE 10.5

An FM transmitter has an unmodulated carrier frequency of 90 MHz and a rated system deviation of 75 kHz. The Armstrong modulator used can only produce a peak frequency deviation of 3 kHz. Calculate (a) the multiplication ratio used, and (b) the frequency of the crystal oscillator.

Solution

(a) $N = 75/3 = 25$ (*Ans.*)
(b) Oscillator frequency $= 90/25 = 3.6$ MHz (*Ans.*)

Figure 10.19 shows the circuit of a crystal oscillator whose output voltage is phase modulated by a modulating signal. The output of the crystal oscillator is applied to the base of transistor T_2. The modulating signal voltage alters the negative bias voltage applied to the varactor diode. This, in turn, alters the capacitance of the varactor diode and its change in capacitance varies the phase of the output signal. The amplified oscillator voltage of the circuit will then be phase modulated.

Fig. 10.19 *Crystal oscillator and phase modulator*

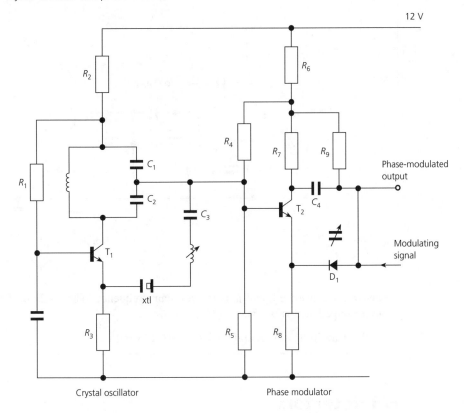

Crystal oscillator   Phase modulator

EXAMPLE 10.6

The varactor diode used in the phase modulator of Fig. 10.20 has the capacitance–voltage characteristic $C_d = 200/\sqrt{V}$ pF. When the d.c. reverse-bias voltage applied to the diode is 4 V the circuit is resonant at 5 MHz and has a Q factor of 20. Calculate the peak phase deviation produced when a 50 mV peak sinusoidal modulating signal is applied to the circuit.

Solution

When the modulating signal voltage V_m is zero $C_d = 200/\sqrt{4} = 100$ pF. When the modulating signal is applied to the circuit the minimum and maximum values of C_d are $200/\sqrt{4.05} = 99.38$ pF and $200/\sqrt{3.95} = 100.63$ pF, respectively. Hence δC_d is either 0.62 pF or 0.63 pF; using the mean value in $\delta f_c/f_c = -\delta C_d/2C_d$ gives $\delta f_c = (5 \times 10^6 \times 0.625)/200 = 15.625$ kHz. Hence bandwidth = 31 250 Hz.

    The impedance Z of the tuned circuit at any frequency is given by $Z = R_d/(1 + jQB/f_0)$, where R_d is the dynamic impedance, Q is the Q factor, B is the

---

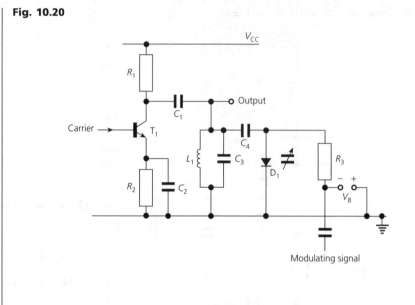

bandwidth considered, and f_0 is the resonant frequency. The angle θ of the tuned circuit impedance is $\theta = \pm\tan^{-1}(QB/f_0)$ or

$$\theta = \pm\tan^{-1}[(20 \times 31\ 250)/(5 \times 10^6)] = \pm0.124\ \text{rad } (\textit{Ans.})$$

FM detectors

An FM detector is required to produce an output voltage that is directly proportional to the instantaneous frequency of its input signal. An FM detector has a transfer function with units of V kHz^{-1}. Before the widespread use of ICs in radio receivers, most FM detectors were based upon the principle of first converting the FM signal into a signal whose amplitude varied in proportion to the frequency deviation and then envelope detecting in the converted signal. This concept is illustrated, in block diagram form, by Fig. 10.21. The two most commonly employed examples of this technique are the Foster–Seeley *phase discriminator* and the *ratio detector*. Nowadays the former is rarely, if ever, used and the latter is employed only in cheap sound broadcast receivers. Most modern radio receivers make full use of widely available ICs and these receivers are most likely to employ either a *quadrature detector* or a *PLL detector*. Another detector that finds application in FM telemetry receivers is the *pulse count detector*.

Fig. 10.21 *Principle of a FM detector*

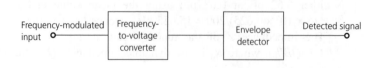

Fig. 10.22 *Quadrature detector*

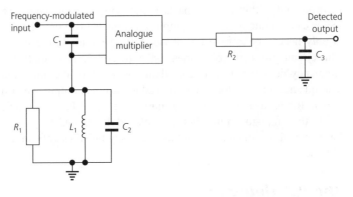

The quadrature detector

The FM signal to be detected is split into two parts. One part is directly applied to one of the two inputs of an analogue multiplier circuit. The other part is passed through a capacitor having a high reactance at the unmodulated carrier frequency and then to a parallel-tuned circuit; see Fig. 10.22. The capacitor C_1 introduces a phase shift of very nearly 90° and the tuned circuit introduces a phase shift that depends upon the instantaneous frequency. The impedance of the tuned circuit is $Z = R/(1 + jQB/f_0)$. At the resonant frequency f_0, the bandwidth $B = 0$ and the circuit is purely resistive; at any frequency off resonance the circuit introduces a phase shift of $\pm\tan^{-1}(QB/f_0)$. The voltage that appears across the tuned circuit is applied to the other input of the multiplier and an output proportional to the product of the two input signals is obtained. The output voltage is then passed through a low-pass filter to obtain the original modulating signal $V_m(t)$.

If the unmodulated carrier frequency is $\omega_c/2\pi$ and the instantaneous frequency of the input signal is $\omega = \omega_c \pm \delta\omega_c$ then the phase shift θ between the two multiplier inputs is

$$\theta = (\pi/2) \pm \tan^{-1}(2Q\delta\omega_c/\omega_c) = (\pi/2) \pm \phi$$

(The plus sign is used if $\omega > \pm\omega_c$ and the minus sign if $\omega < \pm\omega_c$.)

If the input signal is $V \sin \omega t$ the phase-shifted signal will be $V \sin[\omega_c t + (\pi/2) \pm \phi]$, or $V \cos(\omega_c t \pm \phi)$. When the two input signals are multiplied together in the multiplier the result is

$$V^2 \sin \omega t \cos(\omega t \pm \phi) = (V^2/2)[\sin(2\omega t \pm \phi) + \sin(\pm\phi)$$

(using the trigonometric identity $2 \sin A \cos B = \sin(A + B) + \sin(A - B)$).

The output of the low-pass filter is

$$(V^2/2) \sin(\pm\phi) = (V^2/2) \sin[\pm\tan^{-1}(2Q\delta\omega_c/\omega_c)]$$

For $2Q\delta\omega_c \ll \omega_c$ this equation gives

$$\sin[\pm\tan^{-1}(2Q\delta\omega_c/\omega_c)] \approx \pm 2Q\delta\omega_c/\omega_c$$

This output voltage bears a linear relationship to $\delta\omega_c$, i.e. to the frequency deviation of the carrier, and hence it is the wanted modulating signal.

The quadrature detector is widely employed in modern radio receivers and is usually incorporated within an IC that also performs several other circuit functions. The detector can operate with small-amplitude signals (100 µV or so) and is easy to set up; it is only necessary to tune the phase-shifting circuit to the incoming carrier frequency. The circuit provides good linearity, with consequent small distortion, as long as the frequency deviation is not more than about 1% of the unmodulated carrier frequency. The quadrature detector tends to produce a noise output when there is no input signal and so the IC usually includes a muting, or squelch, circuit, too.

If the analogue multiplier is replaced by an AND gate and the input signal is hard limited to produce a variable-frequency pulse waveform, a *coincidence detector* is obtained.

The PLL detector

A PLL can be operated as a detector of FM signals when it has more or less the same performance as the quadrature detector. The PLL detector does not need an externally connected tuned circuit but, on the other hand, an external piezoelectric crystal is required. In some cases the 10.7 MHz output of an IF amplifier may be converted to a lower frequency in the region of 200 kHz before it is applied to the PLL detector. Sometimes the mixer used is on-chip with the PLL.

The block schematic diagram of a PLL FM detector is shown in Fig. 10.23. The free-running frequency f_0 of the VCO is set to be equal to the unmodulated carrier frequency f_c of the signal to be demodulated. The analogue phase detector (which could be a double-balanced mixer) generates an output voltage that is directly proportional to the phase difference, or *phase error*, between the FM signal and the VCO voltage. This error voltage is passed through a low-pass filter and then amplified to produce both the output voltage and a control voltage for the VCO. The free-running frequency of the VCO is varied by the voltage applied to its control terminal. The polarity of the control voltage is always such that it varies the frequency of the VCO in the direction that reduces the difference frequency $\Delta f = f_c - f_0$ and hence reduces the phase error. This means that the frequency of the VCO is forced to try to become equal to the instantaneous frequency of the input signal.

Suppose that, initially, the input signal is not modulated. The action of the PLL reduces the difference between the input carrier frequency f_c and the frequency f_0 of the VCO. Once the VCO frequency has moved to be very close to the carrier frequency the loop attains *lock*. Then the VCO rapidly attains the same frequency as the input signal

Fig. 10.23 *PLL detector*

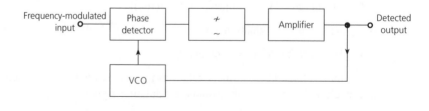

but there is *always* a phase difference between the two voltages. This phase error must always exist in order to maintain the VCO control voltage at the required value. This voltage, and hence the output voltage, is a d.c. voltage.

When the input signal is frequency modulated a similar action takes place. As the input signal frequency deviates from the unmodulated carrier frequency the error voltage also varies to ensure that the VCO tracks to minimise the phase error. As a result the instantaneous frequency of the VCO is always approximately equal to the frequency of the incoming signal. The output of the low-pass filter is the detected modulating signal voltage. The filter must have a cut-off frequency equal to the maximum modulating frequency $f_{m(max)}$ of the FM signal in order to minimise the effects of noise and interference. Should the free-running frequency of the VCO *not* be set to be exactly equal to the unmodulated carrier frequency the detected output voltage will have a d.c. component, but this is (usually) unimportant.

Analysis

Once the loop is in lock the frequency of the VCO is equal to the carrier frequency. The FM input signal is

$$v_s = V_s \sin\left(\omega_c t + 2\pi k f_d \int_0^t V_m(t)\, dt\right)$$

$$= V_s \sin\left(\omega_c t + K_s \int_0^t V_m(t)\, dt\right) = V_s \sin[\omega_c t + \theta_1(t)]$$

The output voltage of the VCO is

$$v_c = V_0 \cos[\omega_c t + \theta_2(t)]$$

These two signals are the inputs to the phase detector which generates an output voltage v_d that is directly proportional to their product.

Thus,

$$v_d = (K_D V_s\, V_0) \sin[\omega_c t + \theta_1(t)] \cos[\omega_c t + \theta_2(t)]$$
$$= (K_D V_s V_0/2) \sin[\theta_1(t) - \theta_2(t)] + \sin[2\omega_c t + \theta_1(t) + \theta_2(t)]$$

Here K_D is the gain factor, in V rad^{-1}, of the phase detector. The low-pass filter will only transmit the lower-frequency components of v_D so that the voltage appearing at the output of the circuit is

$$v_D = (K_D A_v V_s V_0/2) \sin[\theta_1(t) - \theta_2(t)]$$

Since the loop is locked the phase error will be small and $\sin[\theta_1(t) - \theta_2(t)] \approx \theta_1(t) - \theta_2(t)$, giving

$$v_D = (K_D A_v V_s V_0/2)[\theta_1(t) - \theta_2(t)] \tag{10.16}$$

The instantaneous angular velocity ω_0' of the VCO output voltage is

$$\omega_0' = \omega_0 + K_0 v_0(t)$$

where ω_0 is the free-running angular velocity and K_0 is the conversion gain of the VCO in rad s^{-1} V^{-1}. The conversion gain K_0 relates the frequency of the VCO to its control voltage and is expressed in rad s^{-1} V^{-1} or in kHz V^{-1}. Since $\omega = d\theta/dt$, $d\theta_2/dt = K_0 v_0(t)$; also $d\theta_1/dt = K_S V_m(t)$. Equation (10.16) can be written as

$$V_0(t) = (K_D A_v V_S V_0/2)\left(\theta_1(t) - K_0\int_0^t v_0(t)\,dt \right)$$

and differentiating with respect to time,

$$dv_0(t)/dt = (K_D A_v V_S V_0/2)[d\theta_1(t)/dt - K_0 v_0(t)]$$

or

$$d\theta_1(t)/dt = (2 dv_0(t)/dt)/(K_D A_v V_S V_0)/dt + K_0 v_0(t)$$
$$\approx K_0 v_0(t)$$

Therefore, $K_S V_m(t) = K_0 v_0(t)$, or

$$v_0(t) = K_S V_m(t)/K_0 \qquad (10.17)$$

The ratio K_S/K_0 has the dimensions of kHz kHz^{-1} V^{-1} or V and so the output of the detector is the wanted modulating signal $V_m(t)$.

The 565 as a frequency demodulator

The 565 IC is a widely used PLL for operation at frequencies up to about 500 kHz. Figures 10.24(a) and (b) show, respectively, the pin connections and the internal block diagram of the 565. The free-running frequency of the VCO is set by the external components C_1 and R_1 according to the expression

$$f = 0.3/C_1 R_1 \text{ Hz} \qquad (10.18)$$

Capacitor C_1 can be of any value but R_1 should be somewhere in the region of 4000 Ω. R_{int} is an internal 3.6 kΩ resistor which, together with an external capacitor C_2, forms the low-pass filter. The capture range f_c is the bandwidth over which the circuit can be locked:

$$f_c = \pm\sqrt{[f_L/(2\pi R_{int} C_2)]} \qquad (10.19)$$

where f_L is the lock range given by

$$f_L = \pm 8 f_0/(2 V_{CC}) \qquad (10.20)$$

Figure 10.24(c) shows how the 565 should be connected with an op-amp to act as an FM demodulator. The pins 4 and 5 must be connected together so that the VCO output is applied to the phase detector.

Fig. 10.24 *The 565 PLL. (a) pinout, (b) internal block diagram, and (c) use as an FM detector*

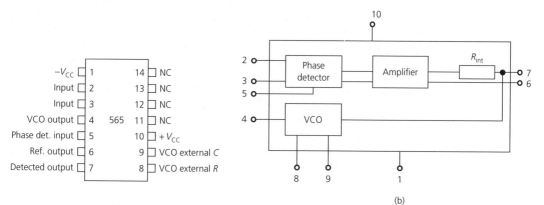

(a)

(b)

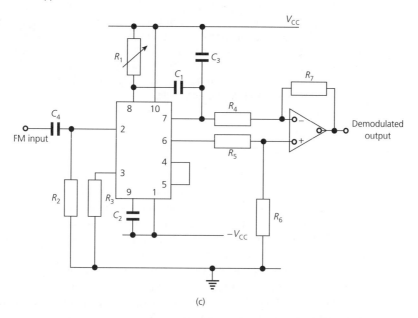

(c)

PRACTICAL EXERCISE 10.5

Aim: To employ the LM565C PLL as an FM detector.
Components and equipment: LM565C PLL. Five resistors and four capacitors (values to be calculated). Power supply. CRO. RF signal generator. Breadboard.
Procedure:

(a) The circuit shown in Fig. 10.24(c) is to be built but first it is necessary to calculate the component values. (i) VCO frequency $= 0.3/C_1R_1$; the maximum VCO frequency is 500 kHz so choose a frequency about half of this, choose

C_1 to be a convenient value, say 1 nF, and calculate R_1. Select the nearest preferred value. (ii) Equal-value biasing resistors R_2 and R_3 must be connected between pins 2 and 3 and earth. Their value can be anywhere in the range 1–12 kΩ and the value chosen sets the input impedance of the demodulator. Make the input coupling capacitor C_2 have a low reactance at the lowest operating frequency – about 10 nF is typical. Capacitor C_3 determines the capture range which in turn sets the largest frequency deviation f_d that the circuit can handle. Select a value for f_d and then calculate C_3 using $C_3 = (4 \times \text{VCO frequency})/(\pi f_c^2 \times 3600 \times 2V_{CC})$. Use the nearest smaller preferred value. The output voltage will be in the region of 0.3 V; decide on the output voltage wanted and hence decide on the gain the op-amp is to provide. If the input resistors R_4 and R_5 are made 10 kΩ each the value of R_5 is gain × 10 kΩ. Lastly, make $R_6 = R_5$. Why?

(b) Build the circuit.
(c) Connect the RF signal generator to the input terminals of the circuit and set it to deliver an FM signal with a carrier frequency equal to the designed VCO frequency and a frequency deviation a little less than the designed capture range. Connect the CRO to the output terminals of the circuit.
(d) Apply FM signals with different deviation ratios to the circuit and determine its performance. If necessary modify some of the component values. Observe the effect of altering the carrier frequency and state the frequency range over which the demodulator worked correctly.

Pulse count detector

The basic block diagram of a pulse count detector is shown by Fig. 10.25. The input FM signal is applied to the amplitude limiter to have any amplitude modulation removed before it arrives at the pulse generator. The pulse generator is leading-edge triggered and generates a number of output pulses that are directly proportional to the frequency of the input signal. Each pulse occupies a fixed time period that is short compared with the periodic time of the unmodulated carrier wave, and hence each pulse supplies the same amount of charge to the integrator. This means that the higher the frequency, the higher will be the output voltage of the integrator, and the lower the frequency, the lower the integrator voltage. The output voltage of the integrator is the wanted modulating signal so the circuit acts as an FM detector.

Relative merits of FM detectors

The Foster–Seely demodulator is sensitive to amplitude variations of the input signal and its alignment is critical. This detector is rarely used in modern receivers. The ratio

Fig. 10.25 *Pulse count FM detector*

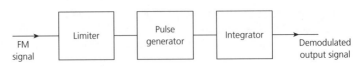

detector is able to reject any amplitude modulation of its input signal but again its alignment is difficult. The ratio detector is still used in some sound broadcast receivers. The pulse count demodulator has very good linearity and good rejection of any amplitude modulation of the input signal, and finds application in telemetry and remote control systems. The quadrature detector is only found inside ICs, along with other circuitry, and is now the most commonly employed type of FM detector. It has a good performance. Lastly, the PLL detector gives a good performance provided the VCO is accurate and stable.

Digital modulators and demodulators

The circuits employed as digital modulators and demodulators are always incorporated within radio ICs and their block diagrams have been considered in Chapter 4.

Frequency synthesisers

A frequency synthesiser is able to generate a large number of precise frequencies which are derived from a single high-stability crystal oscillator source. The disadvantage of using a frequency synthesiser is that the tuning of the receiver is not continuous but can only occur in discrete steps. Each of the derived frequencies has the same accuracy and stability as the crystal oscillator reference source. A frequency synthesiser must be able to cover a wide frequency band so that the receiver can work over the whole of the tuning range. Frequency synthesisers are classified as being either direct or indirect. A direct synthesiser generates multiple output frequencies by mixing the outputs of two or more crystal oscillators, or by dividing or multiplying the output frequency of a single crystal oscillator. An indirect frequency synthesiser employs a feedback-controlled divider/multiplier such as a PLL. Indirect frequency synthesis is slower and more susceptible to noise than direct synthesis but it is cheaper and requires fewer filters. Direct frequency synthesis is employed when rapid changes in frequency are required and many modern systems use *direct digital frequency synthesis* (DDFS).

Indirect frequency synthesis

Most of the frequency synthesisers employed in modern communication receivers are of the indirect type and use a PLL. Figure 10.26 shows the basic arrangement of a PLL indirect frequency synthesiser which consists of a very stable crystal oscillator which acts as the reference source, a phase detector, a low-pass filter and a VCO. The phase detector produces an output d.c. control voltage, the magnitude and polarity of which are determined by the phase difference between the crystal oscillator and VCO voltages. The control voltage is filtered to remove any a.c. components that are present before it is applied to the VCO to vary its frequency. The action of the PLL is to force the frequency of the VCO to change in the direction that reduces any difference between the crystal oscillator frequency and the VCO frequency. Once lock has been achieved

Fig. 10.26 *Basic PLL indirect frequency synthesizer*

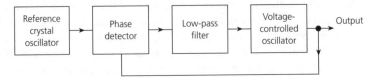

Fig. 10.27 *Frequency synthesizers: (a) using a PLL, (b) with improved frequency resolution*

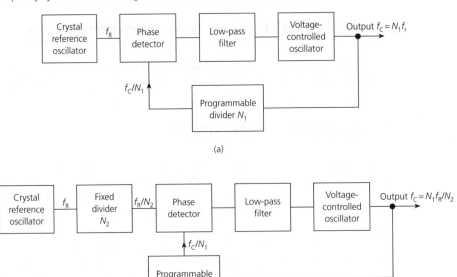

the two inputs to the phase detector are at the same frequency, but there is always a phase difference between them in order to maintain the controlling d.c. voltage.

To obtain more than one output frequency a frequency divider, which may be a programmable type, must be connected in the position shown in Fig. 10.27(a) and a digital phase detector used. The signals applied to the digital phase detector are then at frequencies of f_R and f_c/N_1 and the VCO runs at a frequency of $f_C = N_1 f_R$. The PLL with a frequency divider in the loop allows a large number of frequencies to be obtained by altering the division ratio N_1 of the divider. Each of the possible output frequencies is an integral multiple of the reference frequency. If, for example, $f_R = 1$ MHz and $N_1 = 3$ the VCO frequency will be 3 MHz, but if $N_1 = 20$ the frequency of the VCO will be 20 MHz. Clearly, the increments in frequency that can be obtained are equal to the reference frequency f_R. A digital phase detector is employed because it has a higher sensitivity and is faster switching than an analogue phase detector and requires the logic level input voltages that are supplied by the programmable divider. A digital phase detector may be as simple a circuit as an exclusive-OR gate or an RS latch.

EXAMPLE 10.7

Referring to Fig. 10.27(a), if the reference frequency supplied by the crystal oscillator is 100 kHz and the divider can be programmed to give division ratios of 988 to 1186, determine (a) the range of output frequencies and (b) the increments in frequency.

Solution

(a) Frequency range = 100 kHz × 988 to 100 kHz × 1186
$$= 98.8 \text{ to } 118.6 \text{ MHz } (Ans.)$$
(b) Frequency increments = reference frequency = 100 kHz (*Ans.*)

To improve the frequency resolution the reference frequency can also be divided, as shown by Fig. 10.27(b). If, now, $f_R = 1$ MHz and $N_2 = 100$ the output frequency will be $f_C = N_1 f_R / N_2$ with a frequency resolution of 1 kHz. This method of obtaining a frequency synthesiser is relatively simple, fully digital, and can be obtained in IC form, but it is slow to change from one frequency to another.

To obtain both rapid frequency changes and small frequency resolution a multiple-loop frequency synthesiser is often employed, and Fig. 10.28 shows one example of this technique. The top loop produces an output at frequency $f_R N_A / N_1$ and this is divided down by the ratio N_2 to give frequency $f_R N_A / N_1 N_2$. The lower loop produces an output at frequency $f_R N_B / N_1$ and this is applied to a mixer, along with the output of the system at frequency f_0. The bandpass filter selects the difference frequency $f_0 - f_R N_B / N_1$ so that the

Fig. 10.28 *Multiple-loop frequency synthesizer*

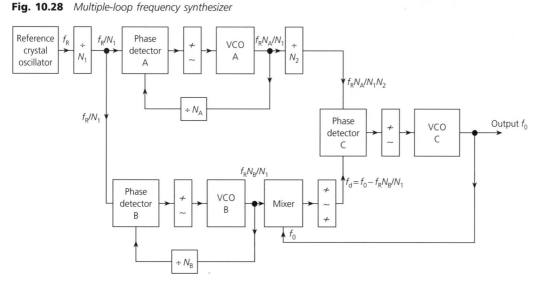

inputs to the phase detector C are at frequencies $f_R N_A / N_1 N_2$ and $f_0 - f_R N_B / N_1$; these frequencies are locked by the output loop to become equal to one another. Then

$$f_0 = (f_R / N_1)(N_A / N_2 + N_B) \qquad (10.21)$$

EXAMPLE 10.8

In the frequency synthesiser of Fig. 10.28, $f_R = 1$ MHz, $N_1 = 10$ and $N_2 = 100$. Determine the range of output frequencies of the synthesiser if N_A is variable from 200 to 300 and N_B can be varied from 350 to 400.

Solution

From equation (10.21)

$$f_{0(\text{min})} = [(1 \times 10^6)/10](200/100 + 350) = 35.2 \text{ MHz}$$

$$f_{0(\text{max})} = [(1 \times 10^6)/10](300/100 + 400) = 40.3 \text{ MHz}$$

Therefore, the frequency range = 35.2 to 40.3 MHz (*Ans.*)

Direct digital frequency synthesis

DDFS employs digital techniques to generate sinusoidal waveforms at a large number of different frequencies. The basic block diagram of a DDFS is given in Fig 10.29(a). The 16-bit counter counts from 0 to 15 under the control of the clock, which is also applied to the *digital-to-analogue converter* (DAC). Each count accesses a different location in the *read-only memory* (ROM). At each location is stored the digital equivalent of an instaneous value of a sinusoidal waveform and these values are shown by Table 10.1.

Fig. 10.29 *(a) Basic DDFS, (b) Double-frequency output*

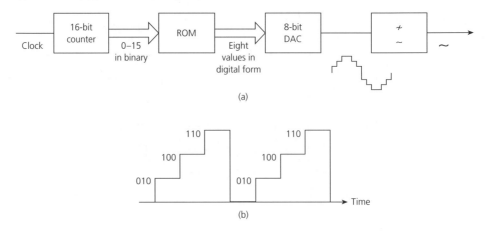

Table 10.1 *Direct digital frequency synthesis*

Address	Data	Represents
0 0 0 0	0 0 0 0 0 0 0 0	$\sin 0° = 0$
0 0 0 1	0 0 1 1 0 0 0 1	$\sin 22.5° = 0.383$
0 0 1 0	0 1 0 1 1 0 1 0	$\sin 45° = 0.707$
0 0 1 1	0 1 1 1 0 1 1 0	$\sin 67.5° = 0.924$
0 1 0 0	0 1 1 1 1 1 1 1	$\sin 90° = 1$
0 1 0 1	0 1 1 1 0 1 1 0	$\sin 112.5° = 0.924$
0 1 1 0	0 1 0 1 1 0 1 0	$\sin 135° = 0.707$
0 1 1 1	0 0 1 1 0 0 0 1	$\sin 157.5° = 0.383$
1 0 0 0	0 0 0 0 0 0 0 0	$\sin 180° = 0$
1 0 0 1	1 0 1 1 0 0 0 1	$\sin 202.5° = -0.383$
1 0 1 0	1 1 0 1 1 0 1 0	$\sin 225° = -0.707$
1 0 1 1	1 1 1 1 0 1 1 0	$\sin 147.5° = -0.924$
1 1 0 0	1 1 1 1 1 1 1 1	$\sin 270° = -1$
1 1 0 1	1 1 1 1 0 1 1 0	$\sin 292.5° = -0.924$
1 1 1 0	1 1 0 1 1 0 1 0	$\sin 315° = -0.707$
1 1 1 1	1 0 1 1 0 0 0 1	$\sin 337.5° = -0.383$

When a ROM location is accessed the data stored at that location is read out at a uniform rate and applied to the DAC. The DAC converts the input digital word to produce a quantised version of the instantaneous value of the sinusoidal waveform. The quantised waveform is then passed through a low-pass filter which transmits only the fundamental frequency of the DAC output waveform to give a sinusoidal waveform. To increase the frequency of the output waveform the counter must access fewer evenly spaced ROM locations; this is shown by Fig. 10.29(b) in which alternate values are outputted at the same rate. Now the count of the counter is required to step from 0 to 14 in increments of 2, i.e. 0, 2, 4, 6, 8, 10, 12, 14, 0, etc. To obtain a frequency increase of n times, every nth instantaneous value is taken out of the ROM, again at the same rate. The frequency resolution is determined by the number of ROM locations that the counter can address and hence by the modulus of the counter. This means that the frequency resolution of a DDFS is the same at all frequencies. The highest frequency that can be generated is determined by the number of instantaneous values that are stored in the ROM. To make it possible for the different frequencies to be obtained the counter must be programmable so that it is able to increment its output by a variable step size.

Figure 10.30 shows how a programmable counter can be obtained. A parallel-in parallel-out (PIPO) shift register and a binary adder are connected to act as an accumulator. The PIPO register has its parallel inputs supplied by the binary adder, while the parallel outputs are connected to the input of both the adder and the ROM. An incrementing digital word W is also applied to the adder. Suppose that a three-bit shift register is employed. If the incrementing digital word is 0001 the count of the register will be incremented in steps of one. The PIPO shift register's output therefore increments

Fig. 10.30 *Programmable DDFS*

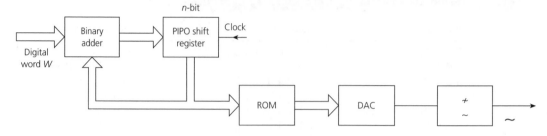

Fig. 10.31 *Increasing frequency of DDFS*

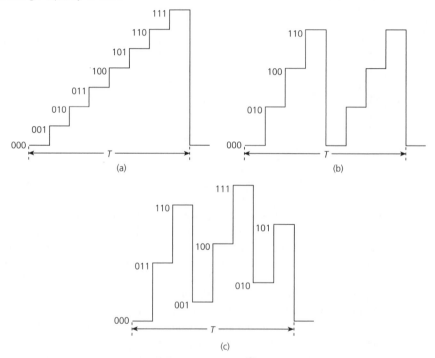

from 000 to 111 as shown by Fig. 10.31(a) and at each step the ROM outputs an instantaneous value of a sine wave. There are eight steps so that the phase of the sine wave is incremented in $2\pi/8$ or $45°$ steps. The frequency of this sinusoidal waveform is the lowest frequency that can be generated. If, now, W is increased to 010 the count will progress in steps of two as shown by Fig. 10.31(b). Alternate samples of the sine wave are now read from the ROM and the accumulator will now overflow after three steps when the count is 110. The phase of the output sinusoid will change in steps of $2\pi/4$ or $90°$. In the time T there are now two cycles of the output waveform so that the frequency has been doubled. If the increment digital word W is increased to 011 the count will proceed in threes as shown by Fig. 11.31(c); now the accumulator overflows when the count is 110, then when it is 111, and finally at 101. Then the output waveform goes through three cycles in time T so that the frequency is three times the minimum value.

EXAMPLE 10.9

Determine the steps of the accumulator output when a four-bit PIPO shift register is employed. Draw the waveforms (a) at the accumulator output and (b) at the output of the low-pass filter when the input digital word $W = 4$.

Solution

Table 10.2 gives the count of the accumulator.
    The required waveforms are shown in Figs 10.32(a) and (b) (*Ans.*)

Table 10.2

	I = 1	*2*	*3*	*4*
0 0 0 0	All	*	*	*
0 0 0 1	steps		*	
0 0 1 0		*	*	
0 0 1 1			*	
0 1 0 0		*	*	*
0 1 0 1			*	
0 1 1 0		*	*	
0 1 1 1			*	
1 0 0 0		*	*	*
1 0 0 1			*	
1 0 1 0		*	*	
1 0 1 1			*	
1 1 0 0		*	*	*
1 1 0 1			*	
1 1 1 0		*	*	
1 1 1 1			*	

Fig. 10.32

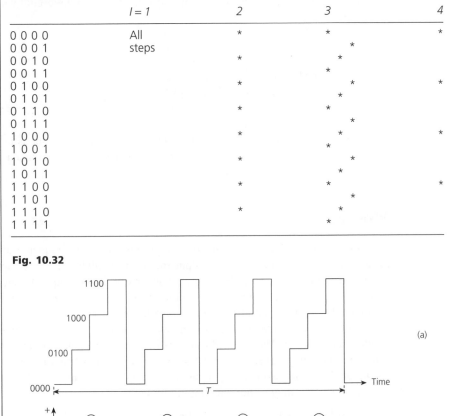

The greater the number of locations in the ROM the smaller will be the quantisation error of the constructed sinusoidal waveform. The frequency of the generated waveform is given by

$$f = [W \text{ (as an integer number)} \times \text{clock frequency}]/2^n \qquad (10.22)$$

where n is the number of bits used by the PIPO shift register. The highest frequency is limited by the DAC's fastest sampling rate.

EXAMPLE 10.10

A DDFS uses a clock frequency of 1 MHz and a four-bit shift register. Determine the frequency of the output waveform when the incrementing digital word W is (a) 1 and (b) 3.

Solution

(a) $f = 1/16$ MHz $= 62.5$ kHz (*Ans.*)
(b) $f = 3 \times 62.5$ kHz $= 187.5$ kHz (*Ans.*)

DDFS has some advantages over other frequency synthesis methods in that it generates less noise than PLL circuits, is very fast to switch from one frequency to another, and can provide a very fine resolution.

Mixers

The function of a mixer is to convert an input signal at one frequency into an output signal at another frequency. If the output frequency is higher than the input frequency the circuit is known as an *up-converter*; conversely, if the output frequency is lower than the input frequency the mixer is acting as a *down-converter*. The mixing process combines the input signal at frequency f_s with the output of a *local oscillator* at frequency f_o to generate the sum and difference frequencies $f_o \pm f_s$, either one of which is selected at the output. The selected sum, or difference, frequency output signal is known as the *intermediate-frequency signal*. Essentially, the action of a mixer is to multiply the two input signals together. If the input signal is $v_s = V_s \sin \omega_s t$ and the local oscillator voltage is $v_o = V_o \sin \omega_o t$, then the output voltage is

$$v_{out} = (kV_sV_o/2)[\cos(\omega_o - \omega_s)t - \cos(\omega_o + \omega_s)t] + \text{many other unwanted frequencies} \qquad (10.23)$$

The *conversion* conductance g_c of a mixer is the ratio (output current at difference (or sum) frequency)/(input signal voltage). If the mixer is to act as a down-converter the difference frequency, $(\omega_o - \omega_s)/2\pi$, component at the output is selected, and for an up-converter the sum frequency $(\omega_o + \omega_s)/2\pi$ is selected.

There are two modes of operation for a mixer: it may be either a *non-linear mixer*, or a *switching mixer*. A non-linear mixer utilises the square-law current–voltage charac-

Fig. 10.33 *Diode ring mixer*

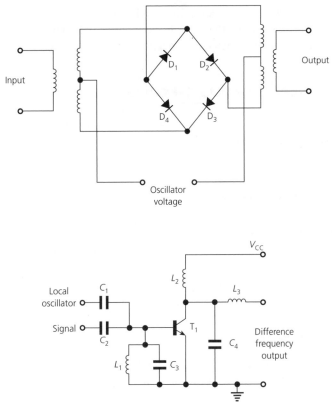

Fig. 10.34 *Active mixer*

teristic that is approximated by a diode or by the circuit of a bipolar transistor or an FET. If the input and local oscillator voltages are applied in series to the non-linear device the output of the mixer will include the term $(V_o \sin \omega_o t + V_S \sin \omega_S t)^2$, and expanding this shows the presence of components at the wanted sum and difference frequencies. Schottky diodes are usually employed in RF mixers.

A mixer may be of either the passive or active type; the former employs diodes and the latter uses transistors and requires a power supply. Most switching mixers are passive and of the double-balanced form shown in Fig. 10.33. Double-balanced ring mixers are used because (a) they have a high degree of isolation between the local oscillator circuit and the RF circuit, (b) the local oscillator voltage that appears at the output is very small, typically 40 dB down, and (c) they have a good even-order intermodulation performance. A ring mixer can be obtained within a single package. The ring mixer has some disadvantages, so it is not employed within radio ICs. These disadvantages are: (a) it requires a relatively high local oscillator voltage, typically +7 dBc; and (b) its *conversion loss* (output power in wanted sideband)/(input signal power) is at least 6 dB, and this figure is increased to about 7 dB by transformer losses. Mixers incorporated within an IC are of the active type and can have a conversion gain. An active mixer is essentially an RF amplifier biased to operate on a non-linear part of its characteristics. A typical active mixer circuit is shown in Fig. 10.34.

The *dynamic range* of a mixer is the range of input signal voltages over which the mixer is able to maintain a linear relationship between the sum (or difference) output voltage and the input voltage as the input signal voltage varies in amplitude. A passive mixer has a wider dynamic range than an active mixer.

Miscellaneous circuits

Most modern communication receivers employ either *crystal filters* or *SAW filters*, to give the desired selectivity. These filters offer the considerable advantages of requiring no IF amplifier alignment, and having a selectivity that is not affected by the application of AGC.

Crystal filters

Standard crystal filters are readily available at a number of fixed frequencies, e.g. 100 kHz, 1.4 MHz, 10.7 MHz and 35.4 MHz, with a bandwidth of between 0.01% and 1% of the centre frequency. The insertion loss of a crystal filter is between 1 and 10 dB, the shape factor is very good, and the generation of spurious responses is small. The frequency accuracy of a crystal is very high and so the bandwidth can be very carefully controlled.

SAW filters

A *surface acoustic wave* (SAW) filter is a four-terminal structure that has a pair of comb-like transducers deposited onto a piezoelectric substrate (see Fig. 10.35). The input transducer converts an electrical signal into a surface acoustic wave, while the output transducer converts the acoustic signal back to electrical form. The 'fingers' of each transducer are spaced apart by a common distance d. When an input voltage is applied to the SAW filter an acoustic wave is excited that propagates along the substrate. The maximum excitation is obtained when the comb spacing is equal to the wavelength λ of the signal. Half of the acoustic power is transmitted to the absorber and is completely lost, while the other half is sent in the opposite direction towards the output transducer. This means that the minimum insertion loss of an SAW filter is 6 dB. When the acoustic wave passes through the output transducer it is converted into an electrical signal.

Fig. 10.35 *SAW filter*

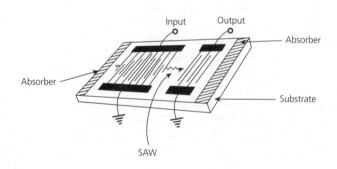

When the frequency of the signal is not at the nominal centre frequency, the comb spacing is no longer equal to the acoustic signal wavelength and the electric/acoustic conversion efficiency is reduced. The roll-off of the conversion efficiency is very rapid and so a highly selective loss–frequency characteristic is obtained. The characteristic can be tailored by the manufacturer by varying the length and/or the number of comb teeth and/or their spacings in each transducer. Like crystal filters, SAW filters are offered by the manufacturers at a number of set frequencies, e.g. 45, 100, 405, 857.65 and 868.95 MHz with a bandwidth of between 1% and 10% of the centre frequency. Their insertion loss varies from 6 dB to about 28 dB. The SAW filter is frequently used to provide IF selectivity because it is small, lightweight, very reliable and requires no adjustments. SAW filters are only available in a limited range of frequencies and their frequency accuracy is not good, typically ±50 kHz centred on 400 MHz. Hence an SAW filter has a wide, loosely specified bandwidth.

Squelch

When a radio receiver is tuned to an RF signal at which there is zero carrier, the AGC system of the receiver (p. 365) will increase the gain of the receiver to its maximum value. The maximum gain will amplify the inevitable noise that is generated within the circuit to produce considerable noise at the loudspeaker. A *squelch*, or *muting*, circuit is used in a radio receiver to prevent the output being noisy when no signal is being received at the tuned-to frequency. A squelch circuit switches the audio amplifier stage(s) out of circuit when there is no carrier and then switches them back into circuit when a carrier is received. The squelch circuit is normally operated by a d.c. voltage generated by the detector stage. Often this d.c. voltage needs to be amplified before it is used to operate the squelch circuit. The block diagram of a squelch system is shown by Fig. 10.36. The noise voltage is amplified, rectified and then applied to a Schmitt trigger circuit, the output of which operates an electronic switch (squelch) circuit that controls the application of the collector supply voltage to the AF amplifier.

Figure 10.37 shows a squelch circuit. When zero carrier is received transistor T_1 turns OFF and the supply voltage V_{CC} is applied to the non-inverting terminal of the op-amp. The op-amp is operated as a voltage comparator and so its output goes high to turn T_2 ON. The collector voltage of T_2 is then almost at earth potential and this prevents noise voltages reaching the AF amplifier. When a carrier is present a d.c. voltage is applied to the base of T_1 to turn it ON and the output of the op-amp goes low. T_2 turns OFF and then the – now present – AF signal is able to pass on to the AF amplifier.

Fig. 10.36 *Squelch system*

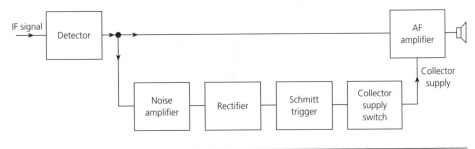

Fig. 10.37 *Squelch circuit*

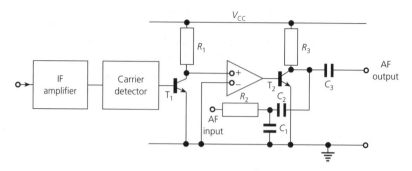

In some circuits the audio amplifier is not completely muted to avoid signals below the squelch threshold being missed. In such circuits the muting is level controlled in an AM receiver and noise controlled in an FM receiver.

PRACTICAL EXERCISE 10.6

Aim: To build and test a squelch circuit.

Components and equipment: Two transistors, one npn AF and the other pnp switching; two IN4148 diodes; capacitors: two 0.1 µF, one 1 µF and two 2.2 µF; resistors: one 1 kΩ, one 3 kΩ, one 15 kΩ and one 47 kΩ. D.C. power supply. 12 V d.c. supply. AF signal source. CRO. D.C. voltmeter. Breadboard.

Procedure:

(a) Build the circuit given in Fig. 10.38 (another squelch circuit).
(b) Connect the 12 V d.c. source to the 12 V input terminal and connect the variable d.c. source to the base of T_1. Connect the d.c. voltmeter across the base–emitter terminals of T_1 to measure its V_{BE} voltage. Connect the CRO to the output terminals of the circuit.

Fig. 10.38

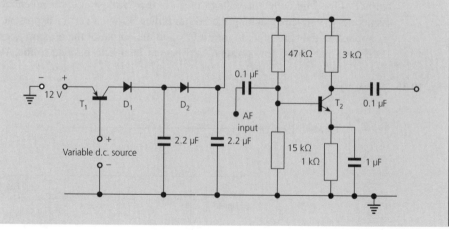

(c) Set the voltage of the variable d.c. supply to 12 V and note the waveform displayed on the CRO screen. Explain. Decrease the voltage of the variable supply in 0.05 V steps and at each step (i) note the V_{BE} value and (ii) observe the output waveform. At what value of V_{BE} did the amplifier start to work? Explain.

(d) A version of this circuit has been employed in commercial VHF radio receivers but, of course, the variable d.c. voltage was not obtained in this way. Suggest how the variable d.c. voltage could be obtained in a practical radio receiver circuit and give some reasons for the use of squelch circuits.

Noise-blanking circuit

A noise-blanking circuit may be used in a communication receiver to reduce the effects of impulse noise. Figure 10.39 is a block diagram of the front end of a radio with noise blanking. The noise-blanking part of the front end consists of a noise receiver, a noise detector and an electronic switch. The noise receiver is able to detect any impulsive noise that might appear in the passband of the receiver proper. Any noise impulse that appears is amplified and detected to produce an output pulse that operates the switch to turn the signal path off for as long as the impulse noise lasts. A delay circuit is inserted in the front end of the main receiver to make sure that there is time for the switch to operate and cut the signal path before the impulse noise gets to the mixer output.

Fig. 10.39 *Noise-blanking circuit*

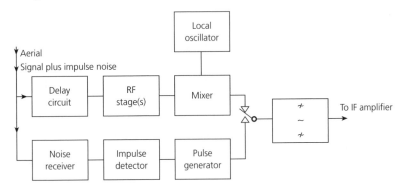

EXERCISES

10.1 Prove that (a) integrating a modulating signal before it is applied to a phase modulator produces an FM wave, and (b) differentiating a modulating signal before it is applied to a frequency modulator produces a PM wave. State how these results can be applied to FM and PM detectors.

10.2 A PLL frequency detector has the following parameters: $f_n = 180$ kHz, $f_1 = 190$ kHz, $K_D = 0.22$ V rad^{-1}, $K_f = 1$, $K_A = 5$ and $K_0 = 21$ kHz V^{-1}. Calculate (a) the open-loop gain A_V, (b) the change in frequency needed to achieve lock, (c) the output voltage, (d) V_D, (e) θ_e and (f) the hold-in range.

10.3 A PLL frequency synthesiser uses a reference frequency of 100 kHz and a programmable counter as a frequency divider. If the count can be altered from 8 to 128 determine (a) the range of output frequencies available and (b) the frequency resolution.

10.4 A diode detector has an input resistance of 1000 Ω and a total load resistance of 1800 Ω. (a) Calculate the efficiency of the detector. (b) The input AM wave has a maximum value of 2V and a minimum value of 0.4 V. Calculate the input power to the detector. (c) If the voltage drop across the diode is 0.25 V calculate the range of audio output voltages. (d) Calculate the maximum capacitance if peak clipping is to be avoided. The maximum modulating frequency is 3 kHz and the load resistance is 8 kΩ.

10.5 Explain how the frequency-determining tuned circuit of an oscillator can be (a) frequency modulated and (b) phase modulated by a variable-reactance circuit. State two types of variable-reactance device and discuss how they vary from one another. (c) If the fractional decrease in capacitance is 0.35% what is the resulting change in frequency?

10.6 Describe the function of a mixer and show how it can produce the sum and difference of the two signal frequencies applied to its input terminals. The signals $v = 1 \sin \omega_c t$ and $0.2 \sin \omega_m t$ are applied to a mixer whose current–voltage characteristic may be represented by $i = 0.4 + 0.2v + 0.1v^2 + \ldots$. Calculate the conversion conductance of the mixer.

Discuss the relative merits of using an active or a passive mixer in a radio receiver.

10.7 Design a 565 PLL FM detector for a 300 kHz carrier with a rated system deviation of 8 kHz. The input resistance of the circuit is to be 12 kΩ.

10.8 A varactor diode has a characteristic $C = 10/\sqrt{V_B}$ pF, where V_B is the reverse-bias voltage applied to the diode. The diode is connected in parallel with a 100 μH inductance. Calculate the resonant frequency of the parallel circuit when the bias voltage is (a) 6V and (b) 4V. (c) If the resonant frequency is to be 8 MHz determine the required bias voltage.

11 Radio transmitters

After reading this chapter you should be able to:

(a) Understand the need for regulation of the operation of radio transmitters.
(b) State that the Radio Communications Agency (in the UK) issues MPT specifications for different radio systems that lay out the requirements for a radio transmitter licence to be granted.
(c) List the main parameters of a radio transmitter that are specified by an MPT document.
(d) Understand the basic operation of AM transmitters and draw and explain a block diagram of an AM transmitter.
(e) Understand the basic operation of FM transmitters and draw and explain a block diagram of an FM transmitter.
(f) Discuss the need for an HF transmitter to employ wideband RF circuitry.

The basic function of a radio transmitter is first to frequency-translate an input signal to a specific part of the frequency spectrum and then transmit the frequency-shifted signal at the required power level. In the lower-frequency bands amplitude modulation is employed almost exclusively but in the VHF and UHF bands both amplitude and frequency modulation are used for analogue systems and digital modulation is employed for digital systems.

Radio regulations

Before any radio transmissions are made it is a legal requirement in most countries that the transmitter has been authorised by the issuing of an appropriate licence. It is a condition of the licence that the performance of the radio equipment meets certain minimum standards. To ensure compatibility between the radio systems employed in different countries around the world the International Telecommunications Union Radio-communication Section (ITU-R) has issued *Radio Regulations* that are legally binding in international law on all member countries, including the UK. The intending operator of a radio transmitter must satisfy these Radio Regulations before the regulatory authority will license its operation. In the UK the regulatory authority is the Radio Communications Agency and in the USA it is the Federal Communication Commission

(FCC). In the UK the Wireless Telegraphy Acts ban the installation or use of radio equipment unless (a) the appropriate licence has been obtained, or (b) the equipment is exempted from licensing, e.g. cordless telephones and radio receivers, but not television receivers and low-power telemetry transmitters.

The Radio Regulations cover a number of fields amongst which are:

- The allocation of carrier frequencies and bandwidths to different services. This is known as *spectrum management* and it is necessary because the unauthorised use of radio frequencies can cause harmful interference to legitimate users.
- The type of, and the effective height of, the transmitting aerial. A new mast and/or aerial must not obstruct an existing radio path.
- The maximum allowable transmitted power.
- Frequency stability tolerance required in different frequency bands.
- Spurious emissions. These are defined as an emission on a frequency (or a band of frequencies) that is (are) outside the necessary bandwidth and whose level may be reduced without affecting information transmission. Spurious emissions include harmonics and intermodulation products and must be limited to avoid interference to other radio systems.
- Radiated spectrum.

MPT specifications

MPT (Ministry of Posts and Telecommunications) specifications are issued in the UK by the Radio Communications Agency and specify the requirements for a radio system. A large number of MPT specifications exist covering all kinds of radio system. As an example, the MPT 1410 specification for digital auxiliary broadcast radio-relay systems in the frequency band 1450 to 1530 MHz, sub-band G, specifies:

(a) Frequency assignments: a plan is given.
(b) Aerial characteristics: states that the polarisation can be either horizontal or vertical.
(c) Transmitted power: EIRP not greater than 20 dBW. Transmitted power not greater than +10 dBW.
(d) Radiated spectrum: bandwidth not wider than 700 kHz.
(e) Frequency stability: not worse than ±15 kHz.
(f) Spurious emissions: not greater than −65 dBW in any 4 kHz band over the 0 to 10 GHz band.

Frequency of operation

The electromagnetic frequency spectrum has been allocated to various radio services by the ITU-R. Specific frequency bands have been allocated to services such as sound and television broadcasting, point-to-point radio links (both narrow band and broadband), mobile radio including marine and aeronautical, radar and radio navigation, radio telemetry, pagers, cordless telephones, etc. Spectrum management is necessary to enable a large number of users to operate on relatively few radio frequencies; often frequencies are allocated to users on a shared basis.

Sound broadcasting

AM sound broadcast signals are transmitted in the MF band at frequencies of 647–1546 kHz with a bandwidth of approximately 9 kHz, as well as a few stations in the LF band. Some broadcast radio stations also broadcast at the following frequencies in the HF band: 5.95–6.2 MHz, 7.1–7.3 MHz, 9.5–9.775 MHz, 11.7–11.975 MHz, 15.1–15.45 MHz, 17.7–17.9 MHz, 21.45–21.75 MHz and 25.6–26.1 MHz. The bandwidth of these HF systems is 10 kHz. FM sound broadcast signals are transmitted in the frequency band 88.1–96.8 MHz. The bandwidth provided is 180 kHz.

Television broadcasting

In the UK terrestrial television broadcasts are in the UHF band at frequencies of 471–575.25 MHz and 615–847.25 kHz, providing a video bandwidth of 5.5 MHz. The sound carrier frequencies are placed 6 MHz above the associated video carrier and give a bandwidth of 20 kHz.

Point-to-point HF radio systems

HF radio links are used to carry telephone calls and/or data signals to overseas destinations where fibre optic cable and/or communications satellite links are not available and/or have inadequate capacity when traffic levels are high. Generally, either SSB or ISB is employed. Several frequency bands have been allotted to such services including, for example, 3.5–3.9 MHz, 5.73–5.95 MHz, 9.04–9.5 MHz, 13.36–14 MHz, 21.75–21.87 MHz and 26.1–27.5 MHz. The bandwidth per channel is 250 Hz to 3 kHz.

Mobile systems

Maritime

Telecommunication services to ships at sea are provided in a number of frequencies in the MF, HF and VHF bands as well as by INMARSAT (p. 420). INMARSAT is a communications satellite system that uses frequency bands centred at 1.5 GHz for ship-to-satellite transmissions, 1.6 GHz for satellite-to-ship transmissions, and frequencies in the band 6/4 GHz for satellite-to-shore links. The VHF band provides short-range services (up to about 80 km) in the band 156–163 MHz. Services over distances of 80 to about 1000 km are provided at frequencies in the 1.6–3.8 MHz band. Longer-distance links to ships at sea use the following frequencies in the HF band: 4, 6, 8, 13, 17 and 22 MHz.

Land

Land mobile services may be divided into three classes: (a) *private land mobile* (PMR), (b) *public land mobile* and (c) cordless telephones and paging systems.

Private land mobile

PMR services do not have access to the *public switched telephone network* (PSTN) and may be subdivided into three categories: (a) *emergency* (ambulance, fire service and police), (b) *public utilities* (electricity, gas, telecommunications and water), and (c) *private* (delivery vans, mini-cabs, taxis, etc.). A large number of different frequency bands have been allocated to maritime and land mobile services and a representative sample of them is given by Table 11.1.

Table 11.1 *Land and sea mobile frequency bands*

Frequency band (MHz)	Used by	Channel bandwidth (kHz)
71.5–78.0	PMR	12.5
80.0–85.0	Emergency	12.5
85.0–88.0	PMR	12.5
97.0–102.0	Emergency	12.5
105.0–108.0	PMR	12.5
138.0–141.0	PMR	12.5
146.0–148.0	Emergency	12.5
156.0–163.0	Maritime	25.0
174.0–225.0	PMR	12.5
451.0–452.0	Emergency	25.0
465.0–466.0	Emergency	25.0

Public land mobile

Public land mobile services give the user access to the PSTN, and each mobile telephone can be called from a local exchange telephone line. Mobile telephones use a cellular radio technique and may (currently) use either analogue techniques (TACS) or digital techniques (GSM). The *Total Access Communication System* (TACS) transmits on frequencies in the 872.0125–904.9875 MHz band and receives on frequencies in the 917.0125–949.9875 MHz band. The *Global System for Mobile Communication* (GSM) uses the frequency bands 890–915 MHz for transmission and 935–960 MHz for reception.

The Radio Communications Agency specifications for land mobile services are known as the MPT 1300 series. Besides mobile telephony, both public and private, the series also includes specifications for applications such as pagers, medical equipment, telemetry, cordless telephones, car alarm systems and security systems.

Cordless telephones and pagers

Cordless telephones use a radio link to connect the handset to the base station instead of the conventional flexible cord. The CT1 system uses 1.7 MHz in the base-to-handset direction and 47 MHz in the handset-to-base direction. The CT2 system employs the frequency band 864–868 MHz. A third system, known as the *Digital European Cordless Telephone* (DECT), operates in the frequency band 1.88–1.9 GHz. Public paging systems operate in the frequency band 138–174 MHz.

Wideband radio systems

The frequencies used by fixed microwave radio systems vary from about 2 GHz up to 60 GHz. Certain bands within this range are allocated to fixed terrestrial and satellite systems. Some frequency bands are allocated for the sole use of telecommunications businesses, such as BT, while other bands are controlled by the Radio Communications Agency and devoted to shared use. Wideband terrestrial radio systems operate in a number of frequency bands in the SHF band. These are: 3.7–4.2 GHz, 5.85–6.425 GHz,

Table 11.2 Telemetry/telecontrol frequency bands

Sub-band (MHz)	Bandwidth (kHz)
A 868.00–868.60	600
B 868.70–869.20	500
C 869.30–869.65	350
D 869.70–870.00	300

6.425–7.11 GHz, 10.7–11.7 GHz, 14.0–14.5 GHz and 17.7–19.7 GHz. Communications satellite systems use some of these bands (p. 405).

Telemetry and telecontrol

Telemetry systems operate over distances of more than 100 m line of sight, or up to 75 m in buildings, with a bit rate that varies from up to 9.6 kb/s to as large as 40 kb/s, and most systems have to follow the UK specification MPT 1340. The 868–879 MHz band is allocated to *short-range device* (SRD) applications such as alarms and social alarms with a maximum transmitted power of 10 mW. For wideband signals this band is subdivided into the sub-bands given in Table 11.2.

The 418 MHz band (changing soon to 433 MHz) is deregulated and used for general-purpose short-range RF devices. The consumer part of the market is high-volume, low-cost, remote control devices such as garage door openers and personal alarms. The maximum transmitted power is 10 mW. Car alarms are operated in the 433.92 MHz band with a maximum transmitted power of 10 mW. The commercial part of the market is mainly data telemetry and is used by utility companies and industry for process control and remote control of machinery. Other telemetry systems operate in the 433 or 450–470 MHz bands to provide multi-channel systems and then the relevant specification is MPT 1329/1361.

Transmitted power

The maximum power that a transmitter may radiate is restricted by the regulatory authority to avoid the station causing interference to other radio stations.

Sound broadcast transmitters are classified according to their operating power. A Class A transmitter can have an output power in the range 10–50 kW, a Class B transmitter generally has a transmitted power of 5 kW, and for a Class C transmitter the maximum power is restricted to 1 kW.

Frequency stability

The carrier frequency at which a transmitter operates must be maintained constant to within the ITU-R specified limits to avoid interference with other adjacent (in frequency) services. *Frequency stability* is the ability of an oscillator or frequency synthesiser to remain at a constant frequency. Frequency stability may be either *short term* or *long term*. Short-term frequency stability is mainly determined by fluctuations in d.c.

operating voltages, while long-term frequency stability is determined by component ageing and changes in the ambient temperature and/or humidity. These may produce changes in inductance and capacitance in the frequency-determining network, and also in resistance, which will lead to changes in the operating point of transistors. The frequency stability of a source can be improved by regulating the power supply and minimising variations in the environmental conditions.

Frequency stability is normally quoted as a percentage change in frequency (the tolerance) from the desired value. Thus a 100 kHz source with ±5% stability will vary between 95 and 105 kHz. Typical stability requirements are:

- AM sound broadcast transmitter: the carrier must not vary by more than ±20 Hz from the allotted carrier frequency.
- FM sound broadcast transmitter: the required stability is ±2 kHz.

Transmitter and receiver codes

The data sheets of radio transmitters and receivers quote the types of signal and modulation used with the equipment using a numeric coding system. The code employs three numeric characters: the first character is a letter that describes the type of modulation employed, the second character is a number that indicates the modulating signal, and the third character, which is another letter, indicates the kind of information that is transmitted/received. Table 11.3 gives the identification code.

Table 11.3 *Transmitter/receiver identification codes*

Numeric character 1 Type of modulation	Numeric character 2 Type of modulating signal	Numeric character 3 Type of information
A DSBAM	0 None	N None
H SSB full carrier	1 Single channel, digital/ quantised info.	A Telegraphy, aural reception
R SSB reduced carrier	2 Single channel, dig./quant. info. + subcarrier	B Telegraphy, auto reception
J SSBSC	3 Single channel, analogue info.	C FAX
B ISB	7 Two or more channels, dig./quant. info.	
C VSB	8 Two or more channels, analogue info.	D Data
F FM	9 Composite signal dig./quant. + analogue	E Telephony
G PM		F Television
D Combined angle/AM		W Combinations of above
P Unmod. pulses		X Any others
K PAM		
L PWM		
M PPM		

Fig. 11.1 *Low-level AM transmitter*

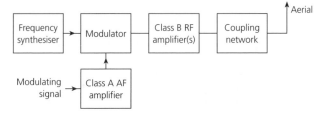

AM transmitters

A radio transmitter must use its input signal to modulate the carrier frequency allocated by the regulatory authority and then amplify the modulated signal to the required power level. The modulated RF signal must then be efficiently coupled to the transmitting aerial, perhaps via a feeder, for radiation to the distant receiving aerial(s). Sound broadcast transmitters employ DSB amplitude modulation but HF radio-telephony transmitters use either ISB or SSB modulation. Modulation of the carrier can be carried out at either a low level or a high level.

Low-level modulation

The basic block diagram of a low-level AM radio transmitter is shown by Fig. 11.1. The carrier voltage is applied to a buffer amplifier whose main function is to provide a constant load for the carrier source and thus help to maintain its frequency stability. The output of the pre-amplifier is applied to a driver amplifier which raises the carrier voltage to the level required by the modulator. The input signal is applied first to a pre-amplifier and then to a driver amplifier to increase it to the input signal level required by the modulator; since the necessary power level is not high the design of the AF amplifier is relatively simple. Both AF amplifiers must operate under Class A conditions to avoid distortion of the signal waveform. The output of the modulator is the wanted DSBAM waveform and it is applied to a linear Class B RF amplifier for amplification to the required transmitted power level. The aerial coupling network is necessary to match the output impedance of the final Class B amplifier to the impedance of the aerial it and must have the minimum possible loss.

Low-level modulation is only used for low-power transmitters because its overall efficiency is poor due to the use of Class B RF power amplifiers.

High-level modulation

High-level amplitude modulation is mainly employed with DSBAM sound broadcast transmitters and VHF/UHF mobile transmitters. HF SSB/ISB transmitters also use high-level modulation but the production of the SSB/ISB signal is carried out in a separate drive unit. The basic block diagram of a high-level AM transmitter is shown by Fig. 11.2. Class C RF amplifiers are used to increase the carrier voltage to the high level required by the anode- or collector-modulated Class C amplifier. The modulating signal

Fig. 11.2 *High-level AM transmitter*

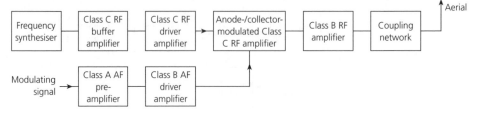

must be amplified to a reach a higher level than in the low-level transmitter and hence it is amplified by first a Class A amplifier and then a Class B power amplifier before it arrives at the modulator. The Class C RF modulator produces a DSBAM wave which is coupled to the aerial, or feeder, by the coupling network.

High-level operation of a radio transmitter offers the advantage that high-efficiency Class C RF amplifiers can be employed throughout the RF section of the system and this gives the transmitter a high overall efficiency. The disadvantage of high-level operation is the need for the modulating signal to be amplified by a Class B power amplifier to obtain the necessary modulating power, although this is of less importance in low-power all-transistor transmitters.

High-level modulation is used for sound broadcast transmitters and VHF/UHF mobile transmitters.

Sound broadcast transmitters

Amplitude modulation

The transmitted power of a sound broadcast transmitter may be up to about 100 kW. To obtain the largest output powers the final stage may still be a Class C anode-modulated valve (usually a tetrode) amplifier but, increasingly, a number of MOSFET modules connected in parallel are employed. A single transistor amplifier is unable to handle kilowatts of power so several modules are employed that are connected in parallel and each module makes its contribution to the total output power. The module system has an advantage in that if one module should fail the transmitter will continue to work albeit at a reduced power level. Some high-power MF transmitters employ tripled or quadrupled lower-power transmitters to obtain a wanted power output; for example, the outputs of four 50 kW transmitters can be combined to give a transmitted power of 200 kW.

Figure 11.3 shows the basic block diagram of an MF sound broadcast transmitter that has a transmitted power of 1 kW. The transmitter operates over the MF broadcast band of 520–1610 kHz using broadband circuits. The system is tuned to a wanted carrier frequency by an output tuning unit that connects the output of the transmitter to the feeder. The RF carrier is fed via a splitting circuit to two RF wideband pre-amplifiers. The split amplified carriers are each then further amplified by a driver power amplifier. The output of each driver amplifier is divided into four equal parts by further splitter circuits and each of the eight parts is applied to its own modulated high-power amplifier,

Fig. 11.3 *MF sound broadcast transmitter*

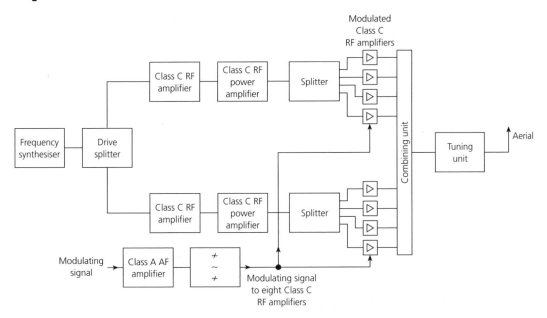

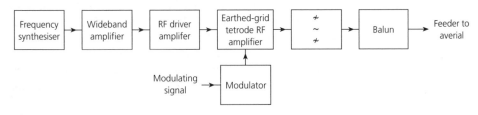

Fig. 11.4 *High-power sound broadcast transmitter*

each of which is able to develop an output power of 125 W. All the 125 W RF amplifiers contain a Class B modulator. The audio input signal is amplified and filtered before it is applied to a Class B modulator to amplitude-modulate one of the eight 125 W RF power amplifiers. The modulated outputs from the eight power amplifiers are combined in a wideband combining unit to produce an output power of 1 kW. The output signal that appears at the output of the combining unit is applied to a tuning unit; here the output signal is tuned to the required frequency of transmission and the output impedance of the combiner is matched to the 50 Ω impedance of the feeder. Typically the frequency stability of the transmitter is ±10 Hz.

If a thermionic valve, such as a tetrode, is employed in the final RF amplifier a high power output can be obtained without the need to combine the outputs of lower-power amplifiers. Figure 11.4 shows the basic block diagram of such a transmitter which uses a tetrode valve in the earthed grid configuration in the Class C anode- (and screen-) modulated RF amplifier.

Fig. 11.5 *FM sound broadcast transmitter*

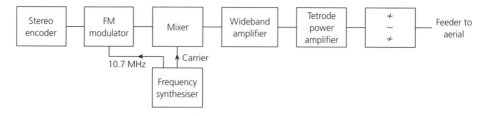

Fig. 11.6 *High-power FM sound broadcast transmitter*

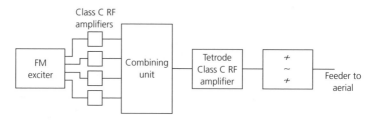

Frequency modulation

In the transmitted power range up to 10 kW all solid-state designs are common, but for higher powers the final power amplifier generally employs a thermionic valve, most often a tetrode. Figure 11.5 shows the block diagram of an FM sound broadcast transmitter that covers the frequency band 87.5–108 MHz in 25 kHz steps and has a peak frequency deviation of ±75 kHz. The frequency stability of the transmitter is ±200 kHz maximum. The high-power Class C RF amplifier uses a tetrode thermionic valve but all other stages in the transmitter use semiconductor devices. The stereo encoder converts the left and right audio signals into a stereo-encoded signal which is applied to the frequency modulator. The FM output of the modulator is centred on 10.7 MHz and this signal is up-converted to the required transmitted frequency by mixing the 10.7 MHz signal with the output of the local oscillator. The frequency stability of the carrier source is maintained at the required level by means of an automatic phase control system (not shown). The output of the mixer is then amplified by a wideband amplifier which raises the signal level to a level somewhere in the range 5–18 W. The modulated signal is then further amplified to the level needed to drive the final amplifier which amplifies the signal to the transmitted power level of 10 kW. The final amplifier is operated under Class C conditions and is tuned to the required frequency of operation by a cavity resonator to provide a gain of about 20 dB.

Similar transmitters are able to provide a higher transmitted power by using four, parallel, solid-state driver amplifiers to provide 250 W maximum drive power each and combining the individual powers to obtain a total drive power of about 800 W. This drive power is then used to drive the wideband input stage of a tetrode amplifier that can produce an output power of 20 kW. The tetrode RF amplifier is tuned to the required frequency of operation by a cavity resonator. Tuning is achieved by varying the lengths of two short-circuiting plungers in the cavity. The parts of the transmitter circuit before

Fig. 11.7 *Self-turning HF transmitter*

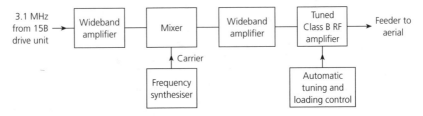

the high-power stage(s) are often known as the exciter. The basic block diagram of such a transmitter is shown by Fig. 11.6.

HF communication transmitters

Communication transmitters operating in the HF band are required to be self-tuning so that it is easy to change frequency rapidly whenever sky-wave propagation conditions vary. A frequency change is accomplished by two operations: first the required frequency is entered into the transmitter by means of a keypad at the control and then an 'action' control is pressed when the frequency is automatically changed. The HF band is subdivided into a large number of bands to make coarse tuning easier. Coarse frequency changes are carried out, with the supply voltage reduced, by altering the lengths of transmission line inductances by moving a short-circuiting bar and hence changing their inductances. Servo-controlled capacitors are then set to the approximate values needed for the new frequency. Then fine tuning is carried out by applying full supply voltage to the equipment and fine tuning the capacitors. Further tuning follows to achieve correct loading of the final power amplifier.

The basic block diagram of a self-tuning HF transmitter is given in Fig. 11.7 in which it is assumed that the input signal is derived from an ISB drive unit. The 3.1 MHz input signal is up-converted to a frequency in the band 4–27.5 MHz by mixing it with the frequency derived from the frequency synthesiser. The output signal of the mixer is amplified by another wideband RF amplifier before it is applied to the automatically tuned final power amplifier. The automatic tuning circuitry also adjusts the loading of the final amplifier; for the maximum power to be transferred from the final power amplifier to the aerial feeder the amplifier must work into its optimum load impedance. The final stage is usually operated under Class B conditions.

VHF/UHF communication transmitters

The output power of a VHF/UHF communication transmitter is only a few tens of watts and so the final high-power amplifier can use a transistor circuit. Figure 11.8 shows the block diagram of a VHF AM transmitter. The input signal is amplified and filtered before it is applied to a Class B power amplifier which increases the signal level so that it is large enough to collector-modulate the final Class C amplifier. The carrier frequency is generated by a frequency synthesiser and is amplified to the required power

Fig. 11.8 *VHF AM communication transmitter*

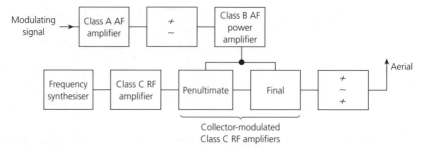

Fig. 11.9 *VHF FM communication transmitter*

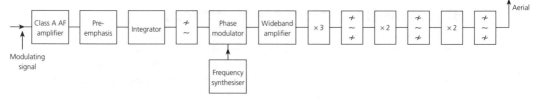

Fig. 11.10 *VHF FM mobile transmitter*

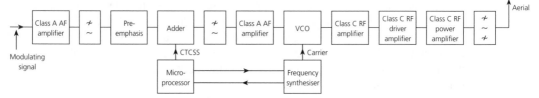

level by a Class C RF amplifier. The AM output of the final amplifier is filtered before it is passed to the aerial to suppress any spurious frequency components that may have been generated.

Figure 11.9 gives the block diagram of a VHF FM transmitter which uses a phase modulator. The input audio signal is amplified and pre-emphasised before it is integrated and low-pass filtered. The processed signal is then applied to the phase modulator to produce an FM signal. The FM signal is amplified before its frequency is increased by a factor of 12 by successive stages of frequency doubling and tripling. If the carrier frequency applied to the phase modulator was 38 MHz the final carrier frequency would be 456 MHz. After each stage of frequency doubling/tripling the output signal is filtered to remove unwanted frequency components.

The block diagram of a VHF FM mobile transmitter that incorporates CTCSS (p. 427) is shown by Fig. 11.10. The input signal is amplified, filtered, pre-emphasised and limited before it is applied to a VCO. The frequency of the VCO is varied by the processed signal to generate an FM signal. The FM signal is then passed through a driver amplifier and amplified to the required transmitted power level by the final amplifier.

Fig. 11.11 *DAB transmitter*

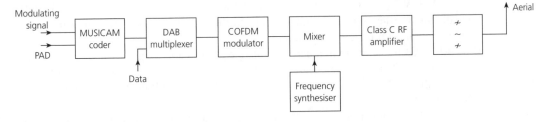

Most VHF/UHF radio transmitters are combined with a radio receiver and are then known as *transceivers*. Transceivers are considered in the next chapter.

Digital audio broadcasting transmitters

The digital audio broadcasting (DAB) system transmits high-quality stereo sound programmes. Digitally coded sound programmes are broadcast by a DAB transmitter. One of the main advantages of digital sound broadcasting is that interference caused by fading, multi-path reception or reflections can be suppressed to give high-quality reception.

The block diagram of a DAB transmitter is shown by Fig. 11.11. Both audio (music and/or speech) signals and *programme-associated data* (PAD) are fed into the *masking-pattern-adapted universal sub-band integrated coding and multiplexing* (MUSICAM) coder. Here the input signals are coded into a digital signal using irrelevance and redundancy reductions. The output-multiplexed signal consists of several coded audio signals that occupy a limited bandwidth. The coded signal plus other data signals are applied to the DAB multiplexer; this circuit combines the incoming audio and data channels to form the *ensemble transport interface* (ETI) at a bit rate of 2.048 Mb/s. This output has two layers: ETI(NI), the independent layer, and ETI(NA), the adapted layer.

The multiplexed output of the DAB multiplexer must then be applied to the *coded orthogonal frequency-division multiplex* (COFDM) modulator. The two pieces of equipment may be on the same rack and if so they are then directly interconnected. If the link between the DAB multiplexer and the COFDM modulator is via a satellite or terrestrial microwave link, ETI(NI) is employed, but if a line in the PSTN is employed ETI(NI) must first be converted to ETI(NA) at the sending end of the line and converted back to ETI(NI) at the transmitter end of the line link. In the COFDM modulator the multiplexed bit stream is spread over 1536 QPSK-modulated carriers if the final signal is to be transmitted in the frequency band 174–230 MHz, or over 384 QPSK-modulated carriers if the 1452–1492 MHz band is used. Using so many carriers ensures that the COFDM demodulator in the DAB receiver always receives an adequate number of signal components to permit demodulation without error. Using QPSK with so many carriers allows the delayed signal components in multi-path reception to be used in the demodulation process as well as the direct signal(s). The bandwidth of the analogue signal is 1.5 MHz.

In the DAB transmitter the DAB signal at the output of the COFDM modulator is converted to the wanted frequency of transmission and is then amplified to the wanted power level. Linear power amplifiers are employed to give output powers of, typically, 50 to 400 W in the 1452–1492 MHz band and 100 W to 1 kW in the 174–230 MHz band. Finally, the amplified signal is passed through a bandpass filter to remove any intermodulation products that might exist.

All DAB transmitters in a network operate at the same frequency and are synchronised together. This practice ensures that the individual transmitters do not interfere with one another and all contribute to the field strength; as a result the transmitted power can be reduced.

The PAD input is used for various extra information signals such as road traffic information, programme/music titles and volume control. The data input carries such features as town maps and hotel information.

EXERCISES

11.1 The data sheet of a high-power transmitter includes the following:

(i) Output power 200 kW carrier with 100% modulation for 10 min and 40% modulation for 50 min in any hour.
(ii) Operates at any one frequency in the band 525–1605 kHz.
(iii) Equipment is protected by a key interlock system to prevent access until the transmitter is switched off.

(a) What kind of transmitter is this? (b) Why is the percentage modulation restricted? (c) Discuss the reasons why a protective interlock system is deemed necessary.

11.2 An MF radio transmitter of the type shown in Fig. 11.3 has the following parameters quoted in its specification: (i) maximum VSWR, 1.4; (ii) frequency stability, ±10 Hz over 30 days; (iii) carrier shift, less than 5% at 100% modulation; AF response, −2 dB, 40–10 000 Hz relative to 400 Hz at 50% modulation. Explain the meaning of each parameter.

11.3 The specification for a UHF transmitter includes: output power adjustable from 1 to 6 W; spurious outputs less than 0.25 µW; FM noise better than −55 dB; modulation variable to a maximum of ±5 kHz; AF response within 3 dB from 300 to 3000 Hz. Explain the meaning of each term used.

11.4 A radio transmitter has the following modes of operation: CW A1A, A1B; MCW A2A, A2B; AM A3E; FM F3E; FSK F1B, SSB H2A, H2B, H3E, J2A, J2B, J3E, R2A, R2B, R3E; ISB B7B, B8E, B9W. Explain each mode of operation.

11.5 Explain the operation of the MF radio transmitter shown by Fig. 11.4.

11.6 (a) Discuss the legal requirements for the operation of a radio transmitter.
(b) List some radio systems that require a licence and some that are deregulated.
(c) Who is the regulatory authority in the UK?
(d) Explain why it is necessary to regulate radio.

12 Radio receivers

After reading this chapter you should be able to:

(a) Explain the principle of operation of a superheterodyne radio receiver and say why it is employed.
(b) Calculate the frequency of the image, or second, channel signal knowing the wanted signal and local oscillator frequencies.
(c) Discuss why double superheterodyne radio receivers are often used and explain their operation.
(d) Discuss the reasons for the choice of intermediate frequency/frequencies for a radio receiver.
(e) State what is meant by co-channel interference and explain why it has more effect on an AM receiver than on an FM receiver.
(f) Calculate intermodulation distortion in a receiver and understand parameters such as intercept point and 1 dB compression point.
(g) Calculate the dynamic range of a receiver.
(h) Explain the meaning of the terms blocking, reciprocal mixing and cross-modulation.
(i) Explain what is meant by the sensitivity of a radio receiver and know how to measure its value.
(j) Explain what is meant by the selectivity of a radio receiver and know how to measure its value.
(k) Explain the function of each stage in a radio receiver.
(l) Understand the application of AGC to a radio receiver and know why it is necessary.
(m) Draw and explain the block diagram of a typical MF/HF communication radio receiver.
(n) Draw and explain the block diagram of a VHF/UHF communication radio receiver.
(o) Draw and explain the block diagram of a VHF/UHF transceiver.
(p) Explain how a digital radio receiver differs from an analogue radio receiver.
(q) Draw and explain the block diagram of a digital radio receiver.

The function of a radio receiver is to select the wanted signal present at the receiving aerial, which may be of very small amplitude, from the background noise and to reject a large number of, possibly stronger, unwanted signals. The radio receiver must then amplify and demodulate the received signal to provide an output baseband signal with at least the minimum required signal-to-noise ratio. The main problem is not in amplifying the received signal to the wanted level but in overcoming the adverse effects of both the received noise and the internally generated noise and interference. Once the signal level has fallen close to the receiver noise level – or *noise floor* – the signal will no longer be intelligible.

Most MF/HF communication radio receivers are able to receive different kinds of signal, such as DSB amplitude modulation, SSBSC, CW and data, and in some cases frequency modulation also. Receivers designed for use in the VHF/UHF bands usually receive either AM or FM signals. Modern communication receivers are always superheterodyne receivers; both single-superheterodyne and double-superheterodyne receivers are employed. There are two main reasons for the use of double-superheterodyne receivers: (a) the first intermediate frequency (IF) can be high, giving a wide separation between the wanted signal frequency and the image channel signal frequency; and (b) the second IF can be low, making good adjacent-channel selectivity easier to obtain. Since many applications for communication radio receivers require the receiver to be remotely controlled and/or able to change frequency both rapidly and accurately, both broadband front ends and frequency synthesis are commonly employed.

Increasingly, digital techniques are being employed in radio receiver design and these obtain sufficient selectivity with the single-superheterodyne principle. Digital receivers tend to be smaller and lighter than those using analogue techniques and consume less power. Traditionally a mobile radio receiver, whether it uses only analogue techniques or is to some extent digitised, is application specific: it may be an AM receiver, or an FM receiver, or a mobile telephone. Some of the latest receivers are software controlled; such receivers process the radio signal in the digital domain instead of the analogue domain throughout using digital signal processors (DSPs). Processing is carried out using general-purpose DSPs; the centre frequency of the receiver, its bandwidth and filters are all configured by software. By using different software the radio can be employed to support a variety of receiver protocols.

Superheterodyne radio receiver

In a superheterodyne radio receiver the frequency of the wanted input signal is always converted to a constant intermediate frequency (IF). Figure 12.1 shows the basic block

Fig. 12.1 *Superheterodyne radio receiver*

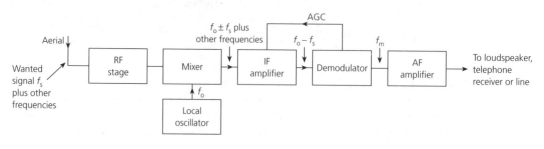

diagram of a superheterodyne radio receiver. The wanted signal, at frequency f_s, together with many unwanted signals at other frequencies that were present at the aerial, are applied to the RF stage or front end. The RF stage will filter out many of the unwanted frequencies. The band-limited signal is then applied to the mixer stage, where the wanted signal frequency f_s is combined with a locally generated frequency f_o, known as the *local oscillator frequency*, to generate a large number of new frequencies. Two of the frequency components generated are (a) the sum frequency $f_o + f_s$ and (b) the difference frequency $f_o - f_s$. Either the difference frequency $f_o - f_s$ or the sum frequency $f_o + f_s$ is selected by the amplifier to be the IF. Since this is a fixed frequency and the wanted signal frequency may lie anywhere in the tuning range of the receiver, the local oscillator frequency must be variable. It is often supplied by a frequency synthesiser. The IF amplifier amplifies the wanted signal and rejects other, unwanted, frequencies that are near to the wanted frequency. The output signal of the IF amplifier is applied to the detector where it is demodulated to receive the baseband signal. The demodulated (detected) AF signal is then applied to the AF amplifier for amplification before it is applied to the loudspeaker, telephone or other device.

The local oscillator frequency may be chosen to make the intermediate frequency higher than, or lower than, the signal frequency. Making $f_{IF} > f_s$ is known as up-conversion and making $f_{IF} < f_s$ is known as down-conversion. Sound broadcast radio receivers always employ down-conversion but communication radio receivers may employ either up- or down-conversion. In either case the local oscillator frequency is chosen to ensure that the IF is outside the tuning range of the receiver. It should also avoid the frequency of nearby sound and television broadcast transmitters.

Image (or second-channel) signal

When a superheterodyne radio receiver is tuned to a signal frequency f_s there is always another signal that will also produce the IF if it is allowed to reach the mixer stage. This other signal is known as the *image (or second-)channel signal* and it is at a frequency f_{IM} such that the difference between it and the local oscillator frequency f_o is equal to the intermediate frequency f_{IF}. Thus

$$f_{IF} = f_{IM} - f_o \qquad (12.1)$$
$$= f_{IM} - (f_s + f_{IF})$$

or

$$f_{IM} = f_s + 2f_{IF} \qquad (12.2)$$

Clearly, the higher the IF the bigger will be the frequency separation between the wanted signal and the image channel signal and this makes it easier for the RF stage to reject the image channel signal. The frequency of the image channel signal will vary as the receiver is tuned to different frequencies and hence either the RF stage should have a variable selectivity or it must employ one or more filters. The use of up-conversion will place the IF signal at a frequency higher than the highest frequency to which the receiver will tune; this practice allows the image channel frequency to be rejected by a low-pass filter. When down-conversion is employed a bank of sub-octave bandpass filters will probably be employed to reject the image channel signal.

A radio receiver has an IF of 39 MHz and is tuned to receive a signal at 5 MHz. Calculate (a) the local oscillator frequency and (b) the image channel signal frequency. Assume that down-conversion is employed.

Solution

(a) $f_o = 39 + 5 = 44$ MHz (*Ans.*)
(b) $f_{IM} = (2 \times 39) + 5 = 83$ MHz (*Ans.*)

The image channel signal must be prevented from reaching the mixer stage because if it does it will produce an interfering signal that the IF amplifier will be unable to remove. In a sound broadcast radio receiver the RF stage contains tuned circuits whose selectivity is good enough to reject the image channel signal. The circuits are tuned by a variable capacitor (perhaps a varactor diode) which is *ganged* with the capacitor in the local oscillator. In an HF communication receiver image channel rejection is usually obtained from either a bank of switchable bandpass filters or a single low-pass filter. In the first case the appropriate bandpass filter is automatically switched into the circuit as the receiver is tuned to a signal frequency. A low-pass filter can provide sufficient image channel rejection when up-conversion is used because all the possible image channel frequencies are then above the tuning range of the receiver. Sound broadcast radio receivers are all of the single-superheterodyne type because the (relatively) narrow tuning range combined with the choice of IF allows adequate image channel rejection. Mobile telephones use single-superheterodyne receivers because the IF signal is applied to an analogue-to-digital (ADC) and this, as well as converting the signal into digital form, also acts as a down-converter. The use of automatic gain control (AGC) in an RF or IF amplifier reduces the necessary dynamic range of the ADC.

Image frequency rejection is the ratio in dB of an unwanted signal above 1 µV e.m.f. that gives the same output as a wanted (on-tune) 1 µV e.m.f. signal. Anything above about 60 dB is typical and 90 dB or more is very good.

Double-superheterodyne radio receiver

Some radio receivers use the double-superheterodyne principle to obtain better image channel rejection. High adjacent-channel rejection demands that the IF be as low as possible while good image channel rejection requires a high IF. In the MF band a reasonable compromise between the two conflicting requirements is always possible but this is not the case in the HF band. For this reason some receivers have two IFs: the first is chosen to be higher than the highest frequency in the tuning range of the receiver, to give good image channel rejection by means of either a low-pass filter or a switchable bank of bandpass filters in the front end; the second is chosen to be a low frequency to allow good adjacent-channel selectivity to be obtained using off-the-shelf filters.

Fig. 12.2 *Double superheterodyne radio receiver*

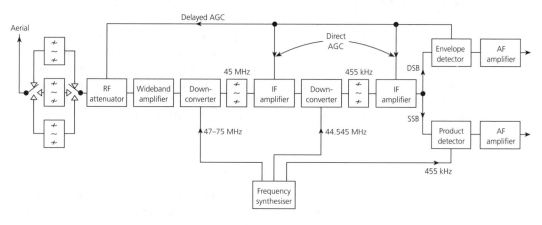

The basic block diagram of a double-superheterodyne communication radio receiver is shown in Fig. 12.2. The aerial is automatically switched to one of the three bandpass filters depending on the required signal frequency in the 0–30 MHz band, and the filtered signal is then applied to a wideband amplifier for amplification. The amplified signal is applied to one input of the first mixer where it is combined with the first local oscillator frequency. This frequency is somewhere in the range 45–75 MHz so that the difference frequency is 45 MHz. The 45 MHz first IF is amplified by the first IF amplifier before it is applied to the second mixer. Here it is mixed with a fixed 44.545 MHz signal to produce a second IF of 455 kHz. This signal is further amplified before it is applied to one of the detectors. The diode detector is used if the signal is DSBAM, while the product detector is used for SSBSC signals. In either case the detected signal is amplified by the audio amplifier and then applied to the loudspeaker or other output device. An AGC voltage (p. 365) is derived from the DSB detector and this is applied to the first and second IF amplifiers to vary their gain. Sometimes AGC is also applied to the RF stage (amplifier or attenuator); this prevents the RF amplifier overloading when a strong signal is received with consequent generation of intermodulation products.

The use of two IFs allows the gain of the receiver to be provided by amplifiers that operate at different frequencies. In turn this allows a high gain to be obtained while minimising the risk of unwanted feedback which makes the receiver more stable and less likely to start oscillating. The greater the number of frequency conversions employed the higher will be the gain that can be provided. The minimum gain necessary for a radio receiver is equal to the ratio

(minimum voltage required at demodulator input)/(minimum RF input voltage)

To ensure the receiver is stable there should not be more than 20 dB RF gain. The remainder of the required gain should be divided between the IF stages, with preferably not more than about 50 dB gain at any one frequency.

The disadvantages of the double-superheterodyne radio receiver are the extra cost and complexity involved and the generation of more spurious frequencies (another image channel, for example) because there are two mixing stages.

Level diagram

A *level diagram* is often used in the specification of a radio receiver. The minimum and maximum input signal voltages must be specified as the starting point for the diagram. Assume that the input signal voltage range is from 1.5 μV to 1.2 V, that the demodulator needs an input power of at least 0 dBm, and the input resistance of the radio receiver is 50 Ω; 1.5 μV is an input power of 4.5×10^{-14} W = −103.5 ≈ −104 dBm. Let the RF gain of the receiver be 20 dB and loss of each mixer be 7 dB. Then

output of RF amplifier = −104 + 20 = −84 dBm

output of first mixer = −84 − 7 = −91 dBm

The input to the demodulator is to be at least 0 dBm so that the minimum required IF gain is 91 + 7 = 98 dB. This gain can be divided equally between the first and second IF amplifiers so that they each have a gain of 49 dB. Now

output of first IF amplifier = −91 + 49 = −42 dBm

output of first mixer = −42 − 7 = −49 dBm

output of second IF amplifier = −49 + 49 = 0 dBm

When the input signal is at its maximum value of 1.2 V, or $1.2^2/50$ = 28.8 mW = +14.6 dBm, the input level at the input terminals of the demodulator will be 14.6 + 20 − 7 + 49 − 7 + 49 = +118.6 dBm. Clearly, the receiver needs the application of AGC to reduce this signal level.

To obtain 0 dBm at the demodulator input when the input signal is +14.6 dBm, assume that the output of each amplifier is reduced to 0 dBm. Then the gain of the RF amplifier must vary from −14.6 to 20 dB; this means that an RF attenuator is necessary. The gains of the IF amplifiers vary from 7 to 49 dB.

Parameters of superheterodyne radio receivers

Choice of the local oscillator frequency

The first IF of a communication radio receiver is equal to the difference between the first local oscillator frequency f_{o1} and the wanted signal frequency f_s. It is usual to make the oscillator frequency higher than the signal frequency since this reduces the ratio $f_{o1(max)}/f_{o1(min)}$. Assuming this, there are two possibilities: *either* the wanted signal can be shifted to a lower IF, known as down-conversion, *or* it can be shifted to a higher IF, known as up-conversion. For modern HF communication radio receivers up-conversion is the more common technique since it ensures that all possible image channel signals lie above the tuning range of the receiver. The image channel signal can then be suppressed by a low-pass filter whose cut-off frequency is equal to the highest frequency to which the receiver can tune. A further advantage of up-conversion is that the ratio $f_{o1(max)}/f_{o1(min)}$ is smaller than for down-conversion.

Image channel interference

When a superheterodyne radio receiver has been tuned to a frequency f_s there will always be another frequency, known as the image channel frequency f_{IM}, that will also produce the first IF, f_{IF1}, if it is allowed to reach the first mixer. From equation (12.2), $f_{IM} = f_s + 2f_{IF1}$. This means that the image channel signal is separated from the wanted signal by a frequency gap equal to twice the first IF. The RF stage must include sufficient selectivity to stop the image channel signal reaching the first mixer.

The frequency of the image channel signal will vary as the receiver is tuned to receive different signals. The RF stage must therefore be able to reject image channel signals at different frequencies. Traditionally, the necessary front-end selectivity has been provided by variable-tuned resonant circuits ganged with the first local oscillator. This technique is still employed with sound broadcast receivers but communication receivers employ either a single low-pass filter or a bank of sub-octave bandpass filters to suppress the image channel signal.

Any vestige of the image channel signal that reaches the first mixer will cause an unwanted signal to appear at the first IF. This signal cannot be rejected by the first IF filter and so it will produce crosstalk at the output of the receiver. The *image response ratio* is the ratio, in dB, of the RF input voltages at the wanted signal frequency, and at the image channel frequency, that are necessary to produce the same audio output power. Typically, an HF communication receiver might have an image response ratio of 100 dB and a VHF/UHF receiver an image response ratio of some 70 to 90 dB.

Choice of the intermediate frequencies

The main factors to be considered when choosing the IFs for a communication receiver are: (a) interference signals, (b) adjacent-channel selectivity, (c) IF breakthrough and (d) the availability of crystal and SAW filters. For broadcast receivers (d) is not applicable.

The first IF should not be in, or near, the tuning range of the receiver nor should it be at the same frequency as a radio or television broadcast transmitter. The front end of the receiver can include filtering to prevent any signals at, or near, the first IF reaching the first mixer. Usually, the first IF stage is isolated from the aerial input terminal by at least 80 dB, but preferably 120 dB.

The smaller the frequency separation between the wanted signal and the image channel signal the harder it is to achieve adequate suppression of the image channel signal. This factor requires the first IF to be as high as possible. Conversely, good adjacent-channel selectivity is easier to obtain if the second IF is low. The actual frequencies chosen are decided by the frequencies at which crystal and SAW filters are readily available.

Co-channel interference

Co-channel interference is caused by an unwanted signal at the same frequency as the wanted signal. Clearly, it cannot be eliminated either by filtering or by the selectivity of the receiver. In a VHF/UHF FM receiver co-channel interference is not important since it is eliminated by the capture effect provided the interfering signal is smaller than the wanted signal.

Intermodulation distortion

Intermodulation distortion within a radio receiver results in the generation of unwanted spurious signals. Whenever two or more signals at frequencies f_1 and f_2 are applied to a non-linear characteristic they will generate intermodulation products. These may be *second-order products* $f_1 \pm f_2$, *third-order products* $2f_1 \pm f_2$, $2f_2 \pm f_1$, *fourth-order products* $3f_1 \pm f_2$, $2f_1 \pm f_2$ and $f_1 \pm 3f_2$, or *fifth-order products* $4f_1 \pm f_2$, $3f_1 \pm 2f_2$, $2f_1 \pm 3f_2$ and $f_1 \pm 4f_2$. The most important of these intermodulation products are the third-order products since they tend to have frequencies that are within the passband of the first IF stage and so will interfere with the reception of wanted signals. Suppose that a wanted signal at 3.01 MHz is accompanied by two unwanted signals at 3.02 MHz and 3.03 MHz. The third-order intermodulation product $(2 \times 3.02) - 3.03$ is at the same frequency as the wanted signal.

Analysis
Any RF circuit with a non-linear current–voltage characteristic has a transfer characteristic that may be represented by

$$i = a + bv + cv^2 + dv^3 + \ldots \tag{12.3}$$

where a, b, c and d are constants.

The unwanted intermodulation products are generated by both the squared and the cubed terms in the equation. Consider the squared term, with inputs $V_1 \cos \omega_1 t$ and $V_2 \cos \omega_2 t$:

$$
\begin{aligned}
i_{\text{out}} &= c(V_1 \cos \omega_1 t + V_2 \cos \omega_2 t)^2 \\
&= cV_1^2 \cos^2 \omega_1 t + cV_2^2 \cos^2 \omega_2 t + 2cV_1 V_2 \cos \omega_1 t \cos \omega_2 t
\end{aligned} \tag{12.4}
$$

The first two terms give components at the second harmonics of the two input signal frequencies but these will not pass through the IF filter and hence are not important. The third term can be expanded to give

$$cV_1 V_2 [\cos(\omega_1 - \omega_2)t + \cos(\omega_1 + \omega_2)t]/2$$

to show that the output voltage contains components at frequencies $f_1 \pm f_2$. These two components are known as the second-order intermodulation products. Their presence causes the output of the circuit to increase in proportion to the *square* of the input (or *twice*, in dB).

Usually, second-order intermodulation products fall outside of the passband of the first IF filter and are suppressed. If, however,

$$f_2 = f_1 + f_{\text{IF1}}/2$$

then

$$f_2 - f_1 = f_{\text{IF1}}/2$$

The second harmonic of this frequency is equal to the first IF and if it is generated it cannot be suppressed. The interfering signal thus produces what is known as *half-IF* or *repeat-spot* interference.

Alternatively, if the receiver is tuned to frequency f_s and there is an unwanted signal at frequency $f_s - f_{IF1}/2$, the second harmonic of the unwanted signal will mix with the second harmonic of the local oscillator frequency to give the intermediate frequency.

Third-order intermodulation products are generated by the cubic term in equation (12.4). Thus

$$
\begin{aligned}
i_{out} &= d(V_1 \cos \omega_1 t + V_2 \cos \omega_2 t)^3 \\
&= d(V_1^3 \cos^3 \omega_1 t + V_2^3 \cos^3 \omega_2 t + 3V_1^2 V_2 \cos^2 \omega_1 t \cos \omega_2 t + 3V_1 V_2^2 \cos \omega_1 t \cos \omega_2^2 t \\
&= (dV_1^3/4)(3 \cos \omega_1 t + 3 \cos 3\omega_1 t) + (dV_2^3/4)(3 \cos \omega_2 t + 3 \cos 3\omega_2 t) \\
&\quad + dV_1^2 V_2[\tfrac{3}{2} \cos \omega_2 t + \tfrac{3}{4} \cos(2\omega_1 + \omega_2)t + \tfrac{3}{4} \cos(2\omega_1 - \omega_2)t \\
&\quad + dV_1 V_2^2[\tfrac{3}{2} \cos \omega_1 t + \tfrac{3}{4} \cos(2\omega_2 + \omega_1)t + \tfrac{3}{4} \cos(2\omega_2 - \omega_1)t
\end{aligned} \tag{12.5}
$$

Either of the $2\omega_1 - \omega_2$ or $2\omega_2 - \omega_1$ components may be at such a frequency that it falls within the passband of the first IF filter. Higher, even-order products are generally out of band while higher-order, odd-order products are usually of negligible amplitude.

The third-order intermodulation level is the level, in dB, relative to 1 μV (dBμV) of two unwanted signals, respectively 10 kHz and 20 kHz off-tune, that generate an unwanted third-order output equivalent to that produced by a wanted signal at 0 dBμV e.m.f. A good communication receiver would have a level of about 85 dBμV. Third-order intermodulation products increase the output of the circuit in proportion to the cube of the input, or three times using decibels. Intermodulation products of fourth order and above are usually ignored since they are much smaller than the second- or third-order products.

To reduce intermodulation, a pre-selector stage, such as a bank of sub-octave filters, is often employed before the first non-linear stage. Alternatively (or in addition), an RF attenuator will reduce the third-order intermodulation level by three times the RF attenuation in dB. If, for example, a 6 dB attenuator is fitted it will reduce each interfering signal by 6 dB but, since the amplitude of the third-order products is proportional to $V_1^2 V_2$ or $V_1 V_2^2$, it will reduce the intermodulation level by 18 dB. Hence, the use of a 6 dB RF attenuator would increase the signal-to-intermodulation level by 18 – 6 or 12 dB.

Intercept point

The *intercept point* is the point at which two extrapolated responses intersect one another. If the amplitudes of the two unwanted signals are equal to one another, i.e. $V_1 = V_2 = V$, the amplitudes V_{1P} of the second-order and the third-order intermodulation products are given by

$$
V_{1P} = k_n V^n \tag{12.6}
$$

where k_n is the nth-order constant and n is the order of the intermodulation products.

This means that whereas the output voltage due to the wanted signal increases in direct proportion to its input voltage V, the intermodulation output voltage increases in proportion to V^n. There must therefore be a level at which the two output voltages are equal to one another. This voltage, V_{PN}, is known as the nth-order intercept point. The intercept point is a purely theoretical level because the amplifier, or mixer, would

Fig. 12.3 *Second- and third-order intercept points*

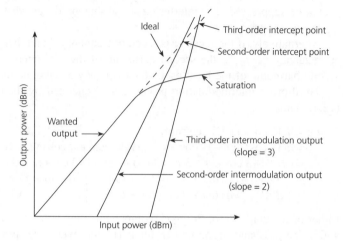

saturate before the level was reached. The intercept point is determined by extending, on a graph of output power in dBm versus input power in dBm, the wanted signal and the nth-order intermodulation product outputs to the point where they intercept each other. Figure 12.3 shows how the output power varies with increase in the wanted input signal, and for both the second- and third-order intermodulation products. Since both axes are logarithmic the second-order plot has twice the slope, and the third-order plot has three times the slope, of the wanted signal output plot. The points at which the curves cross are known respectively as the second-order intercept point and the third-order intercept point. The third-order intercept point is a measure of the ability of a receiver to reject large-amplitude unwanted signals whose frequency is near to that of the wanted signal. This intercept point is primarily determined by the linearity of the first mixer and should be as large as possible. A value of between +10 and +35 dBm is regarded as a good figure. Once the third-order intercept point of an RF circuit has been determined the spurious signal levels for a particular input signal can be read off the graph.

For the third-order intermodulation products $n = 3$ and equation (12.6) can be written in the form

$$P_{3IP} = [k_n(V/2)^3]^2 = (k_n P)^3 \tag{12.7}$$

where $P = V^2/2$ and is the power due to one signal on its own. This means that the intermodulation power is proportional to the cube of the input power, i.e. a 1 dB increase in the input power gives a 3 dB increase in the third-order intermodulation output power.

The ratio D of the intermodulation power to the wanted signal power is $D = P_{3IP}/P_{out}$. P_{3IP} is proportional to P^3 and P_{out} is proportional to P. Hence

$$D = (KP)^2 \tag{12.8}$$

At the third-order intercept point $P_{3IP} = P_{out}$ and so D is equal to unity. Equation (12.8) becomes

$$1 = (KP)^2 = (KP_{3IP})^2 \quad \text{or} \quad K = P_{3IP}^{-1}$$

Consequently, equation (12.8) can be written as

$$D = (P/P_{3IP})^2 \qquad (12.9)$$

EXAMPLE 12.2

Calculate the third-order intercept of a radio receiver if, for an input power of 0 dBm, the ratio (intermodulation power)/(wanted power) at the output is −40 dBm.

Solution

From equation (12.9),

$$-40 = 2 \log_{10}(P/P_{3IP}) = 2 \times (0 - P_{3IP}) = -2P_{3IP}$$

Therefore, the third-order intercept point is +20 dBm (*Ans.*)

Note from this example that for a 0 dBm two-tone signal the third-order intercept point is equal to $-\frac{1}{2}$ times the magnitude of the third-order intermodulation products.

When the two signals are not at 0 dBm they should both be normalised to 0 dBm. The third-order intermodulation level then increases by 3 dB for every 1 dB increase in the two-tone signal level. If the two signals are at different levels then subtract one-third of their level difference in dBm from the larger level and take the result as being their common level.

EXAMPLE 12.3

When two 0 dBm tones are applied to a mixer the level of the third-order intermodulation products is −60 dBm. The mixer has a conversion loss of 6 dB. Calculate, in dBm, the third-order intermodulation output power when the level of the two tones is (a) −10 dBm, (b) +10 dBm, (c) +30 dBm and (d) +20 dBm and +11 dBm.

Solution

The level of the wanted signal at the mixer output is −6 dBm.

(a) The third-order output power is $(-60) + 3 \times (-10) = -90$ dBm (*Ans.*)
(b) The third-order output power is $(-60) + 3 \times 10 = -30$ dBm (*Ans.*)
(c) The third-order output power is $(-60) + 3 \times 30 = +30$ dBm (*Ans.*)
    This answer means that the third-order output level is equal to the input level so this is the third-order intercept point.
(d) The equivalent input level is $20 - (20 - 11)/3 = +17$ dBm
    The third-order output power is $(-60) + 3 \times 17 = -9$ dBm (*Ans.*)

Fig. 12.4 *1 dB compression point*

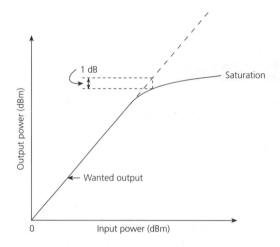

Typical figures for the intercept points of an MF/HF communication receiver are +15 dBm second order and +20 dBm third order. For a VHF/UHF receiver typical figures are second-order intercept point +5 dBm up to 470 MHz, and 0 dBm from 470 MHz to 1.1 GHz.

1 dB compression point

As the input signal voltage applied to an RF amplifier is increased the output voltage will increase more or less linearly until saturation is approached when the gain falls to approximately zero. This effect is usually described as the *1 dB compression point*. The 1 dB compression point of an RF amplifier is the input (or output) level in dB at which the output signal is 1 dB less than the ideal linear output level; see Fig. 12.4. (The input and output 1 dB compression point differ only by the gain of the amplifier.) The third-order intermodulation product level is related to the 1 dB compression point in a simple manner: when the input signal is n dB below the 1 dB compression point the third-order intermodulation level is $2n$ below the output signal level.

Dynamic range

The dynamic range of a radio receiver is the range of input levels that produce output powers lying in between the *noise floor* of the receiver and the input level that makes the *total* intermodulation product power equal to the noise floor. The dynamic range is given by

$$\text{dynamic range} = \tfrac{2}{3}(P_{3IP} - \text{noise floor})$$
$$= \tfrac{2}{3}[P_{3IP} - FkT_0B \ (\text{dB})] \tag{12.10}$$

Reducing the bandwidth of the receiver increases its dynamic range because the noise is reduced. A good receiver has a dynamic range of some 90–120 dB for a 3 kHz bandwidth.

Calculate the dynamic range of a receiver that has a third-order intercept point of +20 dBm, a noise factor of 6 dB and a bandwidth of 8 kHz. $kT = -174$ dBm.

Solution

From equation (12.10),

$$\text{dynamic range} = \tfrac{2}{3}(20 + 174 - 6 - 10 \log_{10} 8000) \approx 99 \text{ dB } (Ans.)$$

The dynamic range of a radio receiver is also related to the 1 dB compression point:

$$\text{dynamic range} = 1 \text{ dB compression point} - \text{noise floor} \tag{12.11}$$

An RF amplifier has a bandwidth of 100 kHz, a noise factor of 3.2 dB, and an input 1 dB compression point of −12 dBm. Calculate (a) the noise floor and (b) the dynamic range of the receiver.

Solution

(a) The noise floor is

$$-174 \text{ dBm} + 10 \log_{10}(10^5) + 3.2 = -120.8 \text{ dBm } (Ans.)$$

(b) The dynamic range is

$$-12 - (-120.8) = 108.8 \text{ dB } (Ans.)$$

Reciprocal mixing

When a large-amplitude off-tune signal appears at the input to the first mixer it will mix with the noise sidebands of the first local oscillator to produce in-band noise that will cause the noise floor to be raised effectively to reduce the sensitivity of the receiver. This process is known as *reciprocal mixing* and it is illustrated by Fig. 12.5 in which both the wanted signal and the unwanted interfering signal are assumed to occupy narrow bandwidths that are much less than the first IF bandwidth. The first local oscillator has upper and lower noise sidebands, sometimes known as *phase noise*, and this is superimposed upon both the converted wanted signal and interfering signal sidebands to produce unwanted signals which lie within the passband of the first IF filter. The added noise degrades the signal-to-noise ratio at the demodulator input.

Reciprocal mixing is defined as the amount of noise introduced by a 20 kHz off-tune signal that will produce an output equivalent to that produced by the wanted signal

Fig. 12.5 *Reciprocal mixing*

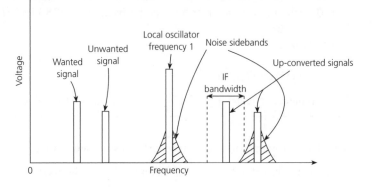

Fig. 12.6 *Effect of reciprocal mixing upon selectivity*

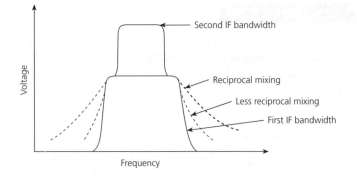

when its voltage is 1 μV e.m.f. Suppose, for example, that the frequency of the wanted signal is 12 MHz and that the first IF is 45 MHz. The first local oscillator frequency is then 57 MHz. If there is a 45.01 MHz, 3 kHz slice of oscillator noise 93 dB down on the oscillator voltage then an unwanted signal at 12.01 MHz would be converted to a 3 kHz noise band at 45 MHz and spuriously received.

The reciprocal-mixing performance of a receiver affects its ability to reject off-tune signals and means that the effective selectivity of the receiver is not as good as the selectivity defined by the IF filters. The effect of reciprocal mixing on selectivity is shown by Fig. 12.6; clearly, the selectivity characteristic has been widened.

Cross-modulation

Cross-modulation is the transfer of the amplitude modulation of an unwanted carrier that appears at the input to the first mixer onto the wanted carrier. Equation (12.5) contains the term $\frac{3}{2}dV_1V_2^2 \cos \omega_1 t$; if V_1 is the wanted signal and V_2 is the unwanted AM signal, i.e. $V_2(1 + m \cos \omega_m t)$, then the amplitude of the unwanted signal is

$$\frac{3}{2}dV_1V_2^2(1 + 2m \cos \omega_m t + m^2 \cos^2 \omega_m t) \qquad (12.12)$$

Usually, the modulation factor m is small enough for the term $m^2 \cos^2 \omega_m t$ to be neglected. Then the total output signal at the wanted frequency ω_1 is

$$bV_1 + \tfrac{3}{4}dV_1^3 + \tfrac{3}{2}dV_1V_2^2 + 3dV_1V_2^2 m \cos \omega_m t$$

The second and third terms are small compared with the first term, since $d \ll b$, and can be neglected. Hence the output at the wanted frequency ω_1 consists of the wanted component bV_1 plus an unwanted cross-modulation component $3dV_1V_2^2 m \cos \omega_m t$.

The *signal-to-cross-modulation ratio* (SCMR) is

$$\begin{aligned} \text{SCMR} &= 20 \log_{10}[(3dV_1V_2^2 m)/bV_1] \\ &= 20 \log_{10}[(3dV_2^2 m)/b] \text{ dB} \end{aligned} \tag{12.13}$$

The *cross-modulation factor* is the ratio of the modulation factors of the superimposed modulation and of the unwanted signal, i.e.

$$\text{cross-modulation factor} = (3dV_2^2 m)/bm = 3dV_2^2/b \tag{12.14}$$

Cross-modulation is specified as the level of the 20 kHz off-tune signal, 30% modulated at 1 kHz, that produces an output signal 30 dB down on the level produced by the wanted signal, 30% modulated at 1 kHz, at 60 dBμV e.m.f.

Since both cross-modulation and third-order intermodulation arise because of the cubic term in a non-linear characteristic, it is to be expected that there is a relationship between them. Approximately, this relationship is

$$V_{CM} \text{ (dBμV)} = \tfrac{3}{2}V_{3IP} \text{ (dBμV)} - 6 \text{ (dB)} - \text{SCMR}/2 \text{ (dB)} \tag{12.15}$$

Spurious responses

Internal spurious responses are signals generated within a receiver which are present even when the aerial is not connected. External spurious signals are generated within the receiver only when the aerial is connected and signals are being received. Both kinds of spurious signal can interfere with a wanted signal. Spurious signal are reduced by making the RF and mixer stages as linear as possible.

Blocking

Blocking is an effect in which the gain of a radio receiver is reduced when a large-amplitude, off-tune signal either overloads a stage or excessively operates the receiver's AGC system and in so doing causes a reduction in the wanted signal output. When blocking occurs the level of the wanted output signal falls each time the interfering signal is received.

The *blocking ratio* is the ratio

(response to a signal at one frequency when there is a simultaneous excitation at another frequency)/(response to the one signal above) (12.16)

The blocking ratio of a receiver depends both upon the magnitudes of the two signals and on their frequency difference. It is specified as the level of an interfering 20 kHz off-tune signal that gives a change in the wanted output signal of 3 dB, when the AGC system of the receiver is inoperative.

If the level of the two signals, in dBμV, to give 1 μV intermodulation product is V_{3IP} then, approximately, the voltage V_B of the blocking signal is

$$V_B = \tfrac{3}{2}V_{3IP} \text{ (dBμV)} - 3 \text{ (dBμV)} \qquad (12.17)$$

If, for example, $V_{3IP} = 82$ dBμV the level of the blocking signal will be $\tfrac{3}{2} \times 82 - 3 = 120$ dBμV, or 1 V. Because of the high levels involved it is quite possible that the fifth-order intermodulation products may also be of significant amplitude; if so,

$$V_B = \tfrac{5}{4}V_{5IP} - 4.5 \text{ dBμV} \qquad (12.18)$$

Sensitivity

The sensitivity of a communication radio receiver is a measure of the capability of the receiver to receive small-level signals. It is defined as the smallest input signal voltage that is required to give a specified output power with a specified output signal-to-noise ratio in a particular bandwidth. It is necessary to include signal-to-noise ratio in the definition because otherwise the output power could consist mainly of noise and be of little use. The modulation level is specified for AM receivers – usually 30% – and the modulation deviation is specified for FM receivers – usually 3 kHz for NBFM receivers and 22.5 kHz for sound broadcast receivers. The lower limit to the sensitivity of a receiver is set by the input thermal noise plus some contribution from the noise factor of the receiver.

If the bandwidth of the receiver is B its sensitivity cannot be better than

$$S_{opt} = -174 + \text{signal-to-noise ratio} + F + 10 \log_{10} B - I \qquad (12.19)$$

where F is the noise factor in dB and I is the improvement in signal-to-noise ratio produced by demodulation.

EXAMPLE 12.6

Calculate the optimum sensitivity for a radio receiver that has a noise factor of 3 dB, a bandwidth of 120 kHz, and a signal-to-noise ratio improvement of 3 dB, if the required output signal-to-noise ratio is to be 12 dB.

Solution

$$S_{opt} = -174 + 12 + 3 + 50.8 + 3 = -105.2 \text{ dBm (Ans.)}$$

For an AM receiver typical figures might be:

(a) a sensitivity of 2 μV with 30% modulation at 400 Hz and 20 dB signal-to-noise ratio (HF receiver);

(b) a sensitivity of 1 μV with 50% modulation at 1 kHz for 12 dB SINAD (p. 361) and 7.5 kHz selectivity (VHF receiver).

An SSB receiver will have a better sensitivity than a DSB receiver because there is no carrier power and the bandwidth is narrower. Typically, the sensitivity is 0.5 µV with 1 kHz output for 12 dB SINAD and 3 kHz selectivity.

For a frequency-modulation receiver the sensitivity is quoted with a specified r.m.s. or peak frequency deviation. Typically, this might be sensitivity 0.5 µV with 2.1 kHz r.m.s. frequency deviation (this is 3 kHz peak deviation) for 12 dB SINAD and 15 kHz selectivity.

If a radio receiver employs one or more tuned RF stages its sensitivity will vary with frequency in the manner shown by Example 12.7.

EXAMPLE 12.7

A radio receiver can be tuned to receive signals in the frequency band 4 to 20 MHz with the tracking error given by Table 12.1. At 20 MHz the sensitivity of the receiver is 2 µV. Calculate its sensitivity at (a) 4 MHz, (b) 8 MHz and (c) 14 MHz, and plot the sensitivity curve of the receiver. Assume the RF stage to have a Q factor of 50.

Table 12.1

Signal frequency (MHz)	4	8	14	20
Tracking error (kHz)	20	80	100	0

Solution

When the receiver is tuned to any particular frequency any tracking error appears in the RF stage.

(a) When the wanted signal is at 4 MHz the RF stage is tuned to 4.02 MHz. Hence

$$\text{sensitivity} = 2 \times R_d/[R_d\sqrt{(1 + Q^2B^2/f_o^2)}]$$
$$= 2\sqrt{[1 + 50^2(40 \times 10^3)^2/(4.02 \times 10^6)^2]} = 2.23 \ \mu V \ (Ans.)$$

(b) The RF stage is tuned to 8.08 MHz. Hence

$$\text{sensitivity} = 2\sqrt{[1 + 50^2(160 \times 10^3)^2/(8.08 \times 10^6)]} = 2.81 \ \mu V \ (Ans.)$$

(c) The RF stage is tuned to 14.1 MHz. Hence

$$\text{sensitivity} = 2\sqrt{[1 + 50^2(200 \times 10^3)^2/(14.1 \times 10^6)^2]} = 2.45 \ \mu V \ (Ans.)$$

The sensitivity curve of the receiver is shown plotted in Fig. 12.7.

Fig. 12.7 *Sensitivity curve of a radio receiver*

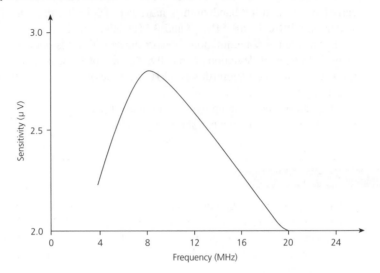

Selectivity

The selectivity of a communication radio receiver is its ability to select a wanted signal from all the signals that are simultaneously present at the aerial terminals and to reject all unwanted signals. Selectivity may be quoted graphically, showing the output of the receiver in dB relative to the maximum output, plotted against frequency off-tune. Alternatively, several points on such a graph may be quoted, e.g. 6 dB down at 3 kHz bandwidth, 60 dB down at 12 kHz bandwidth. Most of the selectivity of a radio receiver is provided by the IF filters. The 6 and 60 dB bandwidths are known, respectively, as the *nose* and *skirt bandwidths*. The nose bandwidth is the band of frequencies over which a signal can be received with little loss of strength. The skirt bandwidth is the band of frequencies over which it is possible to receive a strong signal.

The *shape factor* is the ratio (skirt bandwidth)/(nose bandwidth). The ideal shape factor is unity and typically it is about 4 with 2 being a good figure.

The *adjacent-channel ratio* of a receiver is the ratio, in dB, of the input voltages at the wanted and the adjacent-channel frequencies necessary for the adjacent channel to produce an output power a specified number of decibels down on the wanted signal power.

In HF communication receivers the selectivity is provided mainly by crystal filters and sometimes by ceramic filters, whereas VHF/UHF receivers often employ SAW filters. With the use of either of these types of filter it is possible to achieve almost any desired selectivity. There are a number of standard frequencies at which these filters are available (p. 322) and an IF is chosen with this in mind. When the IF is 455 kHz a ceramic filter is a cost-effective alternative.

Aim: To measure the sensitivity and selectivity of an AM radio receiver.
Components and equipment: AM radio receiver. RF signal generator. AF signal generator (not needed if the RF generator has internal AF modulation). Variable RF attenuator. AF power meter.
Procedure:

(a) Connect up the circuit shown in Fig. 12.8.
(b) Set the frequency of the AF generator (or the internal modulation of the RF generator) to 1 kHz and adjust its voltage to give 30% modulation of the carrier wave.
(c) Set the frequency of the RF generator to the middle of one of the passbands of the receiver. The measurement is often carried out at 210 kHz, or 1, 11.8 or 94 MHz. Set the AF gain of the receiver to about one-half of its maximum value. Tune the receiver to the chosen frequency when the power meter should have its maximum indication, and measure the AF output power.
(d) Now set the percentage modulation to 0% and repeat procedure (c).
(e) The (signal + noise)/noise ratio of the receiver is then equal to the ratio of the power readings obtained in (c) and (d). Calculate the (signal + noise)/noise ratio.
(f) Vary the RF signal voltage until the (signal + noise)/signal ratio is equal to 10 dB, or whatever value is specified, and note the RF signal voltage necessary. This value is the sensitivity of the receiver.
(g) Repeat procedure (f) with a (signal + noise)/noise ratio of 20 dB.
(h) State the sensitivity of the receiver measured for both (e) and (f) and say whether the figures obtained mean that the receiver has a good sensitivity.
(i) Sometimes the measurement of the sensitivity of a receiver specifies that the output power should be of a particular value, often 50 mW. Repeat the measurement but with the RF voltage adjusted so that the measured output power is 50 mW with 20 dB (signal + noise)/noise ratio.
(j) Suggest how the sensitivity measurement could be adapted to measure the selectivity of the receiver.

Fig. 12.8

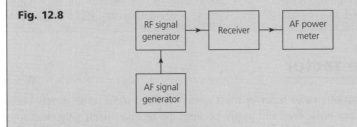

Aim: To measure the selectivity and the adjacent-channel ratio of an AM receiver.
Components and equipment: AM radio receiver. Two RF signal generators. Combining circuit and artificial aerial. AF power meter.

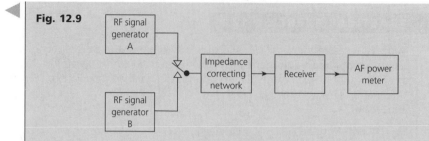

Fig. 12.9

Procedure:

(a) Connect up the circuit given by Fig. 12.9. With zero output from signal generator B adjust the frequency of signal generator A to the centre frequency of the receiver's tuning range. Modulate the carrier to a depth of 30% at 400 Hz, and with the AF gain set to maximum vary the input signal voltage until the AF output power is 10 times the specified value for sensitivity tests; this will often be 500 mW. Switch off the modulation of signal generator A but do not alter the RF voltage.

(b) Tune signal generator B to a frequency corresponding to the adjacent-channel signal and modulated by 30% at 400 Hz. Adjust the RF voltage until the AF output power is 30 dB down on the previous value of (probably) 500 mW. Note this value.

(c) Tune the frequency of signal generator B through the passband of the receiver. At each frequency note the RF voltage needed to produce the −30 dB test output power level. Plotting the RF voltages thus obtained against frequency gives the selectivity curve of the receiver.

(d) Now use an alternative method of measurement. Signal generator A should have 30% modulation at 400 Hz and signal generator B 30% modulation at 1 kHz. With zero output from signal generator B set generator A to the centre frequency of the receiver's tuning range and adjust the RF voltage until the output signal-to-noise ratio is 20 dB (or 10 dB).

(e) Set the frequency of signal generator B to the adjacent-channel frequency for the generator A frequency and adjust its RF voltage until an output signal-to-noise ratio of 17 dB (or 7 dB) is obtained. The ratio of the RF input voltages due to generators A and B is the adjacent channel ratio of the receiver.

Noise factor

The output of a radio receiver must always contain some noise, partly because the input signal is not noise-free and partly because the receiver itself generates some noise. The noise factor F of a radio receiver is a measure of the degradation of the input signal-to-noise ratio caused by the receiver. It is defined as

$$F = \text{(input signal-to-noise ratio)/(output signal-to-noise ratio)} \qquad (12.20)$$

At frequencies up to about 20 MHz the noise picked up by an aerial is generally larger than the noise internally generated by the receiver. There is then little to be gained by the receiver having a low noise factor and often an RF amplifier is not provided. At higher frequencies aerial noise is much smaller than the internally generated noise and then having a low noise factor will improve the sensitivity of the receiver. Consequently, HF communication receivers and VHF/UHF receivers always employ RF gain.

The noise factor of an MF/HF radio receiver is typically in the region of 10 to 12 dB; VHF/UHF receivers have a typical noise factor of 5 to 8 dB but, in some cases, it may be only about 3 dB.

The minimum noise at the output of a receiver is known as the noise floor. The noise floor is equal to the input noise times the noise factor, i.e. *FkTB*. The noise floor is also equal to the minimum detectable signal. Since the sensitivity of a radio receiver is defined in terms of a specified output signal-to-noise ratio it is evident that sensitivity and noise factor are related. If the sensitivity of a receiver is N μV for an output signal-to-noise ratio of S (as a ratio) in a bandwidth of B Hz, then the noise factor of the receiver is

$$F = 61 + 20 \log_{10} N - 10 \log_{10}(S - 1) - 10 \log_{10} B \text{ dB} \qquad (12.21)$$

EXAMPLE 12.8

A radio receiver has a sensitivity of 1.5 μV for an output signal-to-noise ratio of 20 dB in a bandwidth of 3 kHz. Calculate its noise factor.

Solution

From equation (12.21),

$$F = 61 + 20 \log_{10} 1.5 - 10 \log_{10} 99 - 10 \log_{10} 3000 = 9.8 \text{ dB } (Ans.)$$

SINAD ratio

Sometimes it is more helpful to consider the total distortion at the output of a receiver as well as the noise. The SINAD ratio is given by

SINAD = (signal power + noise power + distortion power)/(noise power
         + distortion power) (12.22)

The sensitivity of a radio receiver is often specified in terms of SINAD. The minimum acceptable SINAD is usually taken as being 12 dB.

Stages in a radio receiver

The RF stage

The RF stage, or front end, of a communication radio receiver has two main functions to perform.

1   It must couple the aerial to the receiver in an efficient manner.
2   It must suppress signals at the image channel and intermediate frequencies. For less stringent requirements tuned circuits will be able to provide sufficient selectivity, but for optimum performance either a low-pass filter or a bank of sub-octave bandpass filters will be necessary. The bank of filters will divide up the tuning range of the receiver into sub-bands and any one of the filters can be switched into circuit at a given time. The appropriate filter is switched into circuit by pin diodes.

Some HF receivers which employ up-conversion may use only a single 30 MHz low-pass filter. In a VHF/UHF receiver the bandpass filters may be helical resonators. When filters are used to obtain the RF selectivity any RF amplifiers that are employed will be wideband circuits.

The RF amplifier, or front end, must be designed to have a low noise factor, to operate linearly with even the strongest anticipated input signals, and to generate the minimum intermodulation products. If the amplifier is a wideband type it will be susceptible to second-order intermodulation products as well as to third-order products. The four main parameters that determine the performance of an RF amplifier are the noise figure, the 1 dB compression point, the second-order intercept point, and the third-order intercept point.

The gain of the RF amplifier may be varied by the AGC system of the receiver, or a constant gain amplifier may be employed with the amplifier preceded by an AGC-controlled RF attenuator. The latter technique is often preferred since it enables the RF amplifier to be operated linearly at all input signal levels.

PRACTICAL EXERCISE 12.3

Aim: To investigate an RF attenuator.
Components and equipment: Two 100 Ω resistors; five 0.01 µF capacitors; one 1 mH inductor and three 1N418 diodes RF signal generator. CRO. Two D.C. voltage sources. Breadboard.
Procedure:

(a)   Build the circuit shown by Fig. 12.10. The operation of the circuit is as follows. The incoming RF signal is passed through diode D_3 to the output terminal of the circuit. When the 10 V voltage and the AGC voltage are equal to one another, the voltages at the cathodes of D_2 and D_3 are equal to the AGC voltage minus the voltage drop across R_3. Diodes D_1 and D_2 are turned OFF. As the AGC voltage is reduced the cathode voltages of D_2 and D_3 fall and at some point the diodes conduct. The signal is then shunted to earth via C_4 and C_5. At the same time there will be a voltage drop across diode D_3. When the AGC voltage is zero, D_2 and D_3 are fully ON and there will be a low resistance between the signal input and earth and D_3 will be turned OFF. Then the attenuation of the circuit will be at its maximum value.
(b)   Set the AGC voltage supplied by the d.c. voltage source to 0 V. Set the frequency of the RF generator to 1 MHz and its voltage to 0.5 V. Connect the CRO across the 50 Ω output resistor.
(c)   Note the waveform and value of the voltage appearing across the 50 Ω resistor.

Fig. 12.10

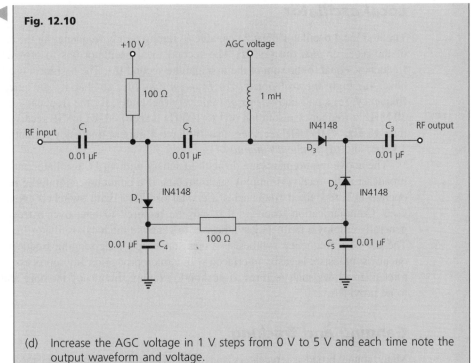

(d) Increase the AGC voltage in 1 V steps from 0 V to 5 V and each time note the output waveform and voltage.
(e) Note the effect of varying the AGC voltage in 1 V steps in the negative direction.
(f) Comment on the operation of the RF attenuator. State where such a circuit is likely to be employed in a radio receiver and comment on the output waveform.

Mixer stage

The function of the first mixer stage is to convert the wanted signal frequency into the first IF. Similarly, the function of the second mixer is to convert the first IF into the second IF. Ideally, a mixer would only generate the wanted sum and difference frequencies but, in practice, a mixer introduces both second- and third-order intermodulation. When a signal is applied to a double-balanced mixer the output signal is proportional to the cube of the input voltage. When two signals of equal amplitude are applied to the mixer, $V_S = V_0$, the output is proportional to V_S^3. Hence if the input signal voltage V_S is increased by 10 dB the mixer output voltage will increase by 30 dB.

A mixer may be either an active or passive circuit. Most passive mixers are of the diode ring type, do not require a power supply and have good isolation between their inputs. The conversion loss of a passive mixer is about 6 dB, which transformer losses may increase to 7 dB, and a relatively high local oscillator power is necessary. On the other hand, an active mixer needs a power supply and has a relatively poor isolation, but has a conversion gain and requires only a small local oscillator power.

Local oscillator

The first local oscillator must be capable of tuning to any frequency in the tuning range of the receiver *plus* the first IF. The second local oscillator has to provide only one frequency, equal to the sum of the first and the second IFs. The first local oscillator must have: (a) high *spectral purity*; (b) *frequency agility*, so that it can quickly change frequency; (c) small *increments of frequency* (generally, for the frequency bands below 30 MHz, a frequency resolution of 1 to 100 Hz is required, with SSB receivers no worse than 10 Hz; VHF/UHF receivers usually have a quoted frequency resolution of about 1 kHz); and (d) *frequency stability*.

The above requirements are difficult to satisfy with an *LC* oscillator and only sound broadcast radio receivers employ such circuits. If a communication radio receiver is to operate at a few fixed frequencies a crystal oscillator with switched crystals may be used. Communication receivers that may be required to tune over a frequency band generally employ a frequency synthesiser to generate the local oscillator frequency(ies). The use of a frequency synthesiser gives stable and wide-ranging frequencies. A frequency synthesiser is easily interfaced with a microprocessor. Microprocessor control of a receiver allows such features as pushbutton tuning, frequency memory and scanning to be provided.

Ganging and tracking

Many sound broadcast receivers and older types of communication receiver employ mechanical control of the tuning of the receiver. The rotation of a tuning-control knob simultaneously varies tuning capacitors in both the RF stage and the first local oscillator. The tuning capacitors are mounted on a common spindle and are said to be ganged. The maintenance of the correct frequency difference (the first IF) between the frequencies to which the RF stage and the oscillator are tuned is called the *tracking*. Usually, identical capacitors are used with different values of inductance in each circuit. Tracking errors are inevitable and result in a variation of both the sensitivity (see Example 12.7) and the image channel rejection of the receiver. More modern radio receivers replace the tuning capacitors with voltage-tuned varactor diodes; this allows rapid frequency changing to take place, often under microprocessor control. Modern communication receivers usually employ a frequency synthesiser and up-conversion and are then able to avoid tracking problems by using either no RF selectivity at all (other than a low-pass filter), or a bank of switched bandpass filters.

IF amplifier

The function of the IF amplifier in a communication receiver is to provide most of the gain and the selectivity of the receiver. Each IF amplifier stage must shape and select a relatively narrow bandwidth at the mixer output and reject adjacent-channel signals. The second IF stage must have a low noise factor and must amplify the signal to the level necessary for the detector to operate satisfactorily. The gain of an IF amplifier is usually controlled by the receiver's AGC system. In sound broadcast receivers, double-tuned coupled circuits may be employed to provide the desired loss–frequency characteristic but, since they have a poor shape factor, they are not employed in communication radio receivers. Most communication receivers employ either crystal filters or SAW filters (p. 322), to give the desired selectivity. These filters offer the considerable advantages of requiring no IF amplifier alignment and having a selectivity that is not affected by the application of AGC to the stage. A number of ICs are readily available that include an IF amplifier usually along with other circuits.

Detector stage

The function of the detector or demodulator stage in a radio receiver is to recover the information modulated onto the received carrier, and often also to generate the AGC voltage. Most AM receivers that employ discrete circuitry in the detector stage still use the diode detector because of its simplicity and its good performance. The main problem is that the input signal level to the detector must be several times larger than the threshold level of the diode, otherwise considerable signal distortion will occur. The demodulation of an SSB or CW signal requires the use of a product detector and this, in turn, needs a local oscillator frequency input. Very often the detection process is carried out within an IC that also provides a number of other circuit functions. FM receivers tend to use the ratio detector in discrete-component designs, and either the quadrature detector or the PLL detector if ICs are employed.

Automatic gain control (AGC)

The amplitude of the wanted carrier that appears at the input of a radio receiver may fluctuate widely, by perhaps 100 dB or more. AGC is applied to a receiver to maintain the carrier level at the detector input at a more or less constant value. The level chosen is such that overload of, and consequent intermodulation product generation in, the final RF stage and/or the first mixer is minimised. The application of the AGC voltage is distributed over a number of stages. Usually, the gain of the IF stages is reduced first and the RF gain is only reduced when the level of the input signal is large enough to ensure a good output signal-to-noise ratio. Typically, delayed AGC begins to reduce the RF gain at an RF input signal level of between 50 and 100 μV.

The basic concept of an AGC system is illustrated by Fig. 12.11. A d.c. voltage is generated in the detector stage (or in a separate AGC generator) that is directly proportional to the amplitude of the carrier at the input to the detector. This d.c. voltage is applied to each of the controlled stages to vary their voltage gains. If the carrier level should rise the AGC voltage will also increase and will reduce the gain of each controlled stage. This will, of course, reduce the overall gain of the receiver and so tend to

Fig. 12.11 *Application of AGC to a radio receiver*

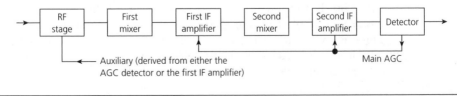

Auxiliary (derived from either the
AGC detector or the first IF amplifier)

Main AGC

Fig. 12.12 *Use of RF attenuators to vary the gain of a radio receiver*

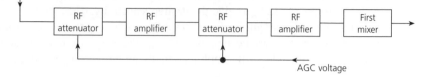

restore the carrier level at the detector input to its original value. Conversely, if the carrier level should fall the AGC system will increase the overall gain of the receiver.

Whenever the RF input signal is large and is likely to cause overloading of one or more stages, the auxiliary AGC will come into action and reduce the gain of the RF stage. If the AGC voltage is used to vary the gain of an RF amplifier problems may arise with regard to both its dynamic range and the production of distortion because of shifts in the operating point of the controlled amplifier(s). Also, changing the gain of an RF amplifier may alter its noise factor and/or detune the amplifier (if it is not wideband). An alternative, which overcomes these problems, is the use of an AGC-controlled RF attenuator. The RF attenuator may have either a continuous loss that is varied by the AGC voltage, or fixed values of loss that are switched into or out of circuit by the AGC voltage. The RF attenuators are often fitted in front of, and in between, the stages of RF gain as shown by Fig. 12.12. ICs that include a detector often have a *received signal strength indicator* (RSSI) circuit as well. The RSSI voltage can be used as the AGC voltage. Most IC RF amplifiers do not include an AGC facility.

Typically, an AGC system is required to reduce input signal variations of anything up to 120 dB to about ±1 dB at the input to the demodulator. This means that the gain of the AGC loop should be at least 119 dB. All AGC systems have an inherent delay in their response to a change in the input signal voltage. It is not desirable for the AGC system to have too rapid a response or it will respond to impulsive noise. The *attack time* is the time taken for the AGC voltage to rise to a predetermined percentage of its final value when the carrier level falls. The *decay time* is the time taken for the AGC voltage to fall to a predetermined percentage of its original value when the carrier level rises. The choice of the attack and delay times depends upon the kind of signal being received:

- For a DSBAM signal the constant-frequency carrier can be used to generate the AGC voltage. The attack and delay times need only be fast enough to allow the AGC system to respond to fading, but slow enough to avoid it responding to low-frequency modulation. Typical figures are in the region 0.1 to 0.2 s.
- When an SSB signal is received the absence of a carrier component means that the AGC voltage must be derived from the peak signal level. The AGC system must therefore be able to respond quickly when a modulated signal appears. To prevent a transient occurring at the end of each syllable of speech the gain of the receiver must only slowly increase at the end of each syllable. If the attack time is too long the system may not be able to follow rapid fades but, on the other hand, if the attack time is too short each new syllable will be accompanied by a 'roaring' sound. Typically, the attack time should be from 2 to 10 ms and the decay time 0.5 to 1 s; the attack and delay times are determined by the time constant of the AGC loop.

There are three ways in which the AGC system for an SSB receiver can be improved: (a) the use of a pilot carrier (which would also be useful for automatic frequency control); (b) the use of *hang AGC*, in which envelope-derived AGC is sustained for about 0.6 s after the signal has fallen to zero; and (c) a combination of envelope AGC with a fast-acting squelch circuit (p. 323) that operates during the intersyllable intervals. Many FM receivers are not provided with an AGC system but instead rely upon amplitude limiting to keep the detected output at a constant level.

Communication radio receivers

A communication radio receiver provides a wide range of features to make the equipment flexible enough to cater for a variety of user requirements. These features may include any, or all, of the following:

- Channel selection with store, tune and receiver facility.
- Mode selection: DSBAM, SSBSC, CW and FM.
- RF attenuator with selectable attenuation.
- AGC selection.
- Scan facility of some or all programmed channels.
- Channel selection by keypad entry.
- Frequency selection by keypad entry.
- Selection of beat-frequency oscillator.
- IF gain and mute level control.
- AF volume control.
- LED signal meter.
- Sweep facility of all, or part, of frequency band.

The quality of the output signal is affected by a number of factors, amongst which are: (a) adjacent-channel, co-channel and image channel signals, (b) reciprocal mixing and (c) cross-modulation and intermodulation. In the design of a communication receiver every effort is made to minimise the adverse effects of these factors; this means that particular attention is paid to RF linearity and filtering and to IF selectivity.

MF/HF communication radio receivers

An MF/HF communication radio receiver must be able to operate in a very congested frequency band and this means it must have good selectivity so that it is able to discriminate against unwanted signals. Such a receiver is often required to be able to receive several different kinds of signal, such as DSBAM, SSBSC, CW and FM signals. The frequencies of operation vary with the user but are always within the frequency band 30 kHz (sometimes lower) to 30 MHz. Many applications demand that the receiver be controlled from a remote location and/or allow the operator to change frequency and/or channel rapidly. This requirement dictates a need for the local oscillator frequency(ies) to be provided by a frequency synthesiser and for wideband RF circuitry. Often the frequency selection is entered digitally by means of a keypad.

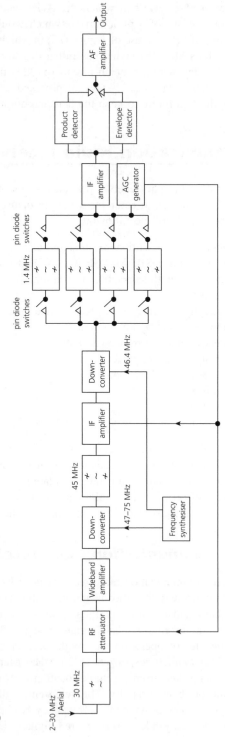

Fig. 12.13 *MF/HF communication receiver*

The block diagram of a typical HF double-superheterodyne communication radio receiver is shown by Fig. 12.13. The first IF of 45 MHz is above the 2–30 MHz tuning range of the receiver. The second IF is at the (more or less) standard value of 1.4 MHz. The first, and the second, local oscillator frequencies which must be supplied to the two mixers are both derived from a frequency synthesiser. Signals picked up by the aerial are passed through the 30 MHz low-pass filter to remove all signals at frequencies above the tuning range, but especially any signals at, or near, the image channel frequency and the first IF. The RF stage should transfer the maximum RF power from the aerial to the receiver and this means that it should be matched to the aerial. This, however, is not always possible since the receiver may be used in conjunction with more than one type of aerial. Some communication receivers employ a bank of sub-octave bandpass filters any one of which may be switched into circuit, quite likely by microprocessor-controlled digital circuitry.

The signals are then passed through an RF attenuator whose attenuation is varied by a d.c. voltage derived from the AGC system. The RF attenuator is followed by a broadband amplifier and the first mixer. Besides amplifying all received signals equally and improving the noise factor of the receiver, the wideband amplifier also isolates the first mixer from the aerial and helps to prevent local oscillator radiation from the aerial. The first mixer mixes the amplified signal with the first oscillator frequency and generates a large number of frequencies amongst which is a component at the difference frequency, $f_{o1} - f_s = 45$ MHz. The frequency supplied by the frequency synthesiser must therefore be variable from 47 to 75 MHz. The difference-frequency component is then selected by the first IF bandpass filter and then applied to the first IF amplifier. This circuit, besides providing gain, also matches the mixer output to the first IF filter. The selected and band-limited (≈ 10 kHz) signal is then applied to the second mixer where it is mixed with the fixed second local oscillator frequency of 46.4 MHz to shift it to the second IF of 1.4 (sometimes 10.7) MHz. The wanted 1.4 MHz component of the output of the second mixer is selected by one of a bank of bandpass filters. Each filter has a centre frequency of 1.4 MHz but a bandwidth appropriate for the different kinds of signals handled by the receiver, e.g. 8 kHz for AM, 2.4 kHz for SSBSC, 1 kHz or 400 Hz for CW signals. The appropriate filter is automatically selected to suit the type of signal being received. After filtering, the narrow-band signal is passed to either one of the two detectors. The AM detector demodulates DSBAM signals and may also generate the AGC voltage. The product detector is used to demodulate all other kinds of signal. Finally, the demodulated signal is filtered and then amplified by the audio amplifier.

Figure 12.14 shows the basic block diagram of a receiver covering the frequency band 10 kHz to 30 MHz which employs a digital signal processor (DSP) to carry out all the IF/AF circuit functions. The receiver is able to receive DSBAM, CW, SSBSC, FM, FSK and FAX signals. The receiver has three main modules, the RF unit, the IF/AF processor and the frequency synthesiser, plus a microprocessor and a power supply. The microprocessor is used to control the functions of the modules and also communicates with the outside world via the keypad on the control panel and the data interface.

The input signal is passed through a low-pass filter to remove the image channel frequency to be applied to the first mixer; here it is converted to the first IF of 41.44 MHz. A crystal filter band limits the mixer output to 10 kHz and rejects the second image frequency. The output of the crystal filter is applied to the second mixer

Fig. 12.14 *MF/HF receiver using a DSP*

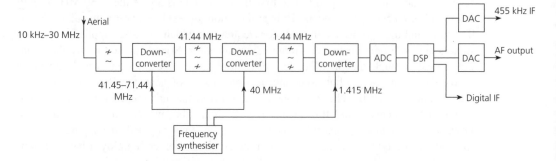

along with a fixed 40 MHz local oscillator signal, and here it is converted to the second IF of 1.44 MHz. The output of the second mixer leaves the RF unit to arrive at the IF/AF processor. Here the signal first passes through another bandpass filter before it reaches the third mixer where it is mixed with a 1.415 MHz signal to give the third IF of 25 kHz. The 25 kHz signal is then applied to a 16-bit ADC where it is converted into digital form. The digitised signal is then passed on to the DSP where a number of signal processing tasks are carried out.

The tasks performed by the DSP include

(a) automatic, manual or remote control;
(b) measurement of the received signal level;
(c) more filtering with adjustable bandwidths;
(d) demodulation;
(e) passband tuning;
(f) noise blanking;
(g) syllabic squelch; and
(h) the generation of
    (i) BFO analogue IF from 0 to 40 kHz,
    (ii) digital IF as a serial data output, and
    (iii) I and Q data streams.

The DSP has three outputs; one output is converted to analogue form to provide an IF of 455 kHz by a DAC, another output provides a digital IF for use for data and/or clock or frame information, and the third output is applied to another DAC that provides the audio signal.

VHF/UHF receivers

Figure 12.15 shows the simplified block diagram of an AM/FM VHF/UHF communication radio receiver that covers the frequency band 20–470 MHz. The incoming signal is filtered and amplified before it is up-converted to the first IF of 515 MHz. The first IF signal is then passed through an RF attenuator whose loss is varied by the AGC voltage. Next the signal is down-converted to the second IF of 10.7 MHz where it receives

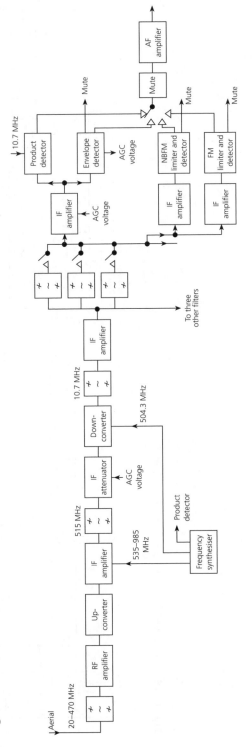

Fig. 12.15 *AM/FM VHF/UHF communication receiver*

Fig. 12.16 *AM/FM VHF/UHF communication receiver with DSP*

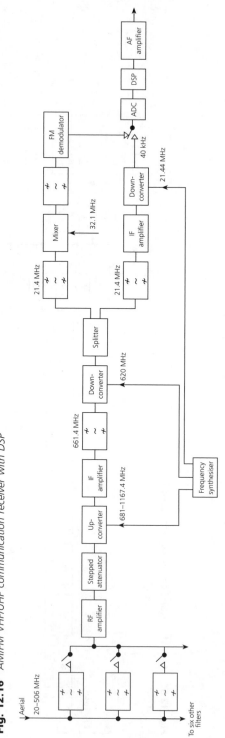

further amplification before it is applied to a bank of six bandpass filters. These filters have varying bandwidth according to the type of signal to be selected, e.g. DSBAM, SSBSC, NFBFM or FM signals. The output of the selected filter is then applied to another IF amplifier and then to the appropriate detector for the type of signal. The envelope detector is used to demodulate DSBAM signals, for example, and it also generates the AGC voltage. The demodulated output signal is then passed through the muting circuit and thence to the AF amplifier where its level is boosted to the required amount.

Figure 12.16 shows the basic block diagram of a VHF/UHF radio receiver that covers the frequency band 20–506 MHz and is able to receive both AM and FM signals. The aerial is connected to a bank of nine bandpass filters and the appropriate filter is selected by means of pin diode switches. The output of the selected bandpass filter is switched to a low-noise RF amplifier and then to an attenuator. The attenuator has stepped values of attenuation that are selected by the operator of the receiver. The signal is next applied to an up-converter where it is converted to the first IF of 661.4 MHz. The output of the up-converter is filtered by a 661.4 MHz bandpass filter having a bandwidth of 10 MHz. The 661.4 MHz first IF signal is then down-converted to the second IF of 21.4 MHz. The second IF signal is then applied to a splitter circuit to provide separate paths for AM and FM signals. In the AM path the signal is filtered to a bandwidth of 30 kHz and amplified before it is down-converted to the third IF of 40 kHz. In the FM path the signal is filtered to a bandwidth of 300 kHz and down-converted to a third IF of 10.7 MHz. The 10.7 MHz signal is then applied to an FM demodulator to produce an audio output signal. Either one of the AM and FM output signals can be switched to the ADC where the signal is converted into digital form. The digital signal is passed to the DSP which processes the signal to produce an audio output signal. The DSP includes a codec to convert the demodulated audio output to analogue form.

VHF transceivers

Many VHF/UHF radio transmitters are combined with radio receivers to give a *transceiver*. Figure 12.17 gives the block diagram of a VHF transceiver. On the transmitter side of the equipment the input audio signal is amplified before it is filtered and then amplitude limited. The band-limited, amplitude-limited signal is then pre-emphasised and again filtered before it is applied to a VCO. The carrier frequency supplied by a frequency synthesiser is frequency modulated by the signal by its varying the frequency of the VCO. The FM output signal is amplified again before it is passed via the aerial switch on to the aerial for radiation.

In the receiving direction the received signal is filtered by an electronically controlled bandpass filter before it reaches the RF amplifier. The amplified RF signal is then passed on to the first mixer where it is down-converted to the first IF of 21.4 MHz. The IF is selected and amplified by the first IF amplifier and then applied to the second mixer. Here the signal is again down-converted to the 455 kHz second IF and then it is demodulated by the quadrature detector. Often much of this circuitry is contained within a single IC. The demodulated output signal is filtered before it is de-emphasised and, after passing through the squelch circuit, amplified by the AF amplifier.

Fig. 12.17 *Microprocessor controlled VHF transceiver*

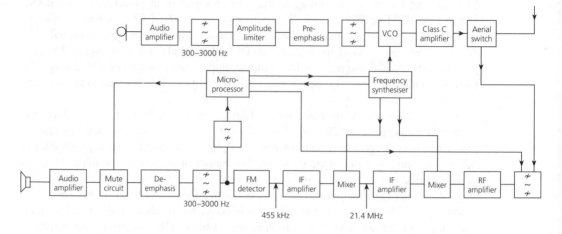

The local oscillator frequencies for the VCO and the first and second mixers are obtained from a frequency synthesiser. The frequency synthesiser, the squelch circuit and the RF bandpass filter are controlled by commands issued by a microprocessor. The frequency synthesiser is programmed to change frequency on receipt of a command from the microprocessor. The microprocessor will also monitor the controls on the front panel of the receiver to detect, and implement, radio operator instructions, and updates the information given on the display, such as the frequency to which the receiver is tuned.

Digital radio receivers

A digital radio receiver uses digital techniques to provide the various circuit functions; it is not a receiver used to receive digital signals. Both analogue and digital radio receivers are designed to receive analogue signals. A digital receiver must employ an ADC to change the received signal from analogue to digital form. The analogue-to-digital conversion process is a form of down-conversion: the operation of an ADC takes an input signal modulated onto a radio, or intermediate, frequency and produces an output at baseband. The minimum sampling rate must be at least twice the highest baseband frequency but oversampling of up to about 10 times is advantageous. The dynamic range of the ADC should be larger than the signal level range after conditioning by filtering, amplification and gain control. Many radio receivers employ digital techniques for read-outs and for the frequency synthesiser but their other circuitry employs analogue techniques. The modern tendency is to employ digital circuitry as much as possible now that DSPs are available to carry out all of the analogue back-end processing, such as IF amplification and filtering, demodulation and AGC voltage generation. One GSM mobile telephone, for example, consists of an LNA, a down-converter, an IF amplifier, an ADC and a DSP. The DSP performs all the circuit functions not provided by the other circuits.

The basic block diagram of a digital radio receiver is given in Fig. 12.18. The received signal is analogue – whether the information is analogue voice/music or digital

Fig. 12.18 *Digital communication receiver*

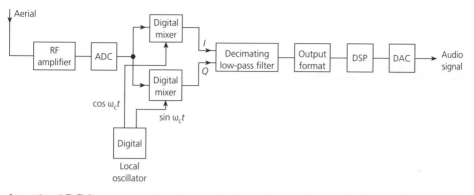

data. An ADC is necessary to change the incoming analogue signal into digital form. The wanted analogue signal is amplified by the RF amplifier and then converted into digital form by the ADC. The ADC must sample the incoming signal at a rate at least twice the highest frequency in the modulating signal; sampling at twice the carrier frequency is not necessary if only the modulation information is to be recovered. A sample of the modulating signal is produced at baseband. Sampling the information carried by a carrier without sampling the carrier itself is known as *undersampling*. By using a sampling frequency much lower than the carrier, the carrier is effectively suppressed and the input signal down-converted. The baseband signal is usually *oversampled*, i.e. the sampling frequency is more than twice the highest baseband frequency. Often the output of the ADC is passed through a low-pass filter to reduce aliasing. The digital signal is applied to a digital mixer; this consists of two mixers driven by digital in-phase (I) and quadrature (Q) components of a local oscillator signal which is derived from a frequency synthesiser. Digital mixing or multiplication consists of taking two digital words and taking their product. Often the multiplication is followed by digital addition in which the product word is added to the previous result. This gives the digital equivalent of analogue mixing and filtering.

In the digital mixer the signal is multiplied by both the sine and the cosine outputs of the local oscillator frequency. The output of the mixer consists of the sum and difference of the wanted signal and the local oscillator frequencies plus a large number of other, unwanted components. The unwanted frequency components are removed, and the baseband signal recovered, by passing the mixer output through a *decimating filter*. This is a digital filter that is able to act as a low-pass filter and reduce the sampling rate of the input signal. The reduction in the sampling rate can be programmed to be a common ratio that is any number between 1 and $2^{17} = 131\,072$. The decimating filter has a very low ripple in the passband, very sharp cut-off characteristic, and a linear phase relationship. The filter output is applied to a circuit that formats the signal to make it available in the required form, such as I and Q signals, floating point, or two's complement, for example. The demodulation process is sometimes carried out in the same DSP chip or it may be performed by a separate DSP. In either case different types of demodulation are made available by downloading the appropriate software. The DSP does all the necessary signal generation and processing tasks. These include: (a) automatic, manual or remote control; (b) filtering, demodulation; (c) noise blanking, syllabic squelch; (d) the generation of a BFO (Beat-frequency Oscillator) signal from 0 to 40 kHz; and (e) the production of a digital IF output for use as serial data and/or an *I/Q* data stream.

EXAMPLE 12.9

Calculate the minimum sampling rate for an ADC when the input signal is (a) a 3 kHz voice signal and (b) a 3 kHz voice signal modulated on to a 10 MHz carrier. State why the calculated sampling rate could not be employed in practice. (c) If the input signal has a dynamic range of 40 dB determine how many bits per sample are needed for one-bit accuracy.

Solution

(a) Minimum sampling rate $= 2 \times 3 = 6$ kHz (*Ans.*)
(b) Minimum sampling rate $= 2 \times 3 = 6$ kHz (*Ans.*)
    The calculated minimum sampling rates could not be used in practice because the roll-off of a practical filters is not sharp enough.
(c) 40 dB $= 10^4$, $\log_2 10^4 = (\log_{10} 10^4)/(\log_{10} 2) = 4/0.3 = 13.3$ (*Ans.*)
    Hence a 14-bit ADC is needed.

A 16-bit microprocessor is employed for such purposes as the control of the operation of modules, and for communication with the outside world via the control panel keypad.

Cellular telephones

A cellular telephone includes both baseband and RF sections. The baseband section performs all the audio processing, command and control circuitry, and analogue-to-digital/digital-to-analogue conversions. The RF section contains all the transmitting and receiving circuitry. The basic block diagram of a cellular telephone is given in Fig. 12.19 and it can be seen to be a digital transceiver.

The audio signal generated by the microphone is applied to an ADC to be converted into digital form before it is passed on to the codec. Here the digital signal is twice

Fig. 12.19 *Cellular telephone*

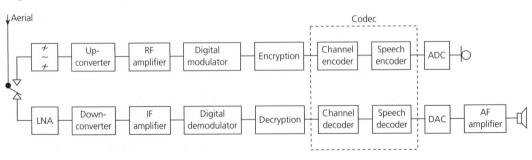

encoded, first by the speech encoder and then by the channel encoder (see p. 445 for reasons). The encoded signal is then encrypted before it is used to modulate a carrier that has been derived from a frequency synthesiser. The digitally modulated signal is then amplified to the wanted transmitted power level before it is passed on to the aerial to be radiated. In the receive direction of transmission the incoming signal is amplified by an LNA before it is down-converted, amplified again and then demodulated. The demodulated signal is decrypted before it is applied to the codec where it is both channel and speech decoded. The digital output signal is then applied to the DAC to recover the analogue speech signal which is then used to activate the receiver.

Base station

The block diagram of a cellular radio system base station is shown by Fig. 12.20. The frequency synthesiser selects one 200 kHz channel from the 25 MHz wide operating bandwidth (75 MHz for DCS 1800). In the receiving half of the base station the incoming signal is filtered and then amplified by the LNA before the first stage of mixing. The first IF signal is amplified before it is again mixed to obtain the second IF. The second IF signal is also filtered and amplified before it is applied to a sample-and-hold amplifier and an ADC and converted into digital form. The digital signal is then applied to a DSP for further processing, such as filtering, equalisation and decoding, to produce the output baseband digital signal. A signal is derived from the DSP and applied to a DAC for conversion to analogue form and the DAC output provides an AGC voltage that is used to control the gain of the IF amplifier.

In the transmitting direction of operation the signal is first applied to the DSP for processing and the processed signal is encoded and then shaped before it is passed to the DACs. The DACs produce I and Q digital signals that are twice up-converted, filtered and amplified before the analogue signal is amplified by the RF amplifier and then transmitted by the aerial.

Fig. 12.20 *Cellular base station*

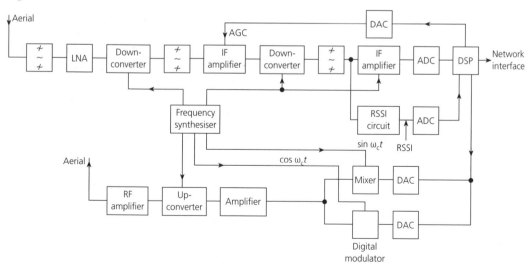

Digital broadcast radio

Digital broadcast radio, also known as *digital audio broadcasting* (DAB), is just being introduced at the time of writing and has been designed to comply with the ITU-R recommendations 1114 and 1130. Digital radio offers the listener (a) good reception even on portable and mobile receivers, (b) CD quality sound, (c) greater choice of programmes with text, data, graphics and still pictures. From the broadcasters' point of view it also offers a more efficient use of the allocated frequency spectrum, and single-frequency networks. The system uses a digital modulation method known as coded orthogonal frequency-division multiplex (COFDM). COFDM uses 1536 closely spaced carrier frequencies each of which is modulated by a subset of the total data being broadcast. The data rate on each carrier is low and this makes it much less sensitive to distortion caused by multi-path propagation. Each symbol is preceded by a guard band which makes the signal resistant to distortion caused by other signals arriving after a time delay and signals from other transmitters operating in the same part of the frequency spectrum. This allows single-frequency networks to be set up in an area in which a common ensemble of digital services is to be provided to the listener. The data representing a range of services is interleaved in both the frequency and the time domains to produce a multiplex of signals. The system also employs baseband audio compression which reduces the amount of data needed to deliver a service. The combination of multiplex and compression gives a high spectrum efficiency and this means that there is room for a wide range of services.

In the UK digital radio operates in the frequency band 217.5–230 MHz divided into seven blocks of 1.55 MHz. One block is used by the BBC and the others are available to commercial operators.

EXERCISES

12.1 Two 0 dBm sinusoidal signals are applied to a double-balanced mixer when the third-order output voltage is −60 dBm. If the conversion loss of the mixer is 6 dB calculate the ratio (IF output voltage)/(third-order output voltage). Calculate the third-order output voltage if the level of each input signal is (a) reduced to −10 dBm, (b) increased to 10 dBm and (c) increased to +20 dBm. (d) Calculate the third-order intercept point.

12.2 A transceiver specification includes: General: simplex/duplex operation, frequency modulation, up to 99 channels, oscillator stability 5 ppm. Receiver: sensitivity 12 dB SINAD for 0.25 μV p.d., squelch sensitivity 9–12 μV p.d., adjacent-channel selectivity 60 dB, spurious emissions attenuation 70 dB. Transmitter: power output 5 W, modulation up to 5 kHz peak deviation. Explain the meaning of each term in the specification.

12.3 (a) Draw the block diagram of an MF/HF radio receiver and briefly explain its operation. (b) Why is an AGC-controlled RF attenuator often used to control RF gain rather than an AGC-controlled RF amplifier?

12.4 (a) State the four main parameters which affect the performance of an RF front end in an MF/HF communication radio receiver. (b) Explain the meaning of each parameter mentioned.

12.5 (a) The second harmonic of a 6 MHz signal beats with a 22 MHz signal. Calculate the frequency of the third-order products. (b) The second harmonic of a 10.4 MHz signal beats with a 10.8 MHz signal. Calculate the frequency of the third-order intermodulation products.

12.6 The features offered by a radio receiver include the following: (a) scan facility of all, or some, programmed channels; (b) required channel and frequency selection by keypad editing; (c) mode selection; (d) selectable RF attenuation; (e) AGC selection; and (f) IF gain and mute control. Briefly discuss the use of each of these features.

12.7 The use of a frequency synthesiser to derive the necessary local oscillator frequencies in a superheterodyne radio receiver can provide very good frequency stability, but suffers from three disadvantages. State what these disadvantages are and briefly discuss each one.

12.8 (a) List two sources of interference to reception in a radio receiver that can be reduced by IF selectivity.
(b) List five sources of interference that can only be reduced by RF selectivity.
(c) A wanted signal at a frequency of 12 MHz is converted to an IF of 1.4 MHz. What local oscillator frequency is needed? At a frequency 10 kHz higher than the local oscillator frequency a 3 kHz slice of synthesiser noise is at a level of −93 dB. Determine the level of the interference at the mixer output.

12.9 (a) A radio receiver has a bandwidth of 120 kHz, a noise factor of 7 dB and a signal-to-noise ratio at the demodulator input of 10 dB. Calculate its sensitivity.
(b) Discuss the steps that can be taken to improve the sensitivity of a radio receiver.

12.10 (a) Explain what is meant by intermodulation in a radio receiver.
(b) Why is it undesirable and how may it be minimised?
(c) Write down the sixth-order intermodulation products when signals at frequencies f_1 and f_2 are applied to a radio receiver.
(d) Signals at 1.4 MHz and 1.41 MHz are applied to a radio receiver. Determine (i) the second-order and (ii) the third-order intermodulation products.

12.11 The specification of an LF/HF radio receiver includes sections on the following: frequency coverage, reception modes, reception bandwidths, frequency stability, stored channels, muting, audio output and sensitivity. Explain (a) the meaning of each term and (b) the importance of each term.

12.12 (a) Explain the importance of the third-order intercept point of a radio receiver.
(b) How is the third-order intercept point related to the dynamic range of the receiver?

(c) A radio receiver has a third-order intercept point of −10 dBm and a noise floor of −110 dBm. Calculate its dynamic range.

(d) Why is a wideband RF amplifier more likely to suffer from intermodulation products than a tuned RF amplifier?

12.13 An HF radio receiver with a bandwidth of 3 kHz has a thermal noise level of −26 dBμV. If the receiver has a noise factor of 10 dB calculate (a) its noise floor and (b) the minimum input signal required to produce an output signal-to-noise ratio of 10 dB. Explain the significance of the result.

12.14 The block diagram of an HF radio receiver is given by Fig. 12.21. Explain the operation of the receiver. If the intermediate frequencies are 45 MHz and 455 kHz suggest a suitable figure for the tuning range of the receiver. Then calculate the range of frequencies that the frequency synthesiser must deliver to each mixer.

Fig. 12.21

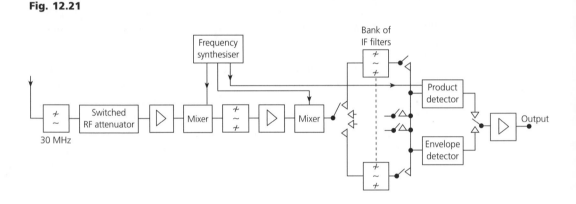

12.15 A digital radio receiver is able to operate with each of the following kinds of signals: A1A, A1B, A2A, A2B, A3E, F3E, H2A, H2B, H3E, J2A, J2B, J3E, R2A, R2B, R3E, B7B, B8E, B9W. Explain each mode of operation.

12.16 Explain what is meant by reciprocal mixing. In a radio receiver a 12 MHz wanted signal is converted to the first intermediate frequency of 1.4 MHz by a diode mixer supplied by a frequency synthesiser signal at 13.4 MHz. At 13.41 MHz a 3 kHz slice of synthesiser noise is −93 dB relative to the fundamental signal. Calculate (a) the frequency of an unwanted signal that would be spuriously converted to a 3 kHz noise band at 1.4 MHz, and (b) the level of this unwanted signal.

12.17 A radio receiver amplifies the incoming signal with an AGC-controlled RF amplifier and then applies the amplified signal to an ADC. Explain how the baseband signal is produced.

12.18 An amplifier has a two-tone input signal applied to its input terminals. Each tone is at −15 dBm. The third-order intercept point of the amplifier is +22 dBm. Calculate the magnitude of the third-order intermodulation products.

13 Radio-relay systems

After reading this chapter you should be able to:

(a) Describe the digital hierarchy used in both the UK and the USA.
(b) Understand the need for relay stations in a microwave point-to-point wideband radio system.
(c) State how, and why, a number of RF channels are multiplexed onto each parabolic dish aerial.
(d) Draw the block diagram of an analogue radio-relay system.
(e) Explain the advantages to be gained by operating a radio-relay system using digital technology as opposed to analogue technology.
(f) Draw the block diagram of a digital radio-relay transmitter and explain its operation.
(g) Draw the block diagram of a digital radio-relay system receiver and explain its operation.
(h) Explain why digital relay stations are necessary and how one works.
(i) Perform link budget calculations and determine fade margin.
(j) Understand the use of scatter propagation systems and say when, and why, one might be employed.

The public telecommunications network of a country is used for the transmission of speech, telegraphy, data and sound/television broadcast signals. The network has two main parts: the *access network* and the *core network*. The core network consists of trunk switching exchanges and trunk lines. All the trunk lines are routed over multi-channel *pulse code modulation* (PCM) systems and these, in turn, are routed over either optical fibre links or terrestrial microwave radio-relay systems. PCM multi-channel telephony systems are based on the 32 channel ITU-T specified system. Two of the channels are used for control and signalling purposes so that the basic system actually provides 30 speech bandwidth channels. The digital multiplexing hierachy specified by the ITU-T is shown by Fig. 13.1. The bit stream labelled as 2 Mb/s is actually equal to 32×64 kb/s or 2.048 Mb/s but it is usual to refer to it as 2 Mb/s. Similarly 8 Mb/s is actually 8.448 Mb/s, 34 Mb/s is 34.369 Mb/s, 140 Mb/s is 139.264 Mb/s, and 565 Mb/s is 564.992 Mb/s. (In the USA the digital hierarchy is 1.544 Mb/s, 6.312 Mb/s, 44.736 Mb/s and 274.176 Mb/s.)

Fig. 13.1 *Digital multiplexing hierarchy*

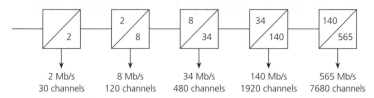

| 2 Mb/s | 8 Mb/s | 34 Mb/s | 140 Mb/s | 565 Mb/s |
| 30 channels | 120 channels | 480 channels | 1920 channels | 7680 channels |

Digital line-of-sight (LOS) radio-relay systems are used to provide a wide range of communication services and their traffic capacity varies from a few to several thousand speech channels. LOS is defined as meaning a 0.577 Fresnel zone clearance over the earth and any object on the earth, such as buildings and trees. Older analogue LOS systems still exist but in the UK they are now used only for the transmission of television signals. Besides the radio-relay systems that form a part of the BT telephone network there are also a number of other telecommunication networks operated by such organisations as Cable & Wireless, and the rail, gas and electricity companies.

Optical fibre cables carry the majority of trunk circuits in the BT network but radio-relay systems do have two advantages which mean that they remain an integral part of the network. These advantages are: (a) a radio-relay system is quicker and easier to provide, particularly over difficult terrain; and (b) it is easier to extend the traffic-carrying capacity of a radio-relay system. On the other hand, there may be some difficulty in obtaining suitable sites for radio-relay stations and the transmission performance of a link may be affected by weather conditions.

Microwave radio-relay systems

A microwave radio-relay system employs LOS space-wave transmissions in both the UHF and the SHF bands. The maximum distance between two aerials is about 60 km but the average length of a microwave link is 40–50 km. Nearly always, the length of a route is much longer than the maximum distance and then a number of radio-relay stations, or repeaters, are employed in the manner shown by Fig. 13.2. The baseband signal, which is most often a 140 Mb/s multiplexed digital PCM signal, is processed and then used digitally to modulate an RF carrier. The modulated signal is transmitted by the transmitting aerial over a path of 40–50 km typical length to the distant receive aerial at the first relay, or repeater, station. At the first relay station the received signal is down-converted, demodulated and then applied to a pulse regenerator. The regener-

Fig. 13.2 *Microwave radio-relay system*

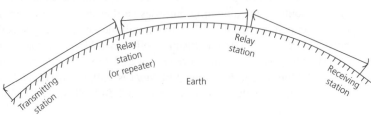

Fig. 13.3 *PCM system transmitted over a radio-relay system: (a) 480 channels and (b) 1920 channels*

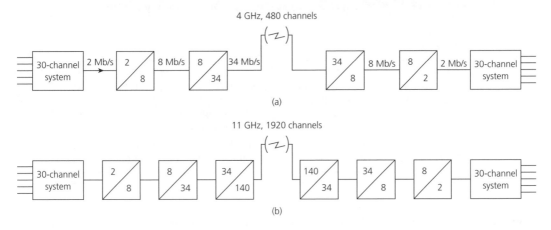

(a)

(b)

ated baseband signal is then up-converted to a microwave frequency and passed to the transmitting aerial for onward transmission to the next relay station. This is repeated several times until the signal arrives at the receiving station.

When the signal arrives at the receiving station it is amplified and down-converted to baseband. The RF signal must be amplified before its amplitude has fallen to such a level that the minimum required signal (carrier)-to-noise ratio cannot be obtained. This is the factor that determines the spacing between the relay stations and hence the number of relay stations required.

Analogue radio-relay systems suffer from a progressive deterioration in the signal-to-noise ratio with increase in the length of the route and this limits the performance of a system. A digital radio-relay system employs either quadrature amplitude modulation (QAM) or some form of phase-shift modulation (PSK). Since the digitally modulated signal can be regenerated at each relay station a required signal-to-noise ratio can be maintained throughout the length of a system.

Figures 13.3(a) and (b) show how a 34 Mb/s 480 channel PCM system and a 140 Mb/s 1920 channel PCM system are routed over a radio-relay system. The baseband PCM signal is applied directly to the input of a digital radio-relay system. The channel spacings and frequency assignments are both specified by ITU-R recommendations. The baseband rate is always nominally 2, 8, 34 or 140 Mb/s. In the BT network 140 Mb/s is used as the trunk transmission rate with 34 Mb/s used for short-distance links.

Various frequency bands have been allocated to microwave radio-relay systems by the ITU-T. Table 13.1 lists the frequency bands that are in use for microwave radio-relay systems in the UK. The 3.7–4.2 GHz band is known as the C band and the 14.0–14.5 band is known as the Ku band. Each frequency band is divided into two blocks each of which contains a number of RF channels. At one relay station all the transmitters operate in the high-frequency block of frequencies and all the receivers operate in the LF block. At the next relay station all the transmitters will operate in the low-frequency block of frequencies and the receivers use frequencies in the high-frequency block. Figure 13.4(a) shows how the lower and upper 6 GHz bands are divided into two blocks

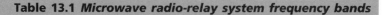

Table 13.1 *Microwave radio-relay system frequency bands*

Frequency (GHz)	Name	Use
3.7–4.2	4 GHz band	2 × 34 Mb/s (8PSK), 140 Mb/s (16QAM, RBQPSK)
5.85–6.425	Lower 6 GHz band	2 × 34 Mb/s (8PSK), 140 Mb/s (RBQPSK)
6.425–7.11	Upper 6 GHz band	2 × 34 Mb/s (8PSK), 140 Mb/s (16QAM)
10.7–11.7	11 GHz band	2 × 34 Mb/s (8PSK), 140 Mb/s (QPSK, 8PSK, 16QAM, 64QAM)
14.0–14.5	14 GHz band	2 × 34 Mb/s (8PSK), 140 Mb/s (QPSK, 8PSK)
17.7–19.7	19 GHz band	140 Mb/s (QPSK), 555 Mb/s (QPSK)

Fig. 13.4 *Frequency allocation of RF channels of a radio-relay system (a) lower and upper 6 GHz bands, and (b) 11/14 GHz bands*

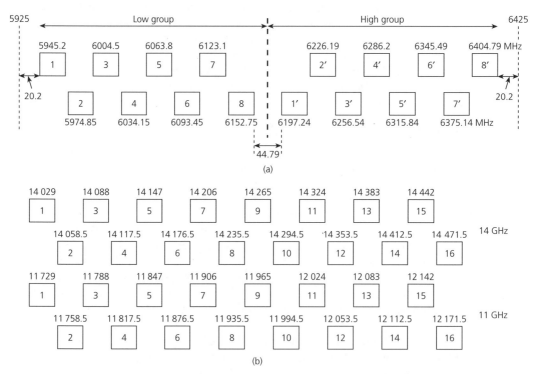

of eight RF channels (frequencies in MHz). Figure 13.4(b) shows the RF channels frequencies employed for both directions of transmission in an 11/14 GHz system. A 140 Mb/s system has six RF channels and can accommodate 6 × 1920 = 11 520 64 kb/s channels. A 2 × 34 Mb/s system provides 6 × 320 = 720 64 kb/s channels and is used to provide short-spur and junction connections.

Fig. 13.5 *Multiplexing RF channels using circulators (Courtesy of British Telecommunication Engineering)*

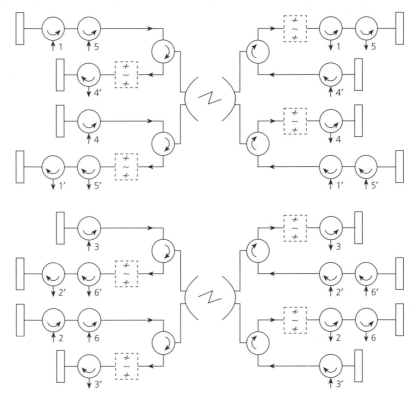

Multiplexing RF channels

The parabolic dish aerials used in radio-relay systems are able to transmit or receive more than one RF channel at the same time and hence it is usual for several channels to be multiplexed at the aerial. To improve the discrimination between channels, adjacent (in frequency) channels use alternate planes of polarisation. Thus if channel 1 is horizontally polarised, channel 2 will be vertically polarised, channel 3 horizontally polarised, and so on for eight channels. Circulators are employed to combine several RF channels at each aerial in a link and this is shown by Fig. 13.5. The circulators and the associated channel filters are collectively known as the *branching network*. In the figures that follow only one channel will be shown.

Analogue radio-relay systems

In the BT network analogue radio-relay systems are now only employed to carry wideband television signals. All multi-channel telephony systems have been transferred to digital systems. The block diagram of one RF channel in an analogue radio-relay system is shown by Fig. 13.6. The eight channels in the system have identical equipment but only the equipment for one channel is shown.

Fig. 13.6 *One RF channel in an analogue radio-relay system (Courtesy of British Telecommunication Engineering)*

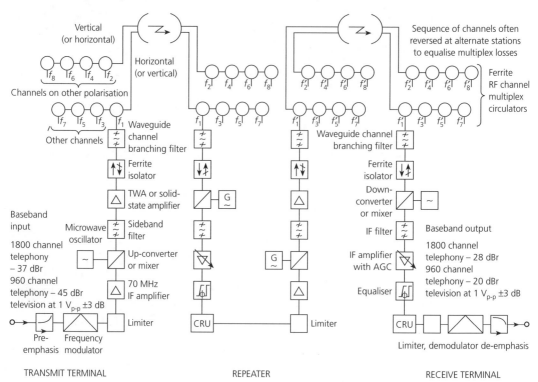

The input baseband signal is first pre-emphasised and then used to frequency-modulate a 70 MHz carrier. The 70 MHz IF is then amplitude limited before it is applied to a mixer together with the output of a microwave oscillator. This oscillator runs at a frequency equal to $(f_t - 70)$ MHz, where f_t is the frequency at which the signal is to be radiated from the aerial. The upper sideband, $[(f_t - 70) + 70]$ MHz $= f_t$, is selected by the sideband filter and then amplified by either a travelling-wave amplifier (TWA), also known as a travelling-wave tube (TWT), or a solid-state amplifier. The amplified signal then passes through first an isolator and then another filter, before it is routed to the transmitting aerial via one or more circulators. The circulators allow the odd-numbered RF channels to be combined together and radiated as a horizontally polarised wave. Similarly, the even-numbered RF channels are also combined together and are radiated with vertical polarisation. At the receiver the signal is selected by the appropriate bandpass channel filter and then mixed with the output of a microwave oscillator. This oscillator runs at a frequency f_o equal to $(f_t + 70)$ MHz and so the mixer output contains a component at $[(f_t + 70) - f_t] = 70$ MHz; this component is selected by the IF filters. The 70 MHz signal is first amplified and equalised before it is demodulated to recover the baseband signal. Finally, the baseband signal is de-emphasised to obtain the original amplitude relationships between the low-frequency and high-frequency components of the signal.

The block marked as CRU is the carrier reinsertion unit. Its function is to inject a noise-free signal into the signal path whenever the incoming carrier fades completely. This prevents the AGC system of the receiver increasing the gain and producing a large output noise. The TWT (or TWA), which can provide a high-power output with a relatively high efficiency, is still employed in both analogue and digital systems, particularly in the 11/14 GHz band. The power output that semiconductor amplifiers can develop at gigahertz frequencies is steadily increasing and such circuits are increasingly employed as the RF power amplifier. At present, a solid-state amplifier can only handle some tens of watts compared with a TWT's hundreds of watts.

Digital radio-relay systems

The main disadvantage of an analogue radio-relay system is that the noise powers generated in each link are additive and so the signal-to-noise ratio inevitably decreases with increase in the length of a route. The problem can be overcome by the use of a digital system, since a digital signal can be regenerated at each relay station and then noise is no longer cumulative, and the signal-to-noise ratio can be maintained at a desired figure. The performance of a digital radio-relay system is quoted in terms of its bit error rate.

Digital radio-relay systems operate in a number of frequency bands (see Table 13.1) with bit rates of either 2×34 Mb/s or 140 Mb/s with a typical repeater spacing of 40–50 km and a transmitted power of 1 to 10 W. The 34 Mb/s bit rate can give 720, and the 140 Mb/s bit rate 11 520, 64 kb/s telephone channels. The 140 Mb/s bit rate has been standardised by the ITU-R because it is compatible with the fourth hierarchical digital multiplexing level of 139.264 Mb/s. In the UK the standard digital radio-relay systems operate in the 11 GHz band and provide six 140 Mb/s RF channels. This gives a capacity of 6×1920, or 11 520, telephony channels.

Bit error rate in digital systems

The performance of a digital microwave system, be it terrestrial or satellite, is expressed in terms of its bit error rate (BER). The BER is equivalent to the output signal-to-noise ratio of an analogue system and is the probability that a transmitted bit will be incorrectly received.

The BER of a digital radio relay system is

BER = (number of bits in error)/(number of bits received) in a specified time

$$(13.1)$$

The BER is quoted as a number; for example, 1×10^{-5} means that, on average, one bit in every 100 000 will be in error. An error in the correct reception of a bit may occur because noise picked up by the system has corrupted the signal waveform to such an extent that the decision circuitry in the receiver cannot accurately determine whether a bit is a one or a zero.

The ITU-R recommendations for a digital radio-relay link are: (a) a BER of 1×10^{-6} over a 1 min period must not be exceeded for more than 0.4% of any month;

and (b) a BER of 1×10^{-3} over a 1 s period must not be exceeded for more than 0.054% of any month. Expressions were given in Chapter 4 for the BER pertaining to a given signal-to-noise ratio for various forms of digital modulation.

The *residual BER* is the BER that exists in the absence of fading in the propagation path. Two other terms are also used: the *errored second* is the time interval of 1 s in which a digital signal is received with one or more errors; and a *severely errored second* is the time interval of 1 s in which a digital signal is received with an error greater than 10^{-3}.

Advantages of digital operation

Further advantages arising from the use of digital techniques are as follows:

● The ever-increasing availability of LSI and VLSI digital ICs allows cheaper, smaller-sized, equipment to be designed and used.
● The widespread use of ICs reduces power consumption and increases reliability.
● Converting a system from analogue to digital operation can considerably increase its channel capacity.
● The BER for data signals sent over a digital system is much lower than if the same signals are transmitted over an analogue system.

Efficiency

The efficiency η of a digital radio system is

$$\eta = \text{(received information bit energy)/(noise density)} = E_b/N_0 \tag{13.2}$$

The noise density N_0 is the noise level in a 1 Hz bandwidth and is equal to -204 dBW $+ F$ dB, where F is the noise figure of the receiving system.

EXAMPLE 13.1

(a) The received power in a radio link is -94 dBW. If the bit rate is 2.048 Mb/s calculate the value of E_b. (b) If the noise factor of the receiver is 8 dB calculate N_0. (c) Calculate the ratio E_b/N_0.

Solution

(a) $E_b = -94$ dBW $- 10 \log_{10}(2.048 \times 10^6) = -157$ dBW (*Ans.*)
(b) $N_0 = -204$ dBW $+ 8 = -196$ dBW (*Ans.*)
(c) $\eta = E_b/N_0 = -157 - (-196) = 39$ dB (*Ans.*)

Digital transmitter

Figure 13.7 shows the block diagram of the transmitter of an 11 GHz, 140 Mb/s, digital radio-relay system. The input baseband signal uses the PCM line code CMI and this is

Fig. 13.7 *Transmitter of a 11 GHz 140 Mb/s digital radio-relay system*

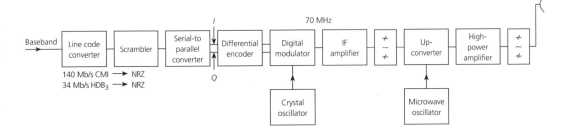

140 Mb/s CMI ⟶ NRZ
34 Mb/s HDB$_3$ ⟶ NRZ

converted into an NRZ waveform by the line code converter. The NRZ signal is then modulated by a pseudo-random digital sequence that scrambles its frequency spectrum to transform repeated bit sequences into pseudo-random sequences. The scrambling process is used because: (a) it improves the spectral and power distributions of the signal, removing any spectral lines, and so reduces interference with other RF channels; (b) it reduces jitter[†]; (c) it makes the system appear transparent; (d) it provides timing information; (e) adaptive equalisers in the receiver will not work correctly unless the received signal is random (or nearly so). The scrambler must establish a clock frequency that will be used in the demodulator at the distant receiver. The scrambled bits are retimed before a frame is established by the insertion of some extra bits for supervisory and error correction purposes.

The scrambled signal is applied to a serial-to-parallel converter which splits the serial NRZ signal into two 70 Mb/s streams which are known as the *I* and *Q* signals. The *I* and *Q* bit streams may be differentially encoded before they are applied to the digital modulator; differential encoding makes it possible for demodulation to take place at the receiver without the need for phase information to be transmitted. Differential encoding means that the phase of one state is changed depending on the previous state. At the receiver the phase at any interval is compared with the phase in the previous interval. The received signal is delayed for one interval and then used as a reference to demodulate the signal in the following interval. At the digital modulator the processed baseband signal modulates a carrier generated by a transistor crystal oscillator. The modulation method may be QPSK, 16QAM or 64QAM at 140 Mb/s. At higher bit rates the modulation will probably be 256QAM. If 16QAM, or higher, is employed the *I* and *Q* signals will also have to be converted into multi-level signals (four for 64QAM). The digitally modulated signal is first filtered and then applied to the IF amplifier. In some transmitters the modulated signal is applied to an RF amplifier pre-distorter circuit before it reaches the IF amplifier; its purpose is to distort the IF signal in such a way that it compensates for the distortion introduced in the RF amplifier which does not have a linear gain–frequency characteristic. The amplified 70 MHz IF signal is further filtered before it is applied to the up-converter for frequency translation to the 11 GHz band. The 11 GHz signal is amplified to the required transmitted power level by the final amplifier; this is usually a gallium arsenide (GaAs) transistor circuit at

---

[†] Jitter is the short-term variation of the significant instants of a digital signal from their ideal position in time. Effectively it is phase modulation of the signal timing.

Fig. 13.8 *Alternative 11 GHz transmitter*

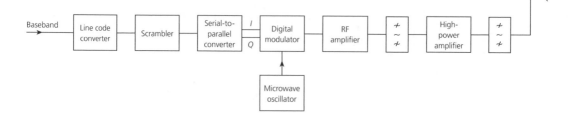

Fig. 13.9 *Use of FEC decoder in digital transmitter*

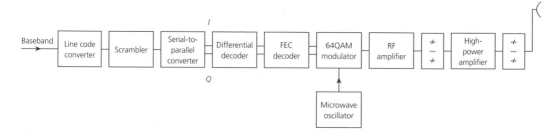

frequencies up about 6 GHz and either a GaAs circuit or a TWT at higher frequencies. The amplified signal is again filtered to shape the transmitted frequency spectrum and limit the occupied bandwidth before it is combined with other RF channels and sent to the transmitting aerial. Filters are constructed using waveguide resonant cavities since stripline filters are too lossy and the up-converter uses a microwave integrated circuit (MIC).

Some digital transmitters apply an 11 GHz carrier, produced by a 1 GHz transistor crystal oscillator and a varactor diode frequency multiplier, to the digital modulator so that the digitally modulated output signal is in the required frequency band; this technique avoids the need for a separate up-converter. The block diagram of such a transmitter is shown by Fig. 13.8.

A 140 Mb/s system that uses 64QAM or higher as the modulation system will include a *forward error control* (FEC) encoder in the transmitter positioned between the differential encoder and the 64QAM modulator; see Fig. 13.9. In the receiver an FEC decoder is fitted between the 64QAM demodulator and the differential decoder.

PRACTICAL EXERCISE 13.1

Aim: To build a simple scrambler circuit and check its operation.
Components and equipment: One 74HC164 SIPO or 74HC194 universal shift register; one 74HC86 quad 2-input exclusive-OR gate IC; one 74HC32 quad 2-input OR gate. Three pulse generators. Logic analyser or CRO, Power supply.

Fig. 13.10

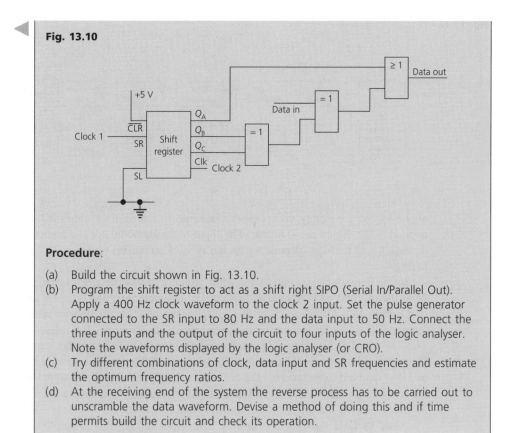

Procedure:

(a) Build the circuit shown in Fig. 13.10.
(b) Program the shift register to act as a shift right SIPO (Serial In/Parallel Out). Apply a 400 Hz clock waveform to the clock 2 input. Set the pulse generator connected to the SR input to 80 Hz and the data input to 50 Hz. Connect the three inputs and the output of the circuit to four inputs of the logic analyser. Note the waveforms displayed by the logic analyser (or CRO).
(c) Try different combinations of clock, data input and SR frequencies and estimate the optimum frequency ratios.
(d) At the receiving end of the system the reverse process has to be carried out to unscramble the data waveform. Devise a method of doing this and if time permits build the circuit and check its operation.

Digital receiver

The block diagram of an 11 GHz digital radio-relay receiver is shown by Fig. 13.11. The received signal is selected and band limited by the appropriate channel filter and then applied to a low-noise amplifier (LNA). It is then passed on to a down-converter where it is mixed with an 11 GHz signal to produce upper and lower sidebands. The lower sideband, centred on either 70 MHz or 140 MHz, is selected by the IF filter and

Fig. 13.11   *11 GHz digital radio-relay receiver*

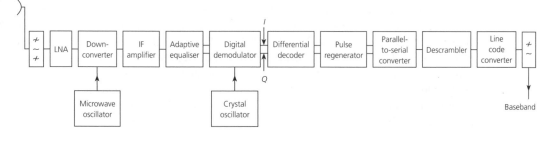

Fig. 13.12 *Digital relay station*

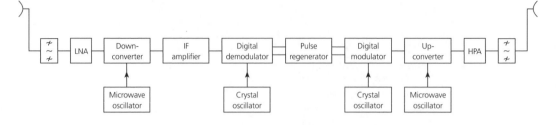

all unwanted frequency components are removed; it is then amplified, before it is applied to the digital demodulator. The input to the demodulator is equalised to remove distortion and perhaps (depending on the type of equaliser) compensate for multi-path fading.

In the demodulator a carrier recovery circuit extracts the clock timing information from the original bit stream and then uses it to synchronise the receiver to the distant transmitter. In a QPSK receiver this may consist of a circuit that by multiplying the received IF signal by 4 removes the phase modulation and gives a reference carrier at $4f_{IF}$. The I and Q bit streams of the demodulated signal are first pulse regenerated and then combined in the parallel-to-serial converter and the resultant bit stream is decoded and descrambled to reconstruct the bit stream. Lastly, the baseband signal is converted from NRZ into the PCM CMI format and frame alignment bits are added. Note that for 34 Mb/s systems the line code is HDB_3 instead of CMI.

Also, 18 GHz equipment operating at 2 Mb/s and 8 Mb/s is employed and often used to provide Megastream circuits.

Adaptive equaliser

Multi-path fading can cause fades as deep as 40 dB or more and to minimise errors caused by such fades an *adaptive equaliser* may be employed. This is an equaliser that has the ability to change its characteristics to suit the distortion suffered by the received signal. The use of an adaptive equaliser will improve the BER to almost the same figure as would be obtained in the absence of multi-path fading.

Digital relay station (or repeater)

A digital relay station, or repeater, consists of the back-to-back linking of parts of a receiver and a transmitter. Figure 13.12 shows the block diagram of the arrangement normally employed. The received signal is filtered and amplified before it is down-converted to the IF of either 70 MHz or 140 MHz. The IF signal is then amplified before it is applied to the digital demodulator to produce the I and Q bit streams. The I and Q signals are applied to the pulse regenerator and the regenerated bit streams are applied to the digital modulator. The modulated output signal is up-converted to the required transmitting frequency and then further amplified and filtered before it arrives at the transmitting aerial.

Aim: To investigate a serial-to-parallel converter.
Components and equipment: Two 74HC74 dual D flip-flops; one 74HC112 dual J–K flip-flop. Two pulse generators. Power supply. Breadboard. Logic analyser.
Procedure:

(a) Build the circuit given by Fig. 13.13.
(b) Set the clock frequency to 1 kHz and apply it to the clock input. Set the other pulse generator to 100 and connect its output terminal to the NRZ input terminal of the circuit. Observe the input and both output waveforms on the logic analyser.
(c) Vary the frequency of the NRZ data input signal to 50 Hz, 200 Hz and 250 Hz, and each time note the two output waveforms.
(d) Remove the NRZ data pulse generator and replace it with a two-way switch connected to logic 1 and logic 0. Use the switch to enter a random bit stream into the circuit. Note the input and output waveforms on the logic analyser.

Fig. 13.13

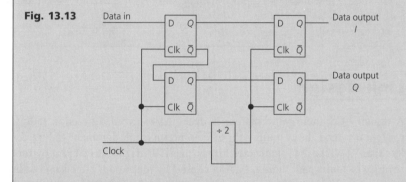

Aim: To investigate an NRZ-to-CMI converter
Components and equipment: One 74HC174 hex D flip-flop or two 74HC74 dual D flip-flops; one 74HC86 exclusive-OR gate; one 74HC02 quad 2-input NOR gate. Two pulse generators. Power supply. Logic analyser and/or CRO. Breadboard.
Procedure:

(a) Build the circuit given in Fig. 13.14.
(b) Set one pulse generator to 100 Hz 50% duty cycle and connect it to the NRZ input terminal of the circuit. Set the other pulse generator to 1000 Hz 50% duty cycle and connect it to the clock inputs of the three D flip-flops.
(c) Use the logic analyser to observe the waveforms at the NRZ input and the output terminals of the circuit. Vary the frequency of the NRZ input and note the effect on the output waveform.
(d) Vary the duty cycle of the NRZ input and observe the output waveform of the circuit.

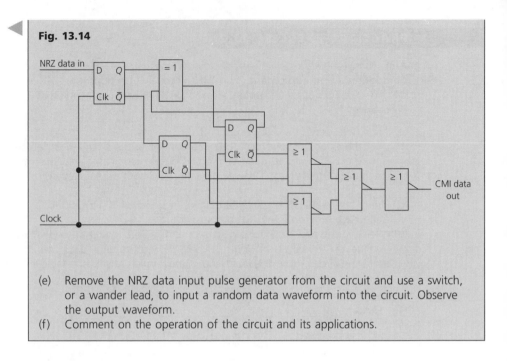

Fig. 13.14

NRZ data in

Clock

(e) Remove the NRZ data input pulse generator from the circuit and use a switch, or a wander lead, to input a random data waveform into the circuit. Observe the output waveform.

(f) Comment on the operation of the circuit and its applications.

Link design

A digital LOS radio-relay system is designed to avoid diffraction fading and surface reflections since these multi-path effects provide the dominant fading for frequencies less than 10 GHz. At frequencies higher than 10 GHz losses caused by rainfall limit the severity of multi-path fading. Fading caused by multi-path effects and fading caused by heavy rainfall are not cumulative; the fade margin is determined by the larger of the two and not their sum. Fading affects a digital system in a different way to an analogue system. In an analogue system fading reduces the output signal-to-noise ratio. In a digital system the *reflective fade margin* is

> the single-frequency fade depth in dB that is exceeded for the same number of seconds as the BER threshold, which is usually 1×10^{-3}.

If intersymbol interference (ISI) is to be avoided the multi-path delay, or dispersion, must be smaller than one-half a symbol period.

EXAMPLE 13.2

A digital radio system operates at a bit rate of 140 Mb/s (139 264 kb/s exactly). Determine the symbol rate when (a) 16QAM and (b) 64QAM is used as the modulation method.

Solution

$T = 1/(139\ 264 \times 10^3) = 7.18$ ns. Hence $T/2 = 3.59$ ns.

(a) The symbol period is four times as long at approximately 14.4 ns (*Ans.*)
(b) The symbol period $= 6 \times 3.59 \approx 21.5$ ns (*Ans.*)

Link budget calculations

The steps to be taken in the calculation of a link budget for a digital LOS system are as follows:

- Calculate the EIRP and the free-space loss.
- Add algebraically the free-space loss to all other losses such as feeder loss.
- Add the gain G_R of the receiving aerial.

Then the received power P_R is given by

$$P_R = \text{EIRP dBW} - \text{losses} + G_R \tag{13.3}$$
$$= P_T + G_T - L_{FS} - L_M + G_R \tag{13.4}$$

where P_T is the transmitted power, G_T and G_R are respectively the gains of the transmitting and receiving aerials, L_{FS} is the free-space loss ($= 10 \log_{10}(4\pi d/\lambda)^2$ dB $= 32.5 + 20 \log_{10} d$ dB $+ 20 \log_{10} f$ dB, where d is in km and f is in MHz), and L_M is the feeder and miscellaneous losses. If the frequency is quoted in GHz then the number 32.5 becomes 92.5.

Fade margin

A radio link must be planned to have a received signal which with zero fading provides a margin that is at least equal to the depth of fading that is to be expected. This safety factor is known as the *fade margin*. The fade margin of a radio-relay link is obtained by subtracting from equation (13.4) the receiver threshold level at which the carrier-to-noise ratio just gives the minimum acceptable BER.

EXAMPLE 13.3

A radio-relay link has the following parameters: $P_T = -6$ dBW, feeder losses $= 6$ dB at both transmitter and receiver, $G_T = 38$ dB, $G_R = 44$ dB and path loss $= 141$ dB. Calculate (a) the received power level and (b) the fade margin if the receiver threshold level is -108 dBW.

Solution

(a) $P_R = -6$ dBW $- 6 + 38 - 141 + 44 - 6 = -77$ dBW (*Ans.*)
(b) Fade margin $= -77 - (-108) = 31$ dB (*Ans.*)

EXAMPLE 13.4

A 28 km path is operated at 6.6 GHz to transmit 140 Mb/s signals using 64QAM. The required bandwidth is 30 MHz and the minimum BER is 2×10^{-6}. The radio receiver has a noise factor of 4 dB, the transmitting and receiving aerials both have a gain of 32 dB and feeder losses are 2 dB at each end. Calculate the necessary transmitted power for a fade margin of 18 dB.

Solution

$E_b/N_0 = 21.4$ dB

$N_0 = -204$ dBW + 4 dB $= -200$ dBW

Therefore,

$E_b = 21.4 - 200 = -178.6$ dBW

The received power is

$P_R = E_b + 10 \log_{10}$(bit rate)
$\quad = -178.6$ dBW + $10 \log_{10}(139\ 264 \times 10^3) = -97.16$ dBW

and the free-space loss is

$32.45 + 20 \log_{10} D$ (km) $+ 20 \log_{10} 6000$ (f in MHz)
$= 32.45 + 28.94 + 75.56 \approx 137$ dB

Then

$P_R = $ EIRP $- 137 + G_R - 2 = $ EIRP $+ 32 - 139 = $ EIRP $- 107$ dBW

EIRP $= P_T$ dBW $- 2 + 32 = P_T + 30$ dBW

If $P_T = 1$ W, then EIRP $= 0 + 30 = 30$ dBW, and $P_R = 30 - 107 = -77$ dBW, which gives a fade margin of $97.16 - 77 = 20.16$ dB. This is 2.16 dB more than is required. The transmitted power could be reduced by 2.16 dB or 1.64 times. Thus

$P_T = 1/1.644 \approx 610$ mW *(Ans.)*

EXAMPLE 13.5

A microwave link is 40 km in length and uses QPSK modulation to transmit signals at a bit rate of 140 Mb/s at 11 GHz. Identical transmitting and receiving aerials are used each having a gain of 48.64 dB. Total feeder losses are 12 dB and the receiver has a noise factor of 4 dB. Determine the required transmitted power for a minimum carrier-to-noise ratio at the receiver of 54 dB.

Solution

$L_{FS} = 32.5 + 20 \log_{10} 40 + 20 \log_{10}(11 \times 10^3) = 32.5 + 32.04 + 80.83 = 145.37$ dB

$G_T = G_R = 48.64$ dB

$$P_R = P_T - 145.37 - 12 + (2 \times 48.64) = P_T - 60.09 \text{ dBW}$$

The received noise power is *FkTB*. The bandwidth is

$$B \approx \text{(bit rate)}/2 = 70 \text{ MHz} \quad F = 4 \text{ dB}$$

Hence the received noise power is

$$2.51 \times 1.38 \times 10^{-23} \times 290 \times 70 \times 10^6 \approx 7 \times 10^{-13} \text{ W} = -121.5 \text{ dBW}$$

and the carrier-to-noise ratio (dB) is

$$54 = P_T - 60.09 - (-121.5) = P_T + 60.41$$

Therefore,

$$P_T = -6.41 \text{ dBW} \approx 0.23 \text{ W } (Ans.)$$

EXAMPLE 13.6

(a) Calculate the path loss for a 50 km route at a frequency of 11.2 GHz. (b) Calculate the fade margin for the route if total feeder and filter losses are 18 dB, the identical aerial gains are 48.5 dB, the average losses caused by water vapour and oxygen are 1 dB, and the transmitted power is 10 W. The receiver has a bandwidth of 80 MHz and a noise factor of 7 dB. Take the carrier-to-noise ratio for the threshold BER of 1 in 10^5 as 18 dB.

Solution

(a)   The path loss is

$$20 \log_{10}(4\pi D/\lambda) \text{ dB} = 20 \log_{10}[(4\pi \times 50 \times 10^3 \times 11.2 \times 10^9)/(3 \times 10^8)]$$
$$= 147.4 \text{ dB } (Ans.)$$

(b)   The overall loss is

$$147.4 + 18 + 1 - (2 \times 48.5) = 69.4 \text{ dB}$$

Therefore,

$$P_R = +10 \text{ dBW} - 69.4 = -59.4 \text{ dBW}$$

The noise level is

$$-204 \text{ dBW} + 10 \log_{10}(80 \times 10^6) + 7 \text{ dB} = -118 \text{ dBW}$$

and the normal carrier-to-noise ratio is

$$-59.4 - (-118) = 58.6 \text{ dB}$$

Now

fade margin = normal carrier-to-noise ratio − carrier-to-noise ratio at threshold error rate

and therefore,

fade margin = 58.6 − 18 = 40.6 dB (*Ans.*)

Tropospheric scatter systems

The basic principle of a tropospheric scatter system was discussed in Chapter 9. Such systems are only employed when no other alternative exists because they require the use of larger aerials and more expensive equipment than their LOS alternatives. A tropopsheric system can operate over water, or inaccessible terrain, or hostile countries.

The scatter angle (p. 280) determines the received power level in an inverse relationship, since P_R falls rapidly as the scatter angle is increased. Either frequency or space diversity, or perhaps both, is always employed to keep short-term fading within reasonable limits. The transmitted power is typically of the order of 10 kW.

EXAMPLE 13.7

A digital tropospheric scatter system operates at 139 264 kb/s at 5 GHz with a transmission loss of 248 dB and an aperture-to-coupling loss of 12 dB. The transmitting and receiving aerials both have a gain of 52 dB and the receiver has a noise factor of 5 dB. Total feeder losses are 3 dB at each end of the system and the transmitted power is 10 kW. The modulation method is QPSK. Calculate the ratio E_b/N_0 for the system.

Solution

$$EIRP = P_T - L_T + G_T = 10 \log_{10}(10\ 000) - 3 \text{ dB} + 52 \text{ dB}$$
$$= 40 - 3 + 52 = 89 \text{ dBW}$$

$$P_R = 89 \text{ dBW} - 248 - 12 + 52 - 3 = -122 \text{ dBW}$$

$$E_b/N_0 = -122 \text{ dBW} - 10 \log_{10}(139\ 264 \times 10^3) - 5 \text{ dB} + 204 \text{ dBW}$$
$$= -4.44 \text{ dB } (Ans.)$$

(If the appropriate curves of BER plotted against E_b/N_0 are available the BER can be determined.)

EXERCISES

13.1 For a radio-relay system that operates in a gigahertz band explain why (a) the transmitted power need only be a few watts, (b) a bandwidth of at least 50 MHz can be made available, (c) internal receiver noise is usually more important than external noise, and (d) tropospheric conditions may affect reception.

A signal-to-noise ratio of 15 dB is required at the output of a receiver that has a bandwidth of 18 MHz and a noise factor of 8 dB. Determine whether this signal-to-noise ratio can be obtained if the input signal power to the receiver is 3×10^{-11} W.

13.2 A radio link transmits at a bit rate of 140 Mb/s and the received power is −86 dBW. If the noise factor of the radio receiver is 5 dB calculate the ratio E_b/N_0.

13.3 A digital radio-relay link operates at 11.2 GHz and is 45 km long. Atmospheric losses are equal to 1.5 dB. The transmitted power is 10 W with 9 dB feeder losses and both the transmitting and receiving aerials have a gain of 49 dB. The receiver has an IF bandwidth of 80 MHz, a noise factor of 8 dB and feeder losses are 8 dB. The minimum carrier-to-noise ratio required for a BER of 1×10^{-6} is 18 dB. Calculate the fade margin.

13.4 Figure 13.15 shows the block diagram of another version of a 64QAM 140 Mb/s transmitter. Explain the function of each block.

Fig. 13.15

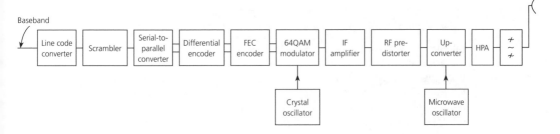

13.5 Describe the operation of the digital transmitter given in Fig. 13.8.

13.6 (a) State the digital hierarchies used in the UK and the USA.

(b) Why does a digital transmitter have a code converter?

(c) What is meant by a branching network in a digital transmitter and why is it used?

(d) Why is the performance of a digital LOS system described in terms of its E_b/N_0 ratio rather than signal-to-noise ratio?

(e) An LOS link operating at 140 Mb/s has a received power of −90 dBW. If the receiver has a noise factor of 7 dB calculate the E_b/N_0 ratio.

14 Communications satellite systems

After reading this chapter you should be able to:

(a) State why communications satellite systems are used and give various applications of satellite systems.
(b) Explain the basic principle of operation of a communications satellite system.
(c) State the various orbits that are used and state their relative merits.
(d) List the various operators of satellite systems.
(e) Calculate the overall carrier-to-noise ratio of a combined up-link/down-link path.
(f) Determine the G/T ratio of a satellite link.
(g) Explain the FDMA and TDMA methods of providing multiple access to a satellite and compare their relative merits.
(h) Give some ways in which the traffic-carrying capacity of a satellite may be increased.
(i) Draw and explain the basic block diagram of a transponder.

International telecommunication networks involve the use of copper and optical fibre cable, both underground and submarine, terrestrial radio-relay systems and communications satellite systems. The traditional application of satellite communication technology has been as an integral part of the international telecommunication network but this application is increasingly challenged by optical fibre systems. Today many international telephone circuits are provided by optical fibre systems. Communications satellite systems cannot compete effectively with optical fibre but they are expected to continue to carry a large proportion of the total long-distance traffic for a long time to come. Other satellite applications, such as television broadcasting, point-to-point business services, e.g. BT's SATSTREAM, and global positioning are also used.

The advantages of a communications satellite system over terrestrial systems are:

- Well suited to broadcast and point-to-multipoint services.
- Well suited to mobile communications.
- Cheaper to provide service to remote areas.
- Transmission costs are independent of distance.

Amongst the applications for communications satellite systems are:

- *The public switched telephone network* (PSTN). Satellite links are used to provide, alongside optical fibre land systems, international telephone circuits.

- *Business*. Increasingly, multi-national companies are leasing satellite capacity and integrating it with their own private telephone networks. In a business system the ground station may be located at the user's premises.
- *Very small aperture terminals* (VSATs). VSATs provide business services over low-traffic routes. A VSAT system is generally employed to allow a company to communicate simultaneously with a number of scattered offices. VSAT systems operate in the Ku band (11–14 GHz) with small, 1–2 m diameter, dish aerials.
- *Satellite news gathering* (SNG). SNG is the use of a mobile earth station to allow news to be transmitted live by up-link to a satellite and thence to the television studio in the home country.
- *Mobile services*. Global services to mobile users on land, on sea or in the air are provided by several organisations, the longest established of which is INMARSAT.
- *Satellite television broadcasting*. Satellite systems are used to broadcast television signals directly into the home.
- *Weather forecasting*. Weather satellites gather information about the weather and radio it by down-link to the weather forecast centre.
- *Global positioning system* (GPS). GPS is employed to track the positions of vehicles of all kinds.

Communications satellite systems

The basic principle of a communications satellite system is illustrated by Fig. 14.1. The satellite is positioned in a geostationary orbit which is 35 786 km above the earth in an equatorial plane. The ground stations are fully integrated with their national telephone networks and, in Europe, with each other. The *space segment* consists of the satellite communication equipment plus the satellite telemetry control equipment that is employed to keep the satellite in the correct orbit and facing in the right direction. The space segment is installed and operated by the satellite operating organisation, e.g. COMSAT. The *ground segment* is provided and operated by the telephone administration, or the licensed operator, in each individual country. The ground segment comprises

Fig. 14.1 *Communication satellite system*

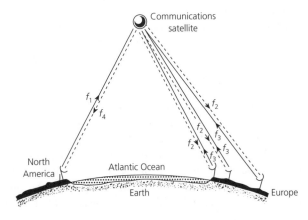

Fig. 14.2 *6 GHz transponder*

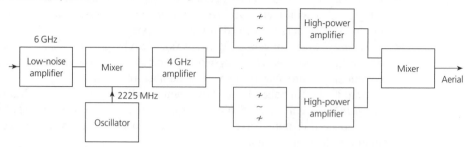

the transmitting and receiving radio equipment in each ground station. The ground stations act as national gateways to the terrestrial telephone network of each country and are directly connected to an international switching centre. A satellite is able to transmit to all locations on earth that are in its coverage area, or *footprint*. A footprint is obtained by the use of several aerials in the satellite. The radiation patterns of the individual aerials are combined to give the wanted beam shape. A satellite produces several different footprints which may cover a very wide area – only one footprint, for example, is needed to cover most of Europe. The onboard aerials are categorised as being *spot*, *zonal* or *global*: the radiated signal from a spot aerial covers a relatively small area of the earth's surface, a zonal aerial covers a much larger area, and a global aerial provides a footprint that covers approximately one-third of the surface of the earth.

Referring to Fig. 14.1, the North American ground station transmits up-link on frequency f_1 and receives down-link on frequency f_4, the European stations transmit up-link on frequency f_3 and receive down-link on frequency f_2. Depending upon the system these frequencies are either in the C band 4/6 GHz or in the Ku band 11/14 GHz. The higher-frequency band is used for the up-link and the lower frequency band is used for the down-link. Some communications satellite systems use the Ka band 27.5–30.5 GHz up-link and 1.7–20.2 GHz down-link.

The main disadvantage of a communications satellite system, other than its cost, is the transmission delay caused by the very long distance over which the signals have to travel. This transmission delay has little, or no, effect upon television signals but it introduces a delay of about 0.25 s into a telephone conversation that may be a little disconcerting to the speakers.

A satellite contains a number of wideband channels or *transponders*. Figure 14.2 shows the block diagram of a 6 GHz satellite transponder. The received 6 GHz signals are amplified by the low-noise amplifier (LNA) and are then mixed with a carrier to be down-converted to 4 GHz. The down-converted signal is filtered and amplified to a power level of, typically, 4 W. Signals transmitted by the satellite towards the earth are received by all the ground stations in the footprint of the satellite. The up-link and down-link equipment used in the ground station are shown by the block diagram in Fig. 14.3. The modulation scheme employed is some version of either PSK or QAM.

Each of the ground stations transmits its traffic to the satellite on the particular carrier frequency allocated to it in the frequency band 5.935–6.425 GHz, or 14–14.5 GHz. This is a bandwidth of 500 MHz and it allows the simultaneous use of a satellite by more than one ground station. The capacity of a satellite is shared between its

Fig. 14.3 *Ground station equipment (a) up-link and (b) down-link*

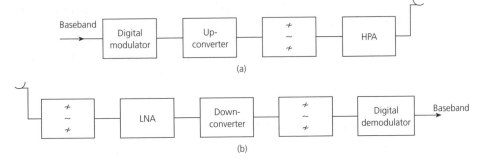

(a)

(b)

various users using either *frequency-division multiple access* (FDMA), *time-division multiple access* (TDMA) or *code-division multiplex* (CDMA). The number of telephone channels that can be provided to a user varies from 12 in a 2.5 MHz bandwidth to 1872 in a bandwidth of 36 MHz. All the signals transmitted to earth by a satellite are received by every ground station in the footprint; each ground station selects the particular carrier frequencies that have been allocated to it, in the frequency bands of either 3.7–4.2 GHz or 10.95–11.2 GHz and 11.45–11.7 GHz.

At frequencies up to the upper 6 GHz band the ground station must be located well away from a town or city to minimise interference from artificial (human) noise. In the UK the BT earth stations are located at Goonhilly in Cornwall and at Madely in Worcestershire. In the 11/14 GHz band, however, artificial noise is no longer a problem and the ground station can be near to a city. The BT Teleport, for example, is situated at North Woolwich, London.

Communications satellite orbits

Geosynchronous orbit

Communications satellites that provide circuits that are an integral part of the international telephone network have been placed in orbit at a height of 35 786 km above the earth in an equatorial plane. At this height the orbiting satellite has an orbital period of 23 hours and 56 minutes and keeps pace with the rotation of the earth, and so it appears to be stationary above a particular point on the earth's surface. This orbit is therefore known as the *geosynchronous orbit* (GEO). The advantages offered by the GEO are (a) since the satellite appears to be stationary, highly directive, and high-gain, aerials can be employed, and (b) each satellite has a large footprint. Disadvantages include a large path loss and a long propagation delay. GEO is used for television broadcasting and for point-to-point telecommunications.

Low-earth orbit

A satellite in low-earth orbit (LEO) is at a height above the earth of between 700 and 2000 km. When the satellite is at 700 km its orbital period is only 1 hour and 39 minutes. Using a satellite in LEO gives two advantages: (a) the path loss is relatively small and (b) the propagation delay is as small as possible. However, the use of

LEO incurs the following disadvantages: (a) the high orbital velocity means that high Doppler effects exist; (b) the footprint of each satellite is small so that many satellites are needed to provide global coverage – which means that much more complex ground stations are needed because of the satellite tracking requirements; and (c) there is a high probability of a satellite *hand-over* being required during the duration of a call. LEO is used for satellite mobile services such as IRIDIUM and these services must use omni-directional low-gain aerials.

Medium-earth orbit

Medium-earth orbit (MEO) is at a height of approximately 10 355 km above the earth with an orbital period of 5 hours and 59 minutes. The 'in between' orbit of an MEO satellite system means that it provides a compromise between the conflicting advantages and disadvantages of GEO and LEO systems.

Commercial operators

Commercial communications satellites are operated by a number of different organisations. Amongst these are:

- The Communication Satellite Corporation (COMSAT). COMSAT operates four GEO satellites in one equatorial plane on behalf of an organisation known as INTELSAT (International Telecommunication Satellite Consortium). COMSAT gives a full range of global fixed satellite services including switched telephony, VSATs and business. The capacity of an INTELSAT satellite has increased considerably since the first satellite was put into service in 1965. Table 14.1 gives a list of the various COMSAT satellites launched over the years since the launch of the first satellite in 1965.
- EUTELSAT. West European countries have launched their own GEO satellites, known as EUTELSAT, which are employed to carry both broadcast television signals and a full range of European fixed services such as switched telephony, VSATs and business systems. Table 14.2 gives details of the various EUTELSAT systems currently in operation.
- INMARSAT. This GEO system has four INMARSAT satellites and one INMARSAT 3 satellite and operates in the 4/6 GHz band (4 GHz up-link). It also has some capacity in INTELSAT satellites. INMARSAT provides a full range of global mobile satellite services including public switched telephony, packet-switched data (X25), telex and paging, and operates to maritime, aeronautical and land mobile terminals.
- The military. The military employs communications satellites for secure communications between troops in the field and their headquarters, but increasingly they make use of public commercial systems.
- ASTRA. ASTRA provides satellite television broadcasts to several countries in Europe, including SKY in the UK. The ASTRA system employs satellites 1A (16 transponders) to 1H (28 transponders) which were launched at regular intervals from 1988 to 1998. There are also two ASTRA 2 satellites with 28 transponders that were launched in 1998.

Table 14.1 INTELSAT systems

INTELSAT No.	Date of first launch	Bandwidth (MHz)	Transponders	Frequency (GHz)	Capacity
I	1965	50		6/4	240 channel
II	1967	130		6/4	or one TV
III	1968	300		6/4	1500 channel and four TV
IV	1971	500		6/4	4000 channel and two TV
IVA	1975	800		6/4	6000 channel and two TV
V	1980	2144	32	6/4 or 14/11	12 000 channel and two TV
VA	1985	2250	32	6/4 or 14/11	15 000 channel and two TV
VI	1987	3300	48	6/4 or 14/11	120 000 channel[†] and three TV
VII	1993	2432	40	6/4 or 14/11	112 500 channel[†] and three TV
VIII	1997		44	6/4 or 14/11	112 500 channel[†] and three TV
IX	(expected 2000)		56	6/4 or 14/11	140 000 channel and three TV

[†] Using digital circuit multiplication equipment (DCME). DCME provides circuit multiplication factors of up to four times by means of a combination of digital compression and interleaving techniques.

Table 14.2 EUTELSAT systems

EUTELSAT system	Date of first launch	Transponders	Uses
1	1983	10	Telephony and TV
2	1990	16	Telephony and TV
Hot bird	1996	20/22	TV
W series	1998	24	Telephony
Se sat	1989	18	Eastern Europe telephony/TV

- IRIDIUM. The IRIDIUM organisation provides communications to mobile hand-held telephones; 66 LEO satellites are employed in six separate planes inclined at 86.4° at 780 km. The satellites are linked together and are able to relay calls between each other. The system uses the 30 GHz band for the up-link and the 20 GHz band for the down-link. An international mobile telephone call will be transmitted from the mobile to its destination using either one of the two methods shown by Figs 14.4(a) and (b). The Ka band is 20–30 GHz.

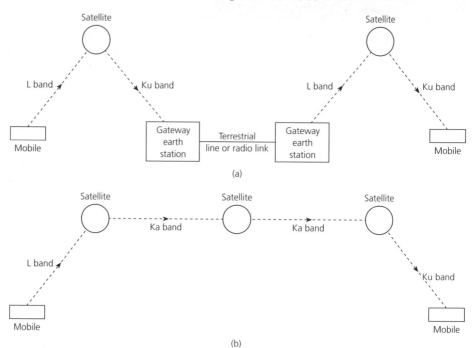

- Globalstar. Globalstar also provides services to mobile users with a system that has 48 LEO satellites in eight planes inclined at 52° at 1410 km. The system uses 6.5 GHz for the up-link and 5.2 GHz for the down-link.
- I-CO, a service to mobile telephones. This system uses 10 MEO satellites in two planes at 45° at 10 355 km. The up-link operates at 5 GHz and the down-link at 7 GHz.
- PanAmSat. This has seven GEO satellites serving South American and transatlantic users. It is used to carry television broadcast signals over the Atlantic.
- Teledisic. Teledisic has 24 LEO satellites in 12 different planes inclined at 98° and 700 km distant.
- Odyssey. This satellite system uses 112 MEO satellites in six planes inclined at 50° at 10 354 km.

Link design

The *power-link budget* of a satellite link is designed to take into account the following factors:

- The carrier-to-noise ratio.
- The modulation method.
- The multiple-access system.
- The ground-station transmitted power.
- The path loss for both the up-link and the down-link.

- The sensitivity of the satellite. This is generally measured in terms of the *gain/temperature ratio* (*G/T* ratio).
- Intermodulation and distortion.
- Interference from other microwave systems, terrestrial as well as satellite.
- Fading caused by heavy rain (at frequencies higher than about 11 GHz).

Carrier-to-noise ratio

The carrier-to-noise ratio of a satellite link is measured at the input terminals of the first amplifier (an LNA) in the receiving system. It is equal to C/N_0, where

$$C = P_R \text{ (dBW)} + G_R \text{ (dB)} - L_P \text{ (dB)} \tag{14.1}$$

and N_0 is the noise power density in a 1 Hz bandwidth $= kT = -228.6 \text{ dBW} + 10 \log_{10} T_{\text{syst}}$.

The most important carrier-to-noise ratio is at the terminal receiver. This ratio is the resultant of the carrier-to-noise ratio for both the up-link and the down-link and is given by

$$\text{carrier-to-noise ratio of satellite link} = 1/[(1/C/N_U) + 1/(C/N_D)] \tag{14.2}$$

EXAMPLE 14.1

A communications satellite system has a system noise temperature of 80 K. Calculate (a) N_0 and (b) the noise in a 5 MHz bandwidth.

Solution

(a) $N_0 = -228.6 + 10 \log_{10} 80 = -209.57 \text{ dBW Hz}^{-1}$ (*Ans.*)
(b) $N = -209.57 + 10 \log_{10}(5 \times 10^6) = -142.6 \text{ dBW}$ (*Ans.*)

EXAMPLE 14.2

Calculate the carrier-to-noise ratio of a satellite link if the up-link carrier-to-noise ratio is 102 dB and the down-link carrier-to-noise ratio is 94 dB.

Solution

Now 102 dB $\approx 1.59 \times 10^{10}$ and 94 dB $\approx 2.51 \times 10^9$. Therefore,

$$\text{carrier-to-noise ratio} = 1/[1/(1.59 \times 10^{10}) + 1/(2.51 \times 10^9)]$$
$$\approx 2.17 \times 10^9 \approx 93.4 \text{ dB} \ (\textit{Ans.})$$

The down-link signal levels at the receiving ground station are very low, typically of the order of -160 to -190 dBW. To obtain a sufficiently high E_b/N_0 ratio at the output of the demodulator it is necessary both to minimise noise and to increase the gain of the system.

Figure-of-merit or G/T ratio

In a communications satellite system the received power levels are always *very* small because of the extremely large distances involved. This means that the noise generated within the receiving system must be reduced to a minimum possible value in order to achieve a satisfactory carrier-to-noise ratio. There are two main requirements that must be satisfied in order to achieve this. First, the bandwidth must be as narrow as possible, and, second, the system noise temperature must be as low as possible.

If the system noise temperature is T_S then the noise power at the input to the demodulator is $P_{IN} = GkT_SB$, where G is the gain of the receiver from the RF input to the demodulator input. Since the received carrier power is P_R W the carrier-to-noise ratio at the demodulator input is

$$C/N = GP_R/(GkT_SB) = [(P_TG_TG_R)/kT_SB]/[\lambda/(4\pi D)]^2$$
$$= [(P_TG_T)/(kB)](\lambda/4\pi D)^2(G_R/T_S) \tag{14.3}$$

The carrier-to-noise ratio is proportional to the ratio (gain of receiving aerial)/(receiver system noise temperature), which is known as the *G/T* ratio.

$$G/T \text{ ratio} = G \text{ dB} - 10 \log_{10} T_S \tag{14.4}$$

Equation (14.3) is often written in the form

$$C/N_0 = \text{EIRP dBW} - L_P \text{ dB} - k \text{ dBWK} + G/T \text{ dB K}^{-1} \tag{14.5}$$

Since, for a given system, $[(P_TG_T/kB)](\lambda/4\pi D)^2$ is a constant, the performance of a communications satellite system can be improved by increasing its G_R/T_S ratio. The higher the *G/T* ratio the greater is the sensitivity of the ground station or satellite. A typical value for the *G/T* ratio is 40 dB K^{-1}. The *G/T* ratio is of constant value throughout a receiving system. The factors which affect the *G/T* ratio of a system are:

- The elevation angle of the aerial. The lower the elevation angle the larger will be the sky noise with a corresponding increase in T_S.
- Feeder losses. An increase in the feeder loss is the same as a reduction in the overall gain of the system and hence it reduces the *G/T* ratio.
- The gain of the LNA.

When the required *G/T* ratio for a satellite system has been calculated a safety margin must be employed to account for any errors in the estimation of losses. The larger the chosen safety margin the more reliable will be the system, but at the expense of increased costs. Typically, a safety margin of 5 dB is chosen.

EXAMPLE 14.3

The parabolic dish aerial used by the ground station of a communications satellite link has a diameter of 28 m and an illumination efficiency of 70%. The down-link operates at a frequency of 4 GHz. Calculate the *G/T* ratio of the system if the system noise temperature is 80 K.

Solution

$\lambda = (3 \times 10^8)/(4 \times 10^9) = 0.075$ m

The gain of the receiving aerial is

$\eta 4\pi A_e/\lambda^2 = (0.7 \times 4\pi^2 \times 14^2)/0.075^2 = 962\ 922.5$ or   59.8 dB

Also, $T = 80$ K $= 19$ dB K^{-1}. Therefore,

G/T ratio $= 59.8 - 19 = 40.8$ dB K^{-1} (*Ans.*)

EXAMPLE 14.4

Calculate the carrier-to-noise ratio for a 4 GHz down-link if the EIRP is 32 dBW, the G/T ratio is 30 dB K^{-1}, the free-space loss is 200 dB and other losses total 5 dB.

Solution

$P_R = 32 - 200 - 5 = -173$ dBW

$P_R + G/T = -173 + 30 = -143$ dBW

Therefore, with $B = 1$ equation (14.1) gives

carrier-to-noise ratio $= -143 - (-228.6) = 85.6$ dB (*Ans.*)

Modulation method

Modern communications satellites employ some form of digital modulation and this is usually QPSK or one of its derivatives, but QAM is also employed. Older satellites use frequency modulation.

Multiple access

Multiple access is the name given to the way in which the traffic-carrying capacity of a satellite can be considerably increased. It allows a large number of earth stations to be given simultaneous access to a satellite and it may employ either frequency-division or time-division techniques. The number of telephone channels made available to an earth station may be fixed (this is known as *fixed access*) or the allocated number may be assigned in response to the traffic demand (this is known as *demand access*).

Frequency-division multiple access

With FDMA each transmission to or from a satellite is allocated a specific bandwidth on a transponder. Several FDMA systems are able to share one transponder. A single ground station transmits a carrier which carries an FDM configuration to the satellite. Each ground station receives and demodulates the carrier from the satellite but it only de-multiplexes those channels that are addressed to it. With FDMA all the ground stations which share a communications satellite do so at the same time, each station being allocated its own part of the frequency spectrum of the transponder. The FDMA system is always employed in conjunction with both frequency modulation and frequency-division multiplexing. Each ground station is allocated one or more carrier frequency(ies) and it modulates all of its outgoing traffic, regardless of its destination, on to that carrier. Every ground station in the network must therefore be able to receive at least one carrier from all the other ground stations.

Large blocks of telephone channels are allocated to individual ground stations on a semi-permanent basis. The number of circuits required on each route can be calculated from traffic studies. For some routes which carry little traffic only a few circuits are required and this results in their having a poor availability. On some other routes there may not be enough traffic to justify economically the provision of even one circuit. In any case, because the telephone traffic varies with the time of day it is unlikely that all the allocated channels would be in use for all of the time. This means that the fixed access version of FDMA is inefficient.

On the routes with lower traffic density the bandwidth of the transponder can be divided into a large number of carriers and a particular channel allocated to each one. Each individual channel independently modulates a separate RF channel. Each channel may use either frequency modulation or some form of digital modulation (often QPSK). This system is known as *single-channel per carrier* (SCPC) working. The INTELSAT SCPC system employs 45 kHz spacing and either frequency modulation or BSK/QPSK modulation. SCPC channels can be either pre-assigned or allotted on demand.

If demand access is employed, a pool of channels is made available to all the ground stations. A channel is only assigned to a particular route between two ground stations as the demand arises. Each RF channel contains a narrow-band common signalling channel that is used to set up a link between two ground stations. The originating ground station sends a signal over the signalling channel that requests the other ground station to establish a link over a specified channel. When the distant ground station signals acceptance via the signalling channel the requested link is established over the specified channel and then communication can begin. When the connection is no longer required it is broken and the channel is returned to general availability status.

The main problem with FDMA occurs because of the use of a TWT as the final power amplifier. A TWT is at its most efficient when it is operated at, or near to, saturation, but this is also the operating condition that gives rise to the most distortion and intermodulation products. A TWT is hence operated 'backed off' in order to reduce intermodulation to a tolerable level. Because of the many intermodulation products generated using FDMA, or SCPC, the expression for the overall carrier-to-noise ratio of a satellite system (equation (14.2)) must be modified to give

$$\text{carrier-to-noise ratio} = 1/[(1/C/N_\text{U}) + (1/C/N_\text{D}) + 1/(C/N_\text{IM})] \qquad (14.6)$$

The number of demand–assignment telephone channels needed to carry a certain amount of telephone traffic can be reduced by the use of *digital speech interpolation* (DSI). DSI equipment monitors the telephone conversations and fills any gaps in the speech with speech from other calls. The activity is monitored by the DSI equipment and every time a speaker pauses the equipment may take away the channel and assign it to another call. A speaker will not be disconnected unless the channel is wanted for another active call. When the speaker speaks again a new channel is assigned. Since, on average, more than 50% of a conversation consists of silent intervals, the circuit capacity can be at least doubled.

FDMA is used for permanent direct and/or high-traffic routes but it is being phased out in favour of a digital system known as *Intermediate Data Rate* (IDR) which employs QPSK modulation at bit rates from 64 kb/s up to 44.736 Mb/s.

Time-division multiple access

TDMA is a technique employed with digital systems which allows a number of earth stations to have access to a common satellite transponder at different times. At any instant in time only one earth station has access to the transponder and it can use all of the available power. Individual time slots are assigned sequentially and give an earth station exclusive use of that transponder. INTELSAT and EUTELSAT systems operate at a bit rate of 120 Mb/s through a 72 MHz transponder. Each earth station takes its turn to transmit data through the transponder for a small fraction of the total time, as shown by Fig. 14.5. There is little distortion and zero intermodulation at the TWT final power amplifier because only one carrier is present at a time. This means that the TWT can be operated near saturation to give maximum power and high efficiency.

TDMA is more efficient than FDMA in its use of the available bandwidth, e.g. 450 FDMA channels and 900 64 kb/s TDMA channels occupy the same bandwidth. TDMA does not employ signal regeneration in the satellite, the transponder effectively acting as a down-converter. The bursts of data from each of the *n* users arrive at the satellite in a pre-assigned sequence. The bandwidth occupied by a burst depends upon the type of modulation used and it may, or may not, occupy the whole of the bandwidth of the transponder. As long as each ground station is able to maintain the correct instants for its bursts to start and to finish its bursts will not overlap those bursts generated by other ground stations. Relatively low-rate continuous digital information inputted to the ground station can be transmitted to the satellite in short bursts at a much higher bit rate. The *frame rate* is the periodicity with which these high-speed bursts are transmitted.

Fig. 14.5 *TDMA*

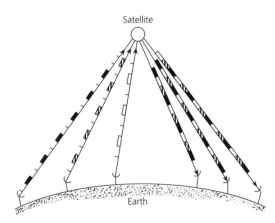

A TDMA system with a frame period of 2 ms and a transmission rate of 120 Mb/s can have a digital input at 10 Mb/s, i.e. 160 60 kb/s voice channels. At 10 Mb/s the ground station receives 5 kbits per 2 ms, which at the transmission rate of 120 Mb/s needs a burst of 167 μs duration. The remainder of the TDMA frame is then free for other users. In the INTELSAT systems the PCM digital signals that are transmitted have an 8 kHz sampling rate so that the pulses are 125 μs wide. The frame size is 2 ms and hence each traffic burst includes $(2 \times 10^{-3})/(125 \times 10^{-6}) = 16$ samples from each of the telephone channels being transmitted.

TDMA frame

A frame is a cycle of bursts; there is one burst per access to the satellite. The burst length can be controlled dynamically depending upon the traffic carried by each access. The number of accesses on a transponder may vary from three to about a hundred. A typical TDMA frame is shown by Fig. 14.6. The carrier recovery (CR) per bit timing recovery (BR) group of bits is used – CR for the recovery of the local carrier for the demodulator and BR for local clock synchronisation. The unique word establishes an accurate time reference in the received burst. This is used to align the local clock and also to act as an identifier for the transmitting station.

The basic block diagram of the equipment needed at each TDMA ground station is shown by Fig. 14.7. The input digital data is fed into a buffer store at 12 Mb/s and is read out of the store at the much higher rate of 120 Mb/s. Since the output bit rate is much higher than the input bit rate it is clear that the data can only be transmitted in short bursts. The bursts are repeated every 2 ms and for the same input and output information $12 \times 10^6 = (120 \times 10^6 T)/(2 \times 10^{-3})$, so the time duration T of a burst is 200 μs. Before it is transmitted each traffic burst must have a *preamble* added; the preamble is the name given to a number of bits which are added to the traffic burst to enable a distant earth station to receive the signal correctly. Preamble bits are generated in the TDMA equipment and added to the traffic burst by the burst assembler. The assembled burst is then applied to a QPSK modulator to produce a burst at the IF. The IF signal is then applied to the transmitting equipment to be frequency shifted to the allocated frequency band and then amplified before it is radiated from the aerial. A receiving earth station must demodulate the received carrier and then recover the synchronisation pulses before it will be able to identify the beginning of each frame. It will then be able to assemble the original telephony signal and pass it on to the destination.

A TDMA system must be synchronised to make sure that the traffic bursts originating from different ground stations do not overlap one another. The necessary synchron-

Fig. 14.6 *TDMA frame*

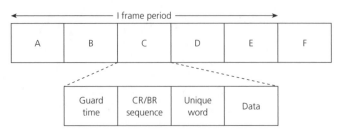

Fig. 14.7 *Ground station TDMA equipment (Courtesy of British Telecommunication Engineering)*

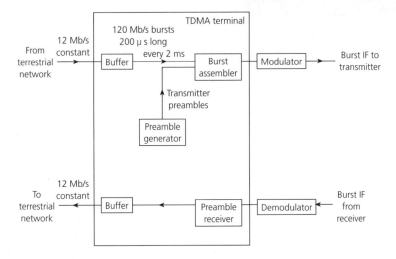

isation is obtained by the use of *reference bursts*. The reference bursts are transmitted by some of the ground stations and are received by all of the ground stations in the network. Each ground station must then ensure that its traffic bursts, with added preamble, are transmitted to the satellite at fixed times relative to each reference burst.

Traffic capacity

A communications satellite system is either bandwidth limited or power limited. When it is bandwidth limited the bit rate B_R is given by

$$B_R = \text{bandwidth (dB)} + \text{bit rate to symbol rate} - 0.75 \text{ dB} \tag{14.7}$$

EXAMPLE 14.5

A satellite transponder has a bandwidth of 38 MHz and handles a QPSK signal. Calculate the bit rate.

Solution

$$B_R = 10 \log_{10}(38 \times 10^6) + 10 \log_{10} 2 - 0.75 \approx 78 \text{ dB}$$

Therefore,

$$B_R = 10^{7.8} = 63.096 \text{ Mb/s } (Ans.)$$

When the channel capacity of a transponder is power limited the bit rate B_R is

$$B_R = \text{EIRP dBW} - L_P + G/T - k - E_b/N_0 \tag{14.8}$$

EXAMPLE 14.6

A communications satellite transmits an EIRP of +25 dBW. The ground station has $G/T = 38$ dB K^{-1} and the modulation method is QPSK. If E_b/N_0 is 10 dB, the path loss is 200 dB, and other losses total 6 dB, calculate the bit rate.

Solution

$$B_R = 25 \text{ dBW} - 200 \text{ dB} + 38 \text{ dB K}^{-1} - (-228.6) \text{ dBW} - 10 - 6 = 75.6 \text{ dB}$$

Therefore,

bit rate $= 10^{7.56} = 36.31$ Mb/s *(Ans.)*

The traffic capacity of each access can be instantaneously modified. The number of digital channels can be approximately doubled by the use of DSI (p. 410).

Code-division multiple access

With CDMA the transmitted signal is spread over part, or all, of the available transponder bandwidth in a time–frequency relationship by means of a code transformation. The same bandwidth is used by all carriers simultaneously but the signals are coded so that they do not interfere with one another. CDMA has been used by the military for some years because of its good security characteristics, but it is now also being used for some commercial systems. The modulated RF bandwidth is between 10 to 100 times greater than the information bandwidth.

Path loss

The path losses of the up-link and the down-link occur because of the inevitable divergence of the transmitted radio waves. The path loss is calculated in exactly the same way as for a terrestrial microwave link. The term $(4\pi D/\lambda)^2$ is known as the path loss. The carrier power P_R received at the end of an up-link or a down-link is given by

$$P_R = \text{EIRP}/(\text{path loss}) \tag{14.9}$$

EXAMPLE 14.7

A communications satellite is 40 000 km from a point on the earth's surface and transmits a power of 2 W from an aerial of 20 dB gain. Calculate the power received at the ground station by an aerial of effective aperture 10 m if the down-link frequency is 11 GHz.

Solution

Method (a):

$\lambda = (3 \times 10^8)/(11 \times 10^9) = 0.027$ m

The flux density at the receiver aerial is

$P_a = P_T G_T/4\pi D^2 = (2 \times 100)/(4\pi \times 40 \times 10^6)^2 = 9.95 \times 10^{-15}$ W m^{-1}

The received power is

$P_R = P_a A_e = 9.95 \times 10^{-15} \times 10 = 9.95 \times 10^{-14}$ W (*Ans.*)

Method (b):

path loss $= [(4\pi \times 40 \times 10^6)/0.027]^2 = 3.466 \times 10^{20}$

The gain of the receiving aerial is

$(4\pi A_e/\lambda^2) = (4\pi \times 10)/0.027^2 = 172\ 378$

Therefore,

received power $= (2 \times 100 \times 173\ 278)/(3.466 \times 10^{20}) = 9.95 \times 10^{-14}$ W (*Ans.*)

Distortion and intermodulation

The circuitry in a transponder is linear and hence it introduces little, if any, distortion and/or intermodulation, with the exception of the HPA. The HPA is either a TWT or a solid-state amplifier. For a TWT to deliver its maximum output power and hence to be operated under the conditions that give maximum efficiency, it must be fully driven by the input signal. This is also the condition when a TWT is non-linear and hence both distortion and intermodulation are likely to be generated. For this reason the TWT final amplifier is usually operated 'backed off' a little at the expense of reduced output power.

Interference

The frequency bands allocated to communications satellite systems are the same as those for terrestrial radio-relay systems. Hence a satellite can receive interfering signals proper to another satellite system. Figure 14.8 illustrates the problem. The utilisation of the geosynchronous orbit is limited because interference restricts the allowable minimum spacing between satellites. To minimise interference the ITU-R has specified (a) the maximum power density at the surface of the earth from a ground station, and (b) the maximum size of the sidelobes of the aerial radiation patterns.

Satellites in geosynchronous orbit must be sufficiently far apart for interference from up-links to adjacent (in the orbit) satellites not to be a problem. This means that

Fig. 14.8 *Interference between satellite links*

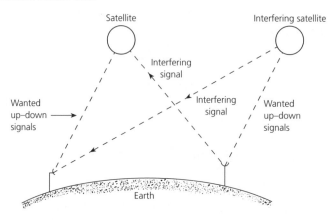

the earth stations must use highly directive aerials, and the ITU-R has specified the maximum sidelobe level which is allowable. The specified aerial gain G is

$$G = 29 - 25 \log_{10} \theta \text{ dBi} \tag{14.10}$$

where θ is the angular distance in degrees between satellites in geosynchronous orbit. Each degree corresponds to a span of about 700 km in that orbit.

EXAMPLE 14.8

A ground station requires an EIRP of 80 dBW in order to obtain the required signal-to-noise ratio at the satellite. Two parabolic dish aerials are available; one aerial has a gain of 40 dBi and, hence, a 40 dBW signal, the other aerial has a 60 dBi gain and a 20 dBW signal. Determine which aerial should be used if $\theta = 2°$.

Solution

Since both of the aerials are able to supply the wanted EIRP the choice of aerial is based upon the sidelobe levels of their radiation patterns. The first aerial will produce an interference EIRP of

$$40 + 29 - 25 \log_{10} 2 = 61.5 \text{ dBW}$$

The second aerial produces an interference EIRP of

$$20 + 29 - 25 \log_{10} 2 = 41.5 \text{ dBW}$$

Assuming the adjacent satellite also receives a wanted 80 dBW signal, the interference is 18.5 dB down for the first aerial and 38.5 dB down for the second aerial. Therefore the second aerial should be chosen. (*Ans.*)

Many satellite services share the 4/6 and 11/14 GHz frequency bands with terrestrial radio-relay systems and here again interference is possible. It is minimised by the use of highly directive aerials and polarisation. Modern ground stations include circuits known as *interference cancellation* which are able to detect, discriminate against, and then eliminate the interfering signals. The ITU-R recommendations restrict the permissible radiated power in the horizontal plane of both satellite earth stations and terrestrial radio-relay stations.

Fading

The path between an earth station and a communications satellite is LOS (if you have *very* keen eyesight!) and hence there are normally no obstacles to cause fading. Atmospheric attenuation varies with time, climate and frequency, being worse in the 11/14 GHz band than in the 4/6 GHz band. When the sky is clear the attenuation is low, of the order of 0.5 dB. When the sky is cloudy the attenuation starts to rise and when it rains increases rapidly. At 11/14 GHz the dimensions of raindrops in heavy rain are of the same order as the wavelength of the signal and this increases the loss to 10 dB or more.

Radiation techniques

The traffic capacity of a communications satellite can be increased still further by the use of spatial polarisation and polarisation diversity. Spatial polarisation means that separate transponders are employed for wide area coverage and for localised spot coverage of the earth. Polarisation diversity means that the same frequency band can be used without mutual interference by two separate signals if one signal is transmitted using horizontal polarisation and the other signal uses vertical polarisation. Alternatively, left- and right-hand circular polarisations are sometimes used.

Frequency reuse

The channel capacity of a transponder can be increased by *frequency reuse*. This term means that an allocated frequency band is used more than once. Interference between carriers at the same frequency but belonging to different transponders is reduced by orthogonal polarisation and multiple spot-beam aerials. The isolation between co-channel transponders should be at least 25 dB.

Ground stations and satellites

Space segment

A communications satellite acts like a microwave radio-relay station. It employs a transponder to relay, or repeat, signals received over the up-link from a ground station. A satellite will have several transponders whose characteristics and performance vary

Fig. 14.9 *INTESAT VI transponder*

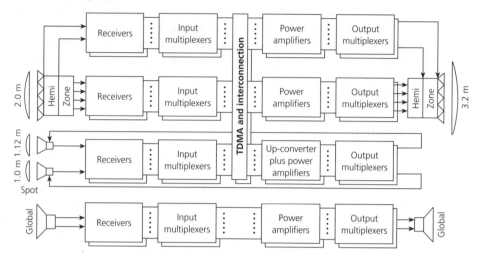

with the type of signals they are designed to handle. The typical transponder has a bandwidth of either 36 or 72 MHz and operates in either the C band (4–6 GHz) or the Ku band (11–14 GHz). Satellites are controlled and monitored by telemetry and command signals sent from ground stations. The equipment on board a satellite is of two sorts: (a) the *communications payload* and (b) the *satellite bus*.

The communications payload comprises the receiving and transmitting aerials, LNAs, down-converters, HPAs, input/output multiplex circuitry to separate/combine the radio channels corresponding to the transponders, and internal switching to enable specific ground stations to be interconnected. The beam coverage of the transmitting aerials is shaped to suit the destination service area, and may be global, hemispherical, zonal or spot. Figure 14.9 shows the basic block diagram of an INTELSAT V1 satellite transponder.

The satellite bus provides power to the communications payload, keeps the satellite pointed in the correct direction at all times, and maintains the internal temperature to within the specified limits.

Ground segment

The ground segment consists of the ground stations which are of a number of standard types. The basic block diagram of a ground station is shown by Fig. 14.10. The terrestrial interface acts as a national gateway and is used, via an international switching centre, to connect the ground station to the national network of the country. On the ground station side the interface is connected to the multiplexing/de-multiplexing equipment. In the direction terrestrial-to-satellite the input signals are combined to produce a composite signal for transmission to the satellite. The composite signal is applied to the modulator and the modulated output signal is up-converted to the up-link frequency band. The up-converted signal is amplified by the HPA, which is either a TWT or a solid-state circuit, and then passed on to the dish aerial.

Fig. 14.10 *Ground station*

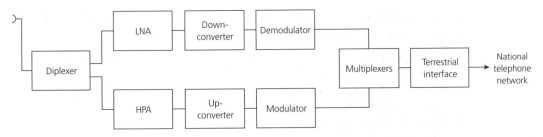

In the direction satellite-to-terrestrial the received signal is applied to the LNA for amplification before it is down-converted and then demodulated. The demodulated composite signal is then applied to the de-multiplexing equipment where the different baseband signals are separated before they are passed via the terrestrial interface to the national telephone network of the country.

INTELSAT

The INTELSAT organisation provides a number of different ground-station types that are labelled alphabetically.

- **INTELSAT A:** Used to provides international telephony and television links in the C band. The ground stations have a G/T ratio of 35 dB K^{-1} at 4 GHz and employ large aerials (diameter 15–18 m) that have a beamwidth of about 0.3°. The transmitted power is of the order of 5 kW giving an EIRP of about +90 dBW. In some cases two 5 kW transmitters are used, one for telephony and the other for television, and their outputs are combined. SCPC is used to cater for traffic overflow during busy periods and to provide service over low-traffic routes.
- **INTELSAT B:** Type B ground stations are smaller than type A ground stations and operate in the 4/6 GHz band with a G/T ratio of 31.7 dB K^{-1} and employ QPSK/SCPC. The EIRP is likely to be in the range 84.5–93.7 dBW. They provide a limited range of services.
- **INTELSAT C:** Type C ground stations operate in the 11/14 GHz Ku band to provide a full range of services. The G/T ratio is 37 dB K^{-1}, the EIRP is in the range 85–90.3 dBW, and the aerials have diameters of 11–14 m.
- **INTELSAT D:** Type D ground stations operate using SCPC with a 30 kHz channel bandwidth to provide telephony services over low-traffic routes. The G/T ratio is either 22.7 or 31.7 dB K^{-1} and the EIRP is either 48.8–51.7 dBW or 53.2–55.6 dBW. The aerials have a diameter of either 5–6 m or 11 m.
- **INTELSAT E:** Type E ground stations are used to provide business services in the Ku band and have a G/T ratio of typically 30 dB K^{-1}. Aerial diameters are 3.5–10 m.
- **INTELSAT F:** Type F ground stations operate to provide business services in the 4/6 GHz C band. The G/T ratio is typically 25 dB K^{-1} and the aerial diameters are 5–10 m.
- **INTELSAT G:** These are non-standard terminals whose use is decided by the leasee who is required to comply with the ITU-R recommendations.

EUTELSAT

The EUTELSAT organisation also provides more than one kind of communications satellite system. The types of system available are:

- **EUTELSAT I:** Used for public telephony in the Ku band using aerials of diameter 3.5–10 m. The G/T ratio is 26–34 dB K^{-1}.
- **EUTELSAT L:** Satellites of this type are leased by the private user. The user must satisfy the ITU-R requirements.
- **EUTELSAT M:** Business service satellites. The user must conform with the ITU-R recommendations.
- **EUTELSAT S:** Open business services. The G/T ratio is 23–30 dB K^{-1}.
- **EUTELSAT T:** Satellites devoted to long-distance telephony. The G/T ratio is 37 dB K^{-1}.
- **EUTELSAT V:** Type V satellites are used for television transmissions only. The G/T ratio is 26–31 dB K^{-1}.
- **EUTELTRACS:** This is a commercial mobile satellite service that provides two-way data exchange and vehicle position reporting for transport firms. Each transport firm has a control point from which messages can be sent, and received, to/from vehicles somewhere in Europe. The dispatch centre is also able to determine the location of a vehicle. Each vehicle has an onboard *mobile communications terminal* (MCT) which allows the driver of the vehicle to transmit/receive messages to/from base.

INMARSAT

INMARSAT uses four GEO satellites to provide air, land and maritime mobile communications.

- **INMARSAT A:** Used for maritime telephony, telex, FAX and data up to 64 kb/s. Aerial diameters of 1 m provide a G/T ratio of about −4 dB K^{-1}. The maximum EIRP is 36 dBW.
- **INMARSAT B:** This is a digital version of INMARSAT A. Voice signals are transmitted at 16 kb/s in a 24 kb/s channel. The maximum EIRP is 33 dBW.
- **INMARSAT C:** This system uses store-and-forward techniques to provide messaging, data, electronic mail, safety/meteorological information and paging. A mobile terminal is physically small enough to fit inside a briefcase-sized container and so it is used by small maritime mobiles such as yachts. It has an EIRP of 12 dBW and a G/T ratio of −23 dB K^{-1}.
- **INMARSAT D:** Provides paging services. If has a G/T ratio of −26 dB K^{-1}.
- **INMARSAT E:** An emergency position indicating and position reporting system.
- **INMARSAT F:** This provides aeronautical voice and data communications. It has a maximum EIRP of 26 dBW and a G/T ratio of −13 dB K^{-1}.
- **INMARSAT H:** Also known as *Skyphone*. Skyphone is provided in long-haul jet aircraft for global voice and 2.4 kb/s data/FAX services.
- **INMARSAT I:** Similar to H but intended for aircraft flying over shorter distances.
- **INMARSAT M:** This system provides low bit-rate (6.4 kb/s) encoded voice data and FAX communications for smaller sea-going vessels, but also finds some land

applications since a terminal is briefcase sized. The maximum EIRP is 24 dBW and the G/T ratio is -10 to -12 dB K^{-1}.

Global positioning system

The *global positioning system* (GPS) is a 24 satellite LEO system that enables users to determine their position accurately on the surface of the earth. Each satellite simultaneously transmits a time code and each user receives the time code signal from at least four satellites. The time it takes for each signal to arrive at the user's receiver depends upon the distance it had to travel. The receiver is able to make use of the time delays of the received signals to determine its exact location – including its altitude. A GPS system can be used to guide a user to his or her destination giving visual and audible instructions. If a traffic jam, or other delay, should occur the system is able to calculate an alternative route, or should the user take a wrong turn the system will recalculate the route.

London teleport

The term *teleport* is used to indicate an inner-city earth station that provides specialised telecommunication services. BT's London teleport provides transmission facilities for both satellite radio and television companies and commerce. The business services include the transfer of data and electronic money for banking concerns and the share prices for stock exchanges. The aerials at the teleport are able to access the GEO satellites of INTELSAT and EUTELSAT for telecommunications and of ASTRA and PanAMSAT for television/radio broadcast signals. The basic arrangement of a teleport television broadcast satellite service is shown by Fig. 14.11. Programmes are passed by the television company from its studio to the BT Tower in central London over either a land line or a radio link. At the BT Tower the signal is switched over another land line to the London teleport; here the signal is transmitted up to the appropriate satellite and then radiated down to earth for reception by television receivers.

Other telecommunication facilities provided by London teleport include SatStream, video conferencing, computer data transfer, and telecommunications such as speech, data, telex and FAX for users who have leased a private circuit.

Fig. 14.11 *TV studio to satellite link via teleport*

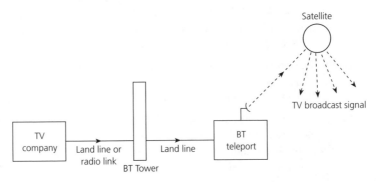

14.1 Calculate the EIRP needed for a power density at a satellite of -90 dBW m^{-2} if the distance between the satellite and earth station is 37 300 km and atmospheric losses total 2.8 dB.

14.2 A down-link operates at 14 GHz. Calculate the G/T of the ground station if $G_R = 48$ dB, feeder losses etc. $= 3$ dB, the LNA has $G = 30$ dB and $F = 3$ dB, and the down-converter has $F = 15$ dB. Sky noise $= 62$ K.

14.3 The signal level at a ground station is -148 dBW. The receiving system has $G_R = 55$ dB, $L = 2.5$ dB and $T_{sys} = 120$ K. Calculate the carrier-to-noise ratio.

14.4 Calculate the required G/T ratio for an up-link operating at 7 GHz with an EIRP of 65 dBW. The carrier-to-noise ratio at the satellite is to be 96 dB. The free-space loss is 210 dB and miscellaneous losses total 5 dB.

14.5 The INMARSAT H system has the following parameters: EIRP $= 25.5$ dBW, G/T ratio $= -13$ dB K^{-1}, $C/N_0 = 44.2$ dB Hz^{-1} for 1×10^{-3} BER, LNA noise figure $= 1.8$ dB. Explain the meaning of each parameter.

14.6 A communications satellite may be in any one of GEO, LEO or MEO. (a) Explain what each term means. (b) Discuss their relative merits for TV broadcasts, fixed telecommunications, and mobile telecommunications.

14.7 Two earth stations are 9650 km apart and are equidistant from a communications satellite that is in orbit at a height of 35 786 km. The up-link operates at 6 GHz and the down-link at 4 GHz. The satellite has a gain of 113 dB and the earth station aerials are each 16.4 m in diameter and have an illumination efficiency of 60%. Calculate (a) the overall path loss and (b) the transmission delay. Assume flat earth between the earth stations.

14.8 A communications satellite has an EIRP of 35 dBW and a path loss of 194 dB. (a) Calculate the received power if the receiving aerial has gain of 42 dB. (b) If the noise temperature of the waveguide feeder is 38 K, the LNA has a gain of 48 dB and a noise temperature of 122 K, and the receiver has a noise temperature of 4000 K and a bandwidth of 27 MHz, calculate the carrier-to-noise ratio at the demodulator input.

14.9 The down-link of a satellite system operates at 21.5 GHz with a receiving aerial gain of 44 dB. Feeder losses are 2 dB. The receiving system has the following data: LNA, gain $= 28$ dB, F $= 2.9$ dB; mixer, F $= 12$ dB. If the aerial noise is 62 K calculate the G/T ratio of the ground station.

14.10 The power received by a ground station on the down-link from a satellite is -160 dBW. The receiving aerial has a gain of 48 dB and feeder losses total 2 dB. If the system noise temperature is 117 K calculate the carrier-to-noise ratio.

14.11 Explain what is meant by the G/T ratio of a ground station. The receiving aerial used by a ground station has a diameter of 30 m and an illumination efficiency of 60%. Calculate the G/T ratio at a frequency of 4.2 GHz if the system noise temperature is 80 K.

14.12 A communications satellite system uses 8PSK to provide a 140 Mb/s link. The ground-station receiving system has $T_S = 380$ K and the carrier-to-noise ratio is 18 dB. Calculate (a) the E_b/N_0 ratio, (b) the received noise power, and (c) the received carrier power. Assume the noise bandwidth is 20 times greater than the theoretical minimum bandwidth.

14.13 (a) Explain why the ratio E_b/N_0 is used instead of the ratio S/N to assess the performance of a digital system.

  (b) Distinguish between C/N and S/N.

  (c) Calculate the C/N for a ground-station receiving system if $C = -80$ dBW, $T_S = 184$ K and the noise bandwidth is 30 MHz.

15 Mobile radio systems

After reading this chapter you should be able to:

(a) Discuss the differences between PMR and public mobile telephony.
(b) Understand why selective signalling and CTCSS may be employed in PMR systems.
(c) Explain why trunking is often employed and describe how it works.
(d) Understand the principle of cellular radio.
(e) State the difference between a macrocell, a microcell and a picocell.
(f) Determine the reuse ratio of a cellular system.
(g) Quote the main parameters of the GSM system.
(h) Explain how the GSM system achieves (i) location updating, (ii) hand-over, (ii) calling a wanted mobile telephone.
(i) Draw and explain the basic architecture of a GSM network.
(j) Compare and contrast the access techniques employed in a GSM network.
(k) Explain how (i) CT2, (ii) DECT and (iii) DCS 1800 differ from GSM.
(l) Draw and explain the operation of the block diagram of a mobile telephone.

Many organisations, both private and public, depend upon mobile radio systems for the operation of their business. Examples of mobile services are many and include (a) *emergency* (ambulance, fire and police services), (b) *utilities* (electricity, gas and water), and (c) *private* (delivery vans, service technicians, mini-cabs and taxis). Despite the inclusion of the emergency services and the utilities these land mobile services are generally lumped together and referred to as the *private land mobile radio* (PMR) service. This is to distinguish those services that do *not* have access to the public switched telephone network (PSTN) from the *public* land mobile services that do have such access. A version of PMR is *public-access mobile radio* (PAMR) which offers PMRs rented access to the PSTN. Public mobile telephone services employ cellular technology. The first cellular systems were introduced in the UK in the early 1980s and employ analogue techniques. In the early 1990s a digital system, known as the *Global System for Mobiles* (GSM), was introduced and this has since been augmented by DCS 1800 (*Digital Cellular System 1.8 GHz*). Cordless telephones have been used since the end of the 1970s, which allow a handset to be used anywhere in the home or garden up to a distance of about 100 m from the base station. Modern digital cordless telephone systems are known as CT2 and DECT (*Digital Enhanced Cordless Telecommunications*).

There are a wide variety of other radio services in use today, such as paging systems, garage door opening systems, and car door opening and engine immobilisation remote controls.

Private land mobile radio

A PMR system is used when there is a need for features that are not available on the public land mobile systems. These features include: (a) dispatcher control for fleet management (a control room may need to contact a large number of mobiles simultaneously and individuals can be sent off on various jobs), (b) different group call types, and (c) short connection times (the average PMR call lasts for only a few seconds and is often urgent, demanding immediate connection). The basic arrangement of a PMR system is shown by Fig. 15.1. The system operates in the *single-frequency simplex mode*. This means that one frequency is used for both directions of transmission and only one person at a time is able to speak. Each mobile transceiver is in radio contact with the control room, or dispatcher, which is sited at the base station.

Most PMR systems are operated using *double-frequency simplex*. This means that two frequencies are used for each call between the base station and a mobile, one frequency for the base-to-mobile direction and the other frequency for the mobile-to-base direction. Although the double-frequency method appears to be wasteful of the frequency spectrum it allows different systems operating at the same frequency to be more closely spaced by a factor of about 3. Since carrier frequencies are allocated on an area basis approximately nine times as many channels can be accommodated in a given area. Since two frequencies are used per call there is a frequency saving of about 4.5 times. Double-frequency operation also gives another advantage; since all base station transmitters are allocated carrier frequencies in one frequency band and all mobile transmitters are given carrier frequencies in another band, the provision of the required adjacent-channel selectivity in the receivers is much easier.

To increase the service area of a PMR system a number of base stations may be interconnected as shown by Fig. 15.2. Several double-frequency RF channels are made available to a system but the mobiles are not allocated any particular carrier frequencies; instead each mobile is allotted an RF channel on demand. The allocation of the frequency bands for different PMR systems is made by the radio telephony administration of the country, which in the UK is the Radio Communications Agency. Blocks of frequencies are selected within a frequency band to give the largest possible number of

Fig. 15.1 *PMR*

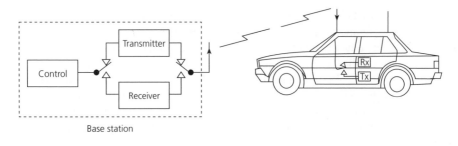

Base station

Fig. 15.2 *Interconnection of PMR base stations*

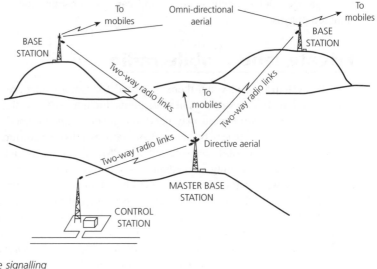

Fig. 15.3 *Five-tone signalling*

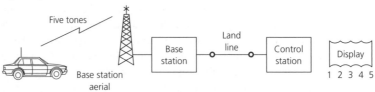

RF channels with the minimum intermodulation. Some examples of the frequency bands allocated to different PMR services are given in Table 11.1 on p. 330.

Selective signalling

In the simple PMR system each mobile must be switched on at all times and the vehicle driver must listen continuously for his or her call sign, or number, to be broadcast by the network controller. This method of operation is known as *open channel* and it has two disadvantages:

1 The need for the driver to listen for any incoming calls.
2 A lack of confidentiality – all other mobiles can also hear the message.

Five-tone signalling

To overcome these disadvantages *five-tone signalling* may be employed. Figure 15.3 shows the basic arrangement of a five-tone signalling system. All the mobiles automatically monitor the codes transmitted by the base station and when a mobile recognises its code it automatically answers the call. An audible alarm is given to alert the driver that he or she is being called. As soon as the driver responds to the call the receiver automatically transmits its code to the base station to acknowledge receipt of the call. Each code consists of five tones that are sequentially transmitted. When a mobile initiates a call its code is transmitted to the base station and then passed on to the control where the number of the calling mobile is displayed on a screen.

Fig. 15.4 *Talkthrough controlled by CTCSS*

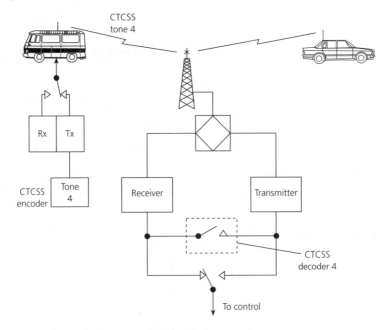

Continuous tone-controlled squelch system

A number of extra facilities can be provided for a PMR system if a *continuous tone-controlled squelch system* (CTCSS) is employed. CTCSS modulates the RF carrier frequency with one of six LF tones. The frequencies of the six tones are: 67, 74.4, 79.7, 85.4, 91.5 and 97.4 Hz. The tones are filtered out at the receiving station so they are not audible. CTCSS provides the following features:

- Remote selection of a facility, such as talkthrough.
- Minimisation of co-channel interference.
- Selective calling of base stations.

Talkthrough

Talkthrough means that a base station can be used as a repeater, or relay, station to allow two mobiles to communicate with one another. The way in which CTCSS can be employed to provide talkthrough is shown by Fig. 15.4. The mobile transceiver is set to operate on one of the six tones (number 4 in the figure) and the CTCSS decoder in the base station is set to respond to this tone only. When the mobile transmits tone 4 the base station operates the talkthrough facility to complete a link between its receiver and transmitter. The mobile is then able to communicate with another mobile.

Co-channel operation

Co-channel interference is minimised by the use of CTCSS. When a CTCSS signal is present in a transmitted signal that is received by a number of mobiles fitted with CTCSS decoders, only the receiver that is set to the same tone will receive that signal. All other CTCSS receivers will be muted. The concept of co-channel reduction is illustrated by Fig. 15.5.

Fig. 15.5 *Co-channel interference reduced by CTCSS*

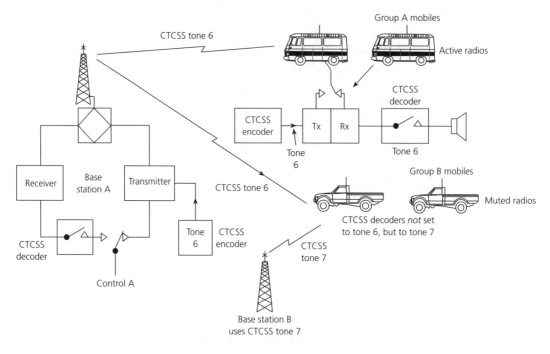

Fig. 15.6 *Selective calling of base stations using CTCSS*

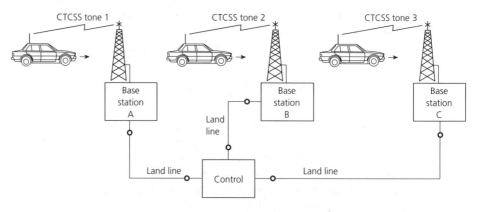

Selective calling

Selective calling of a base station is employed in a PMR system with a number of base stations. Each base station is fitted with a CTCSS decoder which is set to a different tone. A mobile can set its CTCSS encoder to the tone of the base station which gives the best signal strength for the mobile's current location. Figure 15.6 shows the basic concept of selective calling.

Fig. 15.7 *(a) Conventional PMR may block calls, (b) Trunked PMR allows mobiles access to any free channel*

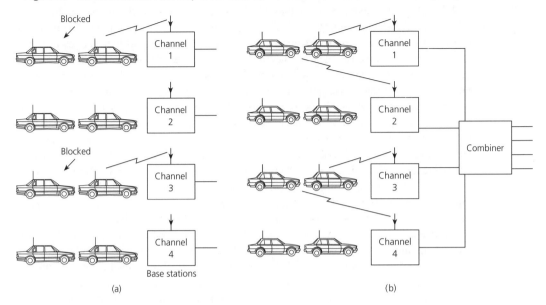

(a) (b)

Trunked PMR systems

A conventional PMR system will often have some of its dedicated RF channels idle for much of the time with a consequent reduction in efficiency. Sometimes one or more channels may be congested while other channels are free but it is not possible to switch one of the free channels to help with the congestion. This means that a user who finds a channel is busy must make repeated attempts to set up a wanted call. Congestion in a conventional PMR system is shown by Fig. 15.7(a). The problem can be overcome by the use of *trunking*.

The basic concept of a trunked PMR system is shown by Fig. 15.7(b). A common 'pool' of RF channels is shared by all the mobiles connected to the system; any mobile can have exclusive use of any free channel whenever it is needed. A controlling computer allocates a free channel for each call and when a call is finished that channel is returned to the pool for use by other mobiles. A trunked system may be operated by a single company or shared by several different companies who do not want the expense of setting up and maintaining their own network. Up to 20 RF channels, in the frequency band 174–225 MHz, each with its own base station, provide coverage of a geographical area. Each mobile in a trunked system is registered with its home base station and is identified by a unique address codeword. When a mobile moves away from its home area it will automatically register with the base station of the area into which it has entered. The new location of the mobile is notified to the home base station by the new base station, and the home base station will then automatically route any calls to the mobile via the new base station. Networks that contain more than about 100 base stations exist and such large networks employ *regional traffic area switching centres* (TASCs) and all base stations are connected to their nearest TASC. The TASCs are fully interconnected with one another.

A trunked PMR system requires the provision of a control channel to which all mobiles are connected whenever they are in communication with another mobile. The allocation of free channels to mobiles is under the control of a computer. To initiate a call a mobile contacts its base station via the control channel and then passes it details of the wanted connection. The connection request is then passed on to all the relevant switching centres and when a connection has been established the calling mobile is notified. As each call terminates the channel that was used is returned to the pool to become available for use by another mobile. Each base station is connected to the control channel for an exclusive period of time. This time period is divided into 20 time slots with the base station and the mobiles using the same time slot on a 'turn-around' basis. Hence, if a mobile makes a call request in time slot 4 the base station will send an acknowledgement in time slot 5. The system employs 100 baud FSK signals and the MPT 1327 signalling protocol ensures efficient half-duplex use of the channels and rapid call set-up. Base stations transmit a power level of up to 50 W in the frequency band 146–225 MHz, and receive signals in the band 390–512 MHz.

A dedicated control channel is used, but if all the traffic channels are busy the control channel may also be used to carry traffic. Then, the first channel to become free will become the control channel. When all channels are busy any further attempts to make a call are placed in a queue with emergency calls being given priority. Callers are automatically called back when a connection has been established and the called number has answered. Because mobiles have access to a larger number of RF channels the average waiting time before a call is set up is considerably reduced.

Figure 15.8 shows how each base station is linked to a switching centre which, in turn, is fully interconnected with the other switching centres in the system.

Fig. 15.8 *Trunked PMR system links base stations via switching centres*

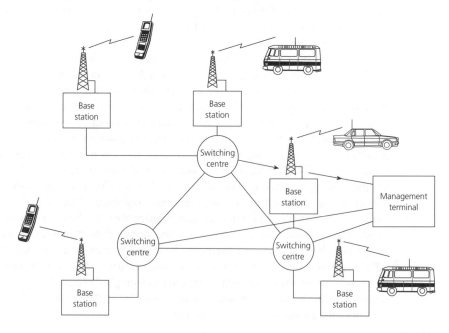

Trans-European trunk radio

Trans-European trunk radio is a suite of standards for digital PMR that were developed under the control of the European Telecommunications Standards Institute (ETSI). The TETRA system is intended to provide both simplex and duplex telephone calls, broadcast calls and mobile-to-mobile calls. The system is able to transmit data simultaneously with voice messages on the same RF channel. All calls, voice or data, are converted into digital packets of information and these are transmitted in sequential time slots.

A single call may occupy one, two, three or all four time slots to obtain a required bit rate. This feature is known as *bandwidth on demand*. The signals in each time slot are transmitted at a bit rate of 9 kb/s but this figure is reduced by signalling etc. bits to 7.2 kb/s. Four calls can be multiplexed onto each 25 kHz channel and hence bit rates of 7.2, 14.4, 21.6 and 28.8 kb/s are possible.

Cellular radio systems

The fundamental principle of cellular radio systems is that the available frequency spectrum is able to support a large number of users by means of trunking and *frequency reuse*. Each radio frequency is used at a number of different locations within the area covered by the system that are sufficiently far apart to avoid co-channel interference. PMR systems in the UK employ cellular radio technology and there are four operators: Cellnet, Vodaphone, Orange and One2one. The first two companies offer both an older analogue system known as the *Total Access Communication System* (TACS) and a modern digital system known as *Global System for Mobiles* (GSM). Both TACS and GSM operate at the following carrier frequencies in the 900 MHz band:

- **TACS:** mobile-to-base 872.0125–904.9875 MHz; base-to-mobile 917.0125–949.9875 MHz;
- **GSM:** mobile-to-base 890–915 MHz, base-to-mobile 935–960 MHz.

Both Orange and One2one offer a digital *Personal Communication Network* (PCN) system using a technology known as *Digital Communication System* (DCS 1800) at 1.8 GHz.

Cellular structure

A geographical area, usually a country, served by a cellular radio system is divided up into a large number of small areas or *macrocells*, each of which has its own base station. Base stations in geographically nearby cells are assigned channel groups that contain different channels. By limiting the coverage area of each base station, the same groups of channels can be used for different cells which are separated from one another by a distance large enough to keep co-channel interference within acceptable limits. This practice is known as frequency reuse. Figure 15.9 illustrates the concept of frequency reuse. The base stations are nominally sited at the centre of a macrocell but, in practice, their positions will vary somewhat. The macrocells, or just cells, are grouped in clusters

Fig. 15.9 *(a) Three 7-cell clusters (b) Frequency allocation for each cluster in (a)*

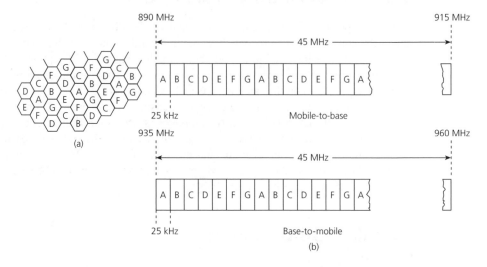

(a)

(b)

and the available bandwidth is allocated to each cluster. Regular patterns of cell clusters are then used to give complete coverage of the geographical area. In this way, each RF channel can be used several times throughout the coverage area in a regular manner. The number of cells per cluster has to be chosen so that the clusters will fit together into contiguous areas. The cells are ideally of hexagonal shape so that they fit closely together without overlap. Only clusters with 4, 7, 12 or 21 cells are suitable; most commonly employed is the seven-cell cluster since it gives the best compromise between co-channel interference and traffic capacity. Because the power transmitted by each base station is restricted maximum use of the available frequency spectrum can be achieved by frequency reuse. Base station carrier frequencies are assigned so that the same frequency can be reused for another base station only a few cells distant. Frequency reuse is limited by co-channel interference between calls.

Cells may vary in size from about 1 km radius up to about 8 km radius. To cope with peaks of telephone traffic at busy times of day some cells may be subdivided into *microcells*, with a radius of 200–300 m, which provide services over a smaller area such as a shopping centre or a railway station. Cell base station aerials are mounted on the top of tall buildings, or towers, and the path loss is mainly determined by diffraction and scattering at roof tops near the mobile's location. The base station aerial of a microcell is mounted at a lower height than the average height of the surrounding buildings to avoid interference with other cells. In areas where the telephone traffic is very high microcells may be further subdivided into *picocells* which provide service to an individual building. Figure 15.10 shows a mixed multi-cell cellular radio system.

The smaller the number of cells per cluster the larger is the number of radio channels per cell which allows it to carry more traffic. Unfortunately, reducing the cluster size reduces the distance between cells operating on channels at the same frequency and this leads to an increase in co-channel interference. The physical distance between the centre of the centre cell and the centre of the repeat cell is known as the repeat, or reuse, distance.

Fig. 15.10 *Mixed-cell cellular ratio system (Courtesy of British Telecommunication Engineering)*

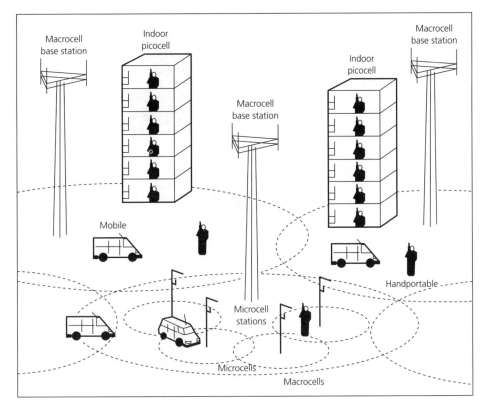

Fig. 15.11 *Calculation of repeat distance and re-use ratio*

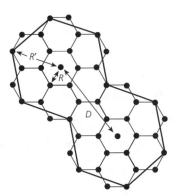

Cell radius and repeat distance

Figure 15.11 shows two seven-cell clusters in which each cell has a radius R and the repeat distance is D. Each cluster can be represented by a larger hexagon with the same area and radius R'. The distance between the centres of the two large hexagons is also D. The ratio (area of larger hexagon)/(area of smaller hexagon) is equal to the number

Fig. 15.12 *Frequency plan for a 4 × 3 re-use pattern*

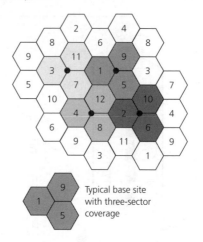

9
1
5
Typical base site
with three-sector
coverage

Fig. 15.13 *Frequency plan for a 3 × 3 re-use pattern*

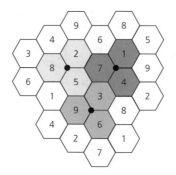

of cells per cluster, i.e. seven. The area of a hexagon is proportional to the square of its radius and hence

$$(R'/R)^2 = 7 \quad \text{or} \quad R'/R = \sqrt{7}$$

From Fig. 15.11, $D = R'\sqrt{3}$, and hence

$$D = \sqrt{3}R\sqrt{7} = R\sqrt{21} \tag{15.1}$$

The reuse ratio is $D/R = \sqrt{21}$. In general, for n cells per cluster,

$$D = R\sqrt{3n} \tag{15.2}$$

The allocation of channels to cells is shown by Fig. 15.12 for a seven-cell cluster. If 12 frequency groups are available a reuse pattern of 4 × 3 can be employed and this is shown in Fig. 15.13.

The basic arrangement of a cellular radio system is shown by Fig. 15.14. Mobiles communicate with the base station of the cell in which they are located. Each base station is connected to a *mobile switching centre* (MSC) and the MSCs are fully inter-connected both with each other and with the PSTN.

Fig. 15.14 *Cellular base stations connected to mobile switching centres*

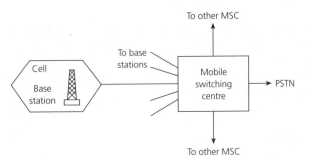

Fig. 15.15 *Use of sectored aerials*

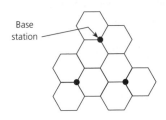

Sectored aerials

Co-channel interference between mobiles can be reduced by the use of a *sectored aerial* at each base station. A three-sectored aerial provides service over a 120° angle and hence its use effectively divides a cell into three parts or sectors. Each sector can act like a separate cell with its own set of channel frequencies. Each sector has its base station situated at one of its corners as shown by Fig. 15.15. Sectoring effectively increases the network capacity three times provided the same number of carriers are assigned to each sector as to each original cell. Sometimes six aerials are employed each covering a 60° sector. Sectoring gives an increase in the signal/interference ratio but increases the number of hand-overs that are required and reduces the trunking efficiency.

GSM

The Global System for Mobiles (GSM) is a digital TDMA/FDD system using GMSK modulation that is based upon cellular radio system technology. As mobile telephones move around the area in which GSM provides service, the precise location of each mobile must be monitored by the system at all times so that they can be communicated with as and when required. Mobile location is achieved by a combination of paging and location updating procedures. There is also a need for reliable communication to be maintained as a mobile moves from one cell to another while a conversation is in progress. This requirement is satisfied by a procedure known as *hand-over*. Although the primary function of GSM is mobile telephony, it also offers data services, text messaging, FAX, and access to the packet data system.

Frequency hopping

The term *frequency hopping* means that the carrier frequency used by an RF channel is constantly changed while a call is in progress. Frequency hopping is used to improve the performance of the system during fading. Frequency hopping shares a bad RF channel between a number of users so that each user only notices a very short gap in the received speech.

Paging

Paging is the process of broadcasting a message which notifies a mobile that there is an incoming call for it to receive. If the system knows the cell in which the mobile is located the broadcast message need only be sent in that cell, otherwise it is necessary for a number of cells to be paged. To reduce the need to page a mobile over several cells, which wastes signalling capacity, location updating is employed.

Location updating

The area covered by the GSM system is divided into a number of *location areas* and the network only pages over one location area. Whenever a mobile leaves one location area and enters a new location area it notifies the network control of its new location. Location areas are larger than individual cells in order to reduce the amount of signalling that would otherwise be necessary. To maintain an up-to-date record of the locations of all mobiles in the system, mobiles may be requested periodically to perform a location update.

Hand-over

When a mobile moves from one cell to another while it is engaged in a conversation the call must automatically be switched from the old cell to the new cell. This requirement is carried out by the hand-over process. The call must be rerouted to the new cell while maintaining the old connection until hand-over can be achieved. The hand-over must be completed before the mobile has moved to a position such that the existing radio link has deteriorated to such an extent that the call is lost. Hand-over should occur as infrequently as possible and the parties to the conversation should be unaware that the hand-over has taken place. The minimum signal level for mobile receivers is typically –90 dBm and so the hand-over level is chosen to be a few decibels higher. If the margin is made too big hand-overs will occur frequently and the MCS will be overloaded; if the margin is too small calls may be lost. A hand-over must take place only as a mobile enters a different cell and not if the signal fades. To ensure this each mobile continually measures the power received from the nearby base stations and informs the serving base station whenever the power received from another base station is larger by at least the fading margin for a set period of time.

Parameters

Speech is initially transmitted at 13 kb/s which is then reduced to 7 kb/s. The carrier frequencies employed in the primary GSM band are 935–960 MHz in the forward (base-to-mobile) direction and 890–915 MHz in the reverse (mobile-to-base) direction, and the channels are spaced 200 kHz apart. In the extended band the frequencies are 880–915 MHz in the reverse direction and 925–960 MHz in the forward direction. Both frequency bands are able to support full-duplex operation using two sub-bands that are spaced 45 MHz apart. This method of operation is known as *frequency-division duplex* (FDD). The modulation rate per carrier is 270.83 kb/s and the voice rate is 22.8 kb/s using an RELP (Residually Excited Linear Predictive) coder voice codec. The transmitted power is in the range 0.25–2.5 W. GSM channels are numbered $n = 1$–124 and the corresponding channel frequencies can be calculated using.

$$\text{mobile transmit frequency} = 890.2 + 0.2(n - 1) \text{ MHz} \tag{15.3}$$

$$\text{base transmit frequency} = 890.2 + 0.2(n - 1) + 45 \text{ MHz} \tag{15.4}$$

Capacity

If a cellular radio system has N duplex channels which are divided equally between the n cells in a cluster, then the number of channels per cell is $m = N/n$. If there are p clusters in the system then the total capacity C of the system is

$$C = mnp = Np \tag{15.5}$$

Architecture

The architecture of a GSM network is shown by Fig. 15.16. Radio links are, of course, used to connect the mobiles to the base stations but other links are carried by 2 Mb/s land circuits. The mobile telephone is identified by a *smart-card identity module* (SIM) that is plugged into the telephone. The SIM stores the user's addressing information and authentication parameters. Mobiles are connected via a radio link to the base station which provides coverage within a cell. It contains both transmitting and receiving radio, as well as signalling, equipment. Base stations are connected to a base station controller which provides the control function and acts as a small switch providing local switching to achieve hand-over between base stations. The base station controller identifies the need for hand-overs and for managing hand-overs between local base stations. This controller also converts the air data rate of 13 kb/s into the network data rate of 64 kb/s. Each controller is linked to an MSC where calls are switched as required. Ideally, each MSC is interconnected with all other MSCs but such *full interconnection* becomes complex and costly in a large network and then *transit switching centres* (TSCs) may be employed. MSCs are directly interconnected whenever the traffic justifies it, otherwise wanted MSC links are established by switching in the TSC. A TSC often also acts as a *gateway mobile switching centre* (GMSC) whose function is to route services within the cellular network to/from the PSTN.

An MSC carries out all switching between mobiles within its area. A local call will be switched by one MSC while another call may require two or more MSCs to be

Fig. 15.16 *GSM architecture*

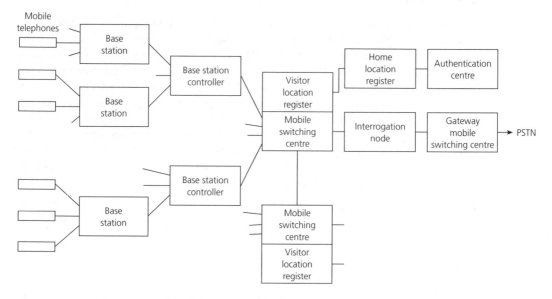

involved. Associated with each MSC is a *visitor location register* (VLR) which stores temporarily the information needed to handle calls set up, or received by, the MSC. This information includes identities, service profiles and authentication data. The *interrogating node* (IN) determines the location of a called mobile and then routes the call to that mobile. The IN is usually combined with an MSC to form a *gateway* MSC. A gateway MSC has links to the PSTN and calls to/from the PSTN must be passed through it. The *home location register* (HLR) keeps records of each mobile in its area, such as which extra services have been made available to the user, and controls some of these services. It also holds location information to enable incoming calls to be routed to the appropriate MSC/VLR. The *authentication centre* (AUC) is a database which ensures that services can only be used by those mobiles that are entitled to do so.

Access techniques

The *air interface* is the interface between the mobile and the base station. Because no mobile is receiving/transmitting continuously some form of multiplexing is used in the air interface. Multiplexing will allow a very large number of mobiles to share the limited frequency spectrum allocated to the system. The multiplexing methods are:

- Time-division multiplex access (TDMA): TDMA is suitable for microcells and for indoor environments where clusters of base stations can be time synchronised. TDMA allows each user to have access to the frequency band for a short period of time – known as a *burst* – during which time speech data is transmitted at a faster bit rate. The available frequency spectrum is shared with other mobiles which have other time slot allocations. The frame and time slot structure employed by GSM (and

Fig. 15.17 *GSM frame and time slot structure*

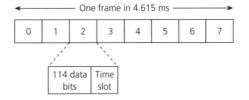

Fig. 15.18 *GSM frame, multi-frame and super-frame*

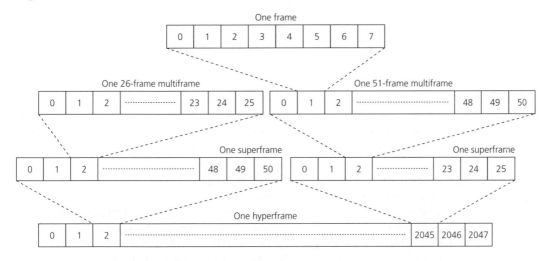

DCS 1800) is shown by Fig. 15.17. Each frame has eight time slots and each time slot contains 156.25 bits. The time slots in the transmitter and receiver are offset by a time period equal to three time slots. This is done to ensure that the transmitter and receiver do not operate simultaneously. Data is transmitted at 270.833 kb/s in each channel. Transmitting and receiving cycles occur on the same carrier frequency but in alternate time slots.

TDMA possesses an advantage in that there is no need for two frequency bands for the forward and reverse links, but also a disadvantage in that there is a need for a guard time between the transmitting and receiving cycles that is proportional to the size of the cell.

With TDMA each RF channel is divided into time slots of 577 µs width. Eight consecutive time slots make up one TDMA frame. TDMA frames are then grouped together in one of two different ways to form multi-frames: (a) a 26-frame multi frame of width 120 ms used to carry traffic channels and an associated control channel; or (b) a 51-frame multi-frame of 235.4 ms width which is only used for the control channel.

The multi-frames are, in turn, combined to produce superframes of width 6.12 s. A superframe consists of 51 26-frame multi-frames or 26 51-frame multi-frames; 2048 superframes form one hyperframe having a width of 12 533.76 s. The frame structure is shown by Fig. 15.18.

Fig. 15.19 *Frequency hopping*

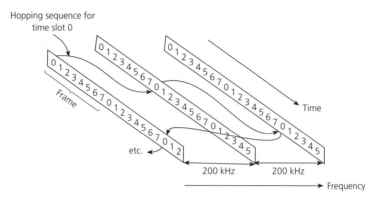

The power transmitted by a mobile is ramped upwards and downwards during each time slot within 28 μs and the power is kept constant to within ±1 dB during each burst. To improve the error correction performance GSM uses frequency hopping, in which the RF carriers may change frequency from one frame to another. This is shown by Fig. 15.19.

● Frequency-division multiplex (FDM): FDM (also known as *dual-frequency time-division duplex*) is more suited to operation with large cells. It has only one-half the carrier bit rate because the system receives and transmits at alternate cycles at the mobile with timing advance allowed for the reverse link. Since the forward and reverse channels are assigned on two sub-bands with a guard band in between, a wider frequency band is occupied. On the other hand, the bit rate is lower and there is less delay. This is the access method used in the TACS analogue system.

● Code-division multiplex (CDMA): With CDMA all mobiles have access to the whole of the frequency band at all times. Signal are coded so that they can be distinguished from one another. The main features of the three access technologies are shown by Figs 15.20(a), (b) and (c).

Operation

Location update

Referring to Fig. 15.16, each time a mobile detects that it has entered a new location area by comparing the last location area stored on its SIM with the information broadcast by the local cell, it instigates a location update. The mobile accesses a radio channel and asks the network for a location update. If the serving MSC/VLR is unchanged the network can immediately record the new location area. If the mobile is now in a location area covered by a different MSC/VLR then the MSC/VLR sends a message to the mobile's HLR, and the HLR records the new position of the mobile and transmits signals to inform the new MSC/VLR of the status of the mobile. The HLR also instructs the old MSC/VLR to delete its record of the mobile.

Fig. 15.20 *Access methods: (a) TDMA, (b) FDMA and (c) CDMA*

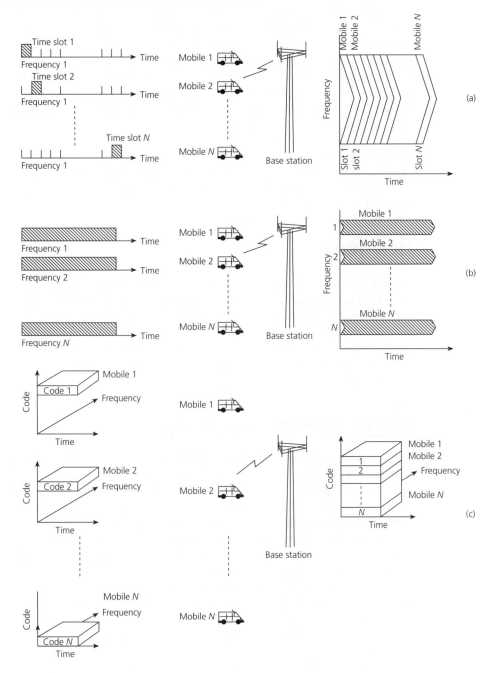

Incoming call

When an incoming call is received by the network it is sent to the GMSC/IN in the mobile's home area. The IN is able to identify the HLR that controls the wanted mobile and it requests routing information from that HLR. The HLR then provides the GMSC/IN with routing information and then the call is routed to the mobile. Now the MSC/VLR attempts to make contact with the mobile by paging it in its last known location area. If the mobile is still in the coverage area of the MSC/VLR and is switched on, it answers the call by requesting a radio channel. A channel is set up and the mobile is rung, and when the user answers the call is completed.

Outgoing call

When the user initiates a call the mobile requests a radio channel. The local MSC/VLR authenticates the mobile and establishes a channel. The call is then routed by the MSC/VLR to the required number.

DCS 1800

The cellular radio systems offered by Orange and by One2One use a system known as DCS 1800, which stands for *Digital Cellular System* at 1800 MHz. This is a form of *personal communication network* (PCN). The parameters of the systems are as follows: forward frequency band 1805–1880 MHz, reverse frequency band 1710–1785 MHz, channel spacing 200 kHz, TDMA access, modulation rate 271 kb/s, voice modulation rate 22.8 kb/s and voice codec RELP. The transmitted power is in the range 30–250 mW.

Digital cordless telephony

The first cordless telephone system in the UK was known as CT1 and using analogue techniques it provided eight RF channels only. It has been superseded by a digital system known as CT2. CT2 provides 32 ADPCM (Adaptive Differential Pulse Code Modulation) channels in both the base-to-handset and handset-to-base directions using full duplex. Signals are transmitted using time-interleaved burst-mode pulses on the same carrier frequency in each direction of transmission. The technique allows identical circuitry to be used in both handset and base and uses only one block of frequencies instead of two as with cellular systems.

Each cordless telephony channel is allocated a 100 kHz bandwidth in the frequency band 864–868 MHz. Employing the ITU-T 32 kb/s ADPCM speech-coding algorithm makes it possible to limit the symbol rate to 72 kb/s. Since only $(4 \times 10^6)/(0.1 \times 10^6) = 40$ channels are available, trunking is employed and a CT2 handset is able to operate on any of these 40 channels. When a handset calls a base station the system automatically selects the available channel that currently has the lowest level of co-channel and adjacent-channel interference and switches to that channel. Because of the single-frequency operation and the use of TDM a large number of telephones are able to work in a given area.

Fig. 15.21 *Use of TDD in CT2 cordless telephony*

The modulation method employed is two-level FSK which is shaped by a Gaussian filter. A frequency deviation of between 14.4 and 25.2 kHz above the carrier frequency represents binary 1, and the same frequency deviation below the carrier represents binary 0. CT2 uses *time-division duplex* (TDD) for communication between the base station and the portable handset. The principle of TDD is shown by Fig. 15.21. Input speech signals in both directions are sampled and then coded into 2 ms packets at 32 kb/s. Each packet contains two leading control bits, 64 data bits, and two final control bits. The digital signal is then transmitted at 72 kb/s between the base station and the handset. The 72 kb/s signals are transmitted in bursts of data 1 ms long.

Digitally enhanced cordless telecommunications

The digitally enhanced cordless telecommunication (DECT) system provides cordless telephony at a frequency of 1.8 GHz. DECT uses the same ADPCM speech-coding algorithm as CT2 but otherwise it differs from CT2 in several respects. The differences between CT2 and DECT are listed in Table 15.1. DECT employs FDMA/TDMA/TDD to provide 120 duplex channels using 10 carriers and multiplexing 12 send and 12 receive channels on each carrier. The frame set-up for each system is shown by Figs 15.22(a) and (b).

Table 15.1 *CT2/DECT parameters*

	CT2	DECT
Bit rate (kb/s)	72	1142
Modulation	GMSK	GMSK
Frequency deviation (kHz)	14.4–25.2	208
Carriers	40	10
Channel spacing (kHz)	100	1728
Frequency band (MHz)	864–868	1880–1900

Fig. 15.22 *Frame set-up for (a) CTZ and (b) DECT*

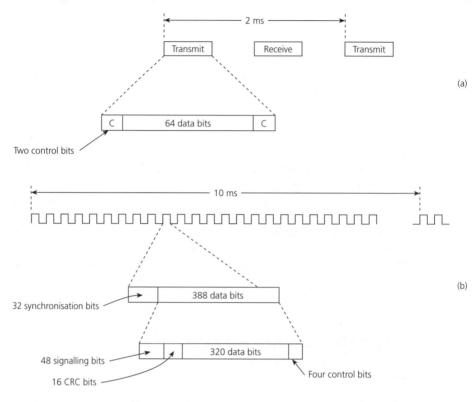

Mobile telephones

The main sections of a mobile telephone are shown by the block diagram of Fig. 15.23. The radio section of the telephone contains all the radio circuitry such as the receiver, the transmitter, the frequency synthesiser and the diplexing filter. The audio section contains circuitry for processing the audio signal both before and after demodulation. The logic section mainly consists of a microprocessor that has several functions:

(a) it controls the frequency synthesiser and ensures that the frequency of transmission is correct;
(b) it controls the transmitted power in response to signals received from the base station;
(c) it controls the telephone so that the power consumption is reduced during standby and sleep periods;
(d) it interfaces with the keypad and the display panel; and
(e) it controls transmissions between the telephone and the base station.

A *speech codec* is a signal processing circuit that employs a set of coding algorithms first to convert input analogue speech into digital form, and then to compress the digital signal so it can be transmitted at a low bit rate. At the receiving end the speech codec

Fig. 15.23 *Main sections of a mobile telephone*

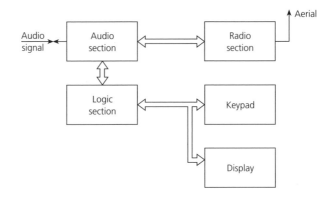

decodes the incoming bit stream and converts it back into analogue form. The speech encoder converts the speech waveform into the digital form using as few bits as possible. Transmission of the digitised waveform over a radio link always introduces errors so a *channel encoder* is employed to encode the speech codec output signal still further and also add some error correction bits. Typically, the bit rate at the speech codec output is either 13 kb/s or 5.6 kb/s and this is increased to either 22.8 kb/s or 11.4 kb/s by the channel encoder. Some equipment uses a *half-rate speech encoder* which only occupies one-half a GSM time slot. If two mobiles have half-rate codecs then two calls can exist in one time slot, which doubles the capacity of the system.

Figure 15.24 gives the block diagram of a typical GSM mobile telephone. Such a telephone is implemented using a number of ICs, the number of which is steadily being reduced as new devices come onto the market. One GSM telephone, for example, uses ICs that include the following circuits:

(a) ADC, speech encoder, DAC and speech decoder;
(b) channel encoder, encryption circuit, GMSK modulator and DAC, channel decoder, decryption circuit, adaptive equaliser and ADC, and a microprocessor;
(c) frequency synthesiser and VCO;
(d) all up/down converters and IF amplifiers;
(e) LNA.

All necessary filters and the HPA are separate modular components.

EXERCISES

15.1 One thousand RF channels are made available in a cellular radio system. Determine the number of radio channels per cell if the cell repeat pattern is (a) seven cells per cluster and (b) 12 cells per cluster.

15.2 (a) A cellular radio system has an allocated bandwidth of 40 MHz. If the bandwidth per duplex channel is 20 kHz calculate the number of channels provided. (b) Determine the repeat distance for a seven-cell cluster if the cells are of 4 km radius.

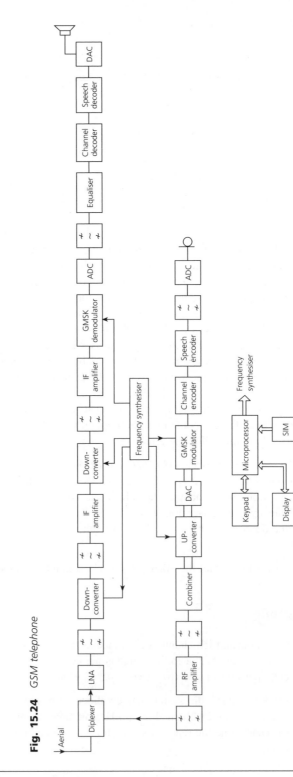

Fig. 15.24   *GSM telephone*

15.3 In the GSM system the power transmitted by a base station is kept constant but the power transmitted by a mobile is a variable that is controlled by signals from the base station. Explain why.

15.4 (a) Suggest a reason why circles are not used to represent cells in a cellular radio system.
   (b) State three shapes that will give complete coverage of an area without overlaps or gaps.
   (c) Which of the three in (b) is used and why?

15.5 (a) What is meant by *hand-over*?
   (b) Discuss the factors that determine the signal level at a mobile at which hand-over will be initiated.
   (c) Quote a typical figure for the received signal power at which hand-over occurs.

15.6 (a) What is meant by sectoring? (b) List its advantages and disadvantages.

15.7 For a GSM frame calculate (a) the duration of each bit, (b) the duration of each time slot, and (c) the duration of each frame.

15.8 A GSM time slot consists of six training bits, 8.25 guard bits, 26 training bits, and two bursts of 58 data bits. Calculate the frame efficiency.

15.9 Determine the channel frequencies used for both directions of transmission for channels 17 and 89 of a CT2 system.

15.10 State the function of each block in the mobile telephone circuit shown in Fig. 15.24, Explain the operation of the telephone.

16 Electronics Workbench

Electronics Workbench is an electronic design tool for use with a PC that provides all the components, measuring equipment and voltage sources needed to design circuits on a computer and then test their performance. Electronics Workbench is an extension of the *Simulation Program with Integrated Circuit Emphasis* (SPICE) industry-standard set of algorithms for the simulation of circuits. In this chapter a number of exercises are given using Electronics Workbench and they correspond with the practical exercises given in earlier chapters.

When Electronics Workbench is first loaded a blank circuit window will appear on the monitor screen. Click **FILE** and when a menu appears click **OPEN**. Select the appropriate file and click **OPEN**. The circuit to be tested will then appear in the circuit window.

- To select a component click on it.
- To delete a component right click on it and then click **DELETE** on the menu that appears.
- To move a component click on it and when it turns red drag it, using the mouse, to its new position.
- To change the default value of a component click on it twice and enter the required value in the appropriate box.
- To wire components together: (a) point at the component's terminal until it highlights and then press and hold the mouse button and drag – a wire will appear; (b) drag the wire to another component, to an instrument, or to another wire; (c) when the terminal on the destination component, or instrument, highlights release the mouse button to make the connection.
- If the wiring looks confusing wires can be given different colours. Double click on a wire and then select the wanted colour.
- If the characteristics of an active device are to be altered, double click on the device and then choose **EDIT** on the displayed menu.

EWB 1.1   Amplitude-modulated waveform

To measure the modulation factor of a DSBAM waveform

Procedure:

(a)   Click **FILE** and then **NEW**. Click on the sources icon and then on AM source and drag it onto the circuit window. Then click on the AM source icon to access its controls and set the carrier frequency to 1 MHz at 10 V. Set the modulation factor to 0.2 at 5 kHz, i.e. $V_m = 2$ V.

(b)   Click on the instruments icon and then on the CRO. Drag the CRO icon to the circuit window. Connect the +terminal of the AM source to the Y1 input terminal of the CRO and the −terminal to earth. Connect the earth terminal of the CRO to earth although this is not really necessary.

(c)   Click on the CRO icon to access its controls and adjust its timebase to 0.2 ms/div. Observe the displayed waveform. Measure the modulation factor using equation (2.7).

(d)   Increase the modulation factor first to 0.5 and then to 0.8, and each time repeat procedure (c).

(e)   Increase the modulating frequency to 10 kHz and then repeat procedures (c) and (d). Reduce the timebase frequency to 0.02 ms/div and note the effect on the displayed waveform.

(f)   With the modulating frequency at 10 kHz increase the timebase frequency in a number of steps and note and explain the effect on the displayed waveform. Draw the waveform obtained when the timebase is set at 0.2 µs/div and explain.

(g)   Turn off the internal timebase (click **Y/T**) and attempt to measure the modulation factor using method (d) in Practical exercise 1.1.

EWB 1.2   Amplitude-modulated waveform

To investigate overmodulation of an AM wave

Procedure:

(a)   Click **FILE** and then **NEW** and then bring both the AM source and the CRO to the circuit window. Connect the +terminal of the AM source to the Y1 input of the CRO. Connect both the AM source −terminal and the CRO earth terminal to earth.

(b)   Click on the AM source icon to access its controls and then set the carrier signal to 1 MHz at 10 V. Set the modulation index to 0.8.

(c)   Click on the CRO icon to access its controls and set the timebase frequency to give a steady display of the AM waveform. Click on 'analysis' at the top toolbar and then click first on 'analysis options' and then on 'instruments'. Now try the effect of changing the 'minimum number of time points'. Set the last named to about 500.

(d) Increase the modulation factor to unity and note and draw the displayed waveform. Is it distorted?

(e) Now increase the modulation factor in steps of 0.1 up to about 1.8 and at each step note and draw the envelope of the modulated waveform. Explain the effect on the modulation envelope of overmodulating the carrier.

EWB 2.1   Frequency-modulated waveform

To observe FM waveforms

Procedure:

(a) Open file rad2.1.ewb and activate the circuit.

(b) Click the FM generator icon and set the carrier frequency to 1 MHz. Then set the modulating frequency to 250 kHz with $m_f = 5$. Double click the CRO icon to access its screen and observe the displayed FM waveform. Click 'analysis', then 'analysis option', then 'instruments', and then, finally, tick 'pause after each screen'.

(c) Vary the value of m_f to, in turn, 8, 10, 3, 2 and 1 and each time note the displayed FM waveform. Comment.

(d) Now reduce the modulating frequency to 10 kHz and try to repeat procedures (a) and (b). What difficulty is experienced?

(e) Observe the effect of setting the modulating frequency first to 0.8 times the carrier frequency and then to the carrier frequency.

EWB 4.1   90° phase-shifting circuit

To investigate a circuit for introducing 90° phase shift into a carrier voltage

Procedure:

(a) Open file rad4.1.ewb and activate the circuit.

(b) Set the frequency of the carrier source to 50 kHz, both resistors to 10 kΩ and both capacitors to 10 nF.

(c) Double click on the CRO icon to access its controls and adjust the timebase control until steady displays are obtained. Measure the phase difference between the output voltages V_{out1} and V_{out2}.

(d) Vary the values of R and/or C until a phase difference of 90° is obtained. State the values of R and C that give this phase difference.

(e) Increase the frequency of the carrier source to 1 MHz and then repeat procedure (d).

(f) Were the amplitudes of the two output voltages equal to one another (i) in procedure (d) and (ii) in procedure (e)? If the amplitudes were unequal in either, or both, case(s), repeat *either* procedure (d) *or* procedure (e) until a 90° phase difference with equal-amplitude voltages is obtained.

EWB 4.2   Digital 90° phase-shifting circuit

To investigate a digital method of obtaining 90° phase shift

Procedure:

(a)   Open file rad4.2.ewb and disconnect the blue line so that the lower D flip-flop is not in circuit. Connect the CRO Y2 terminal to the output of the exclusive-OR gate. Activate the circuit and note that the frequency of the displayed square-wave signal is at twice the frequency of the input. The time constant of the *CR* circuit is equal to the periodic time of the input sine wave. Investigate the effect of altering this time constant.

(b)   Now observe the waveform displayed on the screen and disconnect the blue line so that the lower D flip-flop is not in circuit. Connect the CRO Y2 terminal to the output of the exclusive-OR gate. Activate the circuit and note that the displayed square-wave signal is at twice the frequency of the input. The time constant of the *CR* circuit is equal to the periodic time of the input sine wave. Investigate the effect of altering this time constant.

(c)   Now observe the waveform on the Y2 display. Determine its frequency and compare it with (i) the input frequency and (ii) the frequency of the waveform shown by the Y1 trace.

(d)   To obtain a 90° phase difference between two signals it is necessary to use another J–K flip-flop connected as a divide-by-2 circuit, but this flip-flop must be driven by the inverted exclusive-OR gate output. Replace the blue line connection that was removed in part (a). This puts the lower divide-by-2 into the circuit. Move the Y2 lead from the exclusive-OR gate to the output of the lower D flip-flop. Determine the frequency of each displayed waveform and their relative phase. The output waveforms are rectangular but passing them through suitable low-pass filters will produce a sinusoidal signal. Move the CRO Y2 lead from the lower J–K flip-flop to the output of the circuit so that the *RC* first-order low-pass filter is in the circuit. Adjust the values of *R* and *C* to get the best 'sine wave' possible.

(e)   Discuss the need for a 90° phase-shifting circuit in digital modulators/demodulators and compare this circuit with the one that was the subject of the previous exercise.

EWB 4.3   2-to-4-level converter

To investigate a 2-to-4-level converter

Procedure:

(a)   Open file rad4.3.ewb and activate the circuit.

(b)   Double click on the CRO icon to access its controls and display a waveform on the screen. It will be necessary to adjust the values of the variable resistors in order to obtain a 4-level waveform on the CRO screen. The input waveform may be chosen to be either a periodic waveform or a random waveform by pressing the space bar to operate switch SPACE. When the SPACE switch is in its random position keys A and B must be repeatedly pressed to input a random waveform to the circuit.

(c) When a 4-level waveform has been obtained adjust the resistor values, possibly including the fixed resistors, until the required voltage steps are obtained. Note the resistor values that are required for this.

EWB 5.1   Transmission line

To measure the characteristic impedance and propagation coefficient of a line

Procedure:

(a) Open file rad5.1.ewb and activate the circuit.

(b) Set the source voltage to 10 V at 5 MHz and then use the multimeter to measure the voltage V_{oc} across the input terminals of the line.

(c) Short-circuit the output terminals of the line and again measure the input voltage V_{sc}.

(d) Alter the multimeter connections so that the meter is connected in series with the source and the upper conductor of the line. Click the multimeter to change it to measure current and then note the current I_{sc} flowing into the line.

(e) Open-circuit the output terminals of the line and then measure the input current I_{oc} that flows into the line.

(f) Calculate $Z_{oc} = V_{oc}/I_{oc}$ and $Z_{sc} = V_{sc}/I_{sc}$.

(g) Calculate the characteristic impedance of the line using $Z_0 = \sqrt{(Z_{oc}Z_{sc})}$.

(h) Connect the resistor across the output terminals of the line and set its value to be equal to the calculated value of Z_0. Measure the input voltage to the line which ought to be 5 V. Why should it? Use the CRO to observe the waveform of the load voltage and then disconnect the load resistor and note the effect on the displayed waveform.

(i) Double click on the line icon and then click on **EDIT**. Set the resistance of the line to 5 Ω per unit length. Calculate the value of the attenuation coefficient of the line using $\alpha = R/2Z_0$. Connect the resistor (equal to Z_0) across the output terminals of the line and connect the Y2 terminal of the CRO to the input of the line. Now observe the input and output waveforms of the line and note (i) the phase shift and (ii) the loss over the 10 m length. Measure the two voltages as accurately as possible and hence determine the loss per metre of the line. Does this value agree with the value calculated using $R/2Z_0$?

EWB 10.1   Class C RF amplifier

To investigate Class C bias of a transistor and a Class C RF amplifier

Procedure:

(a)   Open file rad10.1.ewb and activate the circuit.

(b)   Set the signal source to 0 V/50 kHz and the supply voltage V_{CC} to 15 V. Increase the input signal voltage in discrete steps and at each step note the waveform displayed by the CRO. Comment on the results and state the input voltage at which the transistor started to conduct.

(c)   Open file rad10.1a.ewb and activate the circuit. Explain what happens now to the circuit.

(d)   Open file rad10.1b.ewb and activate the circuit. Repeat procedure (b). State the voltage at which the transistor starts to conduct a collector current.

(e)   Vary the bias voltage V_B applied to the transistor and note the effect this has on the output waveform.

(f)   With the bias voltage set to 3 V vary V_{CC} in 2 V steps starting from 0 V and ending at 24 V and note the effect on the output waveform. Determine whether the amplitude of the collector current pulses is directly proportional to V_{CC}.

(g)   Open file rad.10.1c.ewb and activate the circuit. The collector-tuned circuit is resonant at 50 kHz. Set $V_{CC} = 12$ V, $V_B = 3$ V and the input signal to 4 V/50 kHz. Observe the output waveform of the circuit and measure its peak value.

(h)   Vary the collector supply voltage V_{CC} and observe the effect of doing so on the peak voltage of the output waveform.

EWB 10.2   Ring modulator

To investigate a diode balanced or ring modulator

Procedure:

(a)   Open file rad10.2.ewb and activate the circuit.

(b)   Set the carrier voltage to 10 V at 50 kHz and the modulating signal voltage to 1 V at 2 kHz. Click on the CRO icon to access its controls and then observe the displayed waveform. Vary the modulating signal frequency over the range 500 Hz to 3000 Hz in a number of convenient steps, and observe the output voltage at each step.

(c)   With the modulating frequency equal to 3 kHz increase the modulating voltage to 5 V and note the effect upon the output voltage. Increase the modulating signal voltage first to 9 V and then to 10 V and see what effect this has on the output waveform.

(d)   Reduce the carrier voltage to 5 V and the signal voltage to 6 V. Comment on the output waveform. Comment on how the output waveform is a function of the relative values of the carrier and modulating signal voltages. What is the best ratio (carrier voltage)/(modulating signal voltage)? Quote this ratio in dBc.

(e) The ring modulator is also employed as a phase detector. Adjust the two input signal sources to 1 kHz and 1 V and note the output waveform on the CRO. Connect the multimeter across the output terminals and use it measure the d.c. output voltage of the modulator. Vary the frequency of one of the signal sources by a few hertz and note the effect on (i) the output waveform and (ii) the output voltage.

EWB 10.3   Diode detector

To investigate the operation of a diode detector

Procedure:

(a) Open file rad10.3.ewb and activate the circuit.

(b) Set the AM generator to 1 MHz modulated at 4000 Hz with $m = 0.5$. Double click on the CRO icon to access its screen and then observe the displayed waveforms.

(c) The values of the variable resistor and the variable capacitor can be reduced by pressing keys R and C respectively. The values of these components can be increased by pressing the shift key at the same times as either the R or C key. Vary R and/or C and note the effect of different time constants on the detected waveform. Set R and/or C to the values that give the best detected waveform. Note these values.

(d) Calculate the theoretical values of R and C and compare the results with the experimental figures.

(e) Vary the modulating signal frequency and each time note the detected waveform.

(f) With the modulating frequency returned to 4 kHz, vary the depth of modulation. For each value of modulation factor note the detected waveform.

(g) Comment on the results obtained in (e) and (f).

EWB 10.4   Squelch circuit

To investigate the operation of a squelch circuit

Procedure:

(a) Open file rad10.4.ewb and activate the circuit.

(b) Initially the AF amplifier has its 12 V collector supply taken directly from a d.c. source. Set the signal source to 1 kHz at 0.2 V and use the CRO to observe the output waveform of the amplifier. Measure the gain of the amplifier. Determine the sensitivity of the amplifier and say how it might be improved.

(c) Press the space bar on the keyboard. This action (i) disconnects the 12 V collector supply voltage and (ii) provides the supply voltage via the squelch circuit. Measure the value of V_{BE} for T_1 using the multimeter set to d.c. volts. If the value is such that T_1 is conducting the collector supply voltage to the AF amplifier will be 12 V as before. Check that the AF amplifier is working correctly.

(d) Increase the base voltage first to 12 V and then to 13 V and each time note what, if anything, happens. State the V_{BE} value each time.

(e) Decrease the base voltage in steps of 0.05 V to 11 V and note what happens at each step. State the V_{BE} value each time.

(f) Explain the reason for using a squelch circuit in a radio receiver. How would the d.c. voltage applied to the base of T_1 be derived in a radio receiver?

EWB 12.1 RF attenuator

To investigate the operation of an AGC-controlled RF attenuator

Procedure:

(a) Open file rad12.1.ewb and activate the circuit.

(b) Set the AGC voltage to 0 V, the frequency of the RF source to 1 MHz and the RF voltage to 0.5 V. Note the waveform and voltage of the output signal.

(c) Vary the AGC voltage in 1 V steps up to +5 V and each time note the output voltage.

(d) Vary the AGC voltage in −1 V steps from 0 V to −5 V and each time note the output voltage.

(e) Determine the upper frequency at which the circuit will work.

EWB 13.1 Scrambler

To investigate a simple scrambler circuit

Procedure:

(a) Open file rad13.1.ewb and activate the circuit.

(b) Set the clock frequency to 400 Hz and the data input signal to 80 Hz and 50% duty cycle. Observe and note the input and output waveforms displayed by the logic analyser.

(c) Vary the data signal, in turn, to 50, 100, 200 and 400 Hz and each time note the output waveform. A stationary display can be obtained by pressing key F10.

(d) Delete the data input signal pulse generator from the circuit and replace it with a key-operated switch. Connect the switch to the SR input and to logic 1 and 0. Then use the switch to input a random data waveform to the circuit. Observe and note the output waveform.

(e) Discuss the use of such a circuit in a microwave radio transmitter.

(f) Design and implement a method of de-scrambling the data waveform. Test the circuit and then connect its input terminal to the output terminal of the given circuit. Check the operation of the cascaded circuits.

EWB 13.2   Serial-to-parallel converter

To investigate a serial-to-parallel converter

Procedure:

(a)   Open file rad13.2.ewb and activate the circuit.
(b)   Set the NRZ data input to 100 Hz and the clock frequency to 1 kHz. Double click on the logic analyser icon and note the input and two output waveforms that are displayed. Pressing key F10 will give a stationary display.
(c)   Vary the NRZ data input to 200, 250, 400 and 500 Hz and note the effect on the output waveforms. Determine the maximum NRZ data frequency.
(d)   Give some instances of where such a circuit might be employed and why.

EWB 13.3   NRZ-to-CMI converter

To investigate the action of an NRZ-to-CMI converter

Procedure:

(a)   Open file rad13.3.ewb and activate the circuit.
(b)   Double click on the logic analyser icon to access its controls and observe the input and output waveforms of the circuit. The clock waveform is also shown. Also observe the input and output waveform using the CRO.
(c)   Note the effects on the output waveform of changing (i) the frequency of the NRZ input waveform, and (ii) the duty cycle of the input waveform.
(d)   Comment on the applications of such a circuit in a radio system.

Answers to exercises

Chapter 1

1.1 $F_{0(290)} = 2 + (4 - 1)/100 + (4 - 1)/(100 \times 0.25) + (10 - 1)/(25 \times 316.2) = 2.15$.
$F_{0(400)} = 1 + (290/400)(2.15 - 1) = 1.834$.
Minimum output S/N ratio $= 1000 = GS_{IN}/FGkT_SB = S_{IN}/FkT_SB$.
$S_{IN} = 1000 \times 1.834 \times 1.38 \times 10^{-23} \times 400 \times 10^7 = 101$ pW.

1.2 (a) Feeder: $F = 1.46$ dB $= 1.4$ ratio. LNA: $F = t + 1 = 89.9/290 + 1 = 1.31$.
20 dB $= 100$ and 4 dB $= 2.51$ ratio. Hence, $F_{ov} = 1.4 + (1.31 - 1)1.4 + (2.51 - 1)1.4/100$
$= 1.855 = 2.68$ dB.
(b) $t = F - 1 = 0.855$. $T = 0.855 \times 290 = 248$ K.

1.3 (a) 5 dB $= 3.162$ and 60 dB $= 10^6$. $F_{133} = 1 + (3.162 - 1)290/133 = 5.714$.
$N_0 = 5.714 \times 10^6 \times 1.38 \times 10^{-23} \times 133 \times 10^7 = 105$ nW.
(b) 1.76 dB $= 1.5$. $F_{ov} = 1.5 + (3.162 - 1)1.5 = 4.743$.
$F_{133} = 1 + (4.743 - 1)290/133 = 9.161$.
$N_0 = (9.161 \times 10^6)/1.5 \times 1.38 \times 10^{-23} \times 1.33 \times 10^7 = 112$ nW.

1.4 7 dB $= 5$ and 10 dB $= 10$ as a ratio. $F_{ov} = 5 + (10 - 1)/G$.
$T_S = T_{ov} + 290 = 1500$ K, or $T_{ov} = 1210$ K. $t = 1210/290 = 4.172 = F - 1$. So $F = 5.172$.
Therefore, $0.172 = 9/G$, and $G = 52.33 = 17.2$ dB.

1.5 20 dB $= 100$, 7 dB $= 5$, 10 dB $= 10$, 5 dB $= 3.162$, 6 dB $= 3.98$ and 2 dB $= 1.59$ as ratios.
Connect the amplifier with the lowest noise figure first, followed by the amplifier with the next lowest noise figure. Hence, connect in the order 3, 2, 1.
Then $F_{ov} = 1.59 + (3.162 - 1)/3.98 + (5 - 1)/(3.98 \times 10) = 2.23$ or 3.48 dB.

1.6 3 dB $= 2$ and 26 dB $= 398$ ratios.
(a) 110 dBm $= 10 \log_{10}[(1 \times 10^{-3})/N_{IN}]$, $N_{IN} = 1 \times 10^{-14}$ W.
Input S/N ratio $= 10 \log_{10}[(1 \times 10^{-9})/(1 \times 10^{-14})] = 50$ dB.
(b) $1 \times 10^{-14} = 300$ kB, $B = (1 \times 10^{-14})/(1.38 \times 10^{-23} \times 300) = 2.4155$ MHz.
$F_{300} = 1 + (2 - 1)290/300 = 1.967$.
$N_0 = 1.967 \times 398 \times 1.38 \times 10^{-23} \times 300 \times 2.4155 \times 10^6 = 7.83$ pW.
$S_0 = 1 \times 10^{-9} \times 398 - 398$ nW.
Output S/N ratio $= (398 \times 10^{-9})/(7.83 \times 10^{-12}) = 5083 = 47.1$ dB.

1.7 0.3 dB = 1.07 ratio, 20 dB = 100 ratio, 25 dB = 316.23 ratio and 30 dB = 1000 ratio.

For TWT, $T = (10 - 1) \times 290 = 2610$ K. Hence,

$T_s = 20 + 20.3 + 10 \times 1.07 + (2610 \times 1.07)/100 = 78.9$ K.

$N_o = GkT_sB = 1/1.07 \times 100 \times 316.23 \times 1.38 \times 10^{-23} \times 78.9 \times 2.8 \times 10^6$
$ = 9 \times 10^{-11}$ W.

$S_o = 1000 \times 9 \times 10^{-11} = 9 \times 10^{-8}$ W.

Required $S_{in} = (9 \times 10^{-8})/(100 \times 316.23 \times 1/1.07) \approx 3$ pW.

1.8 $V_n = \sqrt{(4 \times 1.38 \times 10^{-23} \times 290 \times 10^4 \times 56 \times 10^3)} = 3$ μV.

R.M.S. side-frequency voltage $= \sqrt{[2(0.3 \times 100)^2/2]} = 3$ μV. Output S/N ratio = 1 or 0 dB. If the carrier is considered, $V = 100\sqrt{(1 + 0.3^2/2)} = 104.4$ μV and then output S/N ratio $= 20 \log_{10}(104.4/3) = 30.83$ dB.

1.9 9 dB = 7.943 and 20 dB = 100 ratios.

$N_0 = 7.943$ $G \times 1.38 \times 10^{-23} \times 290 \times 10^5 = 3.18$ $G \times 10^{-15}$.

Therefore $S_0 = 3.18$ $G \times 10^{-13}$, and hence $S_{IN} = 3.18 \times 10^{-13}$ W.

1.10 (a) $Z = R/(1 + j\omega CR)/V_n = \sqrt{[4kTBR/(1 + j\omega CR)]} = \sqrt{[kTBR(1 - j\omega CR)/(1 + \omega^2 C^2 R^2)]}$
$= \sqrt{\{[kTBR\sqrt{(1 + \omega^2 C^2 R^2)}]/(1 + \omega^2 C^2 R^2)\}} \approx \sqrt{[kTBR(\omega CR)/\omega^2 C^2 R^2]} \approx \sqrt{[kTBR/\omega CR]}$
$= \sqrt{(kTB/\omega C)}$. Hence $V_n = \sqrt{(kT/C)}$. Since B = $\pi f_o/2$.
(b) 0 dB = 1, 2 dB = 1.585. $t = F - 1$, or 0 to 0.585. Therefore, $T = 0$ to 169.7 K.

1.11 (a) Noise power density $= kT = 1.38 \times 10^{-23} \times 290 = 4 \times 10^{-21}$ W Hz^{-1}.
(b) Output noise power $= kTB = 4 \times 10^{-21} \times 20 \times 10^3 = 8 \times 10^{-17}$ W.

1.12 Input $S/N = S_{IN}/N_{IN} = S_{IN}/kT_SB$. Output $S/N = (GS_{IN})/(GkT_SB + GkT_nB)$.
Therefore, (output S/N)(input S/N) = $(T_S + T_n)/T_S$.

1.13 5.8 dB = 3.8, 8 dB = 6.3 ratio. Hence $3.8 = F + (3.8 - 1)/6.3$, or $F = 3.356 = 5.26$ dB.

1.14 20 dB = 100, 2.2 dB = 1.66, 4 dB = 2.51 and 10 dB = 10. Therefore, the overall noise factor is
$F_{ov} = 1.66 + (10 - 1)/100 + (10 - 1)/(100/2.51) = 1.98 = 2.97$ dB.
Input noise $= -174$ dBm $+ 10 \log_{10}(120 \times 10^3) = -123.2$ dBm.
Output noise $= -123.2$ dBm $+ 2.97 = -120.2$ dBm.
Minimum input signal $= (1.2 \times 10^{-6})^2/50 = 2.88 \times 10^{-14}$ W $= -107.3$ dBm.
Hence minimum signal-to-noise ratio at demodulator $= -107.3 - (-120.2) = 12.9$ dB.

1.15 (a) $N = -204$ dBW $+ 10 \log_{10}(25 \times 10^6) + 1.45 = -128.55$ dBW.
(b) $P = kB(T_A + T_S) = 1.38 \times 10^{-23} \times 25 \times 10^6 \times (18 + 21) = 1.35 \times 10^{-14}$ W $= -138.7$ dBW.

1.16 0.25 dB = 1.06. $T = 0.06 \times 290 = 17.4$ K. $T_S = 12 + 17.4 = 29.4$ K.
$N_{IN} = 1.38 \times 10^{-23} \times 29.4 \times 1 \times 10^6 = 4.1 \times 10^{-16}$ W.

1.17 $I_n = \sqrt{(4 \times 1.38 \times 10^{-23} \times 290 \times 5 \times 10^6 \times 100 \times 10^{-6})} = 2.83$ nA.

1.18 8 dB = 6.31, 2.5 dB = 1.78, 12 dB = 15.85.
Before LNA is used: $T_S = 60 + (6.31 - 1)290 = 1600$ K.
With LNA, $T_S = 60 + (1.78 - 1)290 + [(6.31 - 1)290]/15.85 = 383.4$ K.

1.19 2 dB = 1.59, 3 dB = 2.
$F_{ov} = 1.59 + (2 - 1)1.59 = 3.18$. $F_{280} = 1 + (290/280)(3.18 - 1) = 3.26 = 5.13$ dB.
Hence output signal-to-noise ratio = $48 - 5.13 \approx 43$ dB which is within limits.

1.20 (a) $N = -204 + 60 = -144$ dBW. (b) $N = -144 + 3 = -141$ dBW.

Chapter 2

2.1 (a) $4.4 = 4\sqrt{(1 + m^2/2)}$. $1.1^2 = 1 + m^2/2$, $m = \sqrt{0.42} = 0.648 = 64.8\%$.
(b) Maximum current = $\sqrt{2} \times 4(1 + 0.648) = 9.323$ A.
　　Minimum current = $\sqrt{2} \times 4(1 - 0.648) = 1.991$ A.

$$I = \sqrt{\left[(1/T)\left(\int_0^{T/2} 9.323^2 \sin^2 \omega_c t\, dt + \int_{T/2}^T 1.991^2 \sin^2 \omega_c t\, dt\right)\right]}$$

$$= \sqrt{\left[(1/T)\left(\int_0^{T/2} 43.459(1 - \cos 2\omega_c t)\, dt + \int_{T/2}^T 1.982(1 - \cos 2\omega_c t)\, dt\right)\right]}$$

$$= \sqrt{\left[(1/T)\left(\int_0^{T/2} 43.459\, dt + \int_{T/2}^T 1.982\, dt\right)\right]} = \sqrt{[(1/T)(43.459\, T/2 + 1.982(T - T/2))]}$$

$$= \sqrt{(21.73 + 0.991)} = 4.77 \text{ A}.$$

2.2 (a) $10.8 = 10\sqrt{(1 + m^2/2)}$, $1.08^2 = 1 + m^2/2$, $m = \sqrt{0.3328} = 0.577 = 57.7\%$.
(b) $10.8 = 10\sqrt{(1 + 0.4^2/2 + m^2/2)}$, $1.08^2 = 1 + 0.08 + m^2/2$, $m = \sqrt{0.1728} = 0.417 = 41.7$.
(c) $10.8 = 10\sqrt{(1 + m_T^2/2)}$, $m_T = 57.7$, or $m_T = \sqrt{(0.4^2 + 0.4517^2)} = \sqrt{0.334} = 57.7\%$.

2.3 Bandwidth = 10 kHz. Impedance of tuned circuit = $Z = R_d/\sqrt{(1 + Q^2 B^2/f_0^2)}$
$$= R_d/\sqrt{[1 + (10^4 \times 10^8)/10^{12}]} = R_d/1.414.$$
At input $V_{SF} = 0.4V_c$; at output $V_{SF} = 0.4V_c/1.414 = 0.283V_c$.
Output depth of modulation = $2 \times 0.283 = 0.566 = 56.6\%$.

2.4 $V_{m(rms)} = \sqrt{(6^2/2 + 3^2/2)} = 4.743$ V. $m = 4.743/(12/\sqrt{2}) = 0.559 = 55.9\%$.
　　$P_T = (12^2/200)(1 + 0.559^2/2) = 832.5$ mW.

2.5 Diode detector input resistance = $250/(2 \times 0.86) = 145.35$ kΩ.
$R_d = Q/\omega C = (60 \times 10^{12})/(2\pi \times 455 \times 10^3 \times 100) = 209.875$ kΩ.
$R_{d(eff)} = 209.875||145.35 = 85.876$ kΩ. Therefore,
$Q_{eff} = 85.876 \times 10^3 \times 2\pi \times 455 \times 10^3 \times 100 \times 10^{-12} = 24.55$.

2.6 Percentage second harmonic = $(0.6 \times 100)/[8(1 + 0.6^2/4)] = 60/8.72 = 6.88\%$.

2.7 Improvement in output signal-to-noise ratio = $3 + 20 \log_{10}[(1 + 0.8)/0.8] \approx 10$ dB.
Reduction in output signal-to-noise due to reduced power = $10 \log_{10}(10/4) \approx 4$ dB.
Improvement in output signal-to-noise ratio = $10 - 4 = 6$ dB. Output signal-to-noise ratio = 36 dB.

2.8 $10.4 = 10\sqrt{(1 + m^2/2)}$, $m \approx 0.4$. Carrier voltage $= 10$ V, side-frequency voltage $= 10 \times 0.4 = 4$ V.

10 dB is a voltage ratio of $\sqrt{10}$. Hence at the output the lower side-frequency voltage $= 4/\sqrt{10}$ V.

$V = \sqrt{(10^2 + 4^2 + 4^2/10)} = 10.84$ V.

2.10 $m_1 = 4.2/10 = 0.42$, $m_2 = 0.21$ and $m_3 = 0.105$.

$m_T = \sqrt{(0.42^2 + 0.21^2 + 0.105^2)} = 0.481$.

Alternatively, $V = \sqrt{(4.2^2/2 + 2.1^2/2 + 1.05^2/2)} \approx 3.4$ V. Carrier r.m.s. value $= 10/\sqrt{2} = 7.07$ V.

$m_T = 3.4/7.07 = 0.481$.

2.11 $v_{out} = VV_C[(\sin \omega_C t \cos \omega_m t - \cos \omega_C t \sin \omega_m t) \sin \omega_C t] = VV_C[\sin(\omega_C - \omega_m)t] \sin \omega_C t$
$\qquad = (VV_C/2)\{\cos[\omega_C - (\omega_C - \omega_m)]t - \cos[\omega_C + (\omega_C - \omega_m)]t\}$
$\qquad = (VV_C/2)[\cos \omega_m t - \cos(2\omega_C - \omega_m)t]$. The second term is removed by a filter.

2.12 (a) $P_T = 20(1 + 0.65^2/2) = 24.225$ W. (b) Percentage carrier power $= (20/24.225) \times 100 = 82.6\%$. (c) LSF power $= (24.555 - 20)/2 = 2.11$ kW.

2.13 (a) $m_T = \sqrt{(0.25^2 + 0.5^2 + 0.65^2)} = 0.857$. (b) $P_T = 1(1 + 0.857^2/2) = 1367.2$ kW. (c) $P_{SF} = 1367.2 - 1000 = 367.2$ W.

2.14 The amplitude A of the modulated wave $[1 + m \cos \omega t + (m/3) \cos 2\omega t] \cos \omega_C t$ must always be greater than, or equal to, 0.

$dA/dt = -m\omega \sin \omega t - 0.33 \, m \times 2\omega \cos 2\omega t = -m\omega \sin \omega t - 0.66 \, m\omega(2 \sin \omega t \cos \omega t)$
$\qquad = -m\omega \sin \omega t(1 + 1.32 \cos \omega t) = 0$.

Hence, $\cos \omega t = -1/1.32 = -0.758$, and $\omega t = 139.3°$. $2\omega t = 278.6°$.

$A = [1 + m \times \cos 139.3° + (m/3) \cos 278.6°] = 1 - 0.758 \, m + 0.15 \times m/3 = 1 - 0.71m$.

Therefore, $m = 1/0.71 = 1.41$.

2.15 Baseband is the range of frequencies occupied by the moduating signal. Its bandwidth is equal to the highest frequency in the baseband. Bandwidth is the range of frequencies occupied by a signal. For an AM wave it is equal to twice the baseband.

Chapter 3

3.1 (a) $P_T = 1000(1 + 0.5^2/2) = 1125$ W.

(b) No change in voltage so no change in power. $P_T = 1000$ W.

3.2 Output S/N ratio $= 30 + 20 \log_{10}[(\sqrt{3} \times 10)/3] + 10 \log_{10} 2$
$\qquad\qquad\qquad = 30 + 15.23 + 3.01 = 48.24$ dB.

3.3 $f_1 = 1/(2\pi \times 75 \times 10^{-6}) = 2122$ Hz.

(AM noise power)/(FM noise power) $=$

$[(75 \times 10^3)^2 \tan^{-1}(15\,000/2122)]/\{2122^2[15\,000/2122 - \tan^{-1}(15\,000/2122)]\}$
$= (1249.2 \times 1.43)/(7.069 - 1.43) = 316.8 = 25$ dB.

Improvement $= 25 - 18.75 = 6.25$ dB.

3.4 $m_f = 7$. $v = V_c \sin[200\pi \times 10^6 t + 7 \sin(10\pi \times 10^3 t)]$ V.
The amplitudes of the components are obtained from the $J_n(7)$ column of Table 3.1.
Suppose a 1 Ω resistance; then
$P = V_c^2(0.3^2 + 2 \times 0.0047^2 + 2 \times 0.3479^2 + 2 \times 0.3014^2 + 2 \times 0.1676^2 + 2 \times 0.1578^2 + 2 \times 0.3392^2 + 2 \times 0.2336^2 + 2 \times 0.128^2) = 0.967V_c^2$.
Percentage of power in the first $(m_f + 1)$ side frequencies $= (0.967V_c^2)/V_c^2 \times 100 = 96.7\%$.

3.5 Peak frequency deviation $= (V_n/V_c) \times$ frequency difference
$$= (50 \times 10^{-6})/(1.5 \times 10^{-3}) \times 0.1 \times 10^{-6} = 3333.3 \text{ Hz}.$$

3.7 (a) At the output of the third multiplier, $f_0 = 1 \times 6 \times 8 \times 6 = 288$ MHz with a frequency deviation of $1 \times 6 \times 8 \times 6 = 288$ kHz.
The mixer output $= 288 \pm 200$ MHz and 488 MHz is selected.
(b) Multiplication of 75 is required, e.g. $5 \times 5 \times 3$ to give a frequency deviation of 75 kHz.
To obtain a 96 MHz carrier mix with 21 MHz. Then output of mixer $= 75 \pm 21$ and select 96 MHz.

3.8 Rated system deviation $= 5.8 \times 12 = 69.6$ kHz.
(a) $m_f = (15/18) \times (69.6/5) = 11.6$. (b) $m_f = (8/18) \times (69.6/8) = 3.87$.

3.9 (a) $f_d = 15 \times 600 = 9000$ Hz. (b) $kf_d = 9000 \times 10/12 = 7500$ Hz. (c) $kf_d = 9000 \times 8/12 = 6000$ Hz, and $m_f = 6000/1700 = 3.53$. (d) $B = 2(6000 + 1700) = 15.4$ kHz.

3.10 The phasor diagram is shown by Fig. 3.10.

Fig. 3.10

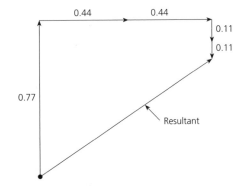

3.11 (a) Peak frequency deviation $= 5 \times 11 = 55$ kHz. (b) $m_f = 55/3 = 18.3$.

3.12 (c) S/N increase $= (4/2.5)^2 = 2.56 \approx 8.2$ dB.

3.13 (a) $f_d = 1.5 \times 8 = 12$ kHz. (b) $m_f = 12/3 = 4$.

Chapter 4

4.2 Increase in M reduces B but increases the required signal level.

4.3 $m_f = 600/1200 = 0.5$.

4.4 (a) $B = (1 \times 10^6)/\log_2 2 = 1$ MHz. (b) $B = 1/\log_2 4 = 500$ kHz. (c) $B = 1/\log_2 8 = 333.3$ kHz.

4.7 0000 gives $- 0.22 \cos \omega_c t - 0.22 \sin \omega_c t = 0.311 \cos(\omega_c t + 135°)$,
0001 gives $- 0.22 \cos \omega_c t - 0.821 \sin \omega_c t = 0.85 \cos(\omega_c t + 105°)$,
0010 gives $- 0.22 \cos \omega_c t + 0.22 \sin \omega_c t = 0.311 \cos(\omega_c t - 135°)$,
0011 gives $- 0.22 \cos \omega_c t + 0.821 \sin \omega_c t = 0.85 \cos(\omega_c t - 105°)$,
0100 gives $- 0.821 \cos \omega_c t - 0.22 \sin \omega_c t = 0.85 \cos(\omega_c t + 165°)$,
0101 gives $- 0.821 \cos \omega_c t - 0.821 \sin \omega_c t = 1.161 \cos(\omega_c t + 135°)$, and, lastly,
0110 gives $- 0.821 \cos \omega_c t + 0.22 \sin \omega_c t = 0.85 \cos(\omega_c t - 165°)$

4.8 (ai) $\eta = 1000/(1000/4) = 4$ b/s/Hz. (aii) $\eta = 1M/(1M/4) = 4$ b/s/Hz.
(bi) $\eta = 1000/(1000/4) = 4$ b/s/Hz. (bii) $\eta = 1M/(1M/4) = 4$ b/s/Hz.
(c) $\eta = 6$ b/s/Hz.

4.9 The input signal is $-\cos \omega_c t + \sin \omega_c t$.
I channel: $I = (-\cos \omega_c t + \sin \omega_c t) \cos \omega_c t = -0.5(1 + \cos 2\omega_c t) + 0.5 \sin 2\omega_c t$. Only the first term is passed by the filter to give $I = -0.5 =$ logic 0.
Q channel: $Q = (-\cos \omega_c t + \sin \omega_c t) \sin \omega_c t = +0.5 =$ logic 1.

4.10 The constellation diagram is shown by Fig. 4.36.

Fig. 4.36

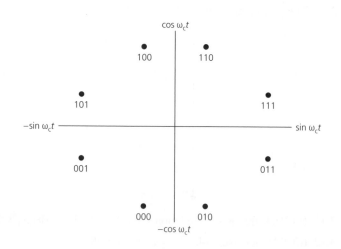

4.11 (a) $E_B = (5 \times 10^{-14})/(33 \times 10^3) = 1.52 \times 10^{-18}$ J.
(b) $E_S = 3E_B = 4.56 \times 10^{-18}$ J. (c) $N_0 = N/B = (5 \times 10^{-17})/(70 \times 10^3) = 7/14 \times 10^{-22}$ WHz^{-1}.
$E_B/N_0 = (1.52 \times 10^{-18})/(7.14 \times 10^{-22}) = 2129$ or 33.3 dB.

4.12 Minimum bandwidth $= 12/3 = 4$ MHz. Hence bandwidth $= 4.8$ MHz $= 10 \log_{10}(4.8 \times 10^6) = 66.8$ dB. $R_B = 10 \log_{10}(12 \times 10^6) = 70.8$ dB. Carrier-to-noise ratio $= 14.7 - 66.8 + 70.8 = 18.7$ dB.

Chapter 5

5.1 $\rho_v = [(1200 + j300) - 600]/(1800 + j300) = 0.368\angle 17.1°$.
At the sending end, V_i and I_i; at the receiving end $-V_i/2$ and $-I_i/2$.
These values are reflected to give $(-0.368V_i/2)\angle 17.1°$ and $(0.368I_i/2)\angle 17.1°$.
At the sending end the reflected waves are: $(0.368V_i/4)\angle 17.1°$ and $(-0.368I_i/4)\angle 17.1°$.
Total sending-end voltage $= V_s = V_i[1 + (0.368/4)\angle 17.1°] = V_i(1.088 + j0.0271)$.
Total sending-end current $= I_s = I_i[1 - (0.368/4)\angle 17.1°] = I_i(0.912 - j0.0271)$.
Input impedance $= V_s/I_s = [V_i(1.088 + j0.0271)]/[I_i(0.912 - j0.0271)] = 716\angle 3.1°$ Ω.

5.2 Required reactance $= j2\pi \times 600 \times 10^6 \times 20 \times 10^{-9} = j75$ Ω. $\lambda = 0.5$ m.
Hence $j75 = j50 \tan(2\pi l/0.5)$, $\tan^{-1}(1.5) = 0.983 = 4\pi l$, and $l = 7.82$ cm.

5.3 $|Z_{in}| = Z_0 = 600$ Ω. $\angle Z_{IN} = \tan^{-1}(600/800 - 800/600) = 30.1°$.
Power in matched load (with $\lambda/2$ section) $= V^2/600$.
Power in mismatched load $= V^2/600 - (\rho_v V)^2/600 = (V^2/600)(1 - 0.02) = 0.98V^2/600$.
Ratio $= 10 \log_{10}[(V^2/600)(600/0.98V^2)] = 0.09$ dB.

5.4 Impedance of fault $= 1/(2\pi \times 500 \times 10^{-6} \times 4.244 \times 10^{-12}) = -j75$ Ω.
Hence, at 2 m from the aerial the total line impedance is $75 - j75$ Ω.
At fault $\rho_v = [(75 - j75) - 75]/[(75 - j75) + 75] = 0.45\angle -63.4°$.
Length of line to fault $= \beta x = 4$ m. $\lambda = 0.6$ m, so $\beta x = 6.66$ λ.
ρ_v at input $= \rho_v e^{-2\beta x} = 0.45\angle -63.4° \times 1\angle -120° = 0.45\angle -183.4°$.

5.8 0.2 dB m^{-1} $= 0.2/8.686 = 0.023$ N m^{-1}. $\lambda = (3 \times 10^8)/(900 \times 10^6) = 1/3$ m.
$Q = \pi/\alpha\lambda = 3\pi/0.023 \approx 410$.

5.9 $\lambda = 1.1628$ m, so 16.28 cm $= 0.01\lambda = 36°$ and 14.5 cm $\approx 0.125\lambda = 45°$.
$Z_A = 100[(166 \cos 36° + j100 \sin 36°)/(100 \cos 36° + j166 \sin 36°)] = 115.62\angle -26.7°$ Ω.
$Z_B = 100[(37.5 \cos 45° + j100 \sin 45°)/(100 \cos 45° + j37.5 \sin 45°)] = 100\angle 45.6°$ Ω.
$Z_T = Z_A Z_B/(Z_A + Z_B) = 54.3\angle 53.5°$ $\Omega = 32.3 + j43.7$ Ω. Hence $\rho_v = (32.3 + j43.7 - 100)/(132.3 + j43.7) = 0.62\angle 128.9°$. $S = 1.62/0.38 = 4.26$.

5.11 (a) $\rho_v = 0.33$. Hence, $40 = V_i(1 + 0.33)$, and $V_i = 30$ V. $V_r = 0.33 \times 30 = 10$ V.
Minima occur along the line at odd $\lambda/4$ intervals from the load and since the line is $3\lambda/4$ long the input voltage is $40 - 10 = 30$ V.
(b) $I_i = 30/75 = 400$ mA. $I_r = -0.33 \times 400 = -133$ mA. Maximum current at the sending end is equal to $400 + 133 = 533$ mA.
(c) Distance from load to first current maximum (or first voltage minimum) $= \lambda/4$.
(d) Fraction of incident power reflected $= \rho^2 = 0.33^2 \approx 0.1$.

5.13 $\rho_v = [(150 - j60) - 100]/[(150 - j60) + 100] = 0.3\angle 36.7°$.
$\lambda/3 = 120°$. Incident I and V at load $= V_i\angle -120°$ and $I_i\angle -120°$. Reflected values $= 0.3V_i\angle(-120° + 36.7°)$ and $-0.3I_i\angle(-120° + 36.7°)$. Reflected values at sending end $= 0.3V_i\angle(-240° + 36.7°)$ and $-0.3I_i\angle(-240° + 36.7°)$.
$V_S = V_i + 0.3V_i\angle -203°$ and $I_S = I_i + 0.3I_i\angle -23.3°$.
$Z_S = V_S/I_S = [V_i(1 + 0.3\angle -203°)]/[I_i(1 + 0.3\angle -23.3°)] = 57.3\angle 14.6$ Ω.

5.14 $|\rho_v| = (S-1)/(S+1) = 2/3$. The incident and reflected voltage phasors must be $180°$ out of phase $\lambda/3$ from the load. $\lambda/3 = 120°$ so $180° = 120° + \angle\rho_v + 120°$, or $\angle\rho_v = -60°$.
$(Z_L - 50)/(Z_L + 50) = (2\angle{-60°})/3$.
$3Z_L - 150 = (2\angle{-60°})Z_L + 100\angle{-60°}$. $Z_L(3 - 2\angle{-60°}) = 100\angle{-60°} + 150$.
$Z_L = [50 + j86.6 + 150]/[3 - 2\angle{-60°}] = (200 - j86.6)/(2 + j1.73) = 82.4\angle{-64.3°}\ \Omega$.

5.15 $I_x = [(V_s e^{-\gamma x})/2Z_0 + (I_s e^{-\gamma x})/2] - [(V_s e^{\gamma x})/2Z_0 - I_s e^{\gamma x}/2]$
$\qquad = I_s[(e^{\gamma x} + e^{-\gamma x})/2 - (V_s/Z_0)[e^{\gamma x} - e^{-\gamma x})/2 = I_s \cosh\gamma x - (V_s/Z_0) \sinh\gamma x$.

5.16 (a) $\rho_v = 50/150 = 1/3$. $S = (1 + 1/3)/(1 - 1/3) = 2$.
(b) $\rho_v = (100 + j100 - 50)/(100 + j100 + 50) = 0.62\angle29.7°$. $S = (1 + 0.62)/(1 - 0.62) = 4.26$.
(c) Return loss for (a) $= 20 \log_{10}(1/3) = 9.54$ dB. Return loss for (b) $= 20 \log_{10} 0.62 = 4.15$ dB.

5.17 $Z_0 = \sqrt{(12 \times 10^{-6})/(4.8 \times 10^{-9})} = 50\ \Omega$.
$Z_{in} = j50 \tan\beta l < j50 \tan(2\pi l\lambda)$
$\lambda = (3 \times 10^8)(15 \times 10^6) = 20$ m
$Z_{in} = j50 \tan(\pi/10) = 0.274\ \Omega$.

Chapter 6

6.1 $1/\lambda_0^2 = 2/\lambda_G^2 = 2/\lambda_C^2 = 2/(2a)^2 = 1/2a^2 = 1/[2(2.8 \times 10^{-2})^2] = 637.755$.
$\lambda_C = \sqrt{(1/637.755)} = 3.96$ cm and $f = c/\lambda_0 = 7.576$ GHz.

6.2 $\lambda_0 = 0.093\,75$ m. For $f = 3.2$ GHz Table 6.1 gives $a = 7.214$ cm and $b = 3.404$ cm. Hence $P_{max} = \{[(1.5 \times 10^6)^2 \times 7.214 \times 3.404 \times 10^{-4}]/480\pi\}\{\sqrt{[1 - (9.375/(2 \times 7.214))^2]}\} = 2.785$ MW.

6.3 $\lambda_0 = 7.5 \times 10^{-3}$ m.
(a) $\lambda_C = 2a = 1.1138$ cm. $f_C = (3 \times 10^8)/(1.1138 \times 10^{-2}) = 26.362$ GHz.
(b) $1/\lambda_G^2 = 1/(7.5 \times 10^{-3})^2 - 1/(1.1138 \times 10^{-2})^2$. $\lambda_G = 1.0145$ cm.
(c) $v_P = c\lambda_G/\lambda_0 = (3 \times 10^8 \times 1.0145)/0.75 = 4.058 \times 10^8$ m s^{-1}.
$v_G = c^2/v_P = (9 \times 10^{16})/(4.058 \times 10^8) = 2.218 \times 10^8$.

6.4 $\rho_v = (1/\sqrt{2} - 1)/(1/\sqrt{2} + 1) = -0.172$. $S = 1.172/0.828 = 1.42$.

6.5 $\lambda_C = 2a = 0.0316$ m. $f_C = c/\lambda_C = 9.4937$ GHz. Therefore $f = 18.987$ GHz and $\lambda_0 = c/f = 0.0158$ m. $1/\lambda_G^2 = 1/0.0158^2 - 1/0.0316^2$, $\lambda_G = 0.0182$ m. $\cos\theta = 0.0158/0.0182 = 0.868$, $\theta = 29.8°$.

6.7 (a) $\lambda_0 = 0.03$ m. (b) $\lambda_C = 2a = 4.6$ cm. $f_C = c/\lambda_C = 6.522$ GHz.
(c) $v_P = f\lambda_G = 10^{10} \times 3.96 \times 10^{-2} = 3.96 \times 10^8$ m s^{-1}.
(d) $v_G = c^2/v_P = (9 \times 10^{16})/(3.96 \times 10^8) = 2.273 \times 10^8$ m s^{-1}.
(e) $\lambda_G = 3.96$ cm.

6.8 (a) $\lambda_C = 2a = 5.7$ cm. $\lambda_0 = \lambda_C/2 = 2.85$ cm. $1/\lambda_G^2 = 1/0.0285^2 - 1/0.057^2$, and $\lambda_G = 3.3$ cm.
(b) $\cos\theta = \lambda_0/\lambda_G = 2.85/3.3 = 0.864$, and $\theta = 30.3°$.

6.9 (a) $v_P = c/\cos\theta = (3 \times 10^8)/0.5 = 6 \times 10^8$ ms^{-1}.
(b) $v_G = c^2/v_P = 1.5 \times 10^8$ m s^{-1}. (e) $\lambda_c = 2a = 4.58$ cm. (c) $6 = 1.5\lambda_G/\lambda_0$, so $\lambda_G = 4\lambda_0$. $1/(4\lambda_0)^2 = 1/\lambda_0^2 - 1/0.0458^2$, and $\lambda_0 = 4.43$ cm.
(d) $\lambda_G = 4\lambda = 17.72$ cm.

6.10 $\lambda_0 = a\sqrt{2}$ m. $f = c/a\sqrt{2} = (3 \times 10^8)/(28 \times 10^{-3} \times \sqrt{2}) = 7.58$ GHz.

6.11 $1/\lambda_0^2 = 1/12^2 + 1/16^2$. $f = (3 \times 10^{10})/9.6 = 3.125$ GHz.

6.12 $\lambda_G = 2\lambda_c = 4a = 4 \times 2.86 = 11.44$ cm. From equation (6.3) $11.44 = \lambda_0/\sqrt{[1 - (\lambda_0/5.72)^2]}$ giving $\lambda_0 = 5.116$ cm and $f = c/\lambda_0 = 5.87$ GHz.

6.13 $f = c\sqrt{[1/(60^2 \times 10^{-6}) + 1/(4 \times 40^2 \times 10^{-6})]} = 5.83$ GHz.

6.14 (a) $1/\lambda_c^2 = 1/\lambda_0^2 - 1/\lambda_G^2 = 1/4.8^2 - 1/8^2$ $\lambda_c^2 = 36$. Hence $\lambda_c = 6$ cm.
(b) $\lambda_0 = \sqrt{(3600/136)} = 5.145$ cm. $f = (3 \times 10^8)/(5.145 \times 10^{-2}) = 5.83$ GHz.

6.15 (a) $1/\lambda_G^2 = (f/c)^2 - (f_c/c)^2 = (f^2 - f_c^2)/c^2$. $\lambda_G = c/\sqrt{(f^2 - f_c^2)}$.
(b) $\lambda_c = 5.7$ cm, $f_c = 5.263$ GHz, so $f = 10.526$ GHz. Hence, $\lambda_G = (3 \times 10^8)/\sqrt{(10.526^2 \times 10^{18} - 5.263^2 \times 10^{18})} = 3.29$ cm.

6.16 $\lambda_G = 16$ cm. $\lambda_0 = (3 \times 10^8)/(3.125 \times 10^9) = 9.6$ cm. Hence $\lambda_c = 12$ cm and $f_c = 2.5$ GHz.

6.17 (c) $\lambda_0 = 1/\sqrt{[(1/10 \times 10^{-2})^2 + (1/12 \times 10^{-2})^2]} = 7.68$ cm
$f = (3 \times 10^8)/(7.68 \times 10^{-2}) = 3.906$ GHz.

6.18 (a) At $1.1f_c$ losses are high, at least double the loss at $1.5f_c$. (b) $\lambda_c = (3 \times 10^8)/(8 \times 10^{-2}) = 3.75$ GHz. Lowest frequency $= 1.25f_c = 4.6875$ GHz. (ii) At 5 GHz $\lambda_0 = 6$ cm. $1/\lambda_G^2 = 1/36 - 1/64$, $\lambda_G = 9.071$ cm.

Chapter 7

7.1 (a) $R_r = 40\pi^2(\lambda/\pi)^2/\lambda^2 = 40$ Ω.
(b) $\lambda/\pi = 23.87$ m, so $l_{eff} = 23.87/2 = 11.94$ m.
(c) $E = (120\pi \times 11.94 \times 10)/(75 \times 30 \times 10^3) = 20$ mV m^{-1}.
(d) $P_R = E^2/120\pi \times A_e = E^2/120\pi \times \lambda^2/4\pi \times G_r$. 12 dB $= 15.85$, so $P_r = [(20 \times 10^{-3})^2/120\pi][75^2/4\pi] \times 15.85 = 7.53$ mW.
(e) $P_T = I^2R_r = 10^2 \times 40 = 4$ kW.

7.2 $\lambda = 0.5$ m. $A_{e(iso)} = \lambda^2/4\pi = 0.02$ m^2. $A_{e(\lambda/2)} = 0.13\lambda^2 = 0.0325$ M^2.
(a) $G = 4/0.02 = 200 = 23$ dBi, $G = 2/0.02 = 100 = 20$ dBi.
(b) $G = 4/0.0325 = 123.08 = 20.9$ dB, $G = 2/0.0325 = 61.54 = 17.9$ dB.

7.3 At a distance of $\lambda/2\pi$ or 15.916 m from the aerial.
(a) $E = 377 \times 265 \times 10^{-6} = 100$ mV m^{-1}.
(b) $P_d = E^2/120\pi = 26.53$ μW m^{-2}.

7.4 $E = (300\sqrt{P_T})/D = (300\sqrt{100})/100 = 30$ mV m^{-1}.

7.5 $\theta = 90°$, so, from equation (7.25), $E_T = 120I/D = 360/10 = 36$ mV m^{-1}.

7.6 $P_T = 160\pi^2 \times 0.1^2 \times 100^2 = 157.91$ kW. EIRP $= 3 \times 157.91 = 431.73$ kW.
$E_{50} = (120\pi \times 100 \times 0.1)/50 = 75.4$ mV m^{-1}.
Alternatively, $E_{50} = \sqrt{(30 \times 157.91 \times 10^3 \times 3)}/50 = 75.4$ mV m^{-1}.

7.7 $\lambda = 450$ m. $\lambda/4 = 112.5$ m.
Distance y varies from $l = 112.5$ m to $(112.5 - 48 - 30) = 34.5$ m.
$I_{in} = 80 = I_0 \cos[360°/450(112.5 - 34.5)] = I_0 \cos 62.4° = 0.463I_0$.
Therefore, $I_0 = 80/0.463 = 172.8$ A.

$$I_{mean} = [172.8/(112.5 - 78)] \int_{78}^{112.5} \cos(2\pi y/450)dy = 5[\sin(2\pi y/450)/(2\pi/450)]_{78}^{112.5}$$

$= 358(\sin 90° - \sin 62.4°) = 40.8$ A.
(a) Effective length $= (78 \times 40.8)/80 = 39.78$ m. (Approximately, $l_{eff} = l_{phys}/2 = 78/2 = 39$ m.)
(b) $E = (120\pi \times 80 \times 39.78)/(450 \times 40 \times 10^3) = 66.7$ mV m^{-1}.

7.8 $\lambda = 0.5$ m. 30 dBi $= 1000$. $P_R/P_T = 10^3 \times 10^3 \times [0.5/(4\pi \times 30 \times 10^3)]^2 = 1.76 \times 10^{-6}$.
Attenuation $= 10 \log_{10}(1.76 \times 10^{-6}) = 57.6$ dB.

7.9 $R_r = 20\pi^2(l_{phys}/\lambda)^2$. The aerial is a monopole so its apparent length is $\lambda/8$.
$R_r = 20\pi^2/8^2 = 3.08$ Ω. But the actual radiated power is only 50% of that predicted, so
$R_r = 3.08/2 = 1.54$ Ω. $P_r = 100^2 \times 1.54 = 15.4$ kW.
Aerial efficiency $= [1.54/(1.54 + 25)] \times 100 = 5.8\%$.

7.10 Apparent physical length $= 200$ m. Since the current distribution is linear, $l_{eff} = 100$ m.
$E = (120\pi \times 200 \times 100 \times 10^5)/(3 \times 10^8 \times 20 \times 10^3) = 126$ mV m^{-1}.

7.11 10 dB $= 10$, and 30 dB $= 1000$ power ratio.
(a) EIRP $= 10$ kW. (b) $P_d = (10 \times 10^3)/(4\pi \times 30 \times 10^3) = 0.884$ μW m^{-2}.
(c) $A_e = 1000 \times \lambda^2/4\pi$ and $\lambda = 3$ m. Hence $A_e = (1000 \times 9)/4\pi$, and
$P_R = A_e P_d = 0.884 \times 10^{-6} \times 9000/4\pi = 633$ μW.

7.12 (a) 10 W $= 10$ dBW. EIRP $= 10 + 28 = 38$ dBW. (b) $E = \sqrt{(30 \times 631)}/10 = 13.76$ mV
m^{-1}. (c) $H = (13.76 \times 10^{-3})/377 = 36.5$ A m^{-1}.

7.13 40 W $= 16$ dBW. Hence, $P_R = 16 + 30 + 30 - 85 = -9$ dBW.

7.14 $R_r = 0.5[80\pi^2(2l_{eff})^2/\lambda^2] = 40\pi^2 l_{eff}^2/\lambda^2 \approx 400l_{eff}^2/\lambda^2 = 400 \times [(10 \times 10^{-2})/(150 \times 10^{-2})]^2$
$= 1.78$ Ω.

7.15 $P_T = 80\pi^2 I^2(l/\lambda)^2 = 40\pi^2 \times 400 \times (1/16)^2 = 616.85$ W. $R_r = 2 \times 616.86/400 = 3.08$ Ω.

Chapter 8

8.1 $E_T = \sqrt{(E_A^2 + E_B^2 + 2E_A E_B \cos \psi)} = \sqrt{[E_A^2 + (1.5E_A)^2 + 2E_A \times 1.5E_A \cos \psi]}$
$\qquad = E_A\sqrt{(3.25 + 3 \cos \psi)} = E_A\sqrt{[3.25 + 3 \cos(\phi + \alpha)]}$.
$\alpha = \pi/2$ and $\phi = (\pi/2) \cos \theta$. Hence $\psi = (\pi/2)(1 + \cos \theta)$. Tabulate for values of θ from
0° to 180°.

8.2 $\psi = (2\pi/\lambda)(\lambda \cos \theta/2) + \pi/2 = \pi \cos \theta + \pi/2$.
Therefore, $E_T = E \sin[(4/2)(\pi \cos \theta + \pi/2)]/[\sin(\pi \cos \theta + \pi/2)]$.

Maximum radiation when $\pi \cos \theta + \pi/2 = 0$, or when $\pi \cos \theta = -\pi/2$. Hence $\theta = \cos^{-1} 0.5 = 120°$.

8.3 $I_P/I_D = -(40 - j30)/(81 + j108) = 0.37\angle -10°$.
In direction parasitic to dipole, field strength is proportional to $1 + 0.37\angle -100° = 1.0043$. In the other direction field strength is proportional to $1 + 0.37\angle 80° = 1.1245$. Greater field strength in direction dipole to parasitic so it is a reflector.

8.4 $Z_A = 73 + (-12 - j30) + (5 + j17.5) = 66 - j12.5 \ \Omega$. Radiated power $= I^2 66$ W.
$Z_B = 73 + (-12 - j30) + (-12 - j30) = 49 - j60 \ \Omega$. Radiated power $= I^2 49$ W.
$Z_C = Z_A$, so radiated power $= I^2 66$ W.
Total power radiated $= I^2(66 + 49 + 66) = I^2 181$ W.
If the same power were radiated by a single dipole the necessary aerial current would be $\sqrt{(181I^2/73)} = 1.575I$. Therefore gain $= 20 \log_{10}(3E/1.575E) = 5.6$ dB. (Note that if the mutual impedances are ignored the gain is $20 \log_{10} \sqrt{3} = 4.77$ dB.)

8.6 $\lambda = 0.06$ m. $60 = 10 \log_{10}[0.6 \times \pi^2(D/0.06)^2]$. Hence $D^2 = (0.06^2 \times 10^6)/0.6\pi^2 \approx 608$ and $D \approx 24.66$ m. $A_e = \pi(24.66/2)^2 = 477 \ m^2$.

8.7 Three dipoles in a line produce $E_T = E \sin(1.5\pi d/\lambda)/\sin(\pi d/\lambda)$
    Five dipoles in a line produce $E_T = E \sin(2.5\pi d/\lambda)/\sin(\pi d/\lambda)$.
Overall field strength $= [E^2 \sin(1.5\pi d/\lambda) \sin(2.5\pi d/\lambda)]/[\sin^2(\pi d/\lambda)]$.

8.8 $\lambda = 0.0273$ m. $G = 56$ dBi $= 398\ 107 = \pi^2 D^2/0.0273^2$, $D^2 = 30.06 \ m^2$.
$A_e = \pi D^2/4 = 23.6 \ m^2$.
Beamwidth $= 70\lambda/D = (70 \times 0.0273)/5.483 = 0.35°$.

8.9 $\phi = (2\pi/\lambda)3\lambda \cos \theta = 6\pi \cos \theta$. $\psi_A = -\pi/2 - 6\pi \cos \theta$. $\psi_B = \pi/2 + 6\pi \cos \theta$
$E_T = E + 0.5E \cos(-\pi/2 - 6\pi \cos \theta) + 0.5E \cos(\pi/2 + 6\pi \cos \theta)$
    $= E + 0.5E[\cos(-\pi/2) \cos(6\pi \cos \theta) + \sin(-\pi/2)\sin(6\pi \cos \theta)]$
    $+ 0.5E[\cos(\pi/2) \cos(6\pi \cos \theta) - \sin(\pi/2) \sin(6\pi \cos \theta)]$
    $= E[1 - \sin(6\pi \cos \theta)]$

8.10 $Z = 60\pi^2/(73.2 + j42.5) = 365 - j212 \ \Omega$.

8.11 (b) $P_d = (1.8 \times 1644)/(4\pi \times 10^8) = 2.36 \ \mu W/m^2$.

(c) At $1.35°$ from the direction of maximum radiation $P_d = 2.36/2 = 1.18 \ \mu W/m^2$.

8.12 The gain is directly proportional to the ratio A/λ^2, where A is the area of the dish. Hence, gain is reduced by the ratio (λ^2 at 6 GHz)/(λ^2 at 4.5 GHz) $= 5^2/6.66^2 = 0.563$. Gain at 4.5 GHz $= 39 - 10 \log_{10} 0.563 = 36.5$ dB.
    Beamwidth is proportional to λ/A. Hence, beamwidth is increased by the ratio $6.66/5 = 1.33$. Beamwidth at 4 GHz $= 1.33 \times 3.75 = 5°$.

8.13 $G = 4\pi A\eta/\lambda^2$. $\lambda = 0.577$ m. Hence, $A = (2500 \times 0.0577^2)/(4\pi \times 0.7) = 0.944 \ m^2$.

8.14 (b) $\lambda = 0.075$ m. $G = 0.72\pi^2(4/0.075)^2 = 20\ 213 = 43.1$ dBi.

Chapter 9

9.1 Required length = grazing height + 0.577 times the first Fresnel zone radius. Thus, $48 \times 10^3 = \sqrt{(2h_t \times 0.65 \times 6400 \times 10^3)}$, or $h_t = 69.23$ m (grazing height).
First Fresnel zone: $r = \sqrt{(D_1^2 \lambda/2D_1)} = \sqrt{(D_1\lambda/2)}$. $\lambda = 0.15$ m.
$$r = \sqrt{[(24 \times 10^3 \times 0.15)/2]} = 42.43 \text{ m}. \quad 0.577r = 24.48 \text{ m}.$$
Therefore required height = 69.23 + 24.48 = 93.71 m.
(b) For flat earth the field strength at the receiving aerial is maximum when $2\pi h^2/\lambda D = \pi/2$, or $h = 42.43$ m. Received field strength is zero when $2\pi h^2/\lambda D = \pi$, or $h = 60$ m. Difference = $60 - 42.43 = 17.57$ m. Therefore, second aerial height = 93.71 + 17.57 = 111.28 m.

9.2 $f_{crit} = 9\sqrt{N_{max}} = 9\sqrt{(1.6 \times 10^{11})} = 3.6$ MHz.
From Fig. 9.10(b), $d = 1000 - 6400 \cos \theta$, or $\theta = 0.156$ rad $= 8.94°$.
$x^2 = 6400^2 + (6400 + 162)^2 - (2 \times 6400 \times 6562 \cos 8.95°)$, or $x = 1024.16$ km.
Hence, $6400/\sin \phi_i = 1024.16/\sin 8.94°$, $\sin \phi_i = 0.972$, and $\phi_i = 76.5°$.
Therefore, MUF $= 3.6/(\cos 76.5°) = 15.4$ MHz.

9.3 (a) With zero ground losses, $E_{110} = 200/110 = 1.818$ mV m^{-1}.
With 9 dB loss, $E_{110} = 1.818/2.82 = 0.65$ mV m^{-1}.
(b) The sky wave travels a distance of $2\sqrt{(120^2 + 55^2)} = 264$ km. Hence sky wave $E = 200/264 = 0.76$ mV m^{-1}.
Maximum E when waves are in phase = $0.76 + 0.65 = 1.41$ mV m^{-1}.
Minimum E when waves are in anti-phase = $0.76 - 0.65 = 0.11$ mV m^{-1}.

9.4 $D_{max} = = \sqrt{(2 \times 110 \times 6400 \times 10^3 \times 4/3)} + \sqrt{(2 \times 60 \times 6400 \times 10^3 \times 4/3)} = 75.33$ km.

9.5 $\lambda = 6$ m. $\phi = 4\pi h_t h_r/\lambda D = (4\pi \times 180 \times 16)/(6 \times 18 \times 10^3) = 0.335$ rad $= 19.2°$.
$E_1/D = \sqrt{(30P_T G_T)/D} = \sqrt{(30 \times 5 \times 4)/18} = 1.36$ mV m^{-1}.
$E_T = 1.36[\sqrt{(1 + 0.8^2 - 2 \times 0.8 \cos 19.2°)}] = 0.49$ mV m^{-1}.

9.6 (a) $\lambda = 0.075$ m. Transmission loss = $[(4\pi \times 35\,800 \times 10^3)/0.075]^2 = 3.598 \times 10^{19}$.
Received power = (EIRP $\times G_r$)/loss = $(10^3 \times 10^6)/(3.598 \times 10^{19}) = 27.8$ pW.
System noise temperature $T_S = 60 + 40 = 100$ K.
Hence input noise = $kT_S B = 1.38 \times 10^{-23} \times 100 \times 30 \times 10^6 = 4.14 \times 10^{-14}$ W.
C/N ratio = $10 \log_{10}[(27.8 \times 10^{-12})/(4.14 \times 10^{-14})] = 28.27$ dB.
(b) G/T ratio = $C/N \times (kB/P_T G_T)(4\pi D/\lambda)^2 = 0.01 = 40$ dB K^{-1}.

9.7 $\lambda = 0.05$ m. (a) $N_{IN} = kT_A B = 1.38 \times 10^{-23} \times 290 \times 20 \times 10^6 = 8 \times 10^{-14}$ W.
$N_0 = FGkT_A B = 2G \times 8 \times 10^{-14} = 16G \times 10^{-14}$ W. $S_{IN} = P_R = 16 \times 10^{-14} \times 1000 = 16 \times 10^{-11}$ W.
$P_R = P_d A_e$. $G_R = 10^5 = A_e/A_{e(iso)} = A_e/(\lambda^2/4\pi)$. Hence $A_e = (10^5 \times 0.05^2)/4\pi$ and $P_d = P_R/A_e = 8 \times 10^{-12}$ W m^{-2}.
(b) $P_a = E^2/120\pi$. Hence $E = \sqrt{(120\pi \times 8 \times 10^{-12})} = 54.92$ μV m^{-1}.
(c) $E = 54.92 \times 10^{-6} = [\sqrt{(30 \times P_T \times 4)}]/(36 \times 10^6)$, or $P_T = 32.58$ kW.

9.8 $f_{crit} = 9\sqrt{N_{max}} = 3.6$ MHz. Hence $5.6 = 3.6/\cos \phi_i$. $\phi_i = \cos^{-1}(3.6/5.6) = 50°$.
Therefore, $6400/\sin 50° = 6562 \sin \beta$, $\beta = \sin^{-1}[(6562 \sin 50°)/6400] = 51.8°$ or $128.2°$.
β must be bigger than 90°, so $\beta = 128.2°$. $\theta = 180° - (50 + 128.2)° = 1.8°$ or 0.03142 rad.
Skip distance = $2 \times 0.031\,42 \times 6400 = 402.176$ km.

9.9 $\lambda = 0.12$ m. $G_R = G_T = (\pi D/\lambda)^2 = 25\,503.3 \approx 44.1$ dB.
$L_P = (4\pi D/\lambda)^2 = 20\log_{10}[(4\pi \times 200 \times 10^3)/0.12] = 146.4$ dB. Total loss $= 146.4 + 62 = 208.4$ dB.
20 kW $= +43$ dBW, so $P_R = 43 - 208.4 + 88.2 = -77.2$ dBW.

9.10 $\lambda = (3 \times 10^8)/(600 \times 10^6) = 0.5$ m. Effective height of obstacle $= (20 \times 10 \times 10^6)/(2 \times 0.7 \times 6400 \times 10^3) = 22.32$ m $+ 42$ m $= 64.32$ m.
First Fresnel zone clearance $= 0.557\sqrt{[(0.5 \times 20 \times 10 \times 10^6)/(30 \times 10^3)]} = 33.31$ m.
From Fig. 9.26, $\tan\theta = [(64.32 + 33.31) - 75]/(20 \times 10^3) = (h_R - 75)/(30 \times 10^3)$, and $h_R = 109$ m.

9.11 Refactivity $= 320$.

9.12 (a) Sound broadcasting, ISB/SSB telephony, ship-to-shore, military, time signals.
(b) Maximum bandwidth only 3 kHz, poor link availability due to fading.

9.13 $L_P = 92.45 + 32.04 + 16.9 = 141.4$ dB.

9.14 (b) EIRP $= 10\log_{10} 5 - 2.6 + 32 = 36.4$ dBW.

9.15 Using equation (9.16) with f in GHz, $P_R = 10\log_{10} 2 - 2.5 + 32 - (92.45 + 29.54 + 16.9) + 32 - 2.5 = -76.9$ dBW.

9.16 (a) $L = 32 + 20\log_{10} 450 + 20\log_{210} 1 = 85.1$ dB.
(b) $P_{T(min)} = 22 + (-120) + 85.1 - 2 \times 0 = -12.9$ dBm $= 51.3$ μW.

9.17 (b) Because the E field would be parallel to the earth's surface and would be short-circuited by the conductivity of the earth.

9.18 (b) $P_d = 1000/[4\pi(25 \times 10^3)^2] = 0.127$ μW m^{-2}.
(c) $E = [\sqrt{(30 \times 1000)}]/(25 \times 10^3) = 6.93$ mV m^{-1}.
(d) $P_d = (6.93 \times 10^{-3})^2/120\pi = 0.127$ μW m^{-2}.

9.19 (a) $P_R = (20 \times 2 \times 2.51)/[3^2 \times 16 \times \pi^2 \times (10 \times 10^3)^2] = 706.4$ pW $= -91.5$ dBW.
(b) $V = \sqrt{(706.4 \times 10^{-12} \times 4 \times 50)} = 0.376$ mV.

Chapter 10

10.2 (a) $K_V = 0.22$ V rad$^{-1} \times 1$ VV$^{-1} \times 5$ VV$^{-1} \times 21$ kHzV$^{-1} = 23.1$ kHz rad$^{-1} = 23.1$ kHz rad^{-1} s$^{-1} \times 2\pi$ rad/cycle $= 145.14$ kHz s^{-2}. (b) $\Delta f = 10$ kHz. (c) $V_{out} = \Delta f/K_0 = 10$ kHz/21 kHz V$^{-1} = 0.476$ V. (d) $V_D = V_{out}/K_f K_A = 0.476/5 = 0.0952$. (e) $\theta_e = V_D/K_D = 0.0952/0.22 = 0.433$. (f) Hold-in range $= (\pi/2 \times 2$ kHz$) = \pm 33$ kHz.

10.3 (a) $f_{0(min)} = 800$ kHz. $f_{0(max)} = 128 \times 0.1 = 12.8$ MHz. (b) Resolution $= 100$ kHz.

10.4 (a) $\eta = (1800/200) \times 100 = 90$. (b) $V_c = (2 + 0.4)/2 = 1.2$ V. Hence $2 = 1.2(1 + m)$, and $m = 0.67$. $P_c = 1.2^2/(2 \times 1000) = 0.72$ mW. $P_{in} = 0.72(1 + 0.67^2/2) = 0.88$ mW.

(d) Maximum output voltage $= 2 - 0.25 = 1.75$, minimum voltage $= 0.4 - 0.25 = 0.15$ V.
(e) $C_{max} = \sqrt{(1 - 0.67^2)}/(0.67 \times 2\pi \times 3000 \times 8000) = 7.35$ nF.

10.5 (c) $0.35/2 = 0.175\%$ increase.

10.6 $i = 0.4 + 0.2(1 \sin \omega_c t + 0.2 \sin \omega_m t) + 0.1(1 \sin \omega_c t + 0.2 \sin \omega_m t)^2$ etc.
The difference/sum components come from the last term. Expanding this:
$i = 0.1 \sin^2 \omega_c t + 0.04 \sin \omega_c t \sin \omega_m t + 0.0004 \sin^2 \omega_m t$. The difference (or sum) component is: $i = 0.02$ mA. Therefore conversion conductance $= (0.02 \times 10^{-3})/0.2 = 1 \times 10^{-4}$ S.

10.7 Choose $C_1 = 1$ nF. $R_1 = 0.3/(300 \times 10^3 \times 1 \times 10^{-9}) = 1$ kΩ. For 12 kΩ input resistance R_2 and $R_3 = 12$ kΩ. Then $C_4 = 1/(2\pi \times 300 \times 10^3 \times 12 \times 10^3) \approx 20$ nF, so choose 47 nF.
$C_2 = (4 \times 300 \times 10^3)/(\pi \times 8000 \times 8000 \times 3600 \times 10) = 166$ nF, so select 150 nF.

10.8 (a) $C = 10/\sqrt{6} = 4.08$ pF. $f_0 = 1/[2\pi\sqrt{(100 \times 10^{-6} \times 4.08 \times 10^{-12})}] \approx 7.88$ MHz.
(b) $f_0 \approx 7.12$ MHz. (c) $C = 1/(4\pi^2 \times 64 \times 10^{12} \times 10^{-6}) = 3.96$ pF. $V_B = 100/3.96^2 = 6.38$ V.

Chapter 12

12.1 (IF output voltage)/(third-order output voltage) $= -60 - (-6) = -54$ dBm.
(a) Third-order output voltage $= -60 - 30 = -90$ dBm.
(b) Third-order output voltage $= -60 + 30 = -30$ dBm.
(c) Third-order output voltage $= -60 + 60 = 0$ dBm.
(d) If the input signal levels are increased to $+30$ dBm the third-order output voltage $= -60 + 90 = +30$ dBm. The third-order output voltage is then equal to the input signal voltage and hence the third-order intercept point $= +30$ dBm.

12.4 Noise factor, the amount of noise that may degrade the reception of weak signals; 1 dB compression point, the level at which a single signal measured at the amplifier output is compressed by 1 dB; second-order intercept point, the level of two signals that introduces second-order intermodulation distortion of the form $A + B = C$; third-order intercept point, the level of two signals that introduces third-order intermodulation of the form $2A - B = C$ or $2B - A = C$.

12.5 (a) $12 \pm 22 = 10$ or 34 MHz. (b) $28.8 \pm 10.8 = 10$ MHz.

12.7 Frequency steps, spurious signals, phase noise.

12.8 (a) Adjacent channel, reciprocal mixing, (b) cross-modulation, blocking, IF breakthrough, image channel, intermodulation. (c) $f_0 = 13.4$ MHz. (d) -99 dB.

12.9 (a) Sensitivity $= -174$ dBm $+ 7$ dB $+ 10$ dB $+ 10 \log_{10}(120 \times 10^3) = -106.2$ dBm.
(b) Reduce the noise factor, reduce the bandwidth, use a better demodulator.

12.10 (c) The sixth-order products are $5f_1 \pm f_2$, $4f_1 \pm 2f_2$, $3f_1 \pm 3f_2$, $2f_1 \pm 4f_2$ and $f_1 \pm 5f_2$.
(d) (i) $1.4 \pm 1.41 = 0.01$ and 2.82 MHz. (ii) $2.82 \pm 1.41 = 1.39$ and 4.21 MHz, $1.4 \pm 2.82 = 1.42$ and 4.22 MHz.

12.12 (c) Dynamic range = $(2/3)[-10 - (-110)] = 200/3 = 66.7$ dB.

12.13 (a) Noise floor = $-26 + 10 = -16$ dBµV.
(b) Minimum input signal = $-16 + 10 = -6$ dBµV = 0.5 µV.
This means that a noise factor of 10 dB is equivalent to a sensitivity of 0.5 µV e.m.f. in a 3 kHz bandwidth.

12.16 (a) $13.41 - 1.4 = 12.01$ MHz. (b) The mixer has 6 dB discrimination against low-level signal conversion, so unwanted signal level = -99 dB.

12.18 The third-order intercept point occurs when the third-order output level is equal to the input level. Hence, $+22 = IM + (3 \times 22)$ and $IM = -44$ dBm.

Chapter 13

13.1 For the input signal to be detected the input signal-to-noise ratio must be greater than or equal to $15 + 8 = 23$ dB. The actual input signal-to-noise ratio is $(3 \times 10^{-11})/(4 \times 10^{-21} \times 18 \times 10^6) = 416.7 = 26.2$ dB. Hence the signal can be detected.

13.2 $E_b/N_0 = -86$ dBW $- 10 \log_{10}(140 \times 10^6) + 204$ dBW $- 5 = -31.5$ dB.

13.3 Path loss = $20 \log_{10}[(4\pi \times 45 \times 10^3 \times 11.2 \times 10^9)/(3 \times 10^8)] = 146.5$ dB.
Overall loss = $146.5 + 1.5 + 8 + 8 - (2 \times 49) = 66$ dB.
$P_R = 10$ dBW $- 66 = -56$ dBW.
Noise level = -204 dBW $+ 10 \log_{10}(80 \times 10^6) + 8 = -117$ dBW.
Normal $C/N = -57 - (-117) = 60$ dB. Therefore fade margin = $60 - 18 = 42$ dB.

13.6 (e) $E_b = -90 - 10 \log_{10}(140 \times 10^6) = -171.5$ dBW. $N_0 = -204 + 7 = -197$ dBW.
$E_b/N_0 = -171.5 + 197 = 25.5$ dB.

Chapter 14

14.1 $P_d = 4\pi(37\ 300 \times 10^3)^2 = 1.748 \times 10^{16}$ W m^{-2}.
EIRP = $10 \log_{10}[1.748 \times 10^{16}] - 90 - 2.8 = 75.23$ dBW.

14.2 $G_{ov} = 48 - 3 = 45$ dB. $L \approx 3$. $T_A = [(2 - 1)290 + 62]/2 = 176$ K.
$F = 3$ dB = $10 \log_{10}[1 + T_e/290]$, $2 = 1 + T_e/290$, or $T_e = 290°$.
Mixer: $15 = 10 \log_{10}(1 + T_e)$, $31.62 = 1 + T_e/290$, or $T_e = 8880$ K.
Therefore, $T_R = 290 + 8880/1000 = 299$ K. $T_s = 176 + 299 = 475$.
Hence G/T ratio = 45 dB $- 10 \log_{10} 475 = 18.23$ dB K^{-1}.

14.3 $C = -148$ dBW $+ 55 + 2.5 = -95.5$ dBW. $N_0 = -228.6$ dBW $+ 10 \log_{10} 120 = -207.8$ dBW. $C/N_0 = -95.5 - (-207.8) = 112.3$ dB.

14.4 Isotropic received level = $+65 - 215 = -150$ dBW. Assume the G/T ratio is 0 dB K^{-1}; then $P_R + G/T = -150$ dBW. $k = -228.6$ dBW, so carrier-to-noise ratio = $-150 - (-228.6) = 78.6$ dB. The wanted carrier-to-noise ratio = 96 dB and hence G/T ratio = $96 - 78.6 = 17.4$ dB K^{-1}.

14.7 The distance from an earth station to the satellite is $\sqrt{(35\ 786^2 + 4825^2)} = 36\ 110$ km. $\lambda_{up} = (3 \times 10^8)/(6 \times 10^9) = 0.05$ m. $\lambda_{down} = 0.05 \times 6/4 = 0.075$ m.
(a) $(4\pi \times 36\ 110 \times 10^3)^2 = 2.0591 \times 10^{17}$. Hence, $loss_{up} = 8.236 \times 10^{19} = 199.2$ dB and $loss_{down} = 195.6$ dB. Transmitting aerial gain $= 10\ \log_{10}[0.6(16.4\pi/0.05)^2] = 58$ dBi. Receiving aerial gain $= 54.5$ dBi. Overall path loss $= 58 - 199.2 + 113 - 195.6 + 54.5 = -169.3$ dB.
(b) Transmission delay $= (2 \times 36\ 110 \times 10^3)/(3 \times 10^8) = 0.241$ s.

14.8 (a) $P_R = 35 - 194 + 42 = -117$ dBW.
(b) Signal power at demodulator input $= -117 + 48 = -69$ dBW. $T_{ov} = 38 + 122 + 4000/63\ 098 \approx 160$ K. $N = kT_{ov}B = -132.2$ dBW. Carrier-to-noise ratio $= -117 - (-132.2) = 15.2$ dB.

14.9 Overall gain of receiving system $= 42$ dB. 2 dB $= 10^{0.2} = 1.58$, so $T'_A = 62/1.58 + 290°(1 - 1/1.58) \approx 39.6$ K. 2.9 dB $= 1.95$ ratio, so $T_{LNA} = 0.95 \times 290 = 275.5$ K. 12 dB $= 15.85$ ratio, so $T_{mix} = 4306.5$ K. $T_{ov} = 275.5 + 4306.5/631 = 282.3$ K. $T_S = T'_A + T_{ov} = 39.6 + 282.3 = 321.9$ K.
G/T ratio $= 42 - 10\ \log_{10} 321.9 = 42 - 25.1 = 16.9$ dB.

14.10 $C = -160 + 48 - 2 = -114$ dBW. $N_0 = -228.6 + 10\ \log_{10} 120 = -207.8$ dBW. Carrier-to-noise ratio $= -114 - (-207.8) = 93.8$ dB.

14.11 $G_R = (0.6\pi^2 \times 30^2)/0.075^2 = 947\ 482 = 59.8$ dBi. $T_S = 10\ \log_{10} 80 = 19.03$ dBK. Hence G/T ratio $= 59.8 - 19.03 \approx 40.8$ dB K^{-1}.

14.12 Minimum theoretical bandwidth $= 140/3 = 46.47$ MHz, so bandwith $= 56$ MHz. (a) $E_b/N_0 = 18 + 10\ \log_{10}(56/140) = 18 - 4 = 14$ dB. (b) $N = 10\ \log_{10}(1.38 \times 10^{-23} \times 380 \times 56 \times 10^6) = -125.3$ dBW. (c) Carrier power $= 18 + (-125.3) = -107.3$ dBW.

14.13 (c) $N_0 = 10\ \log_{10}(1.38 \times 10^{-23} \times 184) \approx -206$ dBW. $N = -206$ dBW $+ 10\ \log_{10}(30 \times 10^6) = -131.2$ dBW. Hence $C/N = -80 - (-131.2) = 51.2$ dB.

Chapter 15

15.1 (a) $1000/7 = 142.86 \approx 142$. (b) $1000/12 = 83.3 \approx 83$.

15.2 $n = (20 \times 10^6)/(20 \times 10^3) = 1000$. $D = 4\sqrt{(3 \times 7)} = 18.33$ km.

15.3 Base station radiated power defines the dimensions of a cell. Mobile transmitted power reduction reduces co-channel interference.

15.4 (a) Circles can only cover area with gaps and/or ovelaps. (b) Square, equilateral triangle, hexagon. (c) Hexagon because it has the largest area for a given distance centre to furthest perimeter point. Hence the fewest number of cells can cover an area.

15.5 (a) Automatic transfer of calls to new cell as mobile moves form one cell to another. MSC overload/calls lost. (c) -90 dBm.

15.6 (a) Using directional aerials to cover a section of a cell. (b) Using three aerials instead of one, more hand-overs, increased capacity, less interference, reduced trunking.

15.7 (a) $1/(270.832 \times 10^3) = 3.692$ μs. (b) 156.25×3.692 μs $= 0.577$ ms. (c) 8×0.577 ms $= 4.615$ ms.

15.8 Time slot $= 156.25$ bits. Frame has $8 \times 156.25 = 1250$ bits. Overhead bits $= 322$. Frame efficiency $\eta = (1 - 322/1250) \times 100 = 74.24\%$.

15.9 $890.2 + 0.2 \times 16 = 893.4$ MHz and $893.4 + 45 = 938.4$ MHz. $890.2 + 0.2 \times 89 = 908$ MHz and $908 + 45 = 953$ MHz.

Index

8PSK   93
8QAM   101
16PSK   97
16QAM   103

access network   381
adaptive equalizer   392
adjacent-channel ratio   358
aerial
  array   204, 209, 210, 211,
      215, 219
  array factor   205
  beamwidth   192, 214, 241
  broadside array   211
  corner reflector   209
  current element   179, 196
  directivity   184, 204, 210
  dish   240
  effective
    aperture   195
    isotropic radiated power
        (EIRP)   195
    length (or height)   182, 187,
        193
  electric field strength   178,
      181, 185, 189
  end-fire array   215
  gain   194, 205, 213, 241
  half-wave dipole   192, 196
  height factor   216
  helical   237
  induction field   180
  isotropic radiator   178, 194,
      197
  log-periodic   226
  long wire radiator   199
  loop   239
  monopole   184
    half-wavelength   189
    top loading   188
    VHF/UHF   191
  mutual impedance   222
  notch   233
  parabolic dish   240
  pattern multiplication   219

radiated power   181
radiation
  field   180
  from   177
  resistance   182, 193
received power   197
rhombic   225
rod   237
slot   235
three-dipole array   210
two-dipole array   204, 208
whip   237
Yagi   229
aerial noise   8
AM transmitter   333
amplitude modulation   29
  non-sinusoidal modulating
      signal   37
    instantaneous voltage   38
    modulation factor   38
    r.m.s. value   39
    sideband   37
  single sideband (SSB)   47
    demodulation of   49
    merits, relative to DSB   50
    peak envelope power   51
    phasor representation of   47
  sinusoidal modulating signal
      29
    depth of modulation   31
    envelope   29
    modulation factor   31
    over modulation   33
    peak envelope power   36
    phasor representation   42, 45
    power   35
    sidefrequency   30
angle modulation   53
Aperture-to-coupling loss   280
Armstrong phase modulator   303
ASTRA   404
atmospheric noise   8
attenuation
  of line   117
  of waveguide   166

automatic gain control (AGC)
    365
available
  noise power   5
  power gain   6

balanced modulator   288, 290
balun   138
bandwidth
  8PSK   95
  8QAM   103
  AM   37
  BPSK   83
  FM   63
  GMSK   100
  MSK   98
  noise   2
  QPSK   88
bandwidth efficiency   108
beamwidth   192, 214, 241
binary phase shift keying (BPSK)
    82
bit error rate (BER)   23, 109,
    387
blocking   355
  ratio   355
branching network   385
broadside array   211

capture effect   68
carrier-to-noise ratio   23, 407
CDMA   403, 414, 440
cellular radio, see mobile radio
    systems
cellular telephone   376
characteristic impedance   116
choke flange   168
circulator   172, 385
class C RF amplifier   286
co-channel interference   347
communication radio receiver
    367
  MF/HF   367
  VHF/UHF   379
  VHF/UHF transceivers   373

Communication satellite operators 404, 419
communications satellite 400, 401
 carrier-to-noise ratio 407
 CDMA 403, 414
 FDMA 402, 409
 footprint 402
 ground segment 401, 418
 G/T ratio 408
 interference with 415
 link design 406
 orbits 403
 path loss 414
 propagation via 281
 space segment 401, 417
 traffic capacity 413
 transponder 402
COMSAT 404
component, transmission line 131
constellation diagram 82, 88, 95, 97, 103, 107
conversion conductance 320
core network 381
corner reflector 209
coupler, waveguide 171
critical frequency 258
cross-modulation 354
crystal filter 322
CT1/CT2 442
CTCSS 427
current
 element 178, 196
 reflection coefficient 120

DCS 1800 442
decimating filter 375
DECT 443
de-emphasis 72
demodulation of SSB 49
depth of modulation 31
detector (demodulator)
 AM 292
  diode detector 292
  non-linear 296
  product 297
 FM 306
  PLL 308
  pulse count 312
  quadrature 307
 stage 364
deviation ratio 56
dibits 86
diffraction
 ground wave 254
 space wave 277
digital
 broadcast radio 378
 cordless telephone 442
 modulation 78

8PSK 93
8QAM 101
16PSK 97
16QAM 103
BPSK 82
GMSK 100
MSK 97
OQPSK 90
QPSK 86
multiplexing hierarchy 381
radio receiver 374
signal waveform 79
diode detector 292
dipole aerial 192, 195, 196, 204, 208
direct digital frequency synthesis (DDFS) 316
dish aerial 240
divergence factor 273
double sideband AM (DSBAM) 29
double-stub matching 137, 149
dynamic range 352

effective
 aperture, or aerial 195
 isotropic power (EIRP) 195
 length (height) of aerial 182, 187, 193
 noise figure (factor) 16
electromagnetic wave 155
end-fire array 215
envelope, of AM wave 29
EUTELSAT 404, 420

fade margin 266, 395
fading 263, 279, 417
Faraday rotation 251
FDMA 402, 409, 440
five-tone signalling 426
flicker noise 7
footprint 402
forward error control (FEC) 390
free-space attenuation 11, 197
frequency
 bands 248
 deviation 54
 diversity 264
 hopping 436
 modulation 54
  advantages over AM 74
  bandwidth 63
  capture effect 68
  de-emphasis 72
  deviation ratio 56
  modulation index 55
  pre-emphasis 72
  signal-to-noise ratio 67, 71
  triangular noise
   spectrum 70

spectrum 57
stability 331
synthesis 313
 direct digital (DDFS) 316
 indirect 313
Fresnel
 zone 274
 radius of 274

gain, of aerial 144, 205, 213, 241
Galactic noise 9
ganging 364
Gaussian
 filter 81
 minimum shift keying (GMSK) 100
general line equations 119
GEO 403
global positioning system 421
Globalstar 406
grazing angle 266
ground segment 401, 418
ground wave 254
group velocity 117, 156
GSM 435
G/T ratio 408
gyro frequency 250

handover 436
height factor 216
helical aerial 237
hybrid ring 170

I-CO 466
IF amplifier 364
image channel signal 343, 344, 347
impedance of free space 178
impulse noise 2
induction field 180
INMARSAT 404, 420
INTELSAT 404, 419
intercept point 349
interference to satellite system 415
intermodulation distortion 348
intermodulation noise 8
ionosphere 248
IRIDIUM 405
isolator 172
isotropic radiator 178, 194, 197

jitter 389

k factor 252

LEO 402
level diagram 346
local oscillator 364
log-periodic aerial 226

long-wire radiator   199
loop aerial   239

magic T   170
matching, of line   134, 165
   λ/4 section   134, 146
   stub   135, 146, 149
maximum usable frequency
      (MUF)   258
measurement of noise factor   22
   of noise temperature   22
MEO   403
minimum shift keying (MSK)
      97
mixers   320
mobile radio systems   424
   cellular   431
      cell (macrocell, microcell,
         picocell)   431, 432
   DCS 1800   424, 442
   DECT   424, 443
   GSM   424, 435
   PMR   424, 425, 426
      trunked   429
mobile telephone   444
modulation
   need for   28
   factor   30, 38
   index   55
modulator
   amplitude   288
   frequency   298, 299, 301,
      303
monopole aerial   184
   gain of   195
   half-wavelength   189
   VHF/UHF   191
MPT specifications   328

narrowband FM (NBFM)   57
near filed   180
noise   2
   aerial   8
   atmospheric   8
   bandwidth   2
   blanking   325
   factor (figure)   11, 360
      effective   16
      lossy circuit   14
      measurement of   22
      overall   14
      relationship with noise
         temperature   17
      variation with frequency
         13
   flicker   7
   floor   21, 352, 361
   galactic   9
   impulse   2
   intermodulation   8
   power   5

power density spectrum (PDS)
      5
   resistance   2, 6
   semiconductor   7
   shot   7
   sky   8
   solar   9
   temperature   17
      aerial   8, 18
      measurement of   22
      system   19
non-linear detector   296
nose bandwidth   358
notch aerial   233

Odyssey   406
offset QPSK (OQPSK)   90
optimum working frequency
      259
over sampling   375
overmodulation   33
over-the-horizon loss   280

paging   436
PanAmSat   406
parabolic dish aerial   240
path loss   197, 414
pattern multiplication   219
PCM system over radio relay
      system   383
peak envelope power (PEP)   36,
      51
phase
   change coefficient   117
   modulation   65, 303
   noise   353
   velocity   158, 162
phasor representation
   of AN wave   42
   of FM wave   61
PLL detector   308
polarisation   155, 263, 267
power
   of DSB wave   35
   density spectrum   5, 80, 83
   efficiency   108
   spectral density   5, 80, 83
pre-emphasis   72
private mobile radio (PMR)
      424, 426, 429, 431
probability of error (in digital
      system)   23, 110
product detector   297
propagation or radio waves   247
   ground wave   254
   ionosphere   248
   sky wave   256
   space wave   266
   via communications satellite
      281
pulse count detector   312

quadrature
   amplitude modulation (QAM)
      101, 103, 106
   FM detector   307
   PSK (QPSK)   86

radiation
   from an aerial   177
   field   180
   resistance   182, 193
radio receivers   341
   1 dB compression point   352
   adjacent channel ratio   358
   automatic gain control (AGC)
      365
   blocking   355
   co-channel interference   347
   communication, see
         communication radio
         receivers
   cross-modulation   354
   detector stage   364
   double superheterodyne   344
   dynamic range   352
   ganging and tracking   364
   IF amplifier   364
   intermodulation   348
   level diagram   346
   local oscillator   364
   mixer stage   353
   noise factor   360
   nose bandwidth   358
   phase noise   353
   reciprocal mixing   353
   RF stage   361
   RSSI   366
   selectivity   357
   sensitivity   357
   shape factor   358
   signal-to-cross modulation-ratio
      355
   SINAD ratio   361
   skirt bandwidth   358
   spurious responses   355
radio regulations   327
radio relay system   381, 382
   analogue   385
   branching network   385
   digital   386
      adaptive equalizer   392
      bit error rate (BER)   386
      efficiency   387
      fade margin   395
      forward error control (FEC)
         390
      link design   394
      receiver   391
      reflective fade margin   394
      relay station/repeater   392
      transmitter   388
radio transmitter, see transmitter

raised-cosine filter 81
reactance frequency modulator
    299
reciprocal mixing 353
rectangular waveguide, see
    waveguide
reflection
    coefficient 120, 121, 140, 266
    loss 129
reflective fade margin 394
resonant cavity 133, 172
return loss 128
RF amplifier, Class C 286
RF stage 361
RFI 10
rhombic aerial 225
r.m.s. value of AM wave 32, 39
rod aerial 237
RSSI 366

SAW filter 322
scatter
    loss 280
    propagation 279
    system 398
selective
    fading 263, 279
    signalling 401, 417
selectivity 357
semiconductor noise 3
sensitivity 356
shape factor 358
shot noise 7
sideband 37
sidefrequency 29
signal-to-cross modulation ratio
    355
signal-to-noise ratio 1, 10, 50,
    67, 70
signal waveform 79
SINAD ratio 361
skip distance 262
skirt bandwidth 358
sky
    noise 8
    wave propagation 256
    critical frequency 258
    fading 263
    frequency diversity 264
    maximum usable frequency
        (MUF) 258
    multi-hop link 262
    optimum working frequency
        (OWF) 259
    skip distance 262
    space diversity 265
slot aerial 235
Smith chart 138
    effect of line attenuation 145
    input impedance 142

matching 146
    double stub 149
    quarter-wave section 146
    single stub 146
    unknown load impedance
        143
    voltage reflection coefficient
        140
    VSWR 141
solar noise 9
space
    diversity 265
    segment 401, 417
    wave propagation 266
        curvature of earth 273
        diffraction 277
        divergence factor 273
        fading 279
        Fresnel zones 274
        height diversity 277
        maximum distance between
            aerials 273
        path profile 276
        reflection coefficient 266
spectral efficiency 108
splatter 33
sporadic E 251
spurious responses 355
squelch 323
stub matching 135, 136, 146
sub refraction 254
super refraction 253

TDMA 403, 411, 438
Teledisic 406
Teleport 421
TE wave 156
TEM wave 155
temperature inversion 253
thermal noise 2
TM wave 156
top loading 188
tracking 364
transceiver 373
transmission lines 113
    balanced 113, 114
    balun 138
    components 131
    current reflection coefficient
        120
    double stub matching 137,
        149
    eighth-wavelength line 125
    general line equations 119
    half-wavelength line 124
    loss-free line 123
    low-loss line 123
    matching of 134, 135, 146,
        146
    mismatched at both ends 129

mismatched load 118, 122, 142
open-circuit line 124
primary coefficients 115
quarter-wavelength line 124,
    134, 146
refection loss 129
return loss 128
secondary coefficients 116
Smith chart 138 (see Smith
    chart)
standing wave 126
transmission loss 129
voltage reflection
    coefficient 120, 121
voltage transmission
    coefficient 128
VSWR 126, 141
Transmitter codes 332
transmitter, radio
    AM 333
    digital audio 339
    FM 336
    sound broadcast 334
    VHF/UHF communications
        337
transponder 402
triangular noise spectrum 70
troposphere 251
    sub refraction 254
    super refraction 253
    temperature inversion 253
tropospheric scatter system 398

undersampling 375

varactor diode FM modulator
    301
velocity of propagation 117,
    152, 156, 162
voltage
    reflection coefficient 120,
        121, 140
    transmission coefficient 128
VSWR 126, 141

waveguide 154
    attenuation 166
    components 168
        bends 169
        choke flange 168
        circulator 172, 385
        coupler 171
        hybrid ring 170
        isolator 172
        magic T 170
        resonant cavity 172
whip aerial 237
white noise 2

Yagi aerial 229